SELLING YOUR COINS &

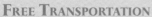

Warwick and Warwick have an expanding requirement for coin and bank
British and worldwide and for coins and notes of individual value. Our cu
is increasing dramatically and we need an ever larger supply of quality ma
to keep pace with demand. The market has never been stronger and if you
considering the sale of your collection, now is the time to act.

FREE VALUATIONS
We will provide a free, professional and without obligation valuation
of your collection. Either we will make you a fair, binding private
treaty offer, or we will recommend inclusion of your property
in our next specialist public auction.

FREE TRANSPORTATION
We can arrange insured transportation of your collection to
our Warwick offices completely free of charge. If you decline
our offer, we ask you to cover the return carriage costs only.

FREE VISITS
Visits by our valuers are possible anywhere in the country or
abroad, in order to assess more valuable collections.
Please telephone for details.

ADVISORY DAYS
We are holding a series of advisory days in all parts of the UK,
please visit our website or telephone for details.

EXCELLENT PRICES
Because of the strength of our customer base
we are in a position to offer prices that we feel
sure will exceed your expectations.

ACT NOW
Telephone or email
Richard Beale today with
details of your property.

LIVE BIDDING
Available on www.easyliveauction.com.

"THE I.A.P.N. dealer, your guide to the world of numismatics"

"More than one hundred of the world's most respected coin dealers are members of the I.A.P.N. (International Association of Professional Numismatists). I.A.P.N. members offer the collector an exceptional selection of quality material, expert cataloguing, outstanding service, and realistic pricing. The I.A.P.N. also maintain the International Bureau for the Suppression of Counterfeit Coins (I.B.S.C.C.) which, for a fee can provide expert opinions on the authenticity of coin submitted to it. A booklet listing the name, address and specialities of all I.A.P.N. members is available without charge by writing to the I.A.P.N. Secretariat". Jean-Luc Van der Schueren, 14, Rue de la Bourse, B-1000, Bruxelles.
Tel: +32–2–513 3400   E-mail: iapnsecret@compuserve.com   Web site: http://www.iapn-coins.org

ARGENTINA
Mariano COHEN, Corrientes 753 Local 49, 1043 CA de BUENOS AIRES

AUSTRALIA
DOWNIES COINS Pty Ltd, P.O. Box 3131, Nunawading, Vic 3131.

NOBLE NUMISMATICS Pty Ltd, 169 Macquarie Street, SYDNEY NSW 2000

AUSTRIA
HERINEK, Gerhard, Josefstädterstrasse 27, 1082 WIEN

BELGIUM
FRANCESCHI & Fils, B, 10, Rue de la Croix-de-Fer, 1000 BRUXELLES

VAN DER SCHUEREN, Jean-Luc, 14, Rue de la Bourse, 1000 BRUXELLES

CZECH REPUBLIC
MACHO & CHLAPOVIČ, Slunna 560/11, 162 00 PRAGUE

EGYPT
BAJOCCHI JEWELLERS, 45 Abdel Khalek Sarwat Street, 11121 CAIRO

FRANCE
BURGAN NUMISMATIQUE—Maison Florange, 8, Rue du 4 Septembre, 75002, PARIS

GUILLARD, Patrick, Eurl, B. P. 41, 75261 Paris Cedex 06

LA PARPAIOLLE, 10 rue Bernex – B. P. 30036, 13251, MARSEILLE Cedex 20

MAISON PLATT SAS, 49, Rue de Richelieu, 75001, PARIS

SAIVE NUMISMATIQUE, 18, rue Dupont des Loges, 57000, METZ

VINCHON-NUMISMATIQUE, 77, Rue de Richelieu, 75002 PARIS

GERMANY
FRITZ RUDOLF KÜNKER GmbH & Co. KG, Nobbenburger Straße 4a, 49076 OSNABRÜCK

GORNY & MOSCH, GIESSENER MÜNZHANDLUNG GmbH, Maximiliansplatz 20, 80333 MÜNCHEN

GERHARD HIRSCH Nachfolger, Prannerstrasse 8, 80333 MUNICH

JACQUIER, Paul-Francis, Honsellstrasse 8, 77694 KEHL am RHEIN

KAPAAN & MADES Münzhandels GbR, Brüderstrasse 2, 44787 BOCHUM

KÖLNER MÜNZKABINETT Tyll Kroha Nachfolger UG, Neven-DuMont-Strasse 15, 50667 KÖLN

KRICHELDORF Hellmut, Verlag e. K. Günterstalstrasse 16, 79100 FREIBURG IM BREISGAU

LEIPZIGER Münzhandlung und Auktion, Nikolaistrasse 25, 04109, LEIPZIG

MANFRED OLDING MÜNZEN-HANDLUNG, Goldbreede 14, 49078, OSNABRÜCK

MEISTER MÜNZENHANDLUNG, Moltkestrasse 6, 71634 LUDWIGSBURG

MÜNZEN-UND MEDAILLEN-HANDLUG STUTTGART,
Charlottenstrasse 4, 70182 STUTTGART

MÜNZGALERIE MÜNCHEN MGM HandelsgmbH & Co. Joker KG, Stiglmaierplatz 2, 80333 MÜNCHEN

PEUS NACHF., Dr. Busso Bornwiesenweg 34, 60322 FRANKFURT/M,

Münzhandlung RITTER GmbH Postfach 24 01 26, 40090 DÜSSELDORF

TIETJEN + CO, Hofweg 14, D-228085 HAMBURG

HUNGARY
NUDELMAN NUMISMATIKA Kft, Petőfi Sándor Utca 16, 1052 BUDAPEST

INDIA
TODYWALLA AUCTIONS, Todywalla House, 80 Ardesher Dadi St., Khetwdai, 400 004 MUMBAI

ITALY
FALLANI , Via del Babuino 58, 00187, ROMA

MORUZZI Numismatica di Moruzzi Umberto, s.n.c., Viale dei Salesiani, 12a, 00175 ROMA

PAOLETTI S.R.L., Via Roma 3, 34 121 TRIESTE

PAOLUCCI Andrea, Via San Francesco 154, 35121 PADOVA

RANIERI Numismatica srl, Piazza Calderini 2/2, 40124 BOLOGNA

VARESI Numismatica s.a.s., Viale Montegrappa 3, 27100 PAVIA

JAPAN
DARUMA INTERNATIONAL GALLERIES, 2–16-32-701, Takanawa, Minato-ku, TOKYO 108-0074

TAISEI COINS Co., UBG Higashi Ikebukuro Bldg., 1F, 2-23-2 Higashi, Ikebukuro, Toshima-ku, TOKYO 170-0013

WORLD COINS JAPAN, 1-15-5, Hamamatsu-cho, Minato-ku, TOKYO 105-0013

MONACO
EDITIONS VICTOR GADOURY, 57 rue Grimaldi, "Le Panorama", 98000 MONACO

MDC MONNAIES de COLLECTION SARL, 27 avenue de la Costa, 98000 MONACO

THE NETHERLANDS
SCHULMAN BV, Herengracht 500, 1017 CB AMSTERDAM

VERSCHOOR MUNTHANDEL, Postbus 5803, 3290 AC STRIJEN

NORWAY
OSLO MYNTGALLERI a/s, P.O. Box 1403, Vika, 0115 OSLO

PORTUGAL
MEP Auctions, Rua do Conde 44a, 1200-637 LISBOA

NUMISMA LEILÕES, Avenida de Igreja 63 C, 1700-235 LISBOA

NUMISPORTO LDA, Av. Combatentes
Grande Guerra 610 LJ6, 4200-186 PORTO

SPAIN
AUREO & CALICO, Plaza del Angel 2, 08002 BARCELONA

CAYON, JANO S.L., Calle Orfila 10, 28010 MADRID

HERVERA Marti, Calle Aribau 45, 08011 BARCELONA.

Jesús VICO S.A., Jorge Juan n-83, Duplicado, 28009 MADRID

SWEDEN
DELZANNO Roberto, Mynthandel, Villa Långbro, Långbrodalsvägen 57, 125 57 ÄLVSJÖ

NORDLINDS MYNTHANDEL AB, PO Box 5132, 102 43 STOCKHOLM

PHILEA AB / MYNTKOMPANIET, Svartensgatan 6, 116 20 STOCKHOLM

SWITZERLAND
ANTIQUA TRADING AG, Mönchhof 1, 8617 MÖNCHALTORF

HESS—DIVO AG, Löwenstrasse 55, 8001, ZÜRICH

LUGDUNUM GmbH, Bielstrasse 3, 4500 SOLOTHURN

MÜNZEN und RARITEITENSHOP GmbH, Schauplatzgasse 1, 3011 BERN

NOMOS AG, Zähringerstrasse 27, 8001 ZÜRICH

NUMISMATICA ARS CLASSICA AG, Niederdorfstrasse 43, 8001 ZÜRICH

NUMISMATICA GENEVENSIS SA, 1 Rond-point de Plainpalais, 1205 GENEVE

SINCONA AG, Limmatquai 112, 8001 ZÜRICH

THAILAND
EUR-SEREE COLLECTING CO., LTD. 1256/8 Nakornchaisri Road, Dusit BANGKOK 10300

HOUSE of COINS, Ltd. Part., P.O. Box 31, Jomtien, CHONBURI 20261

UNITED KINGDOM
BALDWIN & SONS LTD., A.H., 399 Strand, LONDON, WC2R 0LX

PAUL DAVIES LTD, P.O. Box 17, ILKLEY, West Yorkshire LS29 8TZ

KNIGHTSBRIDGE COINS, 43 Duke Street. St. James's, LONDON SW1Y 6DD

LONDON Coins Ltd. (Stephen LOCKETT), 4-6 Upper Street South, NEW ASH GREEN, Kent, DA3 8QH.

NOONANS, 16 Bolton Street, Piccadilly, LONDON W1J 8BQ

RASMUSSEN Mark, P.O. Box 42, BETCHWORTH RH3 7YR

RUDD, Chris, Ltd. P.O. Box 1500, NORWICH NR10 5WS

SAVILLE, Douglas, Chiltern Thameside, 37c St Peters Avenue, Caversham, READING RG4 7DH

THE COIN CABINET Ltd., Suite 47, London Fields Studio, 11-17 Exmouth Market, LONDON E8 3RW

UNITED STATES OF AMERICA
AMOS Publications, P.O. Box 4129, SIDNEY, OH. 45365

ATLAS NUMISMATICS, Inc., 18 Bridge Street, Suite 3A, BROOKLYN, N.Y.11201

BERK, LTD., 31 North Clark Street, CHICAGO, IL 60602

CLASSICAL NUMISMATIC GROUP INC, P.O. Box 479, LANCASTER, PA 17608-0479

COIN AND CURRENCY INSTITUTE INC, P.O. Box 399, WILLISTON, VT 05495

DAVISSON'S LTD, P.O. Box 323, COLD SPRING, MN 56320

DUNIGAN, Mike, 5332 Birchman, FORT WORTH, TX 76107

GILLIO INC. - GOLDMÜNZEN INTERNATIONAL 8 West Figueroa Street, SANTA BARBARA, CA 93101

HARVEY, Stephen, P.O. Box 3778, BEVERLEY HILLS, CA 90212

HERITAGE Auctions, 2801 W. Airport Freeway, DALLAS, TX. 75261

KERN, Jonathan K. Co., 441, S. Ashland Avenue, LEXINGTON, KY 40502–2114

LUSTIG, Andrew, Rare Coins, Inc., P. O. Box 806, NYACK, NY 10960

DMITRY MARKOV COINS & MEDALS, P.O. Box 950, NEW YORK, NY 10272

MILCAREK, Dr. Ron, P.O. Box 2240, AMHERST, MA 01004

RARCOA, Inc, 7550 South Quincy Street, WILLOWBROOK, IL 60527

RARE COIN GALLERIES, P.O. Box 1388, LA CANADA, CA 91012

SEDWICK, Daniel Frank, LLC, 2180 North Park Avenue, Suite 200, Winter Park, FL 32789

Shanna SCHMIDT Numismatic Inc., 637 Highland Avenue, OAK PARK, IL. 60304

STACK's Antiquities, 18 Arlington Lane, BAYVILLE, NY 11709

STACK's BOWERS, 1550 Scenic Avenue, Suite 150, COSTA MESA, CA. 92626

STEPHEN ALBUM RARE COINS, P.O. Box 7386, Santa Rosa, CA 95407

SUBAK Inc., 79 West Monroe Street, Room 1008, CHICAGO, IL 60603

VILMAR Numismatics, LLC, 161 McKenley Hollow Road, BIG INDIAN, NY. 12410

WADDELL, Ltd., Edward J., P.O. Box 3759, FREDERICK, MD 21705–3759

WORLD NUMISMATICS, LLC., P.O. Box 5270, CAREFREE, AZ 85377

WORLD-WIDE COINS OF CALIFORNIA, P.O. Box 3684, SANTA ROSA, CA 95402

VENEZUELA
NUMISMATICA GLOBUS, Apartado de Correos 50418, CARACAS 1050–A

~ Visit our website at www.iapn-coins.org ~

THE

COIN
Yearbook

2023

Edited by
John W. Mussell, FRGS
and the Editorial Team of COIN NEWS

ISBN 978-1-908828-62-0

Published by
TOKEN PUBLISHING LIMITED
8 Oaktree Place, Manaton Close, Exeter, Devon EX2 8WA
Telephone: 01404 46972
email: info@tokenpublishing.com. Website: www.tokenpublishing.com

Printed in Great Britain by Stephens & George Ltd.

Contents

COLIN COOKE

Est. 1984

www.colincooke.com

Foreword

WELCOME to the 2023 edition of the COIN YEARBOOK, the perfect simplified guide to the coins of England, Scotland, Ireland and the Islands. If you're a regular reader of this book, you will notice, I hope, that it is the same price now as it has been for 26 years! I'm not entirely sure how we've managed that to be honest! Partly it's down to us not wanting to pass costs on to you, and partly it's down to the fact that, unlike other things, print has actually come down a little over those two and half decades as technology has made things cheaper. Sadly, I fear this may well be the last YEARBOOK we can keep at this level though—for whilst print might have gone down, paper has gone up a staggering 68 per cent this past year alone. Like everyone else, our industry is not immune from what's going on in the wider world. The "cost of living crisis", as the ever sensationalist press has insisted on calling it, will undoubtedly have an effect on all of us one way or another and we have consciously tried not to increase the cost of this book so that we don't add to the burden of inflation being felt by many. Whether we are able to do so next year remains to be seen, but for now enjoy your 2023 book at the 1997 COIN YEARBOOK price!

As we go to press with this tome, inflation is running at over 10 per cent and it's likely that it will carry on its upward trend until sometime next year when it is predicted it will fall once again. Whether that happens or not remains to be seen, but for now we just have to suck it up and accept that the pandemic, furlough, quantitative easing, the war in Ukraine et al has had an effect on prices across the globe—but does that include the coin market?

Inflation is a funny thing. It's always around whether we notice it or not; a quick look at the aforementioned 1997 COIN YEARBOOK will show you just how much prices have changed over the years without us really noticing them. It's only when we get big jumps of 10 per cent annually that people really sit up and take notice and then only when that jump is on essentials. A 10 per cent increase in the cost of a coin in a year probably wouldn't get the same attention. Indeed, it was only a few years ago that bullion sovereigns were trading at well under £200 and in 1997 they were just £60— today they're round about the £350–360 mark and no one bats an eyelid, not really. Of course, bullion sovereigns aren't a great example as they are influenced by the external gold markets, but look at something like a Gothic crown or Gothic florin, they too have gone up on average 600 per cent in the intervening 26 years. Not even property (outside London) has done that.

Not that I'm advocating coins as investment of course. We always say that coin collecting should be a hobby for fun and not one to try to make money from, but there's no doubt that we all keep one eye on prices and values whenever we buy something—after all no one actually wants to lose money do they? And it's always nice to know that one's collection is still worth something after all the hard work (and hard cash) we put in to developing it. That said, whilst it's good to see that that prices of coins (if not COIN YEARBOOKS) have increased in 26 years, we don't want to see them increase too much. Certainly, if they did then those of us with coins would be (or at least would feel) a little richer but at the same time we'd be unable, or unwilling, to pay the prices necessary to add to our collections and newcomers would very quickly be put off, and that's no good at all. So, whilst prices of coins might not be increasing as quickly as the price of pasta has, might not be making headlines like petrol prices or gas and electricity prices have been, that should be viewed as a good thing. Prices are increasing year on year (we have a complete set of Yearbooks here to prove it) but they aren't going mad and that is how we like it. An inflationary bubble in numismatics will do nobody any good, so let's hope we can avoid one over these next 12 months.

Pricing and values is, of course, what this book is all about. It's not here for the history of coins, or for stories about coins (we have our monthly magazine COIN NEWS for that), it's here to tell you what your coin is worth and we do that by (a) checking dealers' lists and auctions and taking an average, and (b) getting known experts to check our findings to make sure we have got it right and we are always indebted to them. This year we'd like to particularly thank John Philpotts of Silbury Coins who has taken a great deal of time, and gone to a lot of trouble, to update our "Roman Coins used in Britain" section. We would also like to extend our thanks and gratitude to: Chris Rudd and Elizabeth Cottam (Celtic); Stephen Mitchell of Studio Coins (Hammered); Royston Norbury of West Essex Coin Investments (Milled); Nick Swabey (Maundy); David Stuart (Scottish); Mike Southall (Isle of Man); Del Parker (Irish); and Charles Riley (Medals). We also express our gratitude to the Royal Mint for their invaluable assistance and the numerous auction houses who have allowed access to their archives and given us permission to use their illustrations.

We have, quite literally, stopped the presses on this *Yearbook* to add this postscript regarding Her Majesty, Queen Elizabeth II who sadly passed away on the afternoon of September 8, 2022. Her numismatic legacy cannot be understated, both in the UK and across the globe. Her portrait has appeared on billions of coins throughout her 70 years on the throne, and her passing truly is the end of an era. Next year's *Coin Yearbook* will, of course, show the coins of her successor, King Charles III, but this year we pay tribute to her.

Thank you for your service, Ma'am. May you Rest in Peace.

Museum
archive

Every month in **COIN NEWS** we are privileged to feature one of the rare items from the Royal Mint's Museum at Llantrisant. The collection represents one of the most impressive numismatic archives in the world, featuring outstanding rarities alongside the currency we all use in our everyday lives. Here we have chosen a few of the items we have featured, as a "snap shot" of the Museum's treasures.

Celebrating the
Queen's Platinum Jubilee

On February 6, 2022 the nation, and indeed the world, paused to acknowledge the 70th anniversary of the Queen's accession. The main focus of celebration fell over the extended bank holiday in early June but a number of initiatives were already underway and the Royal Mint Museum was for some time planning how best it might mark the occasion. One of the most publicly accessible was the temporary exhibition that opened in the Royal Mint Experience in time for the anniversary. It runs for the rest of the year and explores the evolution of Royal Jubilees in Britain through a range of objects, images and interactives. Building on the success of last year's short-story competition on the theme of decimalisation, the Museum again organised a competition for primary school children but this year taking the theme of the Platinum Jubilee. The response from children right across the country was enthusiastic and entertainingly creative, with the competition winner announced before Easter.

Last year the Museum launched a "reminiscence box" project for care homes in connection with decimalisation. The take-up and the feedback from residents was overwhelming and the project was short listed for a Museum and Heritage Community Impact Award. This success

prompted the Museum to theme the contents of the boxes this year around 70 years of the Queen's reign. It is an interactive experience, providing a rewarding means through which long-forgotten memories can be re-awakened.

In addition there was a digital dimension to the Platinum Jubilee project through specially created content for the learning section on the Museum's website and through the Jubilee Collection pages, highlighting objects from the collection with a connection to Jubilees past and present.

Sir Robert Johnson's Royal Prize Medals

December 2021 marked the 100th anniversary of the appointment of Robert Johnson to the position of Deputy Master of the Royal Mint. The *Pall Mall Gazette* reported the news in January 1922, noting that the role was not very onerous, an observation completely out of place with the energy and reforming zeal Johnson brought to the job.

He was educated at Winchester College, winning the Royal Prize Medal for essays, verse and speeches in both English and Latin in 1892 and 1893. The specimen of the medal illustrated here is one of those awarded to Johnson, inscribed on the edge with his name. He later went on to Oxford and had, as one of his tutors, the historian and numismatist, Sir Charles Oman, unknowingly offering a foretaste of his future career.

At the Mint, Johnson was into his stride from the start and it is no understatement to record that his legacy remains in place to this day. He wanted to keep the Mint's skilled workforce together during the difficult years that followed the First World War and consequently he actively sought work from wherever it could be found. Amongst many others, orders were undertaken for the newly formed Soviet Union, a politically controversial move at the time, and also for Iceland which has remained a regular customer for the Royal Mint. Less than a year into his tenure in office, he established the Royal Mint Advisory Committee with a remit to improve the quality of numismatic design in Britain. The Committee will be marking its own centenary next year, a testament in and of itself to Johnson, and his awareness of the need for the Mint to become a commercial entity laid the foundations for the organisation's continuing evolution.

The Queen's role in coin design

The established process for approving new United Kingdom coins is that they are recommended by the Royal Mint Advisory Committee and then submitted to the Chancellor of the Exchequer who in due course sends them to the Queen for final royal approval. She has, therefore, seen and approved all new coin designs throughout her long reign, including those issued in celebration of the Platinum Jubilee this year and, by extension, all other previous significant royal anniversaries. In 2002, the year of her Golden Jubilee, a design was commissioned from the sculptor, Ian Rank-Broadley, FRBS, and he prepared a typically accomplished low-relief plaster model for the obverse of the coin, an equestrian portrait of the Queen surrounded by an elegant double-arch inscription. In response to the royal submission seeking her approval the Queen demonstrated how closely she observes what is presented to her.

She requested the modest but important alteration that the design show the outline of her legs through the cloak she is depicted wearing. As someone who has ridden from a young age and who is passionate about horses, it was a remark informed by long experience of what a woman should look like riding side-saddle. Although subtle, as can be seen here by comparing the images of the original plaster model and the struck silver coin, the change was made to the design and the result is a handsome coin in celebration of a key milestone in the Queen's reign.

40 years of the 20 pence

Forty years ago, in June 1982, the first 20 pence coins were issued into general circulation, signalling a series of changes to the decimal coinage which went on to include the introduction of a one pound coin the following year and the withdrawal of the halfpenny in 1984. A coin of this value had, though, been seriously considered as part of the original decimal coinage. The Halsbury report into decimalisation, published in 1963, recommended its inclusion and designs were commissioned, resulting in twenty pence decimal pattern pieces being struck and considered by the Chancellor of the Exchequer, James Callaghan, in July 1966. A historical precedent for the coin could be found in the form of the double-florin of 1887. That, however, was an unpopular addition to the currency and the large size of the prospective decimal 20 pence, at 36mm and weighing in at 23grams, was close to the dimensions of a crown piece and not ultimately consistent with the desire to reduce the weight of the new coinage.

A 20 pence did not, therefore, form part of the initial release of decimal coins but a need to review the coinage in the years ahead was anticipated at the time and within a decade of decimalisation the benefit of a 20 pence was recognised. Its equilateral curve heptagon shape was inspired by the decimal 50 pence but it was given a raised edge-flat reminiscent of Matthew Boulton's Cartwheel pennies. A range of trial pieces was created in the lead up to its issue, many specimens of which have been retained in the Royal Mint Museum Collection, and the one illustrated here, slightly thinner than the coin as issued, bears the designs of an orb on one side and Britannia Moneta on the other, a familiar device used on Royal Mint trial pieces. Unlike the 50 pence, it proved possible to strike the 20 pence from a round blank and, initially bearing the handsome design of a crowned rose by William Gardner, it has gone on to be one of the most popular coins of the decimal age.

The Charles Babbage 50 pence— a fitting decimal tribute

The Royal Mint recently issued a new commemorative 50 pence in its "Innovation in Science" series to honour the work of Charles Babbage. He was a gifted mathematician who, as is well known, pioneered work into computers during the first half of the 19 century. The coin has been designed by Nigel Tudman and Jas Bhamra, and an early option submitted at the start of the design commissioning process from the Royal Mint Museum's collection is illustrated here. Other work of theirs may well be familiar to readers of Coin News through the exhibition designs they have created for the Bank of England Museum and in the form of books they have designed, such as Mark Stocker's recently published account of the design of the decimal coinage.

Babbage was something of a polymath and he took an active interest in topical issues of the day, including the movement in support of decimalisation. The cause gained momentum in the years after the Battle of Waterloo; during 1833 it was reported in newspapers that Babbage had prepared proposals for a decimal system which would have had the equivalent of ten shillings in the pound, a solution seriously considered in debates during the 1960s. Given his background in mathematics, it was a cause we should not be surprised to find him championing and for him to be commemorated now on the quintessential decimal coin— the 50 pence—seems wholly appropriate.

Fidei Defensor

In October 1521 Pope Leo X bestowed on Henry VIII the title Fidei Defensor, Defender of the Faith, which makes this month the 500th anniversary. As is well known, it was a gesture made in recognition of a book Henry wrote, dedicated to the Pope, which attacked the teachings of Martin Luther. Use of the title by the English king appears on the second Great Seal of his reign, which was in use from the early 1530s, but it would be almost 200 years before it appeared on the British coins of George I.

There was, though, an earlier outing for the title on the coinage. Pattern shillings and half-groats of Charles I produced at the Mint in the Tower of London by the French engraver Nicholas Briot in the 1630s carry FIDEI DEFENSOR as the reverse legend and a specimen of the shilling from the Royal Mint Museum collection is illustrated here. As with his other machine-struck experimental coins, it is a finely worked piece, with the reverse in particular presenting an elegant balance between inscription and the encircled shield of the Royal Arms. Why Briot chose to use it on these coins is unclear but from early in George I's reign, whether in full or abbreviated, it has remained a reassuringly familiar part of the British coinage.

The scale of design

While all coin designs are conceived at a relatively miniature size there are considerations of scale, even within this small spectrum, to bear in mind. There is a line of reasoning which would regard a design prepared for a crown piece as being inappropriate for a farthing and that this should be applied to portraits and reverse designs alike. When the decimal coins were being designed in the 1960s the Advisory Committee, under the leadership of Prince Philip, debated this very point and there is a clear logic to the view that more detail and complexity can be accommodated within the canvas of a larger coin. A case study arose in relation to the proposed decimal 20 pence at its unwieldy 36mm and the diminutive half penny at 17mm.

As illustrated here, at one point in the selection process the design which ended up appearing on the half penny was considered for the much larger 20 pence. It can be left to the judgement of readers to determine which coin the design most suited but to see the choice provides an insight into the care and attention to detail exercised over what the coins should look like. The decimal half penny was subjected to sustained criticism following its release in February 1971 on account of its awkwardly small size and its design, for some, offered no sanctuary in redeeming its reputation. How the decimal coinage was designed is explored in an authoritative and lavishly illustrated new book by Mark Stocker entitled *When Britain Went Decimal: The coinage of 1971*, which dissects such debates and places the whole story in broader political context of the time.

THE ROYAL MINT®
THE ORIGINAL MAKER

Made Exclusively by
The Royal Mint

For more than 1,100 years, The Royal Mint has struck the coins of every British king and queen. Our history of minting excellence gives us unrivalled knowledge about historic coins from Britain and the rest of the world. Call on our historic coin experts to help you find something to collect and invest in.

 collectorservices@royalmint.com 0800 03 22 153

royalmint.com

CELEBRATE | COLLECT | INVEST | SECURE | DISCOVER

Monarchs
of England

Here we list the Kings and Queens from Anglo-Saxon times to the present, with the dates of their rule. Before Eadgar became the King of all England the country had been divided up into small kingdoms, each with their own ruler.

ANGLO-SAXON KINGS

The Anglo-Saxon monarchs ruled over the various kingdoms which existed in England following the withdrawal of the Romans in the 5th century AD. The most prominent kingdoms in the land were Kent, Sussex, Wessex, Mercia and Northumbria. Each kingdom produced its own coinage but in 973 Eadgar introduced a new coinage that became the standard for the whole of the country.

Eadgar (959–975)
Edward the Martyr (975–978)
Aethelred II (978–1016)
Cnut (1016–1035)
Harold I (1035–1040)
Harthacanut (1035–1042)
Edward the Confessor (1042–1066)
Harold II (1066)

NORMAN KINGS

The Normans came to Britain from their native France following the establishment of a kingdom in Sicily and southern Italy. An expedition led by the powerful Duke William of Normandy culminated in the battle of Hastings in 1066 where he defeated Harold II and was proclaimed King of All England. Their influence spread from these new centres to the Crusader States in the Near East and to Scotland and Wales in Great Britain, and to Ireland. Today their influence can be seen in their typical Romanesque style of architecture.

William I (1066–1087)
William II (1087–1100)
Henry I (1100–1135)
Stephen (1135–1154)

PLANTAGENETS

The Plantagenet kings of England were descended from the first House of Anjou who were established as rulers of England through the Treaty of Wallingford, which passed over the claims of Eustace and William, Stephen of Blois's sons, in favour of Henry of Anjou, son of the Empress Matilda and Geoffrey V, Count of Anjou.

Henry II (1154–1189)
Richard I (1189–1199)
John (1199–1216)
Henry III (1216–1272)
Edward I (1272–1307)
Edward II (1307–1327)
Edward III (1327–1377)
Richard II (1377–1399)

HOUSE OF LANCASTER

The House of Lancaster, a branch of the English royal House of Plantagenet, was one of the opposing factions involved in the Wars of the Roses, the civil war which dominated England and Wales during the 15th century. Lancaster provided England with three Kings

Henry IV (1399–1413)
Henry V (1413–1422)
Henry VI (1422–1461) and again 1470

HOUSE OF YORK

The House of York was the other branch of the House of Plantagenet involved in the disastrous Wars of the Roses. Edward IV was descended from Edmund of Langley, 1st Duke of York, the fourth surviving son of Edward III.

Edward IV (1461–1483 and again 1471–83)
Richard III (1483–1485)

TUDORS

The House of Tudor was an English royal dynasty that lasted 118 years, from 1485 to 1603. The family descended from the Welsh courtier Owen Tudor (Tewdwr). Following the defeat of Richard III at Bosworth, the battle that ended the Wars of the Roses, Henry Tudor, 2nd Earl of Richmond, took the throne as Henry VII.

Henry VII (1485–1509)
Henry VIII (1509–1547)
Edward VI (1547–1553)
Mary (1553–1558)
Philip & Mary (1554–1558)
Elizabeth I (1558–1603)

STUARTS

The House of Stuart ruled Scotland for 336 years, between 1371 and 1707. Elizabeth I of England's closest heir was James VI of Scotland via her grandfather Henry VII of England, who was founder of the Tudor dynasty. On Elizabeth's death, James Stuart ascended the thrones of England and Ireland and inherited the English claims to the French throne. The Stuarts styled themselves "Kings and Queens of Great Britain", although there was no parliamentary union until the reign of Queen Anne, the last monarch of the House of Stuart.

James I (1603–1625)
Charles I (1625–1649)
The Commonwealth (1653–1658)
Charles II (1660–1685)
James II (1685–1688)
William III & Mary (1688–1694)
William III (1694–1702)
Anne (1702–1714)

HOUSE OF HANOVER

The House of Hanover was a Germanic royal dynasty which ruled the Duchy of Brunswick-Lüneburg and the Kingdom of Hanover. George Ludwig ascended to the throne of the Kingdom of Great Britain and Ireland through the female line from Princess Elizabeth, sister of Charles I.

George I (1714–1727)
George II (1727–1760)
George III (1760–1820)
George IV (1820–1830)
William IV (1830–1837)
Victoria (1837–1901)

HOUSES OF SAXE-COBURG-GOTHA AND WINDSOR

The name Saxe-Coburg-Gotha was inherited by Edward VII from his father Prince Albert, the second son of the Duke of Saxe-Coburg-Gotha and husband of Victoria. During World War I the name was changed to Windsor to avoid the Germanic connotatiion.

Edward VII (1901–1910)
George V (1910–1936)
Edward VIII (1936)
George VI (1936–1952)
Elizabeth II (1952–)

PUBLIC AUCTIONS
IN THE NORTH OF ENGLAND
Coins, Medals & Banknotes

WEAR HISTORY ON YOUR WRIST

Connecting two of the world's most sought-after collectables, our unique and exclusive range of watches feature some of the most storied coins in the history of numismatics.

Discover today by calling **0808 109 7836** quoting **92015046** or by visiting **LONDONMINTOFFICE.ORG/WATCHES**

THE
LONDON MINT
OFFICE

Dates
on coins

The vast majority of modern coins bear the date prominently on one side. In most cases dates are expressed in modified Arabic numerals according to the Christian calendar and present no problem in identification. There have been a few notable exceptions to this general rule, however. Morocco, for example, has used European numerals to express dates according to the Moslem calendar, so that a coin dated 1321 actually signifies 1903. Dates are almost invariably written from left to right—even in Arabic script which writes words from right to left. An exception, however, occurred in the Philippines quarto of 1822 where the date appeared as 2281, and the "2"s back to front for good measure.

Dates in Roman numerals have been used since 1234 when this practice was adopted by the Danish town of Roskilde. Such Roman numerals were used sporadically throughout the Middle Ages and in later centuries and survive fitfully to this day. This was the system used in England for the first dated coins, the gold half-sovereigns of Edward VI struck at Durham House in 1548 (MDXLVIII). This continued till 1550 (MDL) but thereafter Arabic numerals were used, beginning with the half-crown of 1551. Notable exceptions of more recent times include the Gothic coinage of Queen Victoria (1847–87).

The first coin with the date in European numerals was a plappart of St Gallen, Switzerland dated 1424, but this was an isolated case. In 1477 Maria of Burgundy issued a guldiner which bore a date on the reverse, in the form of two pairs of digits flanking the crown at the top. The numerals in this instance were true Gothic, an interesting transition between true Arabic numerals and the modified Arabic figures now used in Europe. The Tyrolese guldengroschen of 1484–6 were the first coins to be regularly dated in European numerals and thereafter this custom spread rapidly.

For the numismatist, the problem arises when coins bear a date in the numerals of a different alphabet or computed according to a different era. Opposite is a table showing the basic numerals used in different scripts. The various eras which may be found in coin dates are as listed and explained opposite.

	ARABIC-TURKISH	CHINESE, JAPANESE KOREAN, ANNAMESE (ORDINARY)	CHINESE, JAPANESE KOREAN, ANNAMESE (OFFICIAL)	INDIAN	SIAMESE	BURMESE
1	١	一	壹	۹	ෙ	၁
2	٢	二	貳	۲	๒	၂
3	٣	三	叁	۳	๓	၃
4	٤	四	肆	૪	๔	၄
5	٥	五	伍	५	๕	၅
6	٦	六	陸	૬	๖	၆
7	٧	七	柒	৩	๗	၇
8	٨	八	捌	८	๘	၈
9	٩	九	玖	९	๙	၉
0	٠			٥	๐	၀
10	١٠	十	拾		๑๐	
100	١٠٠	百			๑๐๐	
1000	١٠٠٠	千				

Hijra

The era used on Moslem coins dates from the flight of Mohammed from Mecca to Medina on July 15, 622 and is often expressed as digits followed by AH (Anno Hegirae). Moslems employ a lunar calendar of twelve months comprising 354 11/30 days. Tipu Sultan of Mysore in 1201 AH (the fifth year of his reign) introduced a new era dating from the birth of Mohammed in AD 570 and using a luni-solar system. Tipu also adopted the Hindu cycle of sixty years (the Tamil Brihaspate Cycle), but changed this two or three years later, from Hijra to Muludi.

Afghan coins used the lunar calendar until 1920 and during 1929–31, but at other times have used the solar calendar. Thus the Democratic Republic began issuing its coins in SH 1358 (1979).

To convert an AH date to the Christian calendar you must translate the Arabic into European numerals. Taking an Arabic coin dated 1320, for example, first deduct 3% (to convert from the Moslem lunar year to our solar year). This gives 39.6 which, rounded up to the nearest whole number, is 40. Deduct 40 from 1320 (1280), then add 622. The answer is 1902.

There have been a few notable exceptions. Thus the Khanian era of Ilkhan Ghazan Mahmud began on 1st Rajab 701 AH (1301). This era used a solar calendar, but was shortlived, being confined to coins of Mahmud and his nephew Abu Said down to year 34 (1333).

The era of Tarikh Ilahi was adopted by the Mughal emperor Akbar in the thirteenth year of his reign (922 AH). This era dated from his accession on 5th Rabi al-Sani 963 AH (February 19, 1556). The calendar had solar months and days but no weeks, so each day of the month had a different name. This system was used by Akbar, Jahangir and Shah Jahan, often with a Hijra date as well.

Saphar

The era of the Caesars began on January 1, 38 BC and dated from the conquest of Spain by Augustus. Its use on coinage, however, seems to have been confined to the marabotins of Alfonso VIII of Castile and was expressed in both Latin and Arabic.

Samvat

The era of Vikramaditya began in 57 BC and was a luni-solar system used in some Indian states. Coins may be found with both Samvat and Hijra dates. Conversion to the Christian date is simple; merely subtract 57 from the Samvat to arrive at the AD date.

Saka

This originated in the southwestern district of Northern India and began in AD 78. As it used the luni-solar system it converts easily by adding 78 to the Saka date.

Nepal

Nepalese coins have used four different date systems. All coins of the Malla kings were dated in Nepal Samvat (NS) era, year 1 beginning in 881. This system was also used briefly by the state of Cooch Behar. Until 1888 all coins of the Gurkha dynasty were dated in the Saka era (SE) which began in AD 78. After 1888 most copper coins were dated in the Vikram Samvat (VS) era from 57 BC. With the exception of some gold coins struck in 1890 and 1892, silver and gold coins only changed to the VS era in 1911, but now this system is used for all coins struck in Nepal. Finally, dates in the Christian era have appeared on some commemorative coins of recent years.

Ethiopian

This era dates from August AD 7, so that EE 1885 is AD 1892. Ethiopian dates are expressed in five digits using Amharic numerals. The first two are the digits of the centuries, the third is the character for 100, while the fourth and fifth are the digits representing the decade and year. On modern coins dates are rendered in Amharic numerals using the Christian era.

Thailand

Thai coins mainly use the Buddhist era (BE) which dates from 543 BC, but some coins have used dates from the Chula-Sakarat calendar (CS) which began in AD 638, while others use a Ratanakosind Sok (RS) date from the foundation of the Chakri dynasty in AD 1781.

Hebrew

The coins of Israel use the Jewish calendar dating from the beginning of the world (Adam and Eve in the Garden of Eden) in 3760 BC. Thus the year 1993 is rendered as 5753. The five millennia are assumed in dates, so that only the last three digits are expressed. 735 therefore equates with AD 1975. Dates are written in Hebrew letters, reading from right to left. The first two characters signify 400 and 300 respectively, totalling 700. The third letter denotes the decades (lamedh = 30) and the fourth letter, following the separation mark (") represents the final digit (heh = 5). The Jewish year runs from September or October in the Christian calendar.

Dates from the creation of the world

This system was also used in Russia under Ivan IV. The dating system Anno Mundi (AM) was established by the Council of Constantinople in AD 680 which determined that the birth of Christ had occurred in 5508 AM. Ivan's coins expressed the date as 7055 (1447).

Dynastic dates

The system of dating coinage according to regnal years is a feature of Chinese and Japanese coins. Chinese coins normally have an inscription stating that they are coins of such and such a reign period (not the emperor's name), and during the Southern Sung dynasty this was joined by the numeral of the year of the reign. This system was continued under the republic and survives in Taiwan to this day, although the coins of the Chinese Peoples Republic are dated in western numerals using the Christian calendar.

Early Japanese coins bore a reference to the era (the title assumed by each emperor on his accession) but, like Chinese coins, could not be dated accurately. From the beginning of the Meiji era (1867), however, coins have included a regnal number. The Showa era, beginning in 1926 with the accession of Hirohito, eventually ran to sixty-three (expressed in western numerals on some denominations, in Japanese ideograms on others) to denote 1988, although the rest of the inscription was in Japanese characters.

Dynastic dates were used on Korean milled coins introduced in 1888. These bore two characters at the top Kae Kuk (founding of the dynasty) followed by quantitative numerals. The system dated from the founding of the Yi dynasty in 1392. Curiously enough, some Korean banknotes have borne dates from the foundation of the first dynasty in 2333 BC.

Iran adopted a similar system in 1975, celebrating the 15th anniversary of the Pahlavi regime by harking back to the glories of Darius. The new calendar dated from the foundation of the Persian Empire 2535 years earlier, but was abolished only three years later when the Shah was overthrown.

Political eras

France adopted a republican calendar in 1793 when the monarchy was abolished. Coins were then inscribed L'AN (the year) followed by Roman numerals, but later Arabic numerals were substituted. This continued to the year 14 (1806) but in that year the Emperor Napoleon restored the Christian calendar. The French system was emulated by Haiti whose coins dated from the revolution of 1803. The date appeared as AN followed by a number until AN 31 (1834) on some coins; others had both the evolutionary year and the Christian date from 1828 until 1850 (AN 47). Coins with a date in the Christian calendar appeared only in 1807–9 and then from 1850 onwards.

Mussolini introduced the Fascist calendar to Italy, dating from the seizure of power in October 1922. This system was widely employed on documents and memorials, but was first used on silver 20 lire coins of 1927 and then only in addition to the Christian date and appearing discreetly as Roman numerals. Subsequently it was extended to gold 50 lire and 100 lire coins in 1931 and the subsidiary coinage in 1936, being last used in the year XXI (1943).

Coin
inscriptions

This alphabetical listing is confined to inscriptions found on coins, mainly in the form of mottoes or of a commemorative nature. Names of rulers are, for the most part, excluded. Where the inscription is in a language other than English a translation is given, followed by the name of the issuing country or authority in parentheses.

A Deo et Caesare From God and the Emperor (Frankfurt).

A Domino Factum est Istud et est Mirabile in Oculis Nostris This is the Lord's doing and it is marvellous in our eyes (England, Mary).

A Solo Iehova Sapientia From God alone comes true wisdom (Wittgenstein).

Ab Inimicis Meis Libera Me Deus Free me from enemies (Burgundy).

Ad Legem Conventionis According to the law of the Convention (Furstenberg).

Ad Normam Conventionis According to the standard of the Convention (Prussia).

Ad Palmam Pressa Laeturo Resurgo Pressed to the palm I rise more joyfully (Wittgenstein).

Ad Usam Luxemburgi CC Vallati For the use of the besieged Luxembourgers (Luxembourg siege coins).

Adiuva Nos Deus Salutaris Noster Help us, O God, our Saviour (Lorraine).

Adventus Optimi Principis The coming of the noblest prince (Papacy).

Aes Usibus Aptius Auro Bronze in its uses is more suitable than gold (Brazil).

Aeternum Meditans Decus An ornament intended for all time (Alencon).

Aliis Inserviendo Consumor I spend my life devoted to others (Brunswick-Wolfenbuttel).

Alles Mit Bedacht All with reflection (Brunswick).

Amor Populi Praesidium Regis The love of the people is the king's protection (England, Charles I).

Ang Fra Dom Hib & Aquit (King) of England and France, Lord of Ireland and Aquitaine (England, Edward III).

Anno Regni Primo In the first year of the reign (Britain, edge inscription on crowns).

Apres les Tenebres la Lumiere After the shadows, the light (Geneva).

Archangelus Michael Archangel Michael (Italy, Grimoald IV).

Ardua ad Gloriam Via Struggles are the way to glory (Waldeck).

Arte Mea Bis Iustus Moneta Lud Iust By my art I am twice the just coin of King Louis (France, 1641).

Aspera Oblectant Wild places delight (Nassau-Weilburg).

Aspice Pisas Sup Omnes Specio Behold the coin of Pisa, superior to all (Pisa).

Audiatur Altera Pars Let the other part be heard (Stavelot).

Auf Gott Trawe Ich In God I trust (Brunswick).

Ausen Gefaesen der Kirchen und Burger From the vessels of the Church and citizens (Frankfurt siege, 1796).

Auspicio Regis et Senatus Angliae By authority of the king and parliament of England (East India Company).

Auxilio fortissimo Dei With the strongest help of God (Mecklenburg).

Auxilium de Sanctio Aid from the sanctuary (Papacy).

Auxilium Meum a Dno Qui Fecit Celum e Terram My help comes from God who made heaven and earth (Portugal).

Beata Tranquillitas Blessed tranquillity (Rome, Licinius II).

Beatus Qui Speravit in dom Blessed is he who has hoped in the Lord (Mansfeld).

Benedic Haereditati Tuae Blessings on your inheritance (Savoy).

Benedicta Sit Sancta Trinitas Blessed be the Holy Trinity (Albon).

Benedictio Domini Divites Facit The blessing of the Lord makes the rich (Teschen).

Benedictus Qui Venit in Nomine Domini Blessed is he who comes in the name of the Lord (Flanders).

Beschaw das Ziel Sage Nicht Viel Consider the matter but say little (Quedlinburg).

Besser Land und Lud Verloren als ein Falscher Aid Geschworn   Better to lose land and wealth than swear a false oath (Hesse).

Bey Gott ist Rath und That   With God is counsel and deed (Mansfeld).

Britanniarum Regina   Queen of the Britains (Britain, Victoria).

Britt Omn Rex   King of all the Britains (i.e. Britain and the overseas dominions) (Britain, 1902–52).

Cal et Car Com de Fugger in Zin et Norn Sen & Adm Fam   Cajetan and Carl, Counts of Fugger in Zinnenberg and Nordendorf, Lords and Administrators of the Family (Empire, Fugger).

Candide et Constanter   Sincerely and steadfastly (Hesse-Cassel).

Candide sed Provide   Clearly but cautiously (Osterwitz).

Candore et Amore   With sincerity and love (Fulda).

Candore et Constantia   With sincerity and constancy (Bavaria).

Capit Cath Ecclesia Monasteriensis   Chapter of the Cathedral Church of Munster (Munster).

Capit Eccle Metropolit Colon   Chapter of the Metropolitan Church of Cologne (Cologne).

Capitulum Regnans Sede Vacante   Chapter governing, the See being vacant (Eichstadt).

Carola Magna Ducissa Feliciter Regnante   Grand Duchess Charlotte, happily reigning (Luxembourg).

Carolus a Carolo   Charles (I) to Charles (II) (England).

Cedunt Prementi Fata   The fates yield to him who presses (Ploen, Hese-Cassel).

Charitate et Candore   With charity and sincerity (East Frisia).

Charta Magna Bavariae   The Great Charter of Bavaria (Bavaria).

Christo Auspice Regno   I reign under the auspices of Christ (England, Charles I).

Christus Spes Una Salutis   Christ is our one hope of salvation (Cleve).

Chur Mainz   Electoral Principality of Mainz (Mainz).

Circumeundo Servat et Ornat   It serves and decorates by going around (Sweden).

Civibus Quorum Pietas Coniuratione Die III Mai MDCCXCI Obrutam et Deletam Libertate Polona Tueri Conabatur Respublica Resurgens   To the citizens whose piety the resurgent commonwealth tried to protect Poland overturned and deprived of liberty by the conspiracy of the third day of May 1791 (Poland).

Civitas Lucemborgiensis Millesimum Ovans Expletannum   Completing the celebration of a thousand years of the city of Luxembourg (Luxembourg).

Civium Industria Floret Civitas   By the industry of its people the state flourishes (Festival of Britain crown, 1951).

Cluniaco Cenobio Petrus et Paulus   Peter and Paul from the Abbey of Cluny (Cluny).

Comes Provincie Fili Regis Francie   Court of Provence and son of the King of France (Provence).

Communitas et Senatus Bonon   City and senate of Bologna (Bologna).

Concordia Fratrum   The harmony of the brothers (Iever).

Concordia Patriae Nutrix   Peace, the nurse of the fatherland (Waldeck).

Concordia Res Parvae Crescunt   Little things increase through harmony (Batavian Republic).

Concordia Res Parvae Crescunt, Discordia Dilabuntur   By harmony little things increase, by discord they fall apart (Lowenstein-Wertheim-Virneburg).

Concordia Stabili   With lasting peace (Hildesheim).

Confidens Dno Non Movetur   He who trusts in God is unmoved (Spanish Netherlands).

Confidentia in Deo et Vigilantia   Trust in God and vigilance (Prussian Asiatic Company).

Confoederato Helvetica   Swiss Confederation (Switzerland)

Conjuncto Felix   Fortunate in his connections (Solms).

Conservator Urbis Suae   Saviour of his city (Rome, 4th century).

Consilio et Aequitate   With deliberation and justice (Fulda).

Consilio et Virtutis   With deliberation and valour (Hesse-Cassel).

Constanter et Sincere   Steadfastly and sincerely (Lautern).

Crescite et Multiplicamini   Increase and multiply (Maryland).

Cristiana Religio   Christian religion (Germany, 11th century).

Crux Benedicat   May the cross bless you (Oldenburg).

Cuius Cruore Sanati Sumus   By His sacrifice are we healed (Reggio).

Cultores Sui Deus Protegit   God protects His followers (England, Charles I).

Cum Deo et Die (Jure)   With God and the day (Wurttemberg).

Cum Deo et Jure   With God and the law (Wurttemberg).

Cum Deo et Labore   With God and work (Wittgenstein).

Cum His Qui Orderant Pacem Eram Pacificus   With those who order peace I was peaceful (Zug).

Curie Bonthon to so Doulo   Protect his servant, o Lord (Byzantine Empire).

Custos Regni Deus   God is the guardian of the kingdom (Naples and Sicily).

Da Gloriam Deo et Eius Genitrici Marie   Give glory to God and His mother Mary (Wurttemberg).

Da Mihi Virtutem Contra Hostes Tuos   Give me valour against mine enemies (Netherlands, Charles V).

Dat Wort is Fleis Gworden   The word is made flesh (Muster).

Date Caesaris Caesari et Quae Sunt Dei Deo   Render unto Caesar the things that are Caesar's and unto God the things that are God's (Stralsund).

De Oficina . . .   From the mint of . . . (France, medieval).

Decreto Reipublicae Nexu Confoederationis Iunctae Die V Xbris MDCCXCII Stanislao Augusto Regnante   By decree of the state in conjunction with the joint federation on the fifth day of December 1792, Stanislaus Augustus ruling (Poland).

Decus et Tutamen   An ornament and a safeguard (Britain, pound).

Deducet Nos Mirabiliter Dextera Tua   Thy right hand will guide us miraculously (Savoy).

Denarium Terrae Mariae   Penny of Maryland (Maryland).

Deo Conservatori Pacis   To God, preserver of peace (Brandenburg-Ansbach).

Deo OM Auspice Suaviter et Fortiter sed Luste nec Sibi sed Suis   Under the auspices of God, greatest and best, pleasantly and bravely but justly, not for himself but for his people (Speyer).

Deo Patriae et Subditio   For God, fatherland and neighbourhood (Mainz).

Der Recht Glaubt In Ewig Lebt   Who believes in right will live in eternity (Linange-Westerburg).

Der Rhein ist Deutschlands Strom Nicht Deutschlands Grenze   The Rhine is Germany's River not Germany's Frontier.

Deum Solum Adorabis   You will venerate God alone (Hesse).

Deus Constituit Regna   God establishes kingdoms (Ni jmegen).

Deus Dat Qui Vult   God gives to him who wishes (Hanau-Munzenberg).

Deus et Dominus   God and Lord (Rome, 3rd century).

Deus in Adiutorium Meum Intende   God stretch out in my assistance (France).

Deus Providebit   God will provide (Lowenstein-Wertheim-Virneburg).

Deus Refugium Meum   God is my refuge (Cleve).

Deus Solatium Meum   God is my comfort (Sweden).

Dextera Domini Exaltavit Me   The right hand of God has raised me up (Modena, Spain).

Dextra Dei Exalta Me   The right hand of God exalts me (Denmark).

Dieu et Mon Droit   God and my right (Britain, George IV).

Dilexit Dns Andream   The Lord delights in St Andrew (Holstein).

Dilexit Dominus Decorem Iustitiae   The Lord is pleased with the beauty of justice (Unterwalden).

Dirige Deus Gressus Meos   O God, direct my steps (Tuscany, Britain, Una £5).

Discerne Causam Meam   Distinguish my cause (Savoy).

Divina Benedictiae et Caesarea Iustitia   Sacrifice of blessings and imperial justice (Coblenz).

Dn Ihs Chs Rex Regnantium   Lord Jesus Christ, King of Kings (Rome, Justinian II).

Dns Ptetor Ms Z Lib'ator Ms   The Lord is my protector and liberator (Scotland, David II).

Dominabitur Gentium et Ipse   He himself will also be lord of the nations (Austrian Netherlands).

Domine Conserva Nos in Pace   O Lord preserve us in peace (Basle, Mulhausen).

Domine Elegisti Lilium Tibi   O Lord Thou hast chosen the lily for Thyself (France, Louis XIV).

Domine ne in Furore Tuo Arguas Me   O Lord rebuke me not in Thine anger (England, Edward III).

Domine Probasti Me et Congnovisti Me   O Lord Thou hast tested me and recognised me (Mantua).

Domini est Regnum   The Kingdom is the Lord's (Austrian Netherlands).

Dominus Deus Omnipotens Rex   Lord God, almighty King (Viking coins).

Dominus Mihi Adiutor   The Lord is my helper (Spanish Netherlands).

Dominus Providebit   The Lord will provide (Berne).

Dominus Spes Populi Sui   The Lord is the hope of his people (Lucerne).

Donum Dei ex Fodinis Vilmariens   A gift of God from the Vilmar mines (Coblenz).

Duce Deo Fide et Justicia   By faith and justice lead us to God (Ragusa).

Dum Praemor Amplior   I increase while I die prematurely (Savoy).

Dum Spiro Spero   While I live, I hope (Pontefract siege coins).

Dum Totum Compleat Orbem   Until it fills the world (France, Henri II).

Dura Pati Virtus   Valour endures hardships (Saxe-Lauenburg).

Durae Necessitatis   Through force of necessity (Bommel siege, 1599).

Durum Telum Necessitas   Hardship is a weapon of necessity (Minden).

Dux et Gubernatores Reip Genu   Duke and governors of the republic of Genoa (Genoa).

E Pluribus Unum   One out of more (USA).

Eccl S. Barbarae Patronae Fodin Kuttenbergensium Duo Flor Arg Puri   The church of St Barbara, patron of the Kuttensberg mines, two florins of pure silver (Hungary).

Een en Ondelbaer Sterk   One and indivisible (Batavian Republic).

Eendracht Mag Macht   Unity makes strength (Belgium, South African Republic).

Einigkeit Recht und Freiheit   Union, right and freedom (Germany).

Electorus Saxoniae Administrator   Elector and administrator of Saxony (Saxony).

Elimosina Alms (France, Pepin).

Ep Fris & Ratisb Ad Prum Pp Coad Aug Bishop of Freising and Regensburg, administrator of Pruem, prince-provost, co-adjutant bishop of Augsburg (Trier).

Equa Libertas Deo Gratia Frat Pax in Virtute Tua et in Domino Confido I believe in equal liberty by the grace of God, brotherly love in Thy valour and in the Lord (Burgundy).

Equitas Iudicia Tua Dom Equity and Thy judgments O Lord (Gelderland).

Espoir Me Conforte Hope comforts me (Mansfeld).

Espreuve Faicto Par Lexpres Commandement du Roy Proof made by the express commandment of the King (France, piedforts).

Et in Minimis Integer Faithful even in the smallest things (Olmutz).

Ex Auro Argentes Resurgit From gold it arises, silver again (Sicily).

Ex Auro Sinico From Chinese gold (Denmark).

Ex Flammis Orior I arise from the flames (Hohenlohe-Neuenstein-Ohringen).

Ex Fodinis Bipontio Seelbergensibus From the Seelberg mines of Zweibrucken (Pfalz-Birkenfeld).

Ex Metallo Novo From new metal (Spain).

Ex Uno Omnis Nostra Salus From one is all our salvation (Eichstadt, Mulhouse).

Ex Vasis Argent Cleri Mogunt Pro Aris et Focis From the silver vessels of the clergy of Mainz for altars and for hearths (Mainz).

Ex Visceribus Fodinse Bieber From the bowels of the Bieber mine (Hanau-Munzenberg).

Exaltabitur in Gloria He shall be exalted in glory (England, quarter nobles).

Exemplum Probati Numismatis An example of a proof coin (France, Louis XIII piedforts).

Exemtae Eccle Passau Episc et SRI Princ Prince Bishop of the freed church of Passau, prince of the Holy Roman Empire (Passau).

Expectate Veni Come, o expected one (Roman Britain, Carausius).

Extremum Subidium Campen Kampen under extreme siege (Kampen, 1578).

Exurgat Deus et Dissipentur Inimici Eius Let God arise and let His enemies be scattered (England, James I).

Faciam Eos in Gentem Unam I will make them one nation (England, unites and laurels).

Faith and Truth I will Bear unto You (UK £5, 1993).

Fata Consiliis Potiora The fates are more powerful than councils (Hesse-Cassel).

Fata Viam Invenient The fates will find a way (Gelderland).

Fecit Potentiam in Brachio Suo He put power in your forearm (Lorraine).

Fecunditas Fertility (Naples and Sicily).

Fel Temp Reparatio The restoration of lucky times (Rome, AD 348).

Felicitas Perpetua Everlasting good fortune (Rome, Constantius II).

Felix coniunctio Happy Union (Brandenburg-Ansbach).

Fiat Misericordia Tua Dne Let Thy mercy be O Lord (Gelderland).

Fiat Voluntas Domini Perpetuo Let the goodwill of the Lord last for ever (Fulda).

Fidei Defensor Defender of the Faith (Britain).

Fidelitate et Fortitudine With fidelity and fortitude (Batthanyi).

Fideliter et Constanter Faithfully and steadfastly (Saxe-Coburg-Gotha).

Fidem Servando Patriam Tuendo By keeping faith and protecting the fatherland (Savoy).

Filius Augustorum Son of emperors (Rome, 4th century).

Fisci Iudaici Calumnia Sublata The false accusation of the Jewish tax lifted (Rome, Nerva).

Florent Concordia Regna Through harmony kingdoms flourish (England, Charles I and II).

Fortitudo et Laus Mea Dominu Fortitude and my praise in the Lord (Sardinia).

Free Trade to Africa by Act of Parliment *(Sic)* (Gold Coast).

Friedt Ernehrt Unfriedt Verzehrt Peace nourishes, unrest wastes (Brunswick).

Fulgent Sic Littora Rheni Thus shine the banks of the Rhine (Mannheim).

Fundator Pacis Founder of peace (Rome, Severus).

Gaudium Populi Romani The joy of the Roman people (Rome, 4th century).

Gen C Mar VI Dim Col USC & RAMAI Cons & S Conf M General field marshal, colonel of the only dragoon regiment, present privy councillor of both their sacred imperial and royal apostolic majesties, and state conference minister (Batthanyi).

Gerecht und Beharrlich Just and steadfast (Bavaria).

Germ Hun Boh Rex AAD Loth Ven Sal King of Germany, Hungary and Bohemia, Archduke of Austria, Duke of Lorraine, Venice and Salzburg (Austria).

Germ Jero Rex Loth Bar Mag Het Dux King of Germany, Jerusalem, Lorraine and Bar, Grand Duke of Tuscany (Austrian Netherlands).

Germania Voti Compos Germany sharing the vows (Brandenburg-Ansbach).

Gloria ex Amore Patriae Glory from love of country (Denmark).

Gloria in Excelsis Deo Glory to God in the highest (France, Sweden).

Gloria Novi Saeculi The glory of a new century (Rome, Gratian).

God With Us (England, Commonwealth).

Godt Met Ons God with us (Oudewater).

Gottes Freundt der Pfaffen Feindt God's friend, the Pope's enemy (Brunswick, Christian).

Gratia Dei Sum Id Quod Sum   By the grace of God, I am what I am (Navarre).

Gratia Di Rex   By the grace of God, king (France, 8th century).

Gratitudo Concivibus Exemplum Posteritati   Gratitude to fellow Citizens, an example to posterity (Poland).

Gud och Folket   God and the people (Sweden).

Hac Nitimur Hanc Tuemur   With this we strive, this we shall defend (Batavian Republic).

Hac Sub Tutela   Under this protection (Eichstadt).

Haec Sunt Munera Minerae S Antony Eremitae   These are the rewards of the mine of St Antony the hermit (Hildesheim).

Hanc Deus Dedit   God has given this (Pontefract siege coins).

Hanc Tuemur Hac Nitimur   This we defend, by this we strive (Batavian Republic).

Has Nisi Periturus Mihi Adimat Nemo   Let no one remove these (Letters) from me under penalty of death (Commonwealth, edge inscription).

Henricus Rosas Regna Jacobus   Henry (united) the roses, James the kingdoms (England and Scotland, James VI and I).

Herculeo Vincta Nodo   Bound by a Herculean fetter (Savoy).

Herr Nach Deinem Willen   O Lord Thy will be done (Palatinate, Erbach).

Herre Gott Verleich Uns Gnade   Lord God grant us grace (Brunswick).

Hic Est Qui Multum Orat Pro Populo   Here is he who prays a lot for the people (Paderborn).

Hir Steid te Biscop   Here is represented the bishop (Gittelde).

His Ventis Vela Levantur   By these winds the sails are raised up (Hesse-Cassel).

Hispaniarum Infans   Infante of Spain and its dominions (Spain).

Hispaniarum et Ind Rex   King of Spain and the Indies.

Hispaniarum Rex   King of Spain (Spain).

Hoc Signo Victor Eris   With this sign you will be victor (Rome, Vetranio).

Honeste et Decenter   Honestly and decently (Nassau-Idstein).

Honi Soit Qui Mal y Pense   Evil to him who evil thinks (Britain, George III).

Honni Soit Qui Mal y Pense   (Hesse-Cassel).

Hospitalis et S Sepul Hierusal   Hospital and Holy Sepulchre of Jerusalem (Malta).

Hun Boh Gal Rex AA Lo Wi et in Fr Dux   King of Hungary, Bohemia and Galicia, Archduke of Austria, Dalmatia, Lodomeria, Wurzburg and Duke in Franconia (Austria).

Hung Boh Lomb et Ven Gal Lod III Rex Aa   King of Hungary, Bohemia, Lombardo-Venezia, Galicia, Lodomeria, Illyria, Archduke (Austria).

Ich Dien   I serve (Aberystwyth 2d, UK 2p).

Ich Getrawe Got in Aller Noth   I trust in God in all my needs (Hesse-Marburg).

Ich Habe Nur Ein Vaterland und das Heisst Deutschland   I have only one fatherland and that is called Germany (Germany).

Ielithes Penniae   Penny of Gittelde (Gittelde, 11th century).

Iesus Autem Transiens Per Medium Illorum Ibat   But Jesus, passing through the midst of them, went His way (England, Scotland, Anglo-Gallic).

Iesus Rex Noster et Deus Noster   Jesus is our king and our God (Florence).

Ihs Xs Rex Regnantium   Jesus Christ, King of Kings (Byzantine Empire).

Ihsus Xristus Basileu Baslie   Jesus Christ, King of Kings (Byzantine Empire).

Imago Sanch Regis Illustris Castelle Legionis e Toleto   The image of Sancho the illustrious king of Castile, Leon and Toledo.

In Casus Per Vigil Omnes   In all seasons through vigil (Wertheim).

In Deo Meo Transgrediar Murum   In my God I shall pass through walls (Teschen).

In Deo Spes Mea   In God is my hope (Gelderland).

In Domino Fiducia Nostra   In the Lord is our trust (Iever).

In Equitate Tua Vivificasti Me   In thy equity Thou hast vivified me (Gelderland).

In God We Trust   (USA).

In Hoc Signo Vinces   In this sign shalt thou conquer (Portugal).

In Honore Sci Mavrici Marti   In honour of the martyr St Maurice (St Maurice, 8th century).

In Manibus Domini sortes Meae   In the hands of the Lord are my fates (Mainz siege, 1688–9).

In Memor Vindicatae Libere ac Relig   In memory of the establishment of freedom and religion (Sweden).

In Memoriam Conjunctionis Utriusque Burgraviatus Norice   In memory of the union of both burgraviates in peace (Brandenburg-Ansbach).

In Memorian Connub Feliciaes Inter Princ Her Frider Carol et Dub Sax August Louis Frider Rodas D 28 Nov 1780 Celebrati   In memory of the most happy marriage between the hereditary prince Friedrich Karl and the Duchess of Saxony Augusta Louisa Frederika, celebrated on 28 Nov 1780 (Schwarzburg-Rudolstadt).

In Memorian Felicisssimi Matrimonii   In memory of the most happy marriage (Wied).

In Memoriam Pacis Teschinensis   Commemorating the Treaty of Teschen (Brandenburg-Ansbach).

In Nomine Domini Amen   In the name of the Lord amen (Zaltbommel).

In Omnem Terram Sonus Eorum   In to all the land their shall go sound (Chateau Renault, Papal States).

In Silencio et Spe Fortitodo Mea   In silence and hope is my fortitude (Brandenburg-Kustrin).

In Spe et Silentio Fortitudo Mea   In hope and silence is my fortitude (Vianen).

In Te Domine Confido   In you O Lord I place my trust (Hesse).

In Te Domine Speravi   In You, O Lord, I have hoped (Gurk).

In Terra Pax   Peace in the land (Papacy).

In Via Virtuti Nulla Via   There is no way for virtue on the way. (Veldenz).

Ind Imp, Indiae Imperator, Imperatrix   Emperor (Empress) of India (Britain).

India Tibi Cessit   India has yielded to thee (Portuguese India).

Infestus Infestis   Hostile to the troublesome (Savoy).

Inimicos Eius Induam Confusione   As for his enemies, I shall clothe them in shame (Sardinia, England, Edward VI).

Insignia Capituli Brixensis   The badge of the chapter of Brixen (Brixen).

Isti Sunt Patres Tui Verique Pastores   These are your fathers and true shepherds (Papacy).

Iudicium Melius Posteritatis Erit   Posterity's judgment will be better (Paderborn).

Iure et Tempore   By right and time (Groningen).

Iusques a Sa Plenitude   As far as your plenitude (France, Henri II).

Iuste et Constanter   Justly and constantly (Paderborn).

Iustirt   Adjusted (Hesse-Cassel).

Iustitia et Concordia   Justice and harmony (Zurich).

Iustitia et Mansuetudine   By justice and mildness (Bavaria, Cologne).

Iustitia Regnorum Fundamentum   Justice is the foundation of kingdoms (Austria).

Iustitia Thronum Firmat   Justice strengthens the throne (England, Charles I).

Iustus Non Derelinquitur   The just person is not deserted (Brandenburg-Calenberg).

Iustus Ut Palma Florebit   The just will flourish like the palm (Portugal).

L Mun Planco Rauracorum Illustratori Vetustissimo   To L Municius Plancus the most ancient and celebrated of the Rauraci (Basle).

Landgr in Cleggov Com in Sulz Dux Crum   Landgrave of Klettgau, count of Sulz, duke of Krumlau (Schwarzburg-Sondershausen).

Latina Emeri Munita   Latin money of Merida (Suevi).

Lege et Fide   By law and faith (Austria).

Lex Tua Veritas   Thy law is the truth (Tuscany).

Liberta Eguaglianza   Freedom and equality (Venice).

Libertad en la Ley   Freedom within the law (Mexico).

Libertas Carior Auro   Freedom is dearer than gold (St Gall).

Libertas Vita Carior   Freedom is dearer than life (Kulenberg).

Libertas Xpo Firmata   Freedom strengthened by Christ (Genoa).

Liberte, Egalite, Fraternite   Liberty, equality, fraternity (France).

Lucerna Pedibus Meis Verbum Est   Thy word is a lamp unto mine feet (England, Edward VI).

Lumen ad Revelationem Gentium   Light to enlighten the nations (Papacy).

L'Union Fait la Force   The union makes strength (Belgium)

Macula Non Est in Te   There is no sin in Thee (Essen).

Magnus ab Integro Saeculorum Nascitur Ordo   The great order of the centuries is born anew (Bavaria).

Mandavit Dominus Palatie hanc Monetam Fiert   The lord of the Palatine ordained this coin to be made (Balath).

Manibus Ne Laedar Avaris   Lest I be injured by greedy hands (Sweden).

Mar Bran Sac Rom Imp Arcam et Elec Sup Dux Siles   Margrave of Brandenburg, archchamberlain of the Holy Roman Empire and elector, senior duke of Silesia (Prussia).

Maria Mater Domini Xpi   Mary mother of Christ the Lord (Teutonic Knights).

Maria Unxit Pedes Xpisti   Mary washes the feet of Christ (France, Rene d'Anjou).

Mater Castrorum   Mother of fortresses (Rome, Marcus Aurelius).

Matrimonio Conjuncti   Joined wedlock (Austria).

Me Coniunctio Servat Dum Scinditur Frangor   The relationship serves me while I am being torn to pieces (Lowenstein-Wertheim).

Mediolani Dux   Duke of Milan (Milan).

Mediolani et Man   Duke of Mantua and Milan (Milan).

Memor Ero Tui Iustina Virgo   I shall remember you, o maiden Justina (Venice).

Merces Laborum   Wages of work (Wurzburg).

Mirabilia Fecit   He wrought marvels (Viking coinage).

Misericordia Di Rex   King by the mercy of God (France, Louis II).

Mo Arg Ord Foe Belg D Gel & CZ   Silver coin of the order of the Belgian Federation, duchy of Guelder-land, county of Zutphen (Guelderland).

Moneta Abbatis   Coin of the abbey (German ecclesiastical coins, 13th–14th centuries).

Moneta Argentiae Ord Foed Belgii Holl   Silver coin of the federated union of Belgium and Holland (Batavian Republic).

Mo No Arg Con Foe Belg Pro Hol   New silver coin of the Belgian Federation, province of Holland (Holland).

Mo No Arg Pro Confoe Belg Trai Holl   New silver coin of the confederated Belgian provinces, Utrecht and Holland (Batavian Republic).

Mon Lib Reip Bremens   Coin of the free state of Bremen (Bremen).

Mon Nova Arg Duc Curl Ad Norma Tal Alb   New silver coin of the duchy of Courland, according to the standard of the Albert thaler (Courland).

Mon Nov Castri Imp   New coin of the Imperial free city of . . . (Friedberg).

Moneta Bipont   Coin of Zweibrucken (Pfalz-Birkenfeld-Zweibrucken).

Monet Capit Cathedr Fuld Sede Vacante   Coin of the cathedral chapter of Fulda, the see being vacant (Fulda).

Moneta in Obsidione Tornacensi Cusa   Coin struck during the siege of Tournai (Tournai, 1709).

Moneta Livosesthonica   Coin of Livonia (Estonia).

Moneta Nov Arg Regis Daniae   New silver coin of the king of Denmark (Denmark).

Moneta Nova Ad Norman Conventionis   New coin according to the Convention standard (Orsini-Rosenberg).

Moneta Nova Domini Imperatoris   New coin of the lord emperor (Brunswick, 13th century).

Moneta Nova Lubecensis   New coin of Lubeck.

Moneta Nova Reipublicae Halae Suevicae   New coin of the republic of Hall in Swabia.

Moneta Reipublicae Ratisbonensis   Coin of the republic of Regensburg.

Nach Alt Reichs Schrot und Korn   According to the old empire's grits and grain (Hesse).

Nach dem Conventions Fusse   According to the Convention's basis (German Conventionsthalers).

Nach dem Frankf Schlus   According to the Frankfurt standard (Solms).

Nach dem Schlus der V Staend   According to the standard of the union (Hesse).

Navigare Necesse Est   It is necessary to navigate (Germany).

Nec Aspera Terrent   Nor do difficulties terrify (Brunswick).

Nec Cito Nec Temere   Neither hastily nor rashlly (Cambrai).

Nec Numina Desunt   Nor is the divine will absent (Savoy).

Nec Temere Nec Timide   Neither rashly nor timidly (Danzig, Lippe).

Necessitas Legem Non Habet   Necessity has no law (Magdeburg).

Nemo Me Impune Lacessit   No one touches me with impunity (UK, Scottish pound edge inscription).

Nihil Restat Reliqui   No relic remains (Ypres).

Nil Ultra Aras   Nothing beyond the rocks (Franque-mont).

No Nobis Dne Sed Noi Tuo Da Gloriam   Not to us, o Lord but to Thy name be glory given (France, Francis I).

Nobilissimum Dom Ac Com in Lipp & St   Most noble lord and count in Lippe and Sternberg (Schaumburg-Lippe).

Nomen Domini Turris Fortissima   The name of the Lord is the strongest tower (Frankfurt).

Non Aes Sed Fides   Not bronze but trust (Malta).

Non Est Mortale Quod Opto   What I desire is not mortal. (Mecklenburg).

Non Mihi Sed Populo   Not to me but to the people (Bavaria).

Non Relinquam Vos Orphanos   I shall not leave you as orphans (Papacy).

Non Surrexit Major   None greater has arisen (Genoa, Malta).

Nullum Simulatum Diuturnum Tandem   Nothing that is feigned lasts long (Wittgenstein).

Nummorum Famulus   The servant of the coinage (England, tin halfpence and farthings).

Nunquam Retrorsum   Never backwards (Brunswick-Wolfenbuttel).

O Crux Ave Spes Unica   Hail, o Cross, our only hope (England half-angels, France, Rene d'Anjou).

O Maria Ora Pro Me   O Mary pray for me (Bavaria).

Ob Cives Servatos   On account of the rescued citizens (Rome, Augustus).

Oculi Domini Super Iustos   The eyes of the Lord look down on the just (Neuchatel).

Omnia Auxiliante Maria   Mary helping everything (Schwyz).

Omnia Cum Deo   Everything with God (Reuss-Greiz).

Omnia cum Deo et Nihil Sine Eo   Everthing with God and nothing without Him (Erbach).

Omnis Potestas a Deo Est   All power comes from God (Sweden).

Opp & Carn Dux Comm Rittb SCM Cons Int & Compi Mareschal   Duke of Troppau and Carniola, count of Rietberg, privy councillor of his sacred imperial majesty, field marshal (Liechtenstein).

Opp & Carn . . . Aur Velleris Eques   Duke of Troppau . . . knight of the Golden Fleece (Liechtenstein).

Opportune   Conveniently (Savoy).

Optimus Princeps   Best prince (Rome, Trajan).

Opulentia Salerno   Wealthy Salerno (Siculo-Norman kingdom).

Pace et Iustitia   With peace and justice (Spanish Netherlands).

Pacator Orbis   Pacifier of the world (Rome, Aurelian).

Palma Sub Pondere Crescit   The palm grows under its weight (Waldeck).

Pater Noster   Our Father (Flanders, 14th century).

Pater Patriae   Farther of his country (Rome, Caligula).

Patria Si Dreptul Meu   The country and my right (Roumania).

Patrimon Henr Frid Sorte Divisum   The heritage of Heinrich Friedrich divided by lot (Hohenlohe-Langenbach).

Patrimonia Beati Petri   The inheritance of the blessed Peter (Papacy).

Patrona Franconiae   Patron Franconia (Wurzburg).

Pax Aeterna   Eternal peace (Rome, Marcus Aurelius).

Coin Yearbook 2023

Pax et Abundantia   Peace and plenty (Burgundy, Gelderland).

Pax Missa Per Orbem   Peace sent throughout the world (England, Anne).

Pax Petrus   Peace Peter (Trier, 10th century).

Pax Praevalet Armis   May peace prevail by force of arms (Mainz).

Pax Quaeritur Bello   Peace is sought by war (Commonwealth, Cromwell).

Pecunia Totum Circumit Orbem   Money goes round the whole world (Brazil).

Per Aspera Ad Astra   Through difficulties to the stars (Mecklenburg-Schwerin).

Per Angusta ad Augusta   Through precarious times to the majestic (Solms-Roedelheim, a pun on the name of the ruler Johan August).

Per Crucem Tuam Salva Nos Christe Redemptor   By Thy cross save us, O Christ our Redeemer (England, angels).

Per Crucem Tuam Salva Nos Xpe Redemt   By Thy cross save us, O Christ our Redeemer (Portugal, 15th century).

Perdam Babillonis Nomen   May the name of Babylon perish (Naples).

Perennitati Iustissimi Regis   For the duration of the most just king (France, Louis XIII).

Perennitati Principis Galliae Restitutionis   For the duration of the restoration of the prince of the Gauls (France, Henri IV).

Perfer et Obdura Bruxella   Carry on and stick it out, Brussels (Brussels siege, 1579–80).

Perpetuus in Nemet Vivar   Hereditary count in Nemt-Ujvar (Batthanyi).

Pietate et Constantia   By piety and constancy (Fulda).

Pietate et Iustitia   By piety and justice (Denmark).

Plebei Urbanae Frumento Constituto   Free distribu-tion of grain to the urban working-class established (Rome, Nerva).

Pleidio Wyf Im Gwlad   True am I to my country (UK, Welsh pound edge inscription).

Plus Ultra   Beyond (the Pillars of Hercules) (Spanish America).

Point du Couronne sans Peine   Point of the crown without penalty (Coburg).

Pons Civit Castellana   The bridge of the town of Castellana (Papacy).

Populus et Senatus Bonon   The people and senate of Bologna (Bologna).

Post Mortem Patris Pro Filio   For the son after his father's death (Pontefract siege coins).

Post Tenebras Lux   After darkness light (Geneva).

Post Tenebras Spero Lucem   After darkness I hope for light (Geneva).

Posui Deum Adiutorem Meum   I have made God my helper (England, Ireland, 1351–1603).

Praesidium et Decus   Protection and ornament (Bologna).

Prima Sedes Galliarum   First see of the Gauls (Lyon).

Primitiae Fodin Kuttenb ab Aerari Iterum Susceptarum   First results dug from the Kuttenberg mines in a renewed undertaking (Austria).

Princps Iuventutis   Prince of youth (Roman Empire).

Pro Defensione Urbis et Patriae   For the defence of city and country (France, Louis XIV).

Pro Deo et Patria   For God and the fatherland (Fulda).

Pro Deo et Populo   For God and the people (Bavaria).

Pro Ecclesia et Pro Patria   For the church and the fatherland (Constance).

Pro Fausio PP Reitur VS   For happy returns of the princes of the Two Sicilies (Naples and Sicily).

Pro Lege et Grege   For law and the flock (Fulda).

Pro maximo Dei Gloria et Bono Publico   For the greatest glory of God and the good of the people (Wurttemberg).

Pro Patria   For the fatherland (Wurzburg).

Propitio Deo Secura Ago   With God's favour I lead a secure life. (Saxe-Lauenburg).

Protector Literis Literae Nummis Corona et Salus   A protection to the letters (on the face of the coin), the letters (on the edge) are a garland and a safeguard to the coinage (Commonwealth, Cromwell broad).

Protege Virgo Pisas   Protect Pisa, O Virgin (Pisa).

Provide et Constanter   Wisely and firmly (Wurtem-berg).

Providentia et Pactis   Through foresight and pacts (Brandenburg-Ansbach).

Providentia Optimi Principis   With the foresight of the best prince (Naples and Sicily).

Proxima Fisica Finis   Nearest to natural end (Orciano).

Proxima Soli   Nearest to the sun (Modena).

Pulcra Virtutis Imago   The beautiful image of virtue (Genoa).

Pupillum et Viduam Suscipiat   May he support the orphan and the widow (Savoy).

Quae Deus Conjunxit Nemo Separet   What God hath joined let no man put asunder (England, James I).

Quem Quadragesies et Semel Patriae Natum Esse Gratulamur   Whom we congratulate for the forty-first time for being born to the fatherland (Lippe-Detmold).

Qui Dat Pauperi Non Indigebit   Who gives to the poor will never be in need (Munster).

Quid Non Cogit Necessitas   To what does Necessity not drive. (Ypres).

Quin Matrimonii Lustrum Celebrant   They celebrate their silver wedding (Austria, 1879).

Quocunque Gesseris (Jeceris) Stabit   Whichever way you throw it it will stand (Isle of Man).

Quod Deus Vult Hoc Semper Fit   What God wishes always occurs. (Saxe-Weimar).

Recondüntur non Retondüntur   They are laid up in store, not thundered back (Savoy).

44

Recta Tueri   Defend the right (Austria).

Recte Constanter et Fortiter   Rightly, constantly and bravely (Bavaria).

Recte Faciendo Neminem Timeas   May you fear no one in doing right. (Solms-Laubach).

Rector Orbis   Ruler of the world (Rome, Didius Julianus).

Rectus et Immotus   Right and immovable (Hesse).

Redde Cuique Quod Suum Est   Render to each that which is his own (England, Henry VIII).

Redeunt antiqui Gaudia Moris   There return the joys of ancient custom (Regensburg).

Reg Pr Pol et Lith Saxon Dux   Royal prince of Poland and Lithuania and duke of Saxony (Trier).

Regia Boruss Societas Asiat Embdae   Royal Prussian Asiatic Society of Emden (Prussia).

Regier Mich Her Nach Deinen Wort   Govern me here according to Thy word (Palatinate).

Regnans Capitulum Ecclesiae Cathedralis Ratisbonensis Sede Vacante   Administering the chapter of the cathedral church at Regensburg, the see being vacant (Regensburg).

Regni Utr Sic et Hier   Of the kingdom of the Two Sicilies and of Jerusalem (Naples and Sicily).

Religio Protestantium Leges Angliae Libertas Parliamenti   The religion of the Protestants, the laws of England and the freedom of Parliament (England, Royalists, 1642).

Relinquo Vos Liberos ab Utroque Homine   I leave you as children of each man (San Marino).

Restauracao da Independencia   Restoration of inde-pendence (Portugal, 1990).

Restitutor Exercitus   Restorer of the army (Rome, Aurelian).

Restitutor Galliarum   Restorer of the Gauls (Rome, Gallienus).

Restitutor Generis Humani   Restorer of mankind (Rome, Valerian).

Restitutor Libertatis   Restorer of freedom (Rome, Constantine).

Restitutor Orbis   Restorer of the world (Rome, Valerian).

Restitutor Orientis   Restorer of the east (Rome).

Restitutor Saeculi   Restorer of the century (Rome, Valerian).

Restitutor Urbis   Restorer of the city (Rome, Severus).

Rosa Americana Utile Dulci   The American rose, useful and sweet (American colonies).

Rosa Sine Spina   A rose without a thorn (England, Tudor coins).

Rutilans Rosa Sine Spina   A dazzling rose without a thorn (England, Tudor gold coins).

S Annae Fundgruben Ausb Tha in N Oe   Mining thaler of the St Anne mine in Lower Austria (Austria).

S Ap S Leg Nat Germ Primas   Legate of the Holy Apostolic See, born Primate of Germany (Salzburg).

S Carolus Magnus Fundator   Charlemagne founder (Munster).

S. Gertrudis Virgo Prudens Niviella   St Gertrude the wise virgin of Nivelles (Nivelles).

SI Aul Reg Her & P Ge H Post Mag   General hereditary postmaster, supreme of the imperial court of the hereditary kingdom and provinces (Paar).

S. Ian Bapt F. Zachari   St John the Baptist, son of Zachary (Florence).

S. Kilianus Cum Sociis Francorum Apostoli   St Kilian and his companions, apostles to the Franks (Wurzburg).

S. Lambertus Patronus Leodiensis   St Lambert, patron of Liege (Liege).

Sac Nupt Celeb Berol   For the holy matrimony celebrated at Berlin (Brandenburg-Ansbach).

Sac Rom Imp   Holy Roman Empire (German states).

Sac Rom Imp Provisor Iterum   Administrator of the Holy Roman Empire for the second time (Saxony).

Salus Generis Humani   Safety of mankind (Rome, Vindex).

Salus Patriae   Safety of the fatherland (Italy).

Salus Populi   The safety of the people (Spain).

Salus Provinciarum   Safety of the provinces (Rome, Postumus).

Salus Publica Salus Mea   Public safety is my safety (Sweden).

Salus Reipublicae   The safety of the republic (Rome, Theodosius II).

Salus Reipublicae Suprema Lex   The safety of the republic is the supreme law (Poland).

Salvam Fac Rempublicam Tuam   Make your state safe (San Marino).

Sanctus Iohannes Innoce   St John the harmless (Gandersheim).

Sans Changer   Without changing (Isle of Man).

Sans Eclat   Without pomp (Bouchain siege, 1711).

Sapiente Diffidentia   Wise distrust (Teschen).

Scutum Fidei Proteget Eum / Eam   The shield of faith shall protect him / her (England, Edward VI and Elizabeth I).

Secundum Voluntatem Tuam Domine   Your favourable will o Lord (Hesse).

Securitati Publicae   For the public safety (Brandenburg-Ansbach).

Sede Vacante   The see being vacant (Papal states, Vatican and ecclesiastical coinage).

Sena Vetus Alpha et W Principum et Finis   Old Siena alpha and omega, the beginning and the end (Siena).

Senatus Populus QR   Senate and people of Rome (Rome, 1188).

Si Deus Nobiscum Quis Contra Nos   If God is with us who can oppose us (Hesse).

Si Deus Pro Nobis Quis Contra Nos   If God is for us who can oppose us (Roemhild).

Sieh Deine Seeligkeit Steht Fest Ins Vaters Liebe   Behold thy salvation stands surely in thy Father's love (Gotha).

Signis Receptis   When the standards had been recovered (Rome, Augustus).

Signum Crucis   The sign of the cross (Groningen).

Sincere et Constanter   Truthfully and steadfastly (Hesse-Darmstadt).

Sit Nomen Domini Benedictum   Blessed be the name of the Lord (Burgundy, Strasbourg).

St T X Adiuto Reg Iste Domba   Let it be to you, o Christ, the assistant to the king of Dombes (Dombes).

Sit Tibi Xpe Dat q'tu Regis Iste Ducat   May this duchy which Thou rulest be given to Thee, O Christ (Venice, ducat).

Sit Unio Haec Perennis   May this union last for ever (Hohenlohe-Langenberg).

Sola Bona Quae Honesta   The only good things are those which are honest (Brunswick).

Sola Facta Deum Sequor   Through deeds alone I strive to follow God (Milan).

Soli Deo Honor et Gloria   To God alone be honour and glory (Nassau).

Soli Reduci   To him, the only one restored (Naples and Sicily).

Solius Virtutis Flos Perpetuus   The flower of Virtue alone is perpetual (Strasbourg).

Spes Confisa Deo Nunquam Confusa Recedit   Hope entrusted in God never retreats in a disorderly fashion (Lippe).

Spes Nr Deus   God is our hope (Oudenarde siege, 1582).

Spes Rei Publicae   The hope of the republic (Rome, Valens).

Strena ex Argyrocopeo Vallis S Christoph   A New Year's gift from the silver-bearing valley of St Christopher (Wurttemberg, 1625).

Sub His Secura Spes Clupeus Omnibus in Te Sperantibus   Under these hope is safe, a shield for all who reside hope in Thee (Bavaria).

Sub Pondere   Under weight (Fulda).

Sub Protectione Caesarea   Under imperial protection (Soragna).

Sub Tuum Praesidium Confug   We flee to Thy protection (Salzburg).

Sub Umbra Alarum Tuarum   Under the shadow of Thy wings (Iever, Scotland, James V).

Subditorum Salus Felicitas Summa   The safety of the subjects is the highest happiness (Lubeck).

Sufficit Mihi Gratia Tua Domine   Sufficient to me is Thy grace, o Lord (Ploen).

Supra Firmam Petram   Upon a firm rock (Papacy).

Susceptor Noster Deus   God is our defence (Tuscany).

Sydera Favent Industriae   The stars favour industry (Furstenberg).

Sylvarum Culturae Praemium   Prize for the culture of the forest (Brandenburg-Ansbach).

Tali Dicata Signo Mens Fluctuari Nequit   Consecrated by such a sign the mind cannot waver (England, Henry VIII George noble).

Tandem Bona Caus Triumphat   A good cause eventually triumphs (Dillenburg).

Tandem Fortuna Obstetrice   With good luck ultimately as the midwife (Wittgenstein).

Te Stante Virebo   With you at my side I shall be strong (Moravia).

Tene Mensuram et Respice Finem   Hold the measure and look to the end (Burgundy).

Tert Ducat Secular   Tercentenary of the duchy (Wurttemberg).

Thu Recht Schev Niemand   Go with right and fear no one (Saxe-Lauenburg).

Tibi Laus et Gloria   To Thee be praise and glory (Venice).

Timor Domini Fons Vitae   The fear of the Lord is a fountain of life (England, Edward VI shillings).

Tout Avec Dieu   Everything with God (Brunswick, 1626).

Traiectum ad Mosam   The crossing of the Maas (Maastricht).

Transvolat Nubila Virtus   Marriageable virtue soon flies past (Grueyeres).

Travail, Famille, Patrie   Work, family, country (Vichy France).

Triumphator Gent Barb   Victor over the barbarian people (Byzantine Empire, Arcadius).

Tueatur Unita Deus   May God guard these united (Kingdoms) (England, James I; Britain, 1847).

Turck Blegert Wien   Vienna besieged by the Turks (Vienna, 1531).

Tut Mar Gab Pr Vid de Lobk Nat Pr Sab Car et Aug Pr de Lobk   Regency of Maria Gabriela, widow of the prince of Lobkowitz, born princess of Savoy-Carignan, and August prince of Lobkowitz (Lobkowitz).

Tutela Italiae   The guardianship of Italy (Rome, Nerva).

Ubi Vult Spirat   He breathes where he will (Papacy).

Ubique Pax   Peace everywhere (Rome, Gallienus).

Union et Force   Union and strength (France).

Urbe Obsessa   The city under siege (Maastricht).

Urbem Virgo Tuam Serva   Protects thy city o virgin (Mary) (Strasbourg).

USC & RAM Cons Int Gen C Mar & Nob Praet H Turmae Capit   Privy councillor of both their holy imperial and royal apostolic majesties, general field marshal and captain of the noble praetorian Hungarian squadrons (Eszterhazy).

Veni Luumen Cordium   Come light of hearts (Vatican).

Veni Sancte Spiritus   Come Holy Ghost (Vatican).

Verbum Domini Manet in Aeternum   The word of the Lord abides forever (Hesse-Darmstadt, Veldenz).

Veritas Lex Tua   The truth is your law (Salzburg).

Veritas Temporis Filia   Truth is the daughter of time (England and Ireland, Mary Tudor).

Veritate et Labore   By truth and work (Wittgenstein).

Veritate et Iustitia   By truth and justice (German states).

Victoria Principum   The victory of princes (Ostrogoths).

Videant Pauperes et Laetentur   Let the poor see and rejoice (Tuscany).

Virgo Maria Protege Civitatem Savonae   Virgin Mary Protect the city of Savona (Savona).

Viribus Unitis   With united strength (Austria).

Virtute et Fidelitate   By virtue and faithfulness (Hesse-Cassel).

Virtute et Prudentia   With virtue and prudence (Auersperg).

Virtute Viam Dimetiar   I shall mark the way with valour (Waldeck).

Virtutis Gloria Merces   Glory is the reward of valour (Holstein-Gottorp).

Vis Unita Concordia Fratrum Fortior   United power is the stronger harmony of brothers (Mansfeld).

Visitavit Nos Oriens ex Alto   He has visited us arising on high (Luneburg).

Vivit Post Funera   He lives after death (Bremen).

Vota Optata Romae Fel   Vows taken for the luck of Rome (Rome, Maxentius).

Vox de Throno   A voice from the throne (Papacy).

Was Got Beschert Bleibet Unerwert   What God hath endowed leave undisturbed

Wider macht und List Mein Fels Gott Ist   Against might and trickery God is my rock (Hesse-Cassel).

Xpc Vincit Xpc Regnat   Christ conquers, Christ reigns (Scotland, Spain).

Xpc Vivet Xpc Regnat Xpc Impat   Christ lives, Christ reigns, Christ commands (Cambrai).

Xpe Resurescit   Christ lives again (Venice).

Xpistiana Religio   Christian religion (Carolingian Empire).

Xps Ihs Elegit me Regem Populo   Jesus Christ chose me as king to the people (Norway).

Zelator Fidei Usque ad Montem   An upholder of the faith through and through (Portugal).

Zum Besten des Vaterlands   To the best of the fatherland (Bamberg).

ABBREVIATIONS COMMONLY USED TO DENOTE METALLIC COMPOSITION	
Cu	Copper
Cu/Steel	Copper plated Steel
Ag/Cu	Silver plated copper
Ae	Bronze
Cu-Ni	Cupro-Nickel
Ni-Ag	Nickel Silver (note—does not contain silver)
Brass/Cu-Ni	Brass outer, Cupro-Nickel inner
Ni-Brass	Nickel-Brass
Ag	Silver
Au/Ag	Gold plated silver
Au	Gold
Pt	Platinum

Care
of coins

There is no point in going to a great deal of trouble and expense in selecting the best coins you can afford, only to let them deteriorate in value by neglect and mishandling. Unless you give some thought to the proper care of your coins, your collection is unlikely to make a profit for you if and when you come to sell it. Housing your coins is the biggest problem of all, so it is important to give a lot of attention to this.

Storage

The ideal, but admittedly the most expensive, method is the coin cabinet, constructed of air-dried mahogany, walnut or rosewood *(never oak, cedar or any highly resinous timber likely to cause chemical tarnish)*. These cabinets have banks of shallow drawers containing trays made of the same wood, with half-drilled holes of various sizes to accommodate the different denominations of coins. Such cabinets are handsome pieces of furniture but, being largely handmade, tend to be rather expensive. Occasionally good specimens can be picked up in secondhand furniture shops, or at the dispersal of house contents by auction, but the best bet is still to purchase a new cabinet, tailored to your own requirements. These collectors cabinets are hand-made using certified solid mahogany, as specified by leading museums, as mahogany does not contain any chemicals or resins that could result in the discolouration of the collection inside

the cabinet. The polish used on the outside of the cabinets is based on natural oils and hand applied then finished with bees wax. The trays are left as untreated mahogany so as not to introduce any harmful contaminants. The coin trays are available as single thickness or double thickness for holding thicker coins, capsules or artifacts.

Rob Davis Cabinets of Ticknall, Derbyshire (telephone: 01332 862755, www.robdaviscabinets), provides a first-class bespoke service with cabinets made to client's personal specifications. Made out of mahogany or English walnut, the storage options range from glassed-topped display cabinets suitable for a table top (with "secret" drawers) through to free-standing pieces as used by museums and institutions where security as well as safe-storage is a requirement. **Peter Nichols Cabinet Makers** (telephone 0115 9224149, www.coincabinets.com) was established in 1967 and is now run by Geoff Skinner and Shirley Watts. Based in Nottingham, the family-run business provides specialist display and storage systems to suit every need from standard cabinets for the average collector all the way up to the massive 40-tray specials supplied to the British Museum. All of these manufacturers use materials from sustainable sources and their products are exquisite examples of the cabinet maker's craft.

An excellent storage option is provided by a number of firms who manufacture coin trays in durable, felt-lined, man-made materials with shallow compartments to suit the various sizes of coins. Most of these trays interlock so that they build up into a cabinet of the desired size, and there are also versions designed as carrying cases, which are ideal for transporting coins.

For the coin connoisseur there are beautiful, hand-made cabinets such as this one from Rob Davis Cabinets.

The popular and extensive **Lighthouse** range is available from **Curtis Coin Care**. To view the current range of stock, go to www.curtiscoincare. com. This range includes a wide variety of cases and albums for the general collector in basic or deluxe styles as required, as well as printed albums for the specialist. Their cases, including the popular aluminium range, are manufactured to the highest standards, lined with blue plush which displays any coin to its best advantage. The red-lined single trays come in deep or standard size and make an ideal cabinet when stacked together or housed in their attractive aluminium case, which is available separately. The trays themselves come with a variety of compartments for every size of coin. Their complete range can be viewed on-line.

The extensive **Lindner** range is supplied in the UK by Prinz Publications UK Ltd of Unit 20A, Longrock Industrial Estate, Longrock, Cornwall TR20 8HX (telephone 01736 751910, www.prinz. co.uk). Well-known for their wide range of philatelic and numismatic accessories, but these include a full array of coin boxes, capsules, carrying cases and trays. The basic Lindner coin box is, in fact, a shallow tray available in a standard version or a smoked glass version. These trays have a crystal clear frame, red felt inserts and holes for various diameters of coins and medals. A novel feature of these trays is the rounded insert which facilitates the removal of coins from their spaces with the minimum of handling. These boxes are designed in such a manner that they interlock and can be built up into banks of trays, each fitted with a draw-handle and sliding in and out easily. Various types of chemically inert plastic capsules and envelopes have been designed for use in combination with plain shallow trays, without holes drilled. Lindner also manufacture a range of luxury cases lined in velvet and Atlas silk with padded covers and gold embossing on the spines, producing a most tasteful and elegant appearance.

Safe Albums of 16 Falcon Business Park, 38 Ivanhoe Road, Finchampstead, Berkshire RG40 4QQ (telephone 0118 932 8976, www.safealbums. co.uk) are the UK agents for the German Stapel-Element, a drawer-stacking system with clear plasticiser-free trays that fit into standard bookshelves. The sliding coin compartments, lined with blue velvet, can be angled for display to best advantage. Stackable drawers can be built up to any height desired. A wide range of drawer sizes is available, with compartments suitable for the smallest coins right up to four-compartment trays designed for very large artefacts such as card-cases or cigarette cases. The Mobel-Element cabinet is a superb specialised cabinet constructed of the finest timber with a steel frame and steel grip bars which can be securely locked.

There are also various other storage systems, such as the simple cardboard or plastic box which is made specifically to hold coins stored in see-through envelopes of chemically-inert plastic of various sizes, or white acid-free envelopes, usually 50mm square.

An alternative to these is the card coin holder which has a window made of inert cellophane-type see-through material. The card is folded over with the coin inside and is then stapled or stuck together with its own self-adhesive lining. The cards are a standard 50mm square with windows of various sizes from 15 to 39mm and fit neatly into the storage box or album page.

Coin Albums

When coin collecting became a popular hobby in the 1960s, several firms marketed ranges of coin albums. They had clear plastic sleeves divided into tiny compartments of various sizes and had the merit of being cheap and taking up little room on a bookshelf.

They had several drawbacks, however, not the least being the tendency of the pages to sag with the weight of the coins, or even, in extreme cases, to pull away from the pegs or rings holding them on to the spine.

The Lighthouse range includes a wide selection of de luxe and printed albums.

They required very careful handling as the coins could easily fall out of the top row as the pages were turned. The more expensive albums had little flaps that folded over the top of the coin to overcome this problem.

Arguably the worst aspect of these albums was the use of polyvinyl chloride (PVC) in the construction of the sleeves. Collectors soon discovered to their horror that this reacted chemically with their coins, especially those made of silver and many fine collections were ruined as a result.

Fortunately the lesson has been learned and the coin albums now on the market are quite safe. Lighthouse and Lindner offer a wide range of albums designed to house coins, medals or banknotes. The old problem about sagging pages is overcome by the use of a multi-ring binding welded to a very stout spine, while the sleeves contain neither Styrol nor PVC and will not affect any metals at all. In addition to pages with pockets of uniform size, the Karat range of albums operates on a slide principle which enables the user to insert vertical strips of different sizes on the same page, so that the coins of one country or series, or perhaps a thematic display of coins from different countries, can be displayed side by side.

Safe Albums offer a wide range of albums in the Coinholder System and Coin-Combi ranges. These, too, offer the choice of fixed pages with uniform-sized pockets, or interchangeable sliding inserts for different sizes side by side.

The "slab"

In the United States in the past few decades one of the preferred methods for keeping coins in pristine condition is the use of "slabs"—these tough plastic rectangles cannot be easily broken into, meaning that the coin inside remains in exactly the same condition as when it was placed in there. This has led to the rise of professional grading and encapsulation companies who not only "slab" your coin but also grade it and guarantee that grade. This allows coins to be bought and sold with both vendor and purchaser knowing exactly what the grade is, thus taking out the subjectivity of dealer or collector—an issue that can mean a huge difference in the value of the coin. Slabbing in this way is essentially a tool to help a coin maintain a grade and thus more easily guarantee its value, however, many collectors prefer it as a method of protecting their coins as it allows them to be stored or transported easily with no fear of damage.

The biggest companies in the United States for the encapsulation of coins are **NGC** (Numismatic Gauaranty Corporation) and **PCGS** (Professional Coin Grading Service). They have been in business for many, many years and in America the "slabbed" coin is a common sight. It is less common in the UK, with many collectors still unsure about the benefits of the "slab", but undoubtedly with the US companies opening offices and grading centres throughout the world more and more collectors are using the service and the "slab" is becoming accepted everywhere. However, anyone wishing to photograph a coin undoubtedly has a problem, as can be seen in many auction catalogues offering such items. The tell-tale grips that hold the coin obscure part of the edge of the coin.

Cleaning
coins

This is like matrimony—it should not be embarked on lightly. Indeed, the advice given by the magazine *Punch* in regard to marriage is equally sound in this case—don't do it! It is far better to have a dirty coin than an irretrievably damaged one. Every dealer has horror stories of handling coins that previous owners have cleaned, to their detriment. Probably the worst example was a display of coins found by a metal detectorist who "improved" his finds by abrading them in the kind of rotary drum used by lapidarists to polish gemstones. If you really must remove the dirt and grease from coins, it is advisable to practise on coins of little value.

Warm water containing a mild household detergent or washing-up liquid will work wonders in removing surface dirt and grease from most coins, but silver is best washed in a weak solution of ammonia and warm water—one part ammonia to ten parts water. Gold coins can be cleaned with diluted citric acid, such as lemon juice. Copper or bronze coins present more of a problem, but patches of verdigris can usually be removed by careful washing in a 20 per cent solution of sodium sesquicarbonate. Wartime coins made of tin, zinc, iron or steel can be cleaned in a 5 per cent solution

of caustic soda containing some aluminium or zinc foil or filings, but they must be rinsed afterwards in clean water and carefully dried. Cotton buds are ideal for gently prising dirt out of coin legends and crevices in the designs. Soft brushes (with animal bristles—*never* nylon or other artificial bristles) designed for cleaning silver are most suitable for gently cleaning coins.

Coins recovered from the soil or the sea bed present special problems, due to chemical reaction between the metals and the salts in the earth or sea water. In such cases, the best advice is to take them to the nearest museum and let the professional experts decide on what can or should be done.

There are a number of proprietary coin-cleaning kits and materials on the market suitable for gold, silver, copper and other metals but all of these should be used with caution and always read the instructions that come with them. When using any type of chemical cleaner rubber gloves should be worn and care taken to avoid breathing fumes or getting splashes of liquid in your eyes or on your skin. Obviously, the whole business of cleaning is a matter that should not be entered into without the utmost care and forethought.

POLISHING: A WARNING

If cleaning should only be approached with the greatest trepidation, polishing is definitely OUT! Beginners sometimes fall into the appalling error of thinking that a smart rub with metal polish might improve the appearance of their coins. Short of actually punching a hole through it, there can hardly be a more destructive act. Polishing a coin may improve its superficial appearance for a few days, but such abrasive action will destroy the patina and reduce the fineness of the high points of the surface.

Even if a coin is only polished once, it will never be quite the same again, and an expert can tell this a mile off.

Britain's Coin Shop - since 1955

45 Great Russell Street,
LONDON WC1B 3LU
(opposite the British Museum)
Tel: 020 7636 1188
Web www.coincraft.com
Email info@coincraft.com

Britain's Coin Shop

Auction Price realized £28
Coincraft's Buying Price £100

We have been advertising to buy original £5 bags of BU 1967 Halfpennies for £100, for several years now and have bought several hundred bags at this price. I just saw the prices realized from a large auction house, they sold a bag for just £28! The buyer made a fantastic buy, heck they can make £72 by turning it over to us. The seller, well they didn't do so well, they could have had £78 more if they sold to us and out of that £100. Out of their £28 they have to pay sellers premium.

Let's be honest this is a most unusual case, but it did actually happen in April of 2022. Selling to Coincraft – Britain's Coin Shop is easy, you get paid immediately and you are dealing with knowledgably experts. You are also dealing with a family owned and family run business that has been helping collectors both buying and selling for the past 67 years.

We are right across the street from the British Museum just look out for the Giant Victorian Penny hanging outside. We buy coins, banknotes, medals anything numismatic and quantity doesn't worry us. Immediate payment and most of our offers are accepted on the spot.

If you have something for sale why not deal with the professionals, why not deal with Coincraft – Britain's Coin Shop. Open 5 days a week.

Thank you
Richard Lobel - Founder Coincraft – Britain's Coin Shop

THE ROYAL MINT®

THE ORIGINAL MAKER

Look Right, Look Left,
Look No Further

The Royal Mint has struck the coins of every British monarch since Alfred the Great. We have sourced many rare coins for collectors, such as the George III 1819 Sovereign, which auctioned for £100,000 in July 2019, the George IV 1828 Sovereign that sold for £45,000 in May 2019 and the Edward VIII 1937 Sovereign that sold for £1 million in January 2020. Add to your collection or find a memorable gift by using our Coin Finder Service. Our team of specialists are ready to help you find something remarkable.

 collectorservices@royalmint.com   0800 03 22 153

royalmint.com

CELEBRATE | COLLECT | INVEST | SECURE | DISCOVER

THE ROYAL MINT Experience

Come and watch the UK's coins being made

The Experience offers a grand day out for all the family where the work and issues of one of the oldest mints in the world can be explored at it's purpose-built visitors' centre in Llantrisant.

Walk through Interactive Exhibition

Come and
play, have
fun and learn
all about the
history of coins

Strike your own coin

On the Royal Mint Experience tour you will learn more about the manufacturing process that goes into creating the coins in your pocket. As part of your tour, you will have the opportunity to strike your very own coin (the design of the coin alters, depending on what theme the Royal Mint are celebrating at the time of your visit). The opportunity to strike your own coin can be obtained for £6.90 and is limited to one coin per person. "Strike your own coin" can be purchased when pre-booking your visit and admission tickets.

Want to visit?
See overleaf

A great day out for everyone

BOOK YOUR VISIT today

The visitor centre has been ranked in the top 10% of attractions worldwide for customer experience by TripAdvisor for the past two years

The Royal Mint is located 4 miles from Junction 34 of the M4. Drive past the main entrance to the Mint. The visitors' car park for The Royal Mint Experience is on the left opposite the Three Saints Hotel. The guided tour lasts 45 minutes, but allow a good couple of hours to explore the exhibits in the final exhibition hall. There are plenty of interactive exhibits to keep the children amused. There is a large cafeteria for visitors and a well-stocked shop selling souvenirs as well as coins.

Admission Prices:	Online £
Adult (16+)	13.50 to 17.11
Child (5-15 years)	10.35 to 12.84
Students	11.25 to 13.83
Senior Citizens	11.25 to 13.83
Family of 4	40.49 to 51.25
Child under 5 years	Free
Carer	Free
Blue Peter Badge Holder	Free

There are restrictions on the number of wheelchair users in any one group. Wheelchair users, or others with special needs, should telephone 0333 241 2223. This number can also be used to book a tour. The tours run at regular intervals throughout the day from 9.30am to 3pm. Remember all children under 16 must be accompanied by an adult at all times.

The Royal Mint Experience is open daily from 9.15am to 4.15pm except December 25 and 26 and January 1.

To plan your visit to the Royal Mint Experience go online at www.royalmint.com

Images courtesy of the Royal Mint. Information correct at time of going to press.

Celtic
coinage of Britain

Celtic coins were the first coins made in Britain, from c.120 BC to c.AD 50. They were minted by the rulers of thirteen tribal groups situated to the southeast of a line from the Humber to the Severn. Today's prices typically range from £50 to £5,000. Celtic specialist CHRIS RUDD introduces this increasingly popular series.

Britain was the last part of Celtic Europe to conform to the uniform bureaucracy of Roman colonisation and then only partially. Like Britons themselves, the essence of Ancient British coins is freedom. Tribal rulers were free to mint their own coins to their own designs, often influenced by their local Druids, in my view. The imagery of British Celtic coins is free—surrealistic, not realistic. For me this free spirit is symbolised by two great British freedom fighters and their coins: Cassivellaunos who fought Caesar in 54 BC and Caratacus who fought Claudius from AD 43 to 51.

The first coins made in Britain were made like this

Molten tin-rich bronze was poured into clay moulds.

Coin designs were scribed onto clay strip-moulds with a stylus prior to firing. Tentative reconstruction.

and look like this

Cast bronze
c.120-100 BC

Cast potin
c.80-50 BC

Cassivellaunos with winged sceptre and winged helmet, as seen on silver unit, ABC 2472.

Whaddon Chase gold stater of Cassivellaunos, ABC 2436, with his winged sceptre.

Gold stater of Caratacus, ABC–, sold by Chris Rudd for £88,000, world record price for a Celtic coin.

Marseilles inspired Britain's first homemade coinage: potin coins cast in clay strip-moulds, with Apollo on one side and a bull on the other, plus MA for Massalia (Marseilles). Made in Kent c. 120–100 BC, these cast potins circulated alongside gold coins imported from Gaul. During the Gallic Wars (58–51 BC) many other Gaulish coins—gold, silver and bronze—came to Britain, some brought by refugees, others by British mercenaries, others by trade.

Imported Coriosolites silver stater, ABC 70. Many were in the Jersey hoard, 2012, which contained 70,000 coins and was valued by Chris Rudd at £6 million.

The most famous Gallic migrant was Commios "friend", a former ally of Caesar, who became king of the Regini and Atrebates in the south of England c. 50–25 BC. Commios was the first British ruler to place his name on coins. His three sons—Tincomarus (great in peace), Eppillus (little horse) and Verica (the high one), made the Commian dynasty one of the wealthiest and most powerful in Britain. Most of their coins adopted Roman imagery and archaeology indicates that they imported Roman luxury goods, especially Italian wine. Many coins of Verica show grapes, vine leaves and wine cups.

The main rivals of the Regini and Atrebates were the Catuvellauni of Hertfordshire. Their first known ruler was probably Cassivellaunos "bronze commander", leader of the British coalition against Caesar in 54 BC. Many of Britain's earliest gold coins were probably struck to fund resistance to Caesar and then to pay tribute to him. Cassivellaunos may have organised this war money. Addedomaros "great in chariots" (c. 45–25 BC) was the first ruler north of the Thames to inscribe his coins, perhaps copying Commios.

Thirteen possible tribal groups which were producing coins by c.50-40 BC (Cantiaci much earlier). By c.30 BC the Belgae, East Wiltshire and Berkshire group had apparently stopped minting independently.

Gold stater of Commios (ABC 1022) the first British king to place his name on coins. There are two hidden faces on the obverse.

Verica silver minim with wine cup (ABC 1331) and Verica gold stater with vine leaf (ABC 1193)—evidence of Britain's thirst for fine Italian wine and Roman silverware.

Catuvellaunian expansion continued under Tasciovanos "killer of badgers" whose coins became increasingly Roman in style. His son Cunobelinus "hound of Belenus"—Shakespeare's *Cymbeline*) was the most potent tribal king in Atlantic Europe. Suetonius called him "king of the Britons". During his thirty-year reign (c. AD 8–41) Cunobelinus may have minted well over a million gold staters, most of them displaying a corn ear and CAMV— short for *Camulodunon* (Colchester). When his brother Epaticcus "leader of horsemen" and his son Caratacus "the beloved"—both clad as Hercules on their silver coins—crossed the Thames and attacked the Atrebates, Verica fled to Claudius who invaded Britain in AD 43. The minting of tribal coins ceased shortly afterwards.

Other tribes that issued coins included the Cantiaci of Kent, the Belgae of Hampshire, the Durotriges of Dorset, the Dobunni of the West Midlands, the Trinovantes of Essex, the Iceni of East Anglia and the Corieltavi of Lincolnshire. However, only a minority of people in the British Isles used coins regularly—the moneyed minority in southeast England. Cornwall, Devon, Wales, northern England, Scotland and Ireland remained coinless. Which is why ancient British coins are relatively rare. For example, whereas Greek coins were minted for about 600 years, Roman for about 800 years and Gaulish for about 250 years, ancient British coins were produced for little more than 150 years, and often in much smaller runs.

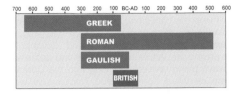

Ancient British coins weren't minted for as long as Greek, Roman or Gaulish coins were. That's one of the reasons they are so scarce.

This century and a half of Ancient British coin production generated a remarkable flowering of insular creativity and insular technology, unmatched by any other northern European nation of the period. Though initially influenced by Gallic minting techniques and Gallic iconography, Ancient British coinage rapidly developed its own denominational systems, its own gold standards and its own highly distinctive coin designs — often inspired by Roman prototypes, but invariably modified to suit local needs. Between c. 110 BC and c. AD 45 around a thousand different coin types were minted in Britain. Many if not most of these thousand types displayed what might loosely be described as "religious" imagery. Not surprising, really, when one recalls that Caesar says that Druidism originated in Britain. Moreover, Tasciovanos struck coins in no fewer than five different denominations, whereas most Gaulish rulers issued no more than two or three.

The history of late iron age Britain, particularly the century prior to the Claudian conquest, has largely been rewritten with the help of Ancient British coins. Most of the recent advances in our knowledge of this period have been due to amateur metal detecting. As a direct result of coin finds made by metal detectorists since the 1970s four new coin-issuing groups and maybe ten new rulers, previously unknown or unrecognised, have been identified. Not bad for barely forty years of unfunded, unofficial fieldwork.

Unlike Gaul, most of the British Isles was virtually coinless throughout the late iron age (and later). Coin production was confined to south-east Britain. That's why, overall, Ancient British coins are much rarer than Gaulish coins.

What is it about Ancient British coins that is making them increasingly popular with collectors all over the world? Having been involved with them for many years (I excavated my first in 1952) I'll tell you why they appeal to me.

I love the *primal antiquity* of Celtic coins. They were the first coins made in Britain over two thousand years ago. When you see the flamboyant freedom of their designs you realise that they are the most boisterously British coins ever minted, unlike the unsmiling Roman, Anglo-Saxon and Norman series that marched soberly in their dancing footsteps.

I love the *anarchic regality* of Celtic coins. Like the rumbustious tribal kings that issued them, their personality is wild, strong and highly irregular. These coins were made by the first British rulers known by name to us — unruly, quarrelsome, beer-swilling, tribal warlords such as Cassivellaunos who fought Julius Caesar in 54 BC and Caratacus, the British resistance leader who opposed Claudius in AD 43.

I love the *imaginative imagery* you find on Celtic coins: all the different gods and goddesses, armed warriors, chariot wheels, hidden faces, decapitated heads, suns, moons, stars, thunderbolts, floral motifs, magic signs and phallic symbols. Plus an amazing menagerie of wild animals, birds and mythical beasts.

I love the *myths, mystery and mysticism* behind Celtic coins. Look closely at this late iron

Ancient British denominations

There was no national currency in pre-Roman Britain and little consistency from region to region. Different tribes issued different mixtures of low, medium and high value coins. Here are the most common denominations used by the ancient Brits. The names are ours, not theirs. We've no idea what they called their coins, shown here actual size.

GOLD STATERS
Can also be silver, billon or bronze

Norfolk Wolf, ABC 1393

GOLD QUARTER STATERS
Can also be silver or billon

Irstead Smiler, ABC 1480

SILVER UNITS

Norfolk God, ABC 1567

SILVER HALF UNITS

Aunt Cost Half, ABC 1953

SILVER MINIMS

Verica Sphinx, ABC 1340

BRONZE UNITS

Cunobelinus Centaur, ABC 2957

BRONZE HALF UNITS

Tasciovanos Goat, ABC 2709

CAST POTIN UNITS

Nipples, ABC 174

age money of Albion and you'll catch glimpses of long-lost legends and ancient pagan rituals such as head-hunting, bull sacrificing and shape-shifting. You'll marvel at the plethora of occult signs and arcane symbols and you may even feel the secret power of the Druids.

I love the *palpitating unpredictability* of Celtic coins. Even after seventy years of heart-racing intimacy they are constantly and delightfully surprising me. Attributions, names and dates are always being revised. Not long ago the Coritani were renamed Corieltavi and Tincommios was rechristened Tincomarus. Almost every month exciting new types and new variants keep leaping out of the ground, thanks to metal detectorists.

Bronze units of Cunobelinus, son of Tasciovanos, showing a bull being sacrificed (ABC 2972) and a man—perhaps a Druid priest?—carrying a severed human head (ABC 2987).

For example, on September 4, 2010 the late Danny Baldock discovered the first recorded coin of Anarevitos, a Kentish ruler previously unknown to history.

I love the *uncommon scarcity* of Celtic coins. Ask any metdet how many Ancient British coins he or she has found and you'll immediately realise that they are rarer than Roman coins—at least a thousand times rarer on average—for the reasons stated above.

Finally I love the *galloping good value* of this horsey money (some Celtic horses have three tails, some breathe fire, others have a human

Silver unit of freedom-fighter Caratacus (ABC 1376) who defied the Roman invaders for eight years until he was betrayed by Cartimandua, queen of the Brigantes.

torso). Their greater rarity doesn't mean they are costlier than other Ancient coins. In fact, they are often cheaper because demand determines price and because there are far fewer collectors of Ancient British coins than there are, say, of Greek or Roman coins. For example, a very fine British gold stater typically costs less than half the price—sometimes even a third the price of a Roman aureus or English gold noble of comparable quality and rarity. But the disparity is gradually diminishing as more and more canny collectors are appreciating the untamed beauty and undervalued scarcity of British Celtic coins.

Coin Yearbook provides a great guide to current prices of commoner Celtic types, but because new types keep turning up and because big hoards are sometimes found (causing values to fluctuate temporarily) you'd be well advised to also keep an eye on dealers' catalogues and prices realised at auction. If you're buying in Britain, buy from people who are members of the BNTA (British Numismatic Trade Association). If you're buying overseas, check that your suppliers belong to the IAPN (International Association of Professional Numismatists). And, if you're a beginner, beware of dodgy traders on the internet, or you could end up with a fistful of fakes and no refund.

I'd also counsel you to spend a day at the British Museum. Its collection of almost 7,000 Ancient British coins is the most comprehensive, publicly accessible collection of its kind in the world. As former curator, Ian Leins, says: "They're public coins . . . your coins, and they're here for you to see. So come and see them. We'll be pleased to show them to you". Access to the collection is free for everyone. But you'll need to make an appointment before you go, and take some photo ID and proof of address. Email: coins@thebritishmuseum.ac.uk or telephone: 020 7323 8607.

Before you buy coins—any coins of any period—it always pays to read about them first. As an old adman I'm not shy about blowing my own trumpet. The best little introduction to Celtic coins is *Britain's First Coins* by Chris Rudd (2013) and the most comprehensive catalogue of the series is *Ancient British Coins* also by Chris Rudd (2010), known in the trade as ABC. If you have even half the fun I've had with Ancient British coins (and am still having)—I can promise you that you'll be a very happy person indeed. Never bored, and never with a complete collection.

A unique gold stater of Anarevitos, a previously unknown ruler of the Cantiaci, probably a son of Eppillus, king of Calleva (Silchester). Sold by Elizabeth Cottam of Chris Rudd for £21,000. (Coin News, December 2010).

Collecting
ancient coins

Ancient coins differ from most other series which are collected in Britain in that every piece has spent the major part of the last two thousand years in the ground. As JOHN CUMMINGS, dealer in ancient coins and antiquities explains here, the effect that burial has had on the surface of the coin determines more than anything else the value of a particular piece. With more modern coins, the only things which affect price are rarity and grade. There may be a premium for coins exhibiting particularly fine tone, or with outstanding pedigrees, but an 1887 crown in "extremely fine" condition has virtually the same value as every other piece with the same grade and of the same date. With ancient coins the story is very different.

A large number of different criteria affect the price of an ancient coin. Factors affecting prices can be broken down into several categories:

Condition

The most important factor by far in determining price. Ancient coins were struck by hand and can exhibit striking faults. Value suffers if the coin is struck with the designs off-centre, is weakly struck, or if the flan is irregular in shape. Many of the Celtic tribes issued coins of varying fineness and those made from low quality gold or silver are worth less than similar specimens where the metal quality is better. Conversely, coins on exceptional flans, particularly well struck, or with fine patinas command a premium.

Many ancient coins have suffered during their stay in the ground. It must be borne in mind that the prices given in the price guide are for uncorroded, undamaged examples. A Roman denarius should be graded using the same criteria as those used for grading modern coins. The surfaces must be good, and the coin intact. The fact that the coin is 2,000 years old is irrelevant as far as grading is concerned. Coins which are not perfectly preserved are certainly not without value, however, the value for a given grade decreases with the degree of fault.

Rarity

As with all other series, rare coins usually command higher prices than common ones. A unique variety of a small fourth century Roman bronze coin, even in perfect condition, can be worth much less than a more worn and common piece from an earlier part of the empire. In the Celtic series, there is an almost infinite variety of minor types and a unique variety of an uninscribed type will rarely outbid an inscribed issue of a known king.

Historical and local significance

Types which have historical or local interest can command a price far above their scarcity value. Denarii of the emperor Tiberius are believed to have been referred to in the New Testament and command a far higher price than a less interesting piece of similar rarity. Similarly, pieces which have British reverse types such as the "VICT BRIT" reverse of the third century AD are more expensive than their scarcity would indicate. The 12 Caesars remain ever popular especially in the American market and this affects prices throughout the world. In the Celtic series, coins of Cunobelin or Boudicca are far more popular than pieces which have no historical interest but which may be far scarcer.

Reverse types

All Roman emperors who survived for a reasonable time issued coins with many different reverse types. The most common of these usually show various Roman gods. When a coin has an unusual reverse it always enhances the value. Particularly popular are architectural scenes, animals, references to Judaism, and legionary types.

Artistic merit

The Roman coinage is blessed with a large number of bust varieties and these can have a startling effect on price. For example, a common coin with the bust facing left instead of right can be worth several times the price of a normal specimen. Like many of the emperors, the coinage of Hadrian has a large number of bust varieties, some of which are extremely artistic and these, too, can command a premium.

The coinage used in Britain from the time of the invasion in AD 43 was the same as that introduced throughout the Empire by the emperor Augustus around 20 BC. The simple divisions of 2 asses equal to one dupondius, 2 dupondii equal to 1 sestertius, 4 sestertii equal to one denarius and 25 denarii equal to one aureus continued in use until the reformation of the coinage by Caracalla in AD 214.

Aureus (gold)

Denarius (silver)

Dupondius (copper)

Sestertius (bronze)

As (copper)

Hammered
coinage

The hammered currency of medieval Britain is among some of the most interesting coinage in the world. The turbulent history of these islands is reflected in the fascinating changes in size, design, fineness and workmanship, culminating in the many strange examples that emanated from the strife of the Civil War.

The Norman Conquest of England in 1066 and succeeding years had far-reaching effects on all aspects of life. Surprisingly, however, it had little impact on the coinage. William the Conqueror was anxious to emphasise the continuity of his reign, so far as the ordinary people were concerned, and therefore he retained the fabric, size and general design pattern of the silver penny. Almost 70 mints were in operation during this reign, but by the middle of the 12th century the number was reduced to 55 and under Henry II (1154–89) it fell to 30 and latterly to only eleven. By the early 14th century the production of coins had been centralised on London and Canterbury, together with the ecclesiastical mints at York and Canterbury. The silver penny was the principal denomination throughout the Norman period, pieces cut along the lines of the cross on the reverse continuing to serve as halfpence and farthings.

Eight types of penny were struck under William I and five under his son William Rufus, both profiles (left and right) and facing portraits being used in both reigns allied to crosses of various types. Fifteen types were minted under Henry I (1100–35), portraiture having now degenerated to crude caricature, the lines engraved on the coinage dies being built up by means of various punches. Halfpence modelled on the same pattern were also struck, but very sparingly and are very rare.

On Henry's death the succession was contested by his daughter Matilda and his nephew Stephen of Blois. Civil war broke out in 1138 and continued till 1153. Stephen controlled London and its mint, but Matilda and her supporters occupied the West Country and struck their own coins at Bristol. Several of the powerful barons struck their own coins, and there were distinct regional variants of the regal coinage. Of particular interest are the coins

Silver pennies of, from left to right, William I, William Rufus, Henry I and Stephen.

struck from obverse dies with Stephen's portrait erased or defaced, believed to date from 1148 when the usurper was under papal interdict.

Peace was restored in 1153 when it was agreed that Matilda's son Henry should succeed Stephen. On the latter's death the following year, Henry II ascended the throne. Coins of Stephen's last type continued to be minted till 1158, but Henry then took the opportunity to overhaul the coinage which had become irregular and sub-standard during the civil war. The new "Cross Crosslet" coins, usually known as the Tealby coinage (from the hoard of over 5,000 pennies found at Tealby, Lincolnshire in 1807), were produced at 30 mints, but when the recoinage was completed this number was reduced to a dozen. The design of Henry's coins remained virtually the same throughout more than two decades, apart from minor variants. Then, in 1180, a new type, known as the Short Cross coinage, was introduced. This was a vast improvement over the poorly struck Cross Crosslet coins and continued without alteration, not only to the end of the reign of Henry II in 1189, but throughout the reigns of his sons Richard (1189–99) and John (1199–1216) and the first half of the reign of his grandson Henry III (1216–46). Throughout that 66 year period, however, there were minor variations in portraits and lettering which enable numismatists to attribute the HENRICUS coins to specific reigns and periods.

"Tealby" type penny (top), and
"Short Cross" penny of Henry II.

The style and workmanship of the Short Cross coinage deteriorated in the reign of Henry III. By the 1220s coin production was confined to the regal mints at London and Canterbury, the sole exception being the ecclesiastical mint maintained by the Abbot of Bury St Edmunds.

Halfpence and farthings were briefly struck in 1221–30, though halfpence are now extremely rare and so far only a solitary farthing has been discovered.

By the middle of this reign the coinage was in a deplorable state, being poorly struck, badly worn and often ruthlessly clipped. In 1247 Henry ordered a new coinage and in this the arms of the cross on the reverse were extended to the rim as a safeguard against clipping. This established a pattern of facing portrait and long cross on obverse and reverse respectively that was to continue till the beginning of the 16th century. Several provincial mints were re-activated to assist with the recoinage but they were all closed down again by 1250, only the regal mints at London and Canterbury and the ecclesiastical mints at Durham and Bury St Edmunds remaining active.

"Long Cross" pennies of Henry III (top),
and Edward I.

In 1257 Henry tentatively introduced a gold penny (worth 20 silver pence and twice the weight of a silver penny). The coin was undervalued and soon disappeared from circulation.

The Long Cross coinage of Henry III continued under Edward I till 1279 when the king introduced a new coinage in his own name. The penny continued the style of its predecessors, though much better designed and executed; but new denominations were now added. Henceforward halfpence and farthings became a regular issue and, at the same time, a fourpenny coin known as the groat (from French *gros*) was briefly introduced (minting ceased in 1282 and was not revived till 1351). Due to the centralisation of coin production the name of the moneyer was now generally dropped, although it lingered on a few years at Bury St Edmunds. The provincial mints were again revived in 1299–1302 to recoin the lightweight foreign imitations of pennies which had flooded in from the Continent.

The coinage of Edward II (1307–27) differed only in minor respects from that of his father, and a similar pattern prevailed in the first years of Edward III. In 1335 halfpence and farthings below the sterling fineness were struck. More

Pre-Treaty Noble of Edward III which contained reference to France in the legend.

importantly, further attempts were made to introduce gold coins. In 1344 the florin or double leopard of six shillings was introduced, along with its half and quarter. This coinage was not successful and was soon replaced by a heavier series based on the noble of 80 pence (6s. 8d.), half a mark or one third of a pound. The noble originally weighed 138.5 grains but it was successively reduced to 120 grains, at which weight it continued from 1351. During this reign the protracted conflict with France known as the Hundred Years' War erupted. Edward III, through his mother, claimed the French throne and inscribed this title on his coins. By the

Noble of Edward IV, issued before he was forced to abandon the throne of England.

Treaty of Bretigny (1361) Edward temporarily gave up his claim and the reference to France was dropped from the coins, but when war was renewed in 1369 the title was resumed, and remained on many English coins until the end of the 18th century. The silver coinage followed the pattern of the previous reign, but in 1351 the groat was re-introduced and with it came the twopence or half-groat. Another innovation was the use of mintmarks at the beginning of the inscriptions. Seven types of cross and one crown were employed from 1334 onwards and their sequence enables numismatists to date coins fairly accurately.

The full range of gold (noble, half-noble and quarter-noble) and silver (groat, half-groat, penny, halfpenny and farthing) continued under Richard II (1377–99). Little attempt was made to alter the facing portrait on the silver coins,

Noble of Henry IV which was reduced in weight due to the shortage of gold.

by now little more than a stylised caricature anyway.

Under Henry IV (1399–1413) the pattern of previous reigns prevailed, but in 1412 the weights of the coinage were reduced due to a shortage of bullion. The noble was reduced to 108 grains and its sub-divisions lightened proportionally. The penny was reduced by 3 grains, and its multiples and sub-divisions correspondingly reduced. One interesting change was the reduction of the fleur de lis of France from four to three in the heraldic shield on the reverse of the noble; this change corresponded with the alteration in the arms used in France itself. The Calais mint, opened by Edward III in 1363, was closed in 1411. There was no change in the designs used for the coins of Henry V (1413–22) but greater use was now made of mintmarks to distinguish the various periods of production. Coins were by now produced mainly at London, although the episcopal mints at Durham and York were permitted to strike pennies.

The supply of gold dwindled early in the reign of Henry VI and few nobles were struck after 1426. The Calais mint was re-opened in 1424 and struck a large amount of gold before closing finally in 1440. A regal mint briefly operated at York in 1423–24. Mintmarks were now much more widely used and tended to correspond more closely to the annual trials of the Pyx. The series of civil upheavals known as the Wars of the Roses erupted in this period.

In 1461 Henry VI was deposed by the Yorkist Earl of March after he defeated the Lancastrians at Mortimer's Cross. The Yorkists advanced on London where the victor was crowned Edward IV. At first he continued the gold series of his predecessor, issuing nobles and quarter-nobles, but in 1464 the weight of the penny was reduced

Groat of Richard III (1483–85).

to 12 grains and the value of the noble was raised to 100 pence (8s. 4d.). The ryal or rose-noble of 120 grains, together with its half and quarter, was introduced in 1465 and tariffed at ten shillings or half a pound. The need for a coin worth a third of a pound, however, led to the issue of the angel of 80 grains, worth 6s. 8d., but this was initially unsuccessful and very few examples are now extant. The angel derived its name from the figure of the Archangel Michael on the obverse; a cross surmounting a shield appeared on the reverse.

In 1470 Edward was forced to flee to Holland and Henry VI was briefly restored. During this brief period (to April 1471) the ryal was discontinued but a substantial issue of angels and half-angels was made both at London and Bristol. Silver coins were struck at York as well as London and Bristol, the issues of the provincial mints being identified by the initials B or E (Eboracum, Latin for York). Edward

defeated the Lancastrians at Tewkesbury and deposed the luckless Henry once more. In his second reign Edward struck only angels and half-angels as well as silver from the groat to halfpenny. In addition to the three existing mints, silver coins were struck at Canterbury, Durham and the archiepiscopal mint at York. Mintmarks were now much more frequent and varied. Coins with a mark of a halved sun and rose are usually assigned to the reign of Edward IV, but they were probably also struck in the nominal reign of Edward V, the twelve-year-old prince held in the Tower of London under the protection of his uncle Richard, Duke of Gloucester. Coins with this mark on the reverse had an obverse mark of a boar's head, Richard's personal emblem. The brief reign of Richard III (1483–5) came to an end with his defeat at Bosworth and the relatively scarce coins of this period followed the pattern of the previous reigns, distinguished by the sequence of mint marks and the inscription RICAD or RICARD.

In the early years of Henry VII's reign the coinage likewise followed the previous patterns, but in 1489 the first of several radical changes was effected, with the introduction of the gold sovereign of 20 shillings showing a full-length portrait of the monarch seated on an elaborate throne. For reverse, this coin depicted a Tudor rose surmounted by a heraldic shield. A similar reverse appeared on the ryal of 10 shillings, but the angel and angelet retained previous motifs. The silver coins at first adhered to the medieval pattern, with the stylised facing portrait and long cross, but at the beginning of the 16th century a large silver coin, the testoon or shilling of 12 pence, was introduced and adopted a realistic profile of the king, allied to a reverse showing a cross surmounted by the royal arms. The same design was also used for the later issue of groat and half groat.

First coinage Angel of Henry VIII which retained the traditional 23.5 carat fineness.

This established a pattern which was to continue till the reign of Charles I. In the reign of Henry VIII, however, the coinage was subject to considerable debasement. This led to the eventual introduction of 22 carat (.916 fine) gold for the crown while the traditional 23 1/2 carat gold was retained for the angel and ryal. This dual system continued until the angel was discontinued at the outset of the Civil War in 1642; latterly it had been associated with the ceremony of touching for "King's Evil" or scrofula, a ritual used by the early Stuart monarchs to bolster their belief in the divine right of kings.

Under the Tudors and Stuarts the range and complexity of the gold coinage increased, but it was not until the reign of Edward VI that the silver series was expanded. In 1551 he introduced the silver crown of five shillings, the first English coin to bear a clear date on the obverse. Under Mary dates were extended to the shilling and sixpence.

The mixture of dated and undated coins continued under Elizabeth I, a reign remarkable for the range of denominations—nine gold and eight silver. The latter included the sixpence, threepence, threehalfpence and threefarthings,

distinguished by the rose which appeared behind the Queen's head.

The coinage of James I was even more complex, reflecting the king's attempts to unite his dominions. The first issue bore the legend ANG: SCO (England and Scotland), but from 1604 this was altered to MAG: BRIT (Great Britain). This period witnessed new denominations, such as the rose-ryal and spur-ryal, the unite, the Britain crown and the thistle crown, and finally the laurel of 20 shillings and its sub-divisions.

In the reign of Elizabeth experiments began with milled coinage under Eloi Mestrell. These continued sporadically in the 17th century, culminating in the beautiful coins struck by Nicholas Briot (1631–39). A branch mint was established at Aberystwyth in 1637 to refine and coin silver from the Welsh mines. Relations between King and Parliament deteriorated in the reign of Charles I and led to the Civil War (1642). Parliament controlled London but continued to strike coins in the King's name. The Royalists struck coins, both in pre-war and new types, at Shrewsbury, Oxford, Bristol, Worcester, Exeter, Chester, Hereford and other Royalist strongholds, while curious siege pieces were pressed into service at Newark, Pontefract and Scarborough.

After the execution of Charles I in 1649 the Commonwealth was proclaimed and gold and silver coins were now inscribed in English instead of Latin. Patterns portraying Cromwell and a crowned shield restored Latin in 1656. Plans for milled coinage were already being considered before the Restoration of the monarchy in 1660. Hammered coinage appeared initially, resuming the style of coins under Charles I, but in 1662 the hand-hammering of coins was abandoned in favour of coins struck on the mill and screw press. The hammered coins of 1660–62 were undated and bore a crown mintmark, the last vestiges of medievalism in British coinage.

The magnificent second coinage Rose-Ryal of James I (1603–25).

BUY AND SELL

through the Premier Auction house you can trust

Where History is Valued

LONDON | NEW YORK | HONG KONG | SINGAPORE | SWITZERLAND

SPEAK TO US TODAY
ABOUT CONSIGNING YOUR MATERIAL

Tel: +44(0)20 7563 4007
Email: concierge@spink.com

69 Southampton Row
Bloomsbury WC1B 4ET
London

Follow us on social media

WWW.SPINK.COM

Coin
grading

Condition is the secret to the value of virtually anything, whether it be antiques, jewellery, horses or second-hand cars—and coins are certainly no exception. When collecting coins it is vital to understand the recognised standard British system of grading, i.e. accurately assessing a coin's condition or state of wear. Grading is an art which can only be learned by experience and so often it remains one person's opinion against another's, therefore it is important for the beginner or inexperienced collector to seek assistance from a reputable dealer or knowledgeable numismatist when making major purchases.

The standard grades as used in the Price Guide are as follows:	
UNC	**Uncirculated** A coin that has never been in circulation, although it may show signs of contact with other coins during the minting process.
EF	**Extremely Fine** A coin in this grade may appear uncirculated to the naked eye but on closer examination will show signs of minor friction on the highest surface.
VF	**Very Fine** A coin that has had very little use, but shows signs of wear on the high surfaces.
F	**Fine** A coin that has been in circulation and shows general signs of wear, but with all legends and date clearly visible.
Other grades used in the normal grading system are:	
BU	**Brilliant Uncirculated** As the name implies, a coin retaining its mint lustre.
Fair	A coin extensively worn but still quite recognisable and legends readable.
Poor	A coin very worn and only just recognisable.
Other abbreviations used in the Price Guide are:	
Obv	**Obverse**
Rev	**Reverse**
Other abbreviations, mintmarks, etc. can be identified under the appropriate section of this Yearbook.	

A SIMPLIFIED PRICE GUIDE TO

ANCIENT COINS USED IN BRITAIN

PART I
Ancient British

The prices given in this section are those that you would expect to pay from a reputable dealer and not the prices at which you could expect to sell coins.

The list below, which has been generously provided by Celtic coin dealer Elizabeth Cottam of Chris Rudd, contains most of the commonly available types: a fully comprehensive guide is beyond the scope of this book. Prices are for coins with good surfaces which are not weakly struck or struck from worn dies. Examples which are struck from worn or damaged dies can be worth considerably less. Particularly attractive examples of bronze Celtic coins command a very high premium. Where a price is given for an issue of which there are many varieties, the price is for the most common type. The illustrations are representative examples only and are not shown actual size.

UNINSCRIBED COINAGE

	F	VF	EF
GOLD STATERS			
Broad Flan	£700	£1775	£5750
Gallic War Uniface	£225	£400	£1000
Remic types	£250	£400	£800
Wonersh types	£250	£450	£2200
Chute	£200	£300	£750
Cheriton	£250	£450	£975
Iceni (various types)	£300	£500	£1350
Norfolk "wolf" type			
fine gold	£250	£475	£1500
brassy gold	£175	£300	£695
very debased	£120	£200	£475
Corieltauvi (various types)	£200	£400	£1000
Dobunni	£250	£500	£1500
Whaddon Chase types	£275	£475	£1300

Cheriton Smiler gold stater

GOLD QUARTER STATERS			
Gallic Imported Types	£80	£175	£395
Kent types	£200	£300	£550
Southern types	£125	£200	£500
Iceni	£150	£250	£500
Corieltauvi	£125	£200	£500
Dobunni	£175	£300	£700
East Wiltshire	£300	£500	£1000
Durotriges	£120	£225	£750
North Thames types	£220	£300	£550

SILVER COINAGE			
Armorican billion staters	£125	£250	£500
Kent Types	£150	£300	£675
South Thames types	£120	£175	£375

Cranborne Chase silver stater

	F	VF	EF
Iceni ('crescent' types)........................	£35	£85	£185
Iceni ('Norfolk God' types)..................	£60	£100	£350
Corieltavi..	£50	£110	£225
Dobunni..	£85	£125	£295
Durotriges full stater			
fine silver...	£80	£175	£350
base silver..	£30	£55	£175
Durotriges quarter silver......................	£25	£35	£95

(Note—most examples are for base coins as better quality items are appreciably higher)

| North Thames types........................... | £110 | £195 | £375 |

Hengistbury cast bronze

POTIN COINAGE

| Kent.. | £25 | £50 | £150 |

BRONZE COINAGE

Durotriges debased stater...................	£30	£75	£125
Durotriges cast bronze........................	£65	£125	£225
North Thames types. Various issues from:	£45	£110	£450

INSCRIBED CELTIC COINAGE

CANTIACI

Dubnovellaunos
stater...	£320	£600	£1500
silver unit..	£135	£220	£575
bronze unit..	£65	£175	£395

Vosenos
stater...	£1100	£2500	£6000
quarter stater....................................	£295	£585	£1250
silver unit..	£140	£300	£675

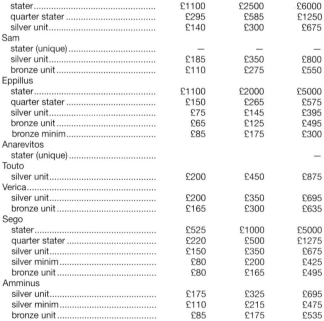

Vosenos gold quarter stater

Sam
stater (unique).................................	—	—	—
silver unit..	£185	£350	£800
bronze unit..	£110	£275	£550

Eppillus
stater...	£1100	£2000	£5000
quarter stater....................................	£150	£265	£575
silver unit..	£75	£145	£395
bronze unit..	£65	£125	£495
bronze minim.....................................	£85	£175	£300

Anarevitos
| stater (unique)................................. | | | — |

Touto
| silver unit.. | £200 | £450 | £875 |

Verica..
| silver unit.. | £200 | £350 | £695 |
| bronze unit.. | £165 | £300 | £635 |

Sego
stater...	£525	£1000	£5000
quarter stater....................................	£220	£500	£1275
silver unit..	£150	£350	£675
silver minim.......................................	£80	£200	£425
bronze unit..	£80	£165	£495

Verica gold stater

Amminus
silver unit..	£175	£325	£695
silver minim.......................................	£110	£215	£475
bronze unit..	£85	£175	£535

Solidus
| silver unit.. | £535 | £1100 | £2350 |
| silver minim....................................... | £535 | £1100 | £1575 |

Sego Warrior gold stater

	F	VF	EF
REGINI & ATREBATES			
Commios			
stater...	£595	£1575	£3000
silver unit......................................	£80	£160	£345
silver minim...................................	£65	£125	£295
Tincomarus			
stater...	£465	£895	£2250
quarter stater	£150	£250	£475
silver unit......................................	£75	£145	£300
silver minim...................................	£65	£125	£200
Eppillus			
stater...	£1000	£2500	£6000
quarter stater	£160	£245	£575
silver unit......................................	£80	£165	£345
Verica			
stater...	£275	£575	£1300
quarter stater	£155	£275	£435
silver unit......................................	£55	£160	£275
silver minim...................................	£50	£120	£245
Epaticcus			
stater...	£1000	£2000	£4250
silver unit......................................	£50	£100	£275
silver minim...................................	£55	£120	£295
Caratacus			
stater (unique)			—
silver unit......................................	£175	£320	£475
silver minim...................................	£110	£220	£345
VECTUARII			
Crab			
silver unit......................................	£165	£325	£695
silver minim...................................	£120	£295	£435
ICENI			
Cani Duro			
silver unit......................................	£115	£275	£575
Antedios			
stater...	£425	£1000	£2500
silver unit......................................	£40	£65	£195
silver half unit................................	£45	£100	£150
Ecen			
stater...	£425	£1200	£2575
silver unit......................................	£45	£85	£195
silver half unit................................	£50	£100	£175
Saenu			
silver unit......................................	£65	£125	£300
Aesu			
silver unit......................................	£65	£125	£300
Ale Scavo			
silver unit......................................	£275	£500	£1275
Esuprasto			
silver unit......................................	£425	£1000	£2000
CORIELTAUVI			
Cat			
silver unit......................................	£400	£1100	£2200
silver half unit (unique)			—
VEPOCUNAVOS			
stater...	£450	£1000	£2600
silver unit......................................	£85	£150	£350
Esuprasu			
stater...	£350	£675	£1375
silver unit......................................	£175	£325	£575

Tincomarus gold stater

Norfolk Wolf gold stater

Ale Scavo silver unit

Vep CorF gold stater

	F	VF	EF
Aunt Cost			
stater	£275	£575	£1395
silver unit	£90	£195	£350
silver half unit	£90	£175	£325
Lat Ison			
stater	£1000	£2100	£4300
silver unit	£175	£425	£1175
silver half unit	£160	£300	£575
Dumnocoveros Tigirseno			
stater	£850	£2000	£3750
silver unit	£100	£195	£595
silver half unit	£100	£210	£625
Volisios Dumnocoveros			
stater	£350	£675	£1350
silver unit	£100	£185	£500
silver half unit	£100	£195	£495
Volisios Cartivellaunos			
stater	£1000	£2000	£4100
silver half unit	£300	£675	£1200
Volisios Dumnovellaunos			
stater	£320	£765	£1675
silver half unit	£150	£325	£675

Bodvoc Bold gold stater

DOBUNNI

	F	VF	EF
Bodvoc			
stater	£1000	£2250	£3250
quarter stater (unique)			—
silver unit	£200	£500	£895
Corio			
stater	£275	£560	£1550
quarter stater	£200	£350	£675
Comux			
stater	£285	£560	£1550
Catti			
stater	£285	£565	£1600
Inamn			
plated stater (unique)			—
silver unit (unique)			—
Anted			
stater	£350	£700	£1600
silver unit	£60	£125	£325
Eisu			
stater	£450	£750	£1600
silver unit	£75	£125	£335

Catti gold stater

TRINOVANTES

	F	VF	EF
Dubnovellaunos			
stater	£275	£475	£1350
quarter stater	£175	£350	£650
silver unit	£75	£150	£375
silver half unit	£100	£200	£475
bronze unit	£65	£140	£295

Dumno Tigir Seno gold stater

CATUVELLAUNI

	F	VF	EF
Addedomaros			
stater	£300	£450	£1300
quarter stater	£300	£550	£675
silver unit	£100	£200	£420
silver half unit	£100	£200	£475
bronze unit	£35	£95	£295

Addedomaros gold stater

	F	VF	EF
Tasciovanos			
stater	£250	£475	£2000
quarter stater	£165	£250	£500
silver unit	£85	£175	£395
bronze unit	£60	£135	£275
bronze half unit	£60	£135	£295
Andoco			
stater	£350	£575	£2000
quarter stater	£200	£420	£775
silver unit	£155	£400	£775
bronze unit	£85	£225	£365
Dias			
silver unit	£100	£200	£425
bronze unit	£50	£150	£425
Rues			
bronze unit	£50	£150	£425
Cat			
plated silver unit (unique)			—

Tasciovanos gold stater

CATUVELLAUNI & TRINOVANTES

	F	VF	EF
Cunobelinus			
stater	£250	£450	£2000
quarter stater	£150	£250	£495
silver unit	£85	£175	£495
bronze unit	£60	£145	£395
bronze half	£60	£145	£285
Trocc			
bronze unit	£50	£150	£550
Agr			
quarter stater	£125	£275	£895
silver unit	£100	£200	£525
bronze unit (only two known)		(too rare to price)	
Dubn			
quarter stater (only three)	£1000	£3000	£7500

Cunobelinus gold stater

Illustrations by courtesy of Chris Rudd

A SIMPLIFIED PRICE GUIDE TO
ANCIENT COINS
USED IN BRITAIN

PART II
Roman Britain

Throughout the centuries, Roman coinage has been subject to many changes, driven by the economic climate of the times giving rise to a range of denominations predominantly in gold, silver and bronze, together with alloys of these metals, typically as a result of debasement. Beginning with the Republican period, we see denominations like the denarius, quinarius and some cast-bronze coinage which was unsuccessful and quickly phased out. Imperatorial and Imperial coinage is a mix of the gold aureus, silver denarius and bronze sestertius, as and dupondius. In the 2nd century AD the silver antoninianus was introduced—a double denarius. The late 3rd century sees the appearance of the silver argenteus, quickly followed by silver siliqua and miliarense, circulated alongside the gold solidus until the Roman's left Britain in AD 410.

All of the coins listed here can be found in Britain and with the increasing popularity of the hobby of metal detecting, more coins are becoming available to budding collectors who in the past may not have seen such coins for sale. This guide offers an indicative price for Fine and Very Fine grade coins; Extremely Fine examples will be worth considerably more and popular types often sell at higher prices. Our grateful thanks go to John Philpotts of Silbury Coins Ltd (www.silburycoins.com) who has completely revised and updated this section.

REPUBLICAN COINAGE 290–41 BC

	F	VF
Republican		
Quadrigatus (or Didrachm) (Janus/Quadriga)	£250	£850
Victoriatus (Jupiter/Victory)	£40	£175
+Denarius (Roma/Biga)	£25	£100
+Denarius (other types)	£35	£150
Denarius (Gallic warrior—L.Hostilius Saserna)	£500	£2500
Quinarius	£35	£125
Cast Aes Grave, As	£250	£900
Struck As/Semis/Litra	£40	£200
Struck Triens/Quadrands	£25	£150

Republican

IMPERATORIAL COINAGE 71–27 BC

	F	VF
Pompey the Great		
Denarius (Hd. of Pompilius/Prow)	£250	£750
Scipio		
Denarius (Jupiter/Elephant............................	£100	£350
Cato Uticensis		
Quinarius (Bacchus/Victory)	£45	£150
Gnaeus Pompey Junior		
Denarius (Roma/Hispania)	£150	£500
Sextus Pompey		
Denarius (his bust)	£275	£800
Denarius (other types)..................................	£150	£500
As..	£160	£600

Gnaeus Pompey Junior

	F	VF
Julius Caesar		
Aureus	£2000	£6000
Denarius ("elephant" type)	£200	£600
Denarius (Ceasar portrait)	£750	£3000
Denarius (heads of godesses).......................	£200	£600
Brutus		
Aureus..............................	Extremely rare	
Denarius (his portrait/EID MAR)	£15,000	£75,000
Denarius (others)...............................	£300	£850
Cassius		
Denarius.......................................	£200	£600
Ahenobarbus		
Denarius	£450	£1500
Mark Antony		
Denarius ("Galley" type)	£75	£300
Denarius (with portrait)	£200	£600
Denarius (other types)	£70	£300
Mark Antony & Lepidus		
AR quinarius	£75	£195
Mark Antony & Octavian		
AR denarius	£250	£850
Quninarius	£50	£175
Mark Antony & Lucius Antony		
AR denarius	£350	£950
Mark Antony & Octavia		
AR Cistophorus	£250	£800
Cleopatra VII & Mark Antony		
AR denarius	£1500	£5000
Fulvia		
AR quinarius	£125	£375
Octavian (later known as Augustus)		
Aureus	£1500	£5500
Denarius	£150	£500
Quinarius (ASIA RECEPTA)	£100	£250
Octavian & Divos Julius Caesar		
AE sestertius	£275	£1500

Julius Caesar

Brutus

Mark Antony

Mark Antony Legionary Series

IMPERIAL COINAGE—Julio-Claudian Dynasty 27 BC–AD 69

	F	VF
Augustus		
Aureus (Caius & Lucius Caesar)	£1500	£5000
AR Cistophorus..............................	£250	£850
Denarius (Caius & Lucius Caesar)	£100	£450
Denarius (other types)	£125	£500
AR quinarius	£75	£250
Sestertius (large SC)	£150	£600
Dupondius or as (large SC)...........................	£55	£250
Quadrans	£25	£100
Divus Augustus (struck under Tiberius)		
As	£70	£450
Augustus & Agrippa		
Dupondius (Crocodile rev)	£100	£350
Livia		
Sestertius or Dupondius	£200	£800
Gaius Caesar		
AR denarius	£250	£1000
Tiberius		
Aureus (Tribute penny)	£1200	£4000
Denarius (Tribute penny)	£100	£350
Sestertius	£200	£650
Dupondius	£125	£500
As	£125	£400
Drusus		
Sestertius......................................	£275	£950
As (Large S C).................................	£125	£450

Augustus

Tiberius

Caligula

Agrippina Senior

	F	VF
Caligula		
Denarius (rev. portrait)	£750	£3000
Sestertius (PIETAS & Temple)	£300	£2000
As (VESTA)	£100	£350
Agrippa (struck under Caligula)		
As..	£75	£300
Germanicus (struck under Caligula or Claudius)		
As (Large S C)	£125	£500
Agrippina Senior (struck under Caligula)		
Sestertius (Carpentum)...................................	£250	£1250
Nero & Drusus (struck under Caligula)		
Dupondius (On horseback, galloping)	£200	£750
Claudius		
Aureus ("DE BRITANN" type)	£2000	£5500
Denarius as above	£500	£2500
Didrachm as above	£375	£1250
Denarius other types	£400	£1250
Sestertius	£225	£750
Dupondius	£60	£350
As	£45	£250
Quadrans	£20	£75
Irregular British Sestertius.............................	£50	£250
Irregular British As	£20	£150
Claudius & Agrippina Junior or Nero		
Denarius	£450	£2000
Nero Cludius Drusus (struck under Claudius)		
Sestertius	£200	£950
Antonia (struck under Claudius)		
Dupondius	£150	£650
Britannicus		
Sestertius	£2500	£17,500
Nero		
Aureus	£1000	£4500
Denarius	£100	£300
Sestertius	£150	£750
Sestertius (Port of Ostia)	£2500	£15000
Dupondius	£85	£350
As	£50	£275
Semis..	£45	£150
Quadrans	£25	£85
Civil War		
Denarius	£200	£650
Galba		
Denarius	£125	£500
Sestertius	£170	£700
Dupondius	£180	£525
As	£110	£400
Otho		
Denarius	£200	£700
Vitellius		
Denarius	£100	£350
Sestertius	£750	£3000
Dupondius	£350	£1000
As	£195	£700

Claudius

Claudius De Britann

Nero

Galba

IMPERIAL COINAGE—Flavian Dynasty AD 69–96

Vespasian		
Aureus	£1000	£4500
Denarius	£40	£150
Denarius (IVDAEA)	£85	£250
Sestertius	£195	£625
Dupondius	£70	£250
As	£55	£210

Vespasian

	F	VF
Titus		
Aureus	£1000	£4500
Denarius as Caesar	£40	£250
Denarius as Augustus	£45	£250
Sestertius	£200	£650
Dupondius	£75	£250
As	£50	£200
As (IVDAEA CAPTA)	£200	£650
Julia Titi		
Denarius	£200	£650
Domitian		
Aureus	£1500	£5000
Cistophorus	£200	£650
Denarius as Caesar	£35	£125
Denarius as Augustus	£35	£125
Sestertius	£100	£550
Dupondius	£50	£200
As	£35	£200
Ae Semis	£30	£120
Ae Quadrands....................................	£25	£100
Domitia		
Cistophorus	£250	£750

Titus

Domitian

IMPERIAL COINAGE—Adoptive Emperors AD 96–138

	F	VF
Nerva		
Aureus	£2000	£7000
Denarius	£50	£200
Sestertius	£140	£750
Sestertius (Palm-tree)	£500	£2500
Dupondius	£70	£250
As	£65	£175
Trajan		
Aureus	£1200	£4000
Denarius	£25	£100
Denarius (Trajan's Column)	£40	£250
Sestertius	£100	£600
Sestertius (Dacian rev.)	£100	£700
Dupondius or as	£35	£250
Ae Quadrands	£25	£95
Plotina, Marciana or Matidia		
Denarius	£450	£1350
Hadrian		
Aureus	£1250	£4500
Cistophourus	£125	£550
Denarius (Provinces)	£45	£200
Denarius other types	£30	£125
Sestertius	£75	£500
Sestertius (RETITVTORI province types)	£150	£600
Sestertius (Britannia std)	£5000	£20,000
Dupondius or As	£35	£250
As (Britannia std)	£200	£1250
Ae Semiis or Quadrands	£30	£125
Egypt, Alexandrian Billon Tetradrachm	£30	£200
Sabina		
Denarius	£30	£250
Sestertius	£115	£475
As or Dupondius	£70	£225
Aelius Ceasar		
Denarius	£70	£250
Sestertius	£150	£550
As or Dupondius	£65	£200

Nerva

Trajan

Hadrian

Sabina

	F	VF

IMPERIAL COINAGE—The Antonines AD 138–193

Antoninus Pius

Aureus	£1200	£3000
Denarius	£25	£125
Sestertius Britannia seated	£500	£3000
Sestertius other types	£40	£350
As - Britannia rev.	£50	£250
Dupondius or As other types	£50	£200

Antoninus Pius

Antoninus Pius & Marcus Aurelius

Denarius (bust each side)	£30	£250

Diva Faustina Senior

Denarius..	£25	£100
Sestertius..	£45	£250
As or Dupondius	£25	£125

Marcus Aurelius

Aureus..	£1200	£4000
Denarius as Caesar	£25	£150
Denarius as Augustus	£25	£150
Sestertius	£45	£450
As or Dupondius	£25	£200

Marcus Aurelius

Faustina Junior

Denarius	£25	£125
Sestertius	£40	£300
As or Dupondius	£30	£125

Lucius Verus

Denarius	£25	£150
Sestertius	£45	£300
As or Dupondius	£30	£150

Lucilla

Denarius	£25	£125
Sestertius	£65	£250
As or Dupondius	£30	£150

Faustina

Commodus

Aureus	£1500	£5000
Denarius as Caesar	£30	£125
Denarius as Augustus	£25	£100
Sestertius	£45	£300
Sestertius (VICT BRIT)	£150	£525
As or Dupondius	£25	£150

Crispina

Denarius	£25	£150
Sestertius	£70	£250
As or Dupondius	£35	£150

Pertinax

IMPERIAL COINAGE—The Severan Dynasty AD 193–235

Pertinax

Denarius..	£225	£750
Sestertius	£500	£2000

Didius Julianus

Denarius..	£400	£1250
Sestertius or Dupondius	£325	£1500

Didius Julianus

Manlia Scantilla or Didia Clara

Denarius	£300	£1500

Pescennius Niger

Denarius	£275	£800

Clodius Albinus

Denarius as Caesar	£45	£150
Denarius as Augustus	£85	£300
Sestertius	£250	£1000
As	£85	£265

Clodius Albinus

85

	F	VF

Septimius Severus

	F	VF
Aureus	£1500	£5000
Aureus (VICT BRIT)	£1500	£6000
+Denarius (Mint of Rome)	£25	£100
+Denarius (Mints of Emesa & Laodicea)	£25	£75
Denarius (LEG XIIII)	£30	£175
Denarius (VICT BRIT)	£30	£150
Sestertius other types.....................................	£75	£350
Sestertius (VICT BRIT)...............................	£300	£1250
Dupondius or as	£50	£225
Dupondius or As (VICT BRIT)	£125	£450

Septimus Severus

Julia Domna

	F	VF
Denarius	£25	£75
Sestertius	£75	£250
As or Dupondius	£50	£175

Julia Domna

Caracalla

	F	VF
Aureus (VICT BRIT)	£1500	£5500
Denarius as Caesar	£25	£75
Denarius as Augustus	£25	£75
Denarius (VICT BRIT)	£30	£100
Antoninianus	£50	£150
Sestertius	£100	£350
Sestertius (VICT BRIT)...............................	£300	£1500
Dupondius or As	£50	£175
Dupondius or As (VICT BRIT)	£100	£325

Caracalla

Plautilla

	F	VF
Denarius	£25	£75

Geta

	F	VF
Denarius as Caesar	£25	£75
Denarius as Augustus	£25	£75
Denarius (VICT BRIT)	£30	£125
Sestertius	£125	£375
Sestertius (VICT BRIT)...............................	£250	£850
Dupondius or as	£75	£250
As (VICT BRIT)	£120	£500

Geta

Macrinus

	F	VF
Antoninianus	£100	£350
Denarius	£45	£150
Sestertius	£125	£425

Macrinus

Diadumenian

	F	VF
Denarius	£75	£350
Dupondius or As	£135	£450

Elagabalus

	F	VF
Aureus	£1500	£5000
Antoninianus	£50	£150
Denarius	£30	£80
Sestertius	£100	£350
Dupondius or As	£60	£185

Diadumenian

Julia Paula

	F	VF
Denarius	£30	£120

Aquilla Severa

	F	VF
Denarius	£55	£200

Julia Soaemias

	F	VF
Denarius	£30	£80
Dupondius or As	£65	£250

Julia Maesa

	F	VF
Denarius	£25	£65
Sestertius	£85	£300

Elagabalus

Severus Alexander

	F	VF
Aureus	£1500	£4500
Denarius as Caesar	£65	£200
Denarius as Augustus	£25	£50
Sestertius	£45	£150
Dupondius or As	£35	£120

Julia Maesa

	F	VF
Orbiana		
Denarius	£65	£300
As	£100	£350
Julia Mamaea		
Denarius	£20	£65
Sestertius	£35	£150

Severus Alexander

IMPERIAL COINAGE—Military Anarchy AD 235–270

	F	VF
Maximinus I		
Denarius	£25	£80
Sestertius, Dupondius or As	£45	£150
Diva Paula		
Denarius	£150	£500
Maximus Caesar		
Denarius	£70	£275
Sestertius	£65	£250
Gordian I & II, Africanus		
Denarius	£550	£2000
Sestertius	£550	£2000
Balbinus & Pupienus		
Antoninanus	£90	£450
Denarius	£80	£425
Gordian III		
Antoninianus	£15	£50
Denarius	£25	£50
Sestertius or As	£25	£100
Tranquillina		
Common Colonial	£30	£115
Philip I		
Antoninianus "Animal":		
Lion, stag, antelope, wolf & twins	£25	£75
Other Antoninianus	£15	£50
Sestertius, Dupondius or As	£35	£100
Otacilla Severa		
Antoninianus	£15	£50
Antoninianus "Hipo"	£25	£125
Sestertius	£25	£125
Philip II		
Antoninianus	£15	£55
Antoninianus "Goat"	£20	£75
Sestertius, Dupondius or As	£35	£100
Pacatian		
Antoninianus	1000	£4000
Trajan Decius		
Antoninianus	£15	£50
Antoninianus (DIVI series Augustus, Trajan etc)	£40	£150
Double Sestertius	£275	£1250
Sestertius, Dupondius or As	£25	£100
Herennius Etruscilla		
Antoniniaus	£15	£50
Sestertius, Dupondius or As	£30	£150
Herennius Etruscus		
Antoninianus	£20	£75
Sesterius, Dupondius or As	£55	£225
Hostilian		
Antoninianus as Caesar	£30	£150
Antoninianus as Augustus	£70	£250
Trebonianus Gallus		
Antoninianus	£15	£50
Sestertius or As	£30	£125
Volusian		
Antoninianus	£15	£55
Sestertius	£30	£150

Maximinus I

Balbinus

Gordian III

Philip I

Trajan Decius

Volusian

	F	VF
Aemilian		
Antoninianus	£45	£175
Valerian I		
Antoninianus	£15	£50
Sestertius & As	£50	£175
Diva Mariniana		
Antoninianus	£35	£150
Gallienus		
Silver Antoninianus	£12	£45
Ae Antoninianus	£5	£25
Ae Antoninianus (Military bust)	£10	£50
Ae Antoninianus (Legionary)	£50	£250
Ae Sestertius	£45	£200
Ae Denarius	£50	£150
Saloninus		
Ae Antoninianus	£5	£25
Valerian II		
Billon Antoninianus	£12	£45
Saloninus		
Antoninianus	£15	£45
Macrianus & Quietus		
Billon Antoninianus	£45	£150
Regalianus or Dryantilla		
Billon Antoninianus	£1500	£5000
Postumus		
Silver Antoninianus	£5	£40
Ae Antoninianus	£5	£25
Radiated sestertius	£50	£250
Laelianus		
Ae Antoninianus	£225	£875
Marius		
Ae Antoninianus	£45	£175
Victorinus		
Ae Antoninianus	£5	£30
Tetricus I & II		
Ae Antoninianus	£5	£30
Claudius II Gothicus		
Ae Antoninianus	£4	£30
Egypt, Alexandrian Billon tetradrachm	£8	£35
DIVO Ae Antoninianus	£8	£35
Quintillus		
Ae Antoninianus	£12	£45

IMPERIAL COINAGE—The Illyrian Emperors—AD 270–285

	F	VF
Aurelian		
Ae Antoninianus	£8	£50
Ae Denarius	£20	£75
Vabalathus & Aurelian		
Ae Antoninianus (bust both sides)	£20	£75
Vabalathus		
Ae Antoninianus	£250	£1000
Severina		
Ae Antoninianus	£15	£50
Ae As	£35	£125
Zenobia		
Eygpt, Alexandrian Billon Tetradrachm	£750	£3000
Tacitus		
Ae Antoninianus	£15	£35
Florian		
Ae Antoninianus	£25	£150

Gallienus

Postumus

Laelianus

Aurelian

Tacitus

Florian

	F	VF
Probus		
Gold Aureus	£1500	£5000
Ae Antoninianus	£10	£50
Antoninianus (military or imp. Busts RIC G or H) ..	£20	£100
Antoninianus		
(Other military or imp NOT BUSTS G or H)....	£50	£250
Antoninianus (VICTOR GERM rev.)	£20	£100
Egypt, Alexandrian Billon tetradrachm	£15	£80
Carus		
Ae Antoninianus	£15	£50
Numerian		
Ae Antoninianus	£15	£50
Carinus		
Ae Antoninianus	£12	£50
Magna Urbica		
Ae Antoninianus	£50	£250
Julian of Pannonia		
Ae Antoninianus	£650	£3000

Probus

Numerian

IMPERIAL COINAGE — The Tetrarchy AD 285–307

Diocletian		
Gold Aureus	£1500	£5000
AR Argenteus	£100	£350
Ae Antoninianus & Radiates	£10	£50
Ae Follis (London Mint)	£15	£75
As above with LON mint mark	£100	£500
Ae Follis (other mints)	£10	£50
Ae Follis (Imperial bust).......................	£25	£150
Maximianus		
AR Argenteus	£100	£350
Ae Follis (London mint)	£15	£75
Ae Follis (other mints)	£10	£50
Ae Follis (MONETA rev.)	£10	£80
Carausius		
Aureus		Extremely rare
Denarius	£500	£2500
Ae Antoninianus (PAX).........................	£25	£175
As above but full silvering	£35	£300
Legionary Antoninianus	£75	£400
Expectate Veni Antoninianus	£100	£425
In the name of Diocletian or Maximian	£35	£150
Allectus		
Aureus		Extremely rare
Ae Antoninianus	£25	£250
As above but full silvering	£45	£400
Quinarius	£25	£150
Constantius I		
AR Argenteus	£20	£350
Ae Follis (London Mint)	£15	£75
Ae Follis (other mints)	£10	£50
Ae Follis (SALVS rev.)	£15	£55
Ae 4 (Lion or Eagle)	£10	£50
Galerius		
Ae Follis (London mint)	£15	£80
Ae Follis (other mints)	£10	£55
Galeria Valeria		
Ae Follis	£35	£100
Severus II		
Ae Follis (London mint)	£35	£200
Ae Follis (other mints)	£30	£125
Ae Radiate...................................	£25	£75
Ae Denarius	£25	£200

Diocletian

Carausius

Allectus

Galerius

	F	VF
Maximinus II		
Ae Follis (London mint)	£15	£75
Ae Follis (other mints)	£10	£55
Ae Radiate	£5	£50
Maxentius		
Ae Follis	£10	£45
Romulus		
Ae Follis	£50	£250
Licinius I		
Billon Argenteus	£50	£175
Ae Follis (London mint)	£12	£50
Ae Follis (other mints)	£12	£40
AE3	£5	£30
Licinius II		
AE3	£10	£35
Alexander or Martinian		
AE	£1200	£4000

Maximinus II

Constantine I

IMPERIAL COINAGE—Family of Constantine AD 307–350

	F	VF
Constantine I		
Billon Argenteus	£50	£175
Ae Follis (London mint)	£12	£50
As above—helmeted bust	£15	£125
Ae Follis (other mints) as Caesar	£15	£50
Ae Follis (other mints) as Augustus	£5	£50
AE3	£5	£30
AE3 (London mint)	£10	£50
AE3 (SARMATIA rev)	£12	£50
Urbs Roma / Wolf & twins AE3/4	£5	£30
Constantinopolis AE3/4	£5	£25
Fausta & Helena		
AE3 (London mint)	£50	£175
AE3 (other mints)	£15	£75
Theodora		
AE4	£10	£35
Crispus		
AE3 (London mint)	£10	£45
AE3	£10	£30
Delmatius		
AE3/4	£15	£50
Hanniballianus Rex		
AE4	£75	£250
Constantine II		
AE3 (London mint)	£10	£40
AE3	£8	£30
AE3/4	£8	£25
Constans		
AE2 (centenionalis)	£10	£30
AE3 (half centenionalis)	£8	£25
AE4	£8	£25
Constantius II		
Gold Solidus	£300	£1000
Siliqua	£25	£100
AE2 (or centenionalis)	£10	£35
AE3 (or half centenionalis)	£8	£20
AE3 (London mint)	£15	£50
AE3	£8	£20

Fausta

Crispus

Constans

IMPERIAL COINAGE—Late period to the collapse of the Empire AD 350 to end

	F	VF
Magnentius		
Gold Solidus	£1000	£4000
Silver Siliqua	£300	£1250
Double centenionalis	£45	£250
Centenionalis	£15	£60

Magnentius

	F	VF
Decentius		
Double centenionalis	£75	£300
Centenionalis	£25	£75
Vetranio		
AE2 (centenionalis)	£40	£150
AE3 (half centenionalis)	£50	£175
Nepotian		
AE2 (centenionalis)	£1500	£6000
Constantius Gallus		
AE2 (centenionalis)	£15	£45
AE3 (half centenionalis)	£8	£30
Julian II		
Siliqua	£30	£100
AE1	£45	£150
AE3 (helmeted bust)	£12	£40
Anonymous, Serapis + Jupiter AE3	£200	£600
Jovian		
AE1	£65	£250
AE3	£15	£55
Valentinian I		
Sold Solidus	£250	£900
Silver Milliarense	£200	£800
Siliqua	£25	£100
AE3	£8	£25
Valens		
Gold Solidus	£250	£800
Silver Milliarense	£200	£700
Siliqua	£25	£100
AE3	£8	£25
Procopius		
AE3	£45	£150
Gratian		
Silver Milliarense	£200	£750
Siliqua	£25	£100
AE3	£8	£45
AE4	£8	£35
Valentinian II		
Solidus	£250	£900
Siliqua	£25	£125
AE2	£12	£35
AE4	£5	£15
Theodosius I		
Solidus	£250	£900
Siliqua	£30	£125
AE2	£12	£50
AE3	£10	£45
Aelia Flaccilla		
AE2	£30	£125
AE4	£15	£50
Magnus Maximus		
Solidus (AVGOB)	£5000	£15,000
Solidus	£1250	£3500
Siliqua	£45	£150
Siliqua (AVGPS)	£750	£2500
AE2	£25	£75
Flavius Victor		
Silver Sliqua	£150	£600
AE4	£30	£85
Eugenius		
Silver Siliqua	£100	£500

Julian II

Jovian

Valens

Magnus Maximus

Gratian

Eugenius

	F	VF
Arcadius		
Gold Solidus...	£250	£900
Silver Siliqua..	£25	£150
Silver Half-siliqua	£150	£500
AE2	£12	£50
AE4	£5	£25
Eudoxia		
AE3	£25	£85
Honorius		
Gold Solidus	£250	£700
Silver Siliqua..	£30	£150
AE4	£8	£25
Constantine III		
Silver Siliqua	£200	£650
Theodosius II		
Gold Solidus	£225	£650
Johannes		
AE4	£125	£500
Valentinian III		
Gold Solidus...	£250	£700
AE4	£25	£75

Arcadius

Honorius

Valentinian III

Ae = bronze; AE 1, 2, 3, 4 = bronze coins in descending order of size.

Coin illustrations by courtesy of Silbury Coins.

Charles II (1660-85), Five Guineas, 1681,
Elephant & Castle below, (S.3332; EGC.193 R6; MCE
24). Good extremely fine for issue. Extremely rare with
much underlying brilliance, some very minor scratches
on reverse. A majestic imposing piece.
£49,500

The Elephant & Castle mark signifying that the gold had come from
Africa. This mark below the monarch's portrait denotes gold had been
Supplied by the Royal African Company. The 'Royal African Company'
was founded in 1660 as 'The Company of Royal Adventurers Trading to
Africa' by Charles II, who was restored to the throne in that year, with
Prince Rupert identifying various regions rich in gold and other precious
commodities.

A SIMPLIFIED PRICE GUIDE TO

ENGLISH HAMMERED COINS

PART I

780–1485

INTRODUCTION

We have taken our starting point for English hammered coin prices from the middle Anglo-Saxon period. This time sees the country divided into separate kingdoms, and Viking divided areas and as well as the introduction of the silver "penny" as the standard unit of currency (and a few struck halfpennies). This is a complicated time in our history and that is reflected numismatically. We have therefore listed only the commonest or most frequently found pieces or rulers within their kingdoms. For many later rulers the price is for the more common non-portait issue.

PRICING

The prices given in the following pages are intended to be used as a "Pocket book guide" to the values of the most common coins within any denomination of any one reign. The price quoted is what a collector may expect to pay for such a piece in the condition indicated. For more detailed information we recommend the reader to one of the many specialist publications.

GRADING

The prices quoted are generally for three different grades of condition: Fine (F), Very Fine (VF) and Extremely Fine (EF). A "Fine" coin is assumed to be a fairly worn, circulated, piece but with all or most of the main features and lettering still clear. "Very Fine" is a middle grade with a small amount of wear and most details fairly clear. For this edition we have included the prices for coins in Extremely Fine condition where appropriate, although very few hammered coins actually turn up in this grade (i.e. nearly mint state with hardly any wear). In some instances the prices quoted are theoretically based and are only included to provide a guide. It is important to note that on all hammered coins the very nature of striking, i.e. individually, by hand, means hammered coinage is rarely a straight grade and when listed by a dealer the overall condition will often be qualified by terms such as: *weak in parts, struck off-centre, cracked or chipped flan, double struck,* etc. When applicable the price should be adjusted accordingly.

HISTORY

Below the heading for each monarch we have given a few historical notes as and when they apply to significant changes in the coinage.

KINGS OF KENT

	F	VF
CUTHRED (798–807)	£900	£3750

ARCHBISHOPS OF CANTERBURY

WULFRED (805–832)	£850	£3500

COELNOTH (833–870)	£775	£2850

PLEGMUND (890–914) (non portrait)	£800	£3000

KINGS OF MERCIA

OFFA (757–796) (non portrait) .	£600	£1750
— — (portrait)	£900	£3250

COENWULF (796–821)	£450	£1400

BURGRED (852–874)	£325	£800

KINGS OF EAST ANGLIA

EDMUND (855–870)	£475	£1400

ST EDMUND (Danish E. Anglia 855–915)

(Many have crude lettering)	£225	£500

VIKING ISSUES OF YORK

	F	VF
CNUT (READS CV N·NET·TI)	£225	£575

| **ST PETER COINAGE (905–915)** | £400 | £1250 |

KINGS OF WESSEX (later all England)

ALFRED THE GREAT (871–99)	£825	£2200

| **EDWARD THE ELDER (899–924)** | £300 | £650 |

| **AETHELSTAN (924–39)**..... | £425 | £1200 |

| **EADMUND (939–46)**........... | £350 | £875 |

| **EADRED (946–55)**................. | £350 | £850 |

| **EADWIG (955–59)**................ | £1000 | £2350 |

EDGAR (First King of All England)
(959–975)

	F	VF	EF
Edgar Penny, non portrait (2 line inscription)	£300	£675	—

EDWARD THE MARTYR
(975–978)

	F	VF	EF
Edward, Penny, Portrait	£1700	£5500	—

AETHELRED II
(978–1016)

	F	VF	EF
Aethelred II, Penny (1st hand type illustrated)	£250	£550	—
Penny, last small cross type	£175	£350	£850

CNUT
(1016–35)

	F	VF	EF
Cnut, Penny (Quatrefoil type illustrated)	£180	£375	£775
Penny (short cross type)	£165	£325	£700

HAROLD I
(1035–40)

	F	VF	EF
Harold I, Penny (long cross type Illustrated)	£350	£1000	—

HARTHACANUTE
(1035–42)

	F	VF	EF
Harthacanute, Penny, English Mint (in his own name)	£1000	£3500	—
Harthacanute Penny (king's name given as "CNUT")	£650	£1800	—
Harthacanute, Penny, Danish type	£400	£1000	—

Danish type

EDWARD THE CONFESSOR
(1042–66)

	F	VF	EF
Edward the Confessor, Penny (helmet type illustrated)	£250	£550	£1400
Edward the Confessor, Penny, facing bust type	£200	£450	£1200

HAROLD II
(1066)

	F	VF	EF
Harold II, Penny	£1400	£3850	—

WILLIAM I
(1066–87)

The Norman Conquest had very little immediate effect on the coinage of England. The Anglo-Saxon standard of minting silver pennies was very high and the practice of the moneyer putting his name and mint town on the reverse continued as before, except with William's portrait of course. It is worth noting here that non-realistic, stylised portraits were used until the reign of Henry VII.

There are eight major types of pennies of which the last, the PAXS type, is by far the commonest.

	F	VF	EF
William I, Penny (PAXS type illustrated).....................................	£365	£725	—

WILLIAM II
(1087–1100)

Very little change from his father's reign except that five new types were issued, most of which were much more crudely designed than previous, all are scarce.

	F	VF	EF
William II, Penny (cross in quatrefoil type illustrated)...	£800	£2200	—

HENRY I
(1100–35)

There are fifteen different types of penny for this reign of which the last two are the most common. Most issues are of a very poor standard both in workmanship and metal, the prices reflect a poor quality of issue.

	F	VF	EF
Henry I, Penny type XV................................	£175	£550	—
Henry I, Penny type XIV (illustrated)...........	£275	£850	—
Halfpenny	£2000	£6000	—

STEPHEN
(1135–54)

This is historically a very complicated time for the coinage, mainly due to civil war and a consequential lack of central control in the country which resulted in very poor quality and deliberately damaged pieces. Coins were struck not only in the name of Stephen and his main rival claimant Matilda rare, but also by their supporters. The commonest issue is the "Watford" type; so named, as are many issues, after the area in which a hoard was found.

	F	VF	EF
Stephen, Penny ("Watford" type illustrated)	£300	£1000	—

(full flan pieces are worth considerably more)

HENRY II
(1154–89)

There were two distinct issues struck during this reign. The first, Cross and Crosslets or "Tealby" coinage (named after Tealby in Lincolnshire, where a large hoard was found), continued to be very poorly made and lasted 20 years. However, in 1180 the new and superior "Short Cross" issue commenced, being issued from only twelve major towns.

	F	VF	EF
Henry II, Penny, Tealby	£125	£400	—
Henry II, Penny, Short Cross	£70	£200	—

RICHARD I
(1189–99)

There were no major changes during this reign, in fact pennies continued to be struck with his father Henry's name throughout the reign. The coins struck under Richard tend to be rather crude in style.

	F	VF	EF
Richard I, Penny	£90	£260	—

JOHN
(1199–1216)

As with his brother before him, there were no major changes during the reign of King John, and pennies with his father's name were struck throughout the reign, although they tended to be somewhat neater in style than those struck during the reign of Richard I.

	F	VF
John, Penny.....................................	£65	£175

HENRY III
(1216–72)

The coinage during Henry III's reign continued as before with the short cross issue. However, in 1247 a new long cross design was introduced to prevent clipping. This design was to last in one form or another for many centuries. Late in the reign saw a brief appearance of the 1st English gold coin.

	F	VF	EF
Henry III, Penny, Short Cross	£40	£120	£325
Henry III, Penny, Long Cross	£30	£75	£250

EDWARD I
(1272–1307)

After a few years of issuing similar pieces to his father, and in his farther's name in 1279 Edward I ordered a major re-coinage. This consisted of well-made pennies, halfpennies and farthings in relatively large quantities, and for a brief period a groat (four pence) was produced. These were often mounted and gilded, the price is for an undamaged piece. The pennies are amongst the most common of all hammered coins.

	F	VF	EF
Edward I (and Edward II)			
Groat (often damaged) see above ...	£2750	£7500	—
Penny..	£25	£75	—
Halfpenny...	£30	£90	—
Farthing..	£25	£90	—

Edward I penny

EDWARD II
(1307–27)

	F	VF	EF
Edward II, long cross Pennies, Halfpennies and Farthings continued in very similar style to his father (Edward I)			
Pennies	£30	£85	—
Halfpennies	£70	£180	—
Farthings	£35	£125	—

EDWARD III
(1327–77)

This was a long reign which saw major changes in the coinage, the most significant being the introduction of a gold coinage (based on the Noble, valued at 6s 8d, and its fractions) and a regular issue of a large silver groat (and half groat). The provincial mints were limited to a few episcopal cities but coins of English type were also struck in the newly-acquired Calais Mint.

	F	VF	EF
Gold			
Noble	£1000	£3500	—
Half Noble	£700	£2000	—
Quarter Noble	£400	£850	—
Silver			
Groat	£60	£180	£900
Half Groat	£40	£135	£600
Penny	£30	£100	£400
Half Penny	£20	£80	£275
Farthing	£40	£120	£350

Gold Noble

RICHARD II
(1377–99)

The denominations continued during this reign much as before. However, coins are quite scarce mainly due to the lack of bullion gold and silver going into the mints, mainly because of an inbalance with European weights and fineness.

	F	VF	EF
Gold			
Noble	£1500	£5000	—
Half Noble	£1450	£4700	—
Quarter Noble	£500	£1350	—
Silver			
Groat	£450	£1800	—
Half Groat	£225	£800	—
Penny	£75	£325	—
Half Penny	£35	£130	—
Farthing	£135	£525	—

Gold Noble

HENRY IV
(1399–1413)

Because of the continuing problems with the scarcity of gold and silver the coinage was reduced by weight in 1412, towards the end of the reign. All coins of this reign are quite scarce.

Noble

	F	VF
Gold		
Noble, Light coinage...................	£1750	£6250
Half Noble, Light coinage	£2350	£7750
Quarter Noble, Light coinage	£775	£2200
Silver		
Groat, Light coinage...................	£1500	£5750
Half Groat, Heavy coinage..........	£750	£2350
Penny..	£450	£1200
Half Penny	£250	£750
Farthing.......................................	£800	£2500

HENRY V
(1413–22)

Monetary reform introduced towards the end of his father's reign in 1412 improved the supply of bullion and hence coins of Henry V are far more common. All of the main denominations continued as before.

	F	VF	EF
Gold			
Noble £1400	£4750	—	
Half Noble £1100	£3150	—	
Quarter Noble £475	£1000	—	
Silver			
Groat, class "C" £175	£575	—	
Half Groat...........................£100	£365	—	
Penny...................................£45	£185	—	
Half Penny...........................£30	£120	—	
Farthing...............................£350	£1200	—	

Groat

HENRY VI
(1422–61 and again 1470–71)

Although there were no new denominations except for the Angel & Halfangel during the 2nd reign (see Edward IV below), Henry's first reign saw eleven different issues, each for a few years and distinguished by privy marks, i.e. annulets, pinecones, mascles, leaves etc.

HENRY VI *continued*

	F	VF	EF
Gold			
First reign—			
Noble, Annulet issue	£1300	£4000	—
Half Noble, Annulet issue	£900	£2750	—
Quarter Noble, Annulet issue	£400	£850	—
2nd reign—			
Angel	£2000	£5750	—
Half Angel	£4600	£13,000	—
Silver			
Groat, Annulet issue	£75	£200	£450
Half Groat, Annulet issue	£35	£125	£400
Penny	£30	£100	£375
Half Penny, Annulet issue	£30	£80	£200
Farthing, Annulet issue	£140	£450	—

Noble

EDWARD IV
(1461–70 and again 1471–83)

The significant changes during these reigns were the replacement of the noble by the rose ryal (and revalued at 10 shillings) and the continuation of the angel at the old noble value. We also start to see mint-marks or initial marks appearing, usually at the top of the coin, they were used to denote the period of issue for dating purposes and often lasted for two to three years e.g. rose, lis, crown etc. Groats were issued at London, Bristol, Coventry, Norwich and York.

	F	VF	EF
Gold			
Noble and quarter noble (Heavy Coinage)			Very rare
Ryal	£1200	£3750	—
"Flemish" copy of Ryal	£850	£2750	—
Half Ryal	£850	£2800	—
Quarter Ryal	£525	£1400	—
Angel, 2nd reign	£1100	£3250	—
Half Angel, 2nd reign	£875	£2500	—
Silver			
Groat	£65	£185	£550
Half Groat Canterbury	£50	£160	£475
Penny	£35	£150	£375
Half Penny	£30	£120	—
Farthing, Heavy coinage	£425	£1250	—

Angel

RICHARD III
(1483–85)

The close of the Yorkist Plantagenet and Medieval period come together at this time. There are no new significant numismatic changes but most silver coins of Richard whilst not really rare, continue to be very popular and priced quite high. The smaller denominations are usually poor condition.

	F	VF	EF
Gold			
Angel	£5750	£18,500	—
Half Angel	£9500	£31,000	—
Silver			
Groat	£825	£2350	—
Half Groat	£1450	£5000	—
Penny	£400	£1200	—
Half Penny	£375	£1000	—
Farthing	£1700	£4750	—

Groat

PART II
1485–1663

Among the more significant features of the post-Renaissance period as it affected coinage is the introduction of realistic portraiture during the reign of Henry VII. We also have a much wider and varied number of new and revised denominations, for example eleven different gold denominations of Henry VIII and the same number of silver for Elizabeth I. Here we only mention the introduction or changes in the main denominations, giving a value for all of them, once again listing the commonest type.

HENRY VII
(1485–1509)

The gold sovereign of 20 shillings makes its first appearance in 1489 as does the testoon (later shilling) in about 1500. The silver penny was re-designed to a rather crude likeness of the sovereign, enthroned.

	F	VF	EF
Gold			
Sovereign	£30000	£110,000	—
Ryal	£32500	£140,000	—
Angel	£925	£2750	—
Half Angel	£750	£2350	—
Silver			
Testoon 1/-	£17500	£42,500	—
Groat, facing bust	£85	£250	£1100
Half Groat	£45	£165	£550
Penny, sovereign type	£45	£140	£400
Half Penny	£30	£90	—
Farthing	£550	£1500	—

Profile Groat

HENRY VIII
(1509–47)

After a long initial period of very little change in the coinage, in 1526 there were many, with an attempt to bring the gold/silver ratio in line with the continental currencies. Some gold coins only lasted a short time and are very rare. The crown (in gold) makes its first appearance. Towards the end of the reign we see large issues of debased silver coins (with a high copper content) bearing the well-known facing portrait of the ageing King. These tend to turn up in poor condition and include the shilling in greater numbers. Similar posthumous issues were minted during early reign of Edward VI.

Gold			
Sovereign, 3rd coinage	£6750	£25,000	—
Half Sovereign	£1050	£3350	—
Angel	£1000	£3000	—
Half Angel	£800	£2500	—
Quarter Angel	£875	£2650	—
George Noble	£11,000	£40,000	—
Half George Noble	£9250	£37,500	—
Crown of the rose	£7000	£25,000	—
Crown of the double rose	£900	£3000	—
Half Crown of the			
double rose	£650	£1850	—
Silver			
Testoon 1/-	£1300	£4750	—
Groat, 2nd coinage	£165	£400	£1350
Half Groat, 2nd coinage	£70	£200	£700
Penny	£50	£150	£425
Half Penny	£35	£135	—
Farthing	£325	£850	—

Gold Sovereign

EDWARD VI
(1547–53)

Some of the coins struck in the first few years of this short reign could really be called Henry VIII posthumous issues as there is continuity in both name and style from his father's last issue. However, overlapping this period are portrait issues of the boy King, particularly shillings (usually poor quality coins). This period also sees the first dated English coin (shown in Roman numerals) MDXLIX (1549). In 1551 however, a new coinage was introduced with a restored silver quality from the Crown (dated 1551) down to the new sixpence and threepence.

Crowned bust half sovereign

	F	VF	EF
Gold			
Sovereign (30s)	£7250	£22,500	—
Half Sovereign (in own name)	£2100	£7250	—
Crown	£2000	£7250	—
Half Crown	£1600	£5250	—
Angel	£14,000	£40,000	—
Half Angel	—	£45,000	—
Sovereign (20s)	£7500	£22,000	—
Silver			
Crown	£1150	£3650	—
Half Crown	£750	£2200	—
Shilling (Fine coinage)	£165	£575	—
Sixpence (Fine coinage)	£170	£650	—
Groat	£800	£4650	—
Threepence	£275	£1350	—
Half Groat	£475	£1600	—
Penny	£75	£250	—
Half Penny	£400	£1450	—
Farthing	£1500	£5000	—

MARY
(1553–54)

The early coins of Mary's sole reign are limited and continue to use some of the same denominations as Edward, except that the gold ryal was reintroduced.

Groat

	F	VF
Gold		
Sovereign (30s)	£9000	£28,500
Ryal	£35,000	—
Angel	£2250	£6000
Half Angel	£6350	£17,000
Silver		
Groat	£225	£750
Half Groat	£725	£2650
Penny	£650	£2350

PHILIP & MARY
(1554–58)

After a very short reign alone, Mary married Philip of Spain and they technically ruled jointly (although not for very long in practise) until her death. After her marriage we see both her and Philip on the shillings and sixpences with both full Spanish and then English titles alone.

	F	VF
Gold		
Angel	£6500	£21,500
Half Angel	£14,000	—
Silver		
Shilling	£500	£2150
Sixpence	£425	£1600
Groat	£225	£775
Half Groat	£550	£2150
Penny	£85	£250

Shilling

ELIZABETH I
(1558–1603)

As might be expected with a long reign there are a number of significant changes in the coinage which include several new denominations—so many in silver that every value from the shilling downwards was marked and dated to distinguish them. Early on we have old base Edward VI shillings countermarked to a new reduced value (not priced here). Also due to a lack of small change and the expense of making a miniscule farthing we have a new threehalfpence and threefarthings. Finally we see the beginnings of a milled (machine produced) coinage for a brief period from 1561–71.

	F	VF	EF
Gold			
Sovereign (30s)	£8000	£25,000	—
Ryal (15s)	£22,500	£65,000	—
Angel	£1300	£4000	—
Half Angel	£1100	£3250	—
Quarter Angel	£1000	£3100	—
Pound (20s)	£4000	£13,500	—
Half Pound	£1900	£5650	—
Crown	£1300	£3850	—
Half Crown	£1250	£3750	—
Silver			
Crown (mm I)	£2000	£5350	—
Half Crown (mm I)	£1150	£3250	—
Shilling	£120	£550	£1850
Sixpence	£80	£260	£1500
Groat	£85	£325	£900
Threepence	£60	£225	£650
Half Groat	£40	£125	£325
Threehalfpence	£65	£235	£450
Penny	£40	£125	£300
Threefarthings	£85	£300	£425
Half Penny	£50	£125	£175

Shilling

WE OFFER FREE VALUATIONS
WE CAN VISIT YOU AT YOUR HOME, WORK OR BANK
SINGLE PIECES OR COLLECTIONS, PURCHASED OR FOR AUCTION

GENEROUS ADVANCES AVAILABLE
THE BEST COMMISSION RATES

WE OFFER 0% COMMISSION

10 CHARLES II STREET, LONDON SW1Y 4AA
PHONE: +44(0)20 7930 7888 | FAX: +44(0)20 7839 5500
info@stjauctions.com | www.stjauctions.com

JAMES I
(1603–25)

Although the size of the gold coinage remains much the same as Elizabeth's reign, the name and weight or value of the denominations have several changes, i.e. Pound = Sovereign = Unite = Laurel. A new four shilling gold coin (thistle crown) was introduced. A number of the silver coins now have their value in Roman numerals on the coin. Relatively few angels were made from this period onwards and they are usually found pierced.

	F	VF	EF
Gold			
Sovereign (20s)	£4000	£15000	—
Unite	£750	£2000	—
Double crown/half unite	£550	£1650	—
Crown	£350	£800	—
Thistle Crown	£350	£1000	—
Half Crown	£300	£625	—
Rose Ryal (30s)	£4000	£14,000	—
Spur Ryal (15s)	£10,000	£33,500	—
Angel (pierced)	£725	£2000	—
Half Angel (Unpierced)	£4000	£11,500	—
Laurel	£725	£2100	—
Half Laurel	£525	£1600	—
Quarter Laurel	£350	£800	—
Silver			
Crown	£900	£2150	—
Half Crown	£375	£950	—
Shilling	£100	£335	—
Sixpence	£70	£275	—
Half Groat	£25	£75	£175
Penny	£25	£70	£135
Half Penny	£20	£55	£135

Gold Unite,
second bust

Silver Halfcrown

CHARLES I
(1625–49)

This reign is probably the most difficult to simplify as there are so many different issues and whole books have been produced on this period alone. From the beginning of the King's reign and throughout the Civil War, a number of mints operated for varying lengths of time, producing both regular and irregular issues. The Tower mint was taken over by Parliament in 1642 but before this a small quantity of milled coinage was produced alongside the regular hammered issues. The Court then moved to Oxford from where, for the next three years, large quantities of gold and silver were struck (including rare triple unites and large silver pounds). The most prolific of the provincial mints were those situated at Aberystwyth, York, Oxford, Shrewsbury, Bristol, Exeter, Truro, Chester and Worcester as well as some smaller mints mainly situated in the West Country. Among the more interesting coins of the period are the pieces struck on unusually-shaped flans at Newark and Pontefract whilst those towns were under siege. As many of the coins struck during the Civil War were crudely struck on hastily gathered bullion and plate, they provide a fascinating area of study. The prices indicated below are the minimum for the commonest examples of each denomination irrespective of town of origin.

	F	VF	EF
Gold			
Triple Unite (£3) (Oxford)	£14,000	£38,000	—
Unite	£850	£2400	—
Double crown/Half unite	£500	£1500	—
Crown	£340	£875	—
Angel (pierced)	£725	£2250	—
Angel (unpierced)	£2600	£9250	—
Silver			
Pound (20 shillings—Oxford)	£4250	£12,000	—
Half Pound (Shrewsbury)	£1500	£4000	—
Crown (Truro, Exeter)	£500	£1400	—
Half Crown	£100	£325	—
Shilling	£60	£200	£1000
Sixpence	£50	£190	£875
Groat (Aberystwyth)	£100	£240	£600
Threepence (Aberystwyth)	£90	£220	£550
Half Groat	£25	£90	£250
Penny	£25	£75	£225
Half Penny	£20	£60	£100

Triple unite

Above: Newark siege shilling.

Oxford Halfcrown

THE COMMONWEALTH
(1649–60)

After the execution of Charles I, Parliament changed the design of the coinage. They are simple non- portrait pieces with an English legend.

	F	VF	EF
Gold			
Unite £2400	£6000	—
Double crown/Half unite...£1800	£5500	—
Crown £1500	£4000	—
Silver			
Crown £1500	£3250	£7500
Half Crown.........................£400	£1000	£3500
Shilling £325	£700	£2750
Sixpence............................£250	£625	£2250
Half Groat £65	£170	£350
Penny..................................£60	£165	£335
Halfpenny £50	£115	£200

Crown

CHARLES II
(1660–85)

Although milled coins had been produced for Oliver Cromwell in 1656–58, after the Restoration of the monarchy hammered coins continued to be produced until 1663, when the machinery was ready to manufacture large quantities of good milled pieces.

	F	VF	EF
Gold			
Unite (2nd issue)..............£2300	£6400	—
Double crown/Half unite...£1700	£5000	—
Crown (1st issue)..............£2000	£5750	—
Silver			
Half Crown (3rd issue) £275	£850	—
Shilling (3rd issue)..............£180	£675	—
Sixpence (3rd issue) £150	£525	—
Fourpence (3rd issue)...........£45	£150	£325
Threepence (3rd issue) £45	£150	£325
Twopence (3rd issue)............£25	£75	£175
Penny (3rd issue) £40	£115	£235

Halfcrown

A COMPREHENSIVE PRICE GUIDE
TO THE COINS OF

THE
UNITED KINGDOM
1656–2022

including

*England, Scotland,
Isle of Man,
Guernsey, Jersey, Alderney,
also Ireland*

When referring to this price guide one must bear a number of important points in mind. The points listed here have been taken into consideration during the preparation of this guide and we hope that the prices given will provide a true reflection of the market at the time of going to press. Nevertheless, the publishers can accept no liability for the accuracy of the prices quoted, which are the prices one could expect to pay for a coin.

1. "As struck" examples with flaws will be worth less than the indicated price.
2. Any coin which is particularly outstanding, with an attractive natural toning or in superb state will command a much *higher* price than that shown.
3. These prices refer strictly to the British market, and do not reflect outside opinions.
4. Some prices given for coins not seen in recent years are estimates based on a knowledge of the market.
5. In the case of coins of high rarity, prices are not generally given.
6. In the listing, "−" indicates, where applicable, one of the following:
    a. Metal or bullion value only
    b. Not usually found in this grade
    c. Not collected in this condition
7. Proof coins are listed in FDC under the UNC column.
8. All prices are quoted in £ sterling, exclusive of VAT (where applicable).

FIFTY SHILLINGS

	F	VF	EF

OLIVER CROMWELL (1656–58)

	F	VF	EF
1656..	£30,000	£85,000	£220,000

Opinions differ as to whether the portrait coinage of Oliver Cromwell was ever meant for circulation but for the sake of completeness it has been decided to include it in this Yearbook. The fifty shillings gold coin is unique as it was only struck during Cromwell's time using the same dies that were used for the broad or 20 shillings coin but with a weight of approximately 2.5 times that of the broad.

FIVE GUINEAS

CHARLES II (1660–85)

	F	VF	EF
1668 First bust	£8000	£18,000	£90,000
1668 — Elephant below bust	£8000	£17,000	£90,000
1669 —	£8000	£17,000	—
1669 — Elephant..................................	£8000	£17,000	—
1670 —	£8500	£17,000	£90,000
1670 — Proof		Exceedingly Rare	
1671 —	£8000	£17,000	£95,000
1672 —	£8000	£16,000	£90,000
1673 —	£8000	£18,000	£90,000
1674 —	£6000	£17,000	£90,000
1675 —	£5500	£15,000	£90,000
1675 — Elephant..................................	£9000	£20,000	—
1675 — Elephant & Castle below bust...	£9500	£19,000	£100,000
1676 —	£8000	£17,000	£92,500
1676 — Elephant & Castle	£8500	£20,000	£95,000
1677 —	£8000	£19,000	£90,000
1677/5 — Elephant...............................	£9500	£20,000	£100,000
1677 — Elephant & Castle	£8500	£19,000	£90,000
1678/7 — 8 over 7................................	£8000	£18,000	£90,000
1678/7 — Elephant & Castle	£8500	£19,000	£100,000
1678/7 Second Bust.............................	£8000	£17,000	£92,500
1679 —	£8500	£17,000	£92,500
1680 —	£8500	£17,000	£92,500
1680 — Elephant & Castle	£9000	£19,000	£100,000
1681 —	£8000	£17,000	£90,000
1681 — Elephant & Castle	£9000	£19,000	£105,000
1682 —	£8000	£17,500	£90,000
1682 — Elephant & Castle	£9000	£19,000	£100,000
1683 —	£8000	£17,000	£92,500
1683 — Elephant & Castle	£9000	£20,000	£102,000
1684 —	£7500	£20,000	£92,500
1684 — Elephant & Castle	£8000	£21,000	£90,000

Charles II

JAMES II (1685–88)

	F	VF	EF
1686..	£8000	£18,000	£100,000
1687..	£7000	£18,000	£95,000
1687 Elephant & Castle.........................	£8000	£18,000	£100,000
1688	£7000	£16,000	£85,000
1688 Elephant & Castle.........................	£9500	£22,000	£105,000

	F	VF	EF

WILLIAM AND MARY (1688–94)

	F	VF	EF
1691	£7000	£18,000	£110,000
1691 Elephant & Castle	£7000	£19,000	£115,000
1692	£7000	£17,000	£110000
1692 Elephant & Castle	£7500	£20,000	£115,000
1693	£7000	£18,000	£110,000
1693 Elephant & Castle	£7500	£18,000	£120,000
1694	£7000	£18,000	£90,000
1694 Elephant & Castle	£7500	£19,000	£100,000

WILLIAM III (1694–1702)

	F	VF	EF
1699 First bust	£8000	£18,000	£95,000
1699 — Elephant & Castle	£9000	£20,000	£100,000
1700 —	£7500	£19,000	£95,000
1701 Second bust "fine work"	£7500	£20,000	£95,000

(1701 "fine work"—beware recent forgeries)

ANNE (1702–14)

Pre-Union with Scotland

	F	VF	EF
1703 VIGO below bust	£65,000	£170,000	£650,000
1705	£12,000	£35,000	£125,000
1706	£11,000	£32,000	£120,000

Post-Union (different shields)

	F	VF	EF
1706	£9000	£20,000	£90,000
1709 Narrow shields	£9000	£20,000	£93,000
1711 Broader shields	£9000	£20,000	£95,000
1713 —	£10,000	£19,000	£94,000
1714 —	£10,000	£20,000	£95,000
1714/3	£10,000	£21,000	£95,000

William & Mary

GEORGE I (1714–27)

	F	VF	EF
1716	£9500	£22,000	£105,000
1717	£9500	£23,000	£105,000
1720	£9500	£22,000	£105,000
1726	£9500	£22,000	£100,000

GEORGE II (1727–60)

	F	VF	EF
1729 Young head	£9000	£18,000	£95,000
1729 — E.I.C. below head	£8000	£18,000	£95,000
1731 —	£8000	£18,000	£85,000
1735 —	£8000	£18,000	£100,000
1738 —	£8000	£18,000	£100,000
1741	£8000	£17,000	£80,000
1741/38 41 over 38	£7500	£18,000	£80,000
1746 Old head, LIMA	£7500	£18,000	£80,000
1748 —	£7500	£18,000	£75,000
1753 —	£7500	£19,000	£78,000

GEORGE III (1760–1820)

	F	VF	EF
1770 Patterns	—	—	£400,000
1773	—	—	£400,000
1777	—	—	£400,000

Anne

TWO GUINEAS

	F	VF	EF

CHARLES II (1660–85)

	F	VF	EF
1664 First bust	£2700	£7000	£24,000
1664 — Elephant	£2500	£6000	£22,000
1665 —		Extremely rare	
1669 —		Extremely rare	
1671 —	£3500	£9000	£35,000
1673 First bust		Extremely rare	
1675 Second bust	£3000	£7000	£22,000
1676 —	£3000	£7000	£28,000
1676 — Elephant & Castle	£3000	£7000	£28,000
1677 —	£3000	£7000	£25,000
1677 — Elephant & Castle		Extremely rare	
1678/7 —	£2800	£6500	£26,000
1678 — Elephant		Extremely rare	
1678 — Elephant & Castle	£2800	£6500	£32,000
1679 —	£2800	£6500	£28,000
1680 —	£2800	£6000	£29,000
1681 —	£2800	£5500	£29,000
1682 — Elephant & Castle	£2700	£7000	£31,000
1683 —	£2700	£6000	£32,000
1683 — Elephant & Castle	£2700	£7000	£34,000
1684 —	£2700	£7000	£32,000
1684 — Elephant & Castle	£2700	£7500	£40,000

Charles II

JAMES II (1685–88)

	F	VF	EF
1687	£3500	£11,000	£36,000
1688/7	£3750	£11,500	£37,000

WILLIAM AND MARY (1688–94)

	F	VF	EF
1691 Elephant & Castle		Exceedingly rare	
1693	£3000	£9000	£30,000
1693 Elephant & Castle	£3250	£9000	£32,500
1694 — 4 over 3	£3000	£8000	£30,000
1694/3 Elephant & Castle	£3500	£9000	£30,000

James II

WILLIAM III (1694–1702)

	F	VF	EF
1701 "fine work"	£3250	£8000	£35,000

ANNE (1702–14)

	F	VF	EF
1709 Post Union	£2000	£6500	£24,000
1711	£2000	£6500	£24,000
1713	£2200	£7000	£25,000
1714/3	£2200	£7000	£26,000

GEORGE I (1714–27)

	F	VF	EF
1717	£2500	£6500	£30,000
1720	£2500	£6500	£30,000
1720/17	£2750	£6500	£30,000
1726	£2350	£7000	£32,000

Anne

	F	VF	EF

GEORGE II (1727–60)

	F	VF	EF
1733 Proof only FDC		Extremely Rare	
1734 Young head 4 over 3	£3000	£7500	—
1735 —	£2500	£6000	£17,500
1738 —	£950	£3000	£7000
1739 —	£950	£3000	£6500
1739 Intermediate head	£950	£3000	£8000
1740 —	£1000	£2500	£8000
1748 Old head	£1350	£3000	£8000
1753 —	£1700	£3000	£9000

GEORGE III (1760–1820)

	F	VF	EF
1768 Patterns only	—	Extremely Rare	
1773 Patterns only	—	Extremely Rare	
1777 Patterns only	—	Extremely Rare	

George II

GUINEAS

	F	VF	EF

CHARLES II (1660–85)

	F	VF	EF
1663 First bust	£4000	£13,000	£50,000
1663 — Elephant below	£4000	£12,000	—
1663 Second bust	£3500	£11,000	£40,000
1664 Second bust	£3500	£11,000	—
1664 — Elephant	£4000	£12,000	£47,000
1664 Third bust	£1200	£4000	£15,000
1664 — Elephant	£1800	£5000	£18,000
1665 —	£1200	£4000	£15,000
1665 — Elephant	£2000	£6000	£22,000
1666 —	£1000	£3200	£13,000
1667 —	£1000	£3200	£13,000
1668 —	£1050	£3500	£13,500
1668 — Elephant		Extremely rare	
1669 —	£1200	£3200	£14,000
1670 —	£1200	£3200	£13,500
1671 —	£1200	£3200	£14,000
1672 —	£1200	£3500	£16,000
1672 Fourth bust	£1100	£3000	£11,000
1673 Third bust	£1200	£3200	£16,000
1673 Fourth bust	£900	£2800	£12,000
1674 —	£900	£2800	£12,000
1674 — Elephant & Castle		Extremely rare	
1675 —	£1000	£3000	£12,000
1675 — CRAOLVS Error		Extremely rare	
1675 — Elephant & Castle	£1100	£3400	£15,000
1676 —	£800	£2500	£11,000
1676/4 — 6 over 4	£800	£2500	£11,000
1676 — Elephant & Castle	£900	£4000	£18,000
1677 —	£800	£2500	£10,000
1677 — GRATIR Error		Extremely rare	
1677/5 — Elephant 7 over 5		Extremely rare	
1677 — Elephant & Castle	£1000	£3000	£13,000
1678 —	£950	£2500	£13,000
1678 — Elephant		Extremely rare	
1678 — Elephant & Castle	£1000	£3200	£14,000

Charles II, third bust

Charles II, fourth bust, elephant & castle below

	F	VF	EF
1679 —	£1000	£2500	£11,000
1679 — Elephant & Castle	£1100	£3500	£14,000
1680 —	£950	£2500	£10,000
1680 — Elephant & Castle	£1100	£4000	£13,500
1681 —	£1000	£3000	£12,000
1681 — Elephant & Castle	£1100	£4000	£15,000
1682 —	£1000	£3200	£11,000
1682 — Elephant & Castle	£1100	£4200	£16,000
1683 —	£950	£2500	£11,000
1683 — Elephant & Castle	£1000	£4000	£15,000
1684 —	£900	£3000	£12,000
1684 — Elephant & Castle	£1100	£4250	£17,500

James II,
first bust,
elephant
& castle
below

JAMES II (1685–88)

	F	VF	EF
1685 First bust	£1400	£3500	£13,000
1685 — Elephant & Castle	£1500	£4000	£14,000
1686 —	£1200	£3000	£13,000
1686 — Elephant & Castle		Extremely rare	
1686 Second bust	£1300	£3500	£11,000
1686 — Elephant & Castle	£1400	£4000	£15,000
1687 —	£1500	£4500	£13,000
1687 —Elephant & Castle	£1400	£4000	£16,500
1688 —	£1250	£2750	£11,000
1688 — Elephant & Castle	£1250	£3750	£14,000

WILLIAM AND MARY (1688–94)

	F	VF	EF
1689..	£1000	£3000	£12,000
1689 Elephant & Castle	£1100	£3250	£13,000
1690..	£1000	£3400	£13,000
1690 GVLIFLMVS	£1000	£3400	£13,000
1690 Elephant & Castle	£1100	£3500	£15,000
1691..	£1000	£3250	£12,500
1691 Elephant & Castle	£1000	£3250	£12,500
1692..	£1000	£3250	£12,500
1692 Elephant	£1150	£4000	£13,500
1692 Elephant & Castle	£1100	£4000	£13,500
1693..	£1100	£2750	£12,000
1693 Elephant	£1250	£4500	£18,500
1693 Elephant & Castle	£1200	£4500	£17,500
1694..	£1100	£3250	£12,500
1694/3	£1100	£3250	£12,500
1694 Elephant & Castle	£1200	£3500	£13,000
1694/3 Elephant & Castle...............	£1200	£3500	£13,500

James II,
second bust

(Note: there are several overstamp errors of this reign. Prices are similar to standard issues)

WILLIAM III (1694–1702)

	F	VF	EF
1695 First bust	£900	£3000	£10,500
1695 — Elephant & Castle	£1400	£6000	£16,500
1696 —	£900	£3000	£10,500
1696 — Elephant & Castle		Extremely rare	
1697 —	£900	£4000	£11,500
1697 Second bust	£900	£3250	£11,000
1697 — Elephant & Castle	£1800	£7000	£20,000
1698 —	£900	£3000	£10,000
1698 — Elephant & Castle	£1600	£5000	£13,500
1699 —	£950	£3250	£12,000
1699 — Elephant & Castle		Extremely rare	
1700 —	£925	£2500	£9500
1700 — Elephant & Castle	£1350	£5500	—
1701 —	£850	£2750	£9000
1701 — Elephant & Castle		Extremely rare	
1701 Third bust "fine work"............	£2000	£6500	£20,000

William III,
second bust

	F	VF	EF

ANNE (1702–14)

	F	VF	EF
1702 (Pre-Union) First bust	£1400	£5000	£18,000
1703 — VIGO below	£25,000	£65,000	£135,000
1705 —	£1500	£5000	£14,000
1706 —	£1500	£5000	£15,000
1707 —	£1500	£5000	£15,000
1707 — (Post-Union)	£800	£3000	£12,000
1707 — Elephant & Castle	£1300	£5500	£16,000
1707 Second bust	£800	£3000	£11,000
1708 First bust	£850	£3250	£12,000
1708 Second bust	£750	£2500	£8000
1708 — Elephant & Castle	£1500	£6000	£18,000
1709 —	£900	£2200	£10,000
1709 — Elephant & Castle	£950	£4000	£15,000
1710 Third bust	£800	£1600	£6000
1711 —	£800	£1600	£6000
1712 —	£800	£1900	£7000
1713 —	£700	£1800	£5500
1714 —	£700	£1800	£5500
1714 GRATIA	£900	£2000	£12,000

Anne, third bust

GEORGE I (1714–27)

	F	VF	EF
1714 First bust (Prince Elector)	£2200	£6000	£20,000
1715 Second bust	£900	£2000	£5500
1715 Third bust	£600	£1800	£5750
1716 —	£750	£1900	£6000
1716 Fourth bust	£675	£1800	£5500
1717 —	£675	£1800	£5500
1718/7 — 8 over 7			Extremely rare
1718 —			Extremely rare
1719 —	£700	£1800	£6000
1720 —	£700	£1800	£5000
1721 —	£750	£1950	£5500
1721 — Elephant & Castle			Extremely rare
1722 —	£800	£1750	£6000
1722 — Elephant & Castle			Extremely rare
1723 —	£700	£1800	£6500
1723 Fifth bust	£700	£1800	£6500
1724 —	£700	£1800	£6500
1725 —	£700	£1800	£6500
1726 —	£750	£1800	£6500
1726 — Elephant & Castle	£2200	£8000	£25,000
1727 —	£900	£2400	£7500

George I, fifth bust

GEORGE II (1727–60)

	F	VF	EF
1727 First young head, early large shield	£1400	£4750	£16,000
1727 — Larger lettering, early small shield	£1400	£5000	£16,000
1728 — —	£1650	£5500	£14,000
1729 2nd young head E.I.C. below	£1800	£4250	£17,500
1729 — Proof			Very Rare
1730 —	£700	£1800	£7000
1731 —	£700	£2000	£8000
1731 — E.I.C. below	£1600	£5000	£16,500
1732 —	£700	£2500	£8000
1732 — E.I.C. below	£900	£3000	£11,000
1732 — Larger lettering obverse	£700	£2000	£8000
1732 — — E.I.C. below	£1400	£4000	£16,000
1733 — —	£650	£1600	£5000
1734 — —	£650	£1600	£5000
1735 — —	£650	£1600	£5000
1736 — —	£650	£1700	£5000
1737 — —	£650	£1700	£5000

George II, 1760, old head, large lettering

	F	VF	EF
1738 — —	£700	£1800	£6000
1739 Intermediate head	£800	£1800	£7000
1739 — E.I.C. below..	£1450	£4000	£15,000
1740 —	£800	£1800	£9000
1741/39 —	£1000	£3000	£11,000
1743 —	£1000	£3000	£11,000
1745 — Larger lettering obv. Older bust	£700	£1800	£6000
1745 — LIMA below..	£2500	£7000	£28,000
1746 — (GEORGIVS) Larger lettering obv.......	£750	£1800	£7000
1747 Old head, large lettering	£650	£1500	£4800
1748 —	£650	£1400	£5000
1749 —	£650	£1500	£5000
1750 —	£650	£1450	£5000
1751 — small lettering..................................	£600	£1400	£5000
1753 —	£600	£1400	£5000
1755 —	£600	£1500	£4500
1756 —	£600	£1500	£4500
1758 —	£600	£1500	£4500
1759 —	£600	£1500	£4500
1760 —	£600	£1500	£4250

George III third head

GEORGE III (1760–1820)

	F	VF	EF
1761 First head...	£2200	£6000	£15,000
1763 Second head	£1600	£4000	£12,000
1764 —	£1400	£4000	£13,000
1764 – No stop above bust.............................	£2200	£5000	£13,000
1765 Third head	£500	£800	£2000
1766 —	£500	£800	£2000
1767 —	£550	£1000	£2500
1768 —	£500	£800	£2000
1769 —	£500	£800	£2200
1770 —	£1500	£3250	£8000
1771 —	£500	£700	£1800
1772 —	£500	£700	£1800
1773 —	£500	£700	£1950
1774 Fourth head	£450	£700	£1400
1775 —	£475	£700	£1500
1776 —	£425	£675	£1600
1777 —	£425	£625	£1600
1778 —	£850	£1400	£4000
1779 —	£500	£725	£1350
1781 —	£450	£675	£1450
1782 —	£450	£675	£1450
1783 —	£400	£625	£1450
1784 —	£400	£625	£1350
1785 —	£425	£675	£1400
1786 —	£475	£725	£1450
1787 Fifth head, "Spade" reverse	£400	£575	£1150
1788 —	£400	£575	£1150
1789 —	£400	£575	£1200
1790 —	£425	£650	£1350
1791 —	£400	£600	£1200
1792 —	£400	£600	£1200
1793 —	£400	£650	£1250
1794 —	£400	£650	£1200
1795 —	£400	£650	£1200
1796 —	£400	£650	£1200
1797 —	£400	£700	£1250
1798 —	£400	£675	£1250
1799 —	£500	£825	£2000
1813 Sixth head, "Military" reverse	£1300	£2500	£7000

(Beware of counterfeits of this series—many dangerous copies exist)

Fourth head

Fifth head, Spade reverse

Sixth "Military" head

HALF GUINEAS

	F	VF	EF
CHARLES II (1660–85)			
1669 First bust	£600	£1850	£7000
1670 —	£600	£1850	£6500
1671 —	£650	£1850	£7500
1672 —	£650	£1750	£6000
1672 Second bust	£650	£1600	£6250
1673 —	£650	£1800	£6250
1674 —	£650	£1950	£6500
1675 —	£650	£1950	£6500
1676 —	£600	£1700	£5750
1676 — Elephant & Castle	£800	£3250	—
1677 —	£650	£1800	£6000
1677 — Elephant & Castle	£700	£2400	£9000
1678 —	£600	£1600	£6500
1678/7 —	£550	£1600	£6500
1678/7 — Elephant & Castle	£800	£2100	£9000
1679 —	£600	£1750	£6000
1680 —	£600	£2200	£7000
1680 — Elephant & Castle	£850	£2400	£9250
1681 —	£625	£1800	£7000
1682 —	£650	£1800	£6000
1682 — Elephant & Castle	£725	£2450	£10,000
1683 —	£625	£1750	£5500
1683 — Elephant & Castle		Extremely rare	
1684 —	£625	£1650	£6000
1684 — Elephant & Castle	£725	£2400	£9000

Charles II, second bust

James II

JAMES II (1685–88)			
1686	£600	£1800	£6000
1686 Elephant & Castle	£1000	£4000	£10,500
1687	£600	£1800	£6000
1688	£575	£1850	£6250

WILLIAM AND MARY (1688–94)			
1689 First busts	£700	£2200	£6000
1690 Second busts	£650	£2000	£6000
1691 —	£700	£1900	£6250
1691 — Elephant & Castle	£750	£2400	£7250
1692 —	£750	£2200	£7250
1692 — Elephant		Extremely rare	
1692 — Elephant & Castle	£750	£2500	£7250
1693 —		Extremely rare	
1694 —	£675	£2000	£6500

William & Mary, second busts

WILLIAM III (1694–1702)			
1695	£500	£1450	£6000
1695 Elephant & Castle	£750	£2500	£8000
1696 —	£650	£1850	£6500
1697 Larger Harp rev.	£750	£2200	£7500
1698	£650	£1500	£5250
1698 Elephant & Castle	£750	£2200	£7000
1699		Extremely rare	
1700	£600	£1400	£6000
1701	£525	£1350	£5750

William III

	F	VF	EF

ANNE (1702–14)

	F	VF	EF
1702 (Pre-Union)	£1300	£3500	£13,000
1703 VIGO below bust	£12,000	£35,000	£80,000
1705	£1100	£3500	£11,000
1707 (Post-Union)	£500	£1200	£4750
1708	£475	£1300	£5250
1709	£475	£1200	£4500
1710	£450	£1100	£4500
1711	£450	£1100	£4500
1712	£475	£1200	£4600
1713	£450	£1100	£4500
1714	£450	£1100	£4500

Anne

GEORGE I (1714–27)

	F	VF	EF
1715 First bust	£750	£1600	£6000
1717 —	£450	£850	£4750
1718 —	£450	£850	£4750
1718/7 —	£450	£850	£4750
1719 —	£450	£800	£4250
1720 —	£425	£750	£4500
1721 —			Extremely rare
1721 — Elephant & Castle			Extremely rare
1722 —	£450	£1000	£4250
1723 —	£525	£1050	£4400
1724 —	£450	£1100	£5000
1725 Second bust	£450	£900	£3850
1726 —	£450	£900	£4200
1727 —	£450	£950	£4350

George I, second bust

GEORGE II (1727–60)

	F	VF	EF
1728 Young head	£700	£1600	£6000
1729 —	£600	£1500	£4800
1729 — E.I.C.	£750	£1800	£6500
1730 —	£500	£1100	£4350
1730 — E.I.C.	£900	£2250	—
1731 —	£450	£1100	£3850
1731 — E.I.C.			Extremely rare
1732 —	£400	£1100	£3800
1732 — E.I.C.			Extremely rare
1733 —			Unknown
1734 —	£400	£950	£3750
1735 —			Unknown
1736 —	£500	£950	£3750
1737 —	£500	£950	£4200
1738 —	£450	£950	£3800
1739 —	£450	£950	£3750
1739 — E.I.C.			Extremely rare
1740 Intermediate head	£450	£1050	£4000
1743 —			Extremely rare
1745 —	£450	£1100	£4250
1745 — LIMA	£1300	£4000	£13,000
1746 —	£350	£850	£3000
1747 Old head	£400	£850	£3250
1748 —	£375	£800	£3000
1749 —	£400	£900	£3250
1750 —	£375	£800	£3250
1751 —	£350	£850	£3000
1752 —	£350	£850	£3000
1753 —	£350	£850	£3000
1755 —	£350	£750	£2900
1756 —	£400	£750	£3000
1758 —	£350	£750	£3000
1759 —	£350	£750	£2600
1759/8 —	£350	£700	£3000
1760 —	£350	£750	£2950

George II, young head

George II, old head

GEORGE III (1760–1820)

	F	VF	EF
1762 First head	£725	£2000	£5500
1763 —	£850	£2700	£6500
1764 Second head	£325	£600	£1700
1765 —	£550	£1600	£4250
1766 —	£350	£625	£1950
1768 —	£350	£625	£1950
1769 —	£375	£625	£1900
1772 —	Extremely rare		
1773 —	£370	£750	£2150
1774 —	£400	£800	£2400
1774 Third head	Extremely rare		
1775 —	£1500	£4000	£11,000
1775 Fourth head	£275	£500	£1200
1775 — Proof	Extremely rare		
1776 —	£275	£550	£1500
1777 —	£275	£550	£1200
1778 —	£275	£550	£1250
1779 —	£275	£550	£1300
1781 —	£275	£550	£1250
1783 —	£500	£1800	—
1784 —	£250	£500	£1100
1785 —	£225	£500	£1000
1786 —	£225	£500	£1000
1787 Fifth head, "Spade" rev.	£225	£400	£1000
1788 —	£225	£400	£1000
1789 —	£225	£400	£1000
1790 —	£225	£400	£950
1791 —	£225	£400	£950
1792 —	£1500	£4000	—
1793 —	£225	£475	£1000
1794 —	£225	£475	£950
1795 —	£225	£525	£1100
1796 —	£225	£475	£950
1797 —	£225	£475	£950
1798 —	£225	£475	£950
1800 —	£375	£1000	£2750
1801 Sixth head, Shield in Garter rev.	£225	£375	£875
1802 —	£225	£375	£875
1803 —	£225	£375	£875
1804 Seventh head	£225	£375	£875
1805	Extremely rare		
1806 —	£225	£425	£800
1808 —	£225	£425	£800
1899 —	£225	£425	£800
1810 —	£225	£425	£800
1811 —	£400	£600	£1600
1813 —	£350	£600	£1200

George III,
first head

George III,
second head

George III,
third head

George III,
fourth head

George III,
fifth head

George III,
sixth head

George III,
seventh head

THIRD GUINEAS

DATE	F	VF	EF
GEORGE III (1760–1820)			
1797 First head, date in legend	£150	£275	£700
1798 — —	£150	£275	£700
1799 — —	£475	£1100	£2000
1800 — —	£160	£325	£800
1801 Date under crown	£170	£350	£800
1802 —	£170	£350	£800
1803 —	£170	£350	£775
1804 Second head	£150	£275	£700
1806 —	£150	£275	£675
1808 —	£150	£350	£750
1809 —	£150	£350	£750
1810 —	£150	£350	£750
1811 —	£600	£1300	£3000
1813 —	£300	£600	£1350

George III, date in legend

George III, date under crown

QUARTER GUINEAS

	F	VF	EF
GEORGE I (1714–27)			
1718	£250	£400	£1050
GEORGE III (1760–1820)			
1762	£250	£525	£900

George I

FIVE POUNDS

DATE	Mintage	F	VF	EF	UNC
GEORGE III (1760–1820)					
1820 (pattern only)	—			Extremely rare	
GEORGE IV (1820–30)					
1826 proof only	—	—	—	£65,000	
VICTORIA (1837–1901)					
1839 Una & The Lion. Proof .					*

* In recent months the prices paid for Una & the Lion coins has risen astronomically. In August 2021 Hertiage Auctions sold an example for over $1 million.

DATE	Mintage	F	VF	EF	UNC
1887	53,844	£1600	£2500	£3500	£4500
1887 Proof	797	—	—	—	£20,000
1887 S on ground on rev. (Sydney Mint)				Excessively rare	
1893	20,405	£2000	£2800	£5000	£8000
1893 Proof	773	—	—	—	£19,000
EDWARD VII (1902–10)					
1902	34,910	£1750	£2200	£2750	£4000
1902 Matt proof	8,066	—	—	—	£3500

DATE	MINTAGE	F	VF	EF	UNC

GEORGE V (1911–36)
1911 Proof only .... 2,812 — — — £10,000

GEORGE VI (1937–52)
1937 Proof only .... 5,501 — — — £8000

Later issues are listed in the Decimal section.

TWO POUNDS

GEORGE III (1760–1820)
1820 (pattern only)............ — — — Extremely rare

GEORGE IV (1820–30)
1823 St George reverse..... — £800 £1100 £2500 £4500
1826 Proof only, shield reverse — — — Extremely rare

WILLIAM IV (1830–37)
1831 Proof only .... 225 — — — £22,500

VICTORIA (1837–1901)
1887................................... 91,345 £800 £1100 £1500 £2000
1887 Proof......................... 797 — — — £3500
1887 S on ground of rev. (Sydney Mint) Excessively rare
1893................................... 52,212 £800 £1100 £2000 £3000
1893 Proof......................... 773 — — — £7000

EDWARD VII (1902–10)
1902................................... 45,807 £700 £850 £1200 £2000
1902 Matt proof................ 8,066 — — — £1800

GEORGE V (1911–36)
1911 Proof only .... 2,812 — — — £3000

GEORGE VI (1937–52)
1937 Proof only .... 5,501 — — — £2750
Later issues are listed in the Decimal section.

CROMWELL GOLD

	F	VF	EF

OLIVER CROMWELL (1656–58)
1656 Fifty Shillings £35,000 £100,000 £300,000
1656 Twenty Shillings............................. £8,000 £20,000 £50,000

SOVEREIGNS

DATE	MINTAGE	F	VF	EF	UNC

GEORGE III (1760–1820)

DATE	MINTAGE	F	VF	EF	UNC
1817	3,235,239	£550	£900	£2000	£5000
1818	2,347,230	£700	£1300	£5000	£8500
1819	3,574	Exceedingly rare			
1820	931,994	£550	£850	£1800	£4000

George III

GEORGE IV (1820–30)

DATE	MINTAGE	F	VF	EF	UNC
1821 First bust, St George reverse	9,405,114	£500	£750	£1800	—
1821 — Proof	incl. above	—	—	—	£12,000
1822 —	5,356,787	£450	£750	£2000	£3500
1823 —	616,770	£1000	£2750	£8000	—
1824 —	3,767,904	£500	£900	£2250	£4000
1825 —	4,200,343	£800	£2400	£8000	£10,000
1825 Second bust, shield reverse	incl. above	£425	£700	£1750	£2750
1826 —	5,724,046	£425	£700	£1500	£2750
1826 — Proof	—	—	—	—	£9000
1827 —	2,266,629	£475	£750	£1750	£3500
1828 —	386,182	£6000	£15,000	£30,000	—
1829 —	2,444,652	£475	£800	£2500	£4000
1830 —	2,387,881	£500	£825	£2500	£4000

George IV, shield reverse

WILLIAM IV (1830–37)

DATE	MINTAGE	F	VF	EF	UNC
1831	598,547	£600	£1000	£3250	£5000
1831 Proof, plain edge	—	—	—	—	£22,000
1832	3,737,065	£500	£900	£2500	£4200
1833	1,225,269	£500	£900	£2500	£4200
1835	723,441	£500	£900	£2500	£4200
1836	1,714,349	£500	£900	£2000	£4200
1836 N. of Anno struck on shield	—	£6000	£11,000	—	—
1837	1,172,984	£525	£950	£2400	£4500

Note—from the Victoria reign onwards, the prices of coins in lower grade are usually subject to the bullion price of gold.

William IV

VICTORIA (1837–1901)

Many of the gold coins struck at the colonial mints found their way into circulation in Britain, for the sake of completeness these coins are listed here. These can easily be identified by a tiny initial letter for the appropriate mint which can be found below the base of the reverse shield or, in the case of the St George reverse, below the bust on the obverse of the Young Head issues, or on the "ground" below the horse's hoof on the later issues.

YOUNG HEAD ISSUES

Shield reverse

(Note—Shield back sovereigns in Fine/VF condition, common dates, are normally traded as bullion + a percentage)

DATE	MINTAGE	F	VF	EF	UNC
1838	2,718,694	£800	£1500	£4000	£8000
1839	503,695	£1100	£2750	£4000	£9500
1839 Proof, plain edge	—	—	—	—	£27,000
1841	124,054	£5000	£10,000	£22,000	—
1842	4,865,375	£350	£500	£1000	£2000
1843	5,981,968	£350	£500	£1000	£2000
1843 "Narrow shield" variety	incl. above	£5250	£10,000	—	—
1843 Roman I in date	—	£750	£1500	—	—
1844	3,000,445	£350	£400	£1000	£1950
1845	3,800,845	£350	£400	£1000	£1950
1846	3,802,947	£350	£400	£1000	£1950
1847	4,667,126	£350	£420	£1000	£2000

Victoria Young Head

DATE	MINTAGE	F	VF	EF	UNC
1848	2,246,701	£350	£420	£1000	£2000
1849	1,755,399	£350	£420	£1000	£1800
1850	1,402,039	£350	£420	£1000	£1800
1851	4,013,624	£350	£420	£750	£1800
1852	8,053,435	£350	£420	£850	£1800
1853	10,597,993	£350	£420	£750	£1850
1853 Proof..............................	—	—	—	−£22,000	
1854 Incuse WW	3,589,611	£350	£420	£750	£1800
1854 Surface raised WW	3,589,611	£350	£420	£750	£2100
1855	4,806,160	£350	£420	£750	£1860
1856	8,448,482	£350	£420	£750	£1860
1857	4,495,748	£350	£420	£750	£1860
1858	803,234	£350	£420	£750	£1860
1859	1,547,603	£350	£420	£750	£1860
1859 "Ansell" (additional line on lower part of hair ribbon).........	—	£750	£1800	£10,000	—
1860	2,555,958	£350	£400	£650	£1300
1861	7,624,736	£350	£400	£600	£1300
1862	7,836,413	£350	£400	£650	£1300
1863	5,921,669	£350	£400	£600	£1300
1863 Die No 827 on Truncation...				Extremely rare	
1863 with Die number below shield	incl. above	£350	£400	£600	£1100
1864 —	8,656,352	£350	£400	£650	£1100
1865 —	1,450,238	£350	£400	£650	£1100
1866 —	4,047,288	£350	£400	£600	£1100
1868 —	1,653,384	£350	£400	£550	£1150
1869 —	6,441,322	£350	£400	£550	£1150
1870 —	2,189,960	£350	£400	£550	£1100
1871 —	8,767,250	£350	£400	£500	£1100
1872 —	13,486,708	£350	£400	£500	£1000
1872 no Die number	incl. above	£350	£400	£500	£1000
1873 with Die number	2,368,215	£350	£400	£600	£1000
1874 —	520,713	£2000	£4000	£12,000	—

M below reverse shield (Melbourne Mint)

1872.............................	748,180	£350	£400	£500	£1250
1873.............................	—			Extremely rare	
1874.............................	1,373,298	£350	£400	£500	£1250
1879.............................				Extremely rare	
1880.............................	3,053,454	£700	£1650	£3000	£6000
1881.............................	2,325,303	£350	£400	£450	£1600
1882.............................	2,465,781	£350	£400	£450	£1150
1883.............................	2,050,450	£350	£400	£600	£3500
1884.............................	2,942,630	£350	£400	£450	£1000
1885.............................	2,967,143	£350	£400	£450	£1000
1886.............................	2,902,131	£1800	£4000	£6500	£8500
1887.............................	1,916,424	£600	£1350	£3500	£6000

S below reverse shield (Sydney Mint)

1871	2,814,000	£350	£400	£450	£1300
1872.............................	1,815,000	£350	£400	£450	£1600
1873.............................	1,478,000	£350	£400	£450	£1300
1875.............................	2,122,000	£350	£400	£450	£1300
1877.............................	1,590,000	£350	£400	£450	£1300
1878.............................	1,259,000	£350	£400	£450	£1400
1879.............................	1,366,000	£350	£400	£450	£1300
1880.............................	1,459,000	£350	£400	£450	£1500
1881.............................	1,360,000	£350	£400	£450	£1500
1882.............................	1,298,000	£350	£400	£450	£1300
1883.............................	1,108,000	£350	£400	£450	£1100
1884.............................	1,595,000	£350	£400	£450	£1100
1885.............................	1,486,000	£350	£400	£450	£1100
1886.............................	1,667,000	£350	£400	£450	£1100
1887.............................	1,000,000	£350	£400	£450	£1600

The die number appears between the wreath and the bottom rose, below the shield

The mint initial appears between the wreath and the bottom rose, below the shield, i.e. "S" indicates that this coin was struck at the Sydney Mint

IMPORTANT NOTE: The prices quoted in this guide are set at August 2022 with the price of gold at £1,500 per ounce and silver £15.80 per ounce— market fluctuations can have a marked effect on the values of modern precious metal coins.

DATE	MINTAGE	F	VF	EF	UNC
St George & Dragon reverse					
1871	incl. above	£350	£365	£400	£550
1872	incl. above	£350	£365	£400	£550
1873	incl. above	£350	£365	£400	£550
1874	incl. above	£350	£365	£400	£550
1876	3,318,866	£350	£365	£400	£550
1878	1,091,275	£350	£365	£400	£550
1879	20,013	£600	£1500	£4500	—
1880	3,650,080	£350	£365	£400	£550
1884	1,769,635	£350	£365	£400	£550
1885	717,723	£350	£365	£400	£550
M below bust on obverse (Melbourne Mint)					
1872	incl. above	£350	£500	£600	£2500
1873	752,199	£350	£375	£460	£600
1874	incl. above	£350	£375	£460	£600
1875	incl. above	£350	£375	£460	£600
1876	2,124,445	£350	£375	£460	£600
1877	1,487,316	£350	£375	£460	£600
1878	2,171,457	£350	£375	£460	£600
1879	2,740,594	£350	£375	£460	£600
1880	incl. above	£350	£375	£460	£600
1881	incl. above	£350	£375	£460	£600
1882	incl. above	£350	£375	£460	£600
1883	incl. above	£350	£375	£460	£600
1884	incl. above	£350	£375	£460	£600
1885	incl. above	£350	£375	£460	£600
1886	incl. above	£350	£375	£460	£600
1887	incl. above	£350	£375	£460	£600
S below bust on obverse (Sydney Mint)					
1871	2,814,000	£350	£375	£460	£525
1872	incl. above	£350	£375	£460	£700
1873	incl. above	£350	£375	£460	£550
1874	1,899,000	£350	£375	£460	£550
1875	inc above	£350	£375	£460	£550
1876	1,613,000	£350	£375	£460	£550
1877	—			Unknown	
1879	incl. above	£350	£375	£460	£550
1880	incl. above	£350	£375	£460	£550
1881	incl. above	£350	£375	£460	£550
1882	incl. above	£350	£375	£460	£550
1883	incl. above	£350	£375	£460	£550
1884	incl. above	£350	£375	£460	£550
1885	incl. above	£350	£375	£460	£550
1886	incl. above	£350	£375	£460	£550
1887	incl. above	£350	£375	£460	£550
JUBILEE HEAD ISSUES					
1887	1,111,280	£350	£375	£450	£550
1887 Proof	797	—	—	—	£4000
1888	2,717,424	£350	£375	£450	£550
1889	7,257,455	£350	£375	£450	£550
1890	6,529,887	£350	£375	£450	£550
1891	6,329,476	£350	£375	£450	£550
1892	7,104,720	£350	£375	£450	£550
M on ground on reverse (Melbourne Mint)					
1887	940,000	£350	£375	£450	£550
1888	2,830,612	£350	£375	£450	£550
1889	2,732,590	£350	£375	£450	£550
1890	2,473,537	£350	£375	£450	£550
1891	2,749,592	£350	£375	£450	£550
1892	3,488,750	£350	£375	£450	£550
1893	1,649,352	£350	£375	£450	£550

M below bust indicates Melbourne Mint

S below bust indicates Sydney Mint

Jubilee head type

"M" below the horse's hoof above the date indicates that the coin was struck at the Melbourne Mint

DATE	MINTAGE	F	VF	EF	UNC
S on ground on reverse (Sydney Mint)					
1887	1,002,000	£350	£375	£1600	£2750
1888	2,187,000	£350	£375	£450	£550
1889	3,262,000	£350	£375	£450	£550
1890	2,808,000	£350	£375	£450	£550
1891	2,596,000	£350	£375	£450	£550
1892	2,837,000	£350	£375	£450	£550
1893	1,498,000	£350	£375	£450	£550

OLD HEAD ISSUES

DATE	MINTAGE	F	VF	EF	UNC
1893	6,898,260	£350	£375	£450	£550
1893 Proof	773	—	—	—	£4000
1894	3,782,611	£350	£375	£450	£550
1895	2,285,317	£350	£375	£450	£550
1896	3,334,065	£350	£375	£450	£550
1898	4,361,347	£350	£375	£450	£550
1899	7,515,978	£350	£375	£450	£550
1900	10,846,741	£350	£375	£450	£550
1901	1,578,948	£350	£375	£450	£550
M on ground on reverse (Melbourne Mint)					
1893	1,914,000	£350	£375	£450	£550
1894	4,166,874	£350	£375	£450	£550
1895	4,165,869	£350	£375	£450	£550
1896	4,456,932	£350	£375	£450	£550
1897	5,130,565	£350	£375	£450	£550
1898	5,509,138	£350	£375	£450	£550
1899	5,579,157	£350	£375	£450	£550
1900	4,305,904	£350	£375	£450	£550
1901	3,987,701	£350	£375	£450	£550
P on ground on reverse (Perth Mint)					
1899	690,992	£350	£375	£500	£2500
1900	1,886,089	£350	£375	£450	£550
1901	2,889,333	£350	£375	£450	£550
S on ground on reverse (Sydney Mint)					
1893	1,346,000	£350	£375	£450	£550
1894	3,067,000	£350	£375	£450	£550
1895	2,758,000	£350	£375	£450	£550
1896	2,544,000	£350	£375	£450	£550
1897	2,532,000	£350	£375	£450	£550
1898	2,548,000	£350	£375	£450	£550
1899	3,259,000	£350	£375	£450	£550
1900	3,586,000	£350	£375	£450	£550
1901	3,012,000	£350	£375	£450	£550

Old head type

EDWARD VII (1902–10)

DATE	MINTAGE	F	VF	EF	UNC
1902	4,737,796	£350	£375	£450	£550
1902 Matt proof	15,123	—	—	—	£750
1903	8,888,627	£350	£375	£450	£550
1904	10,041,369	£350	£375	£450	£550
1905	5,910,403	£350	£375	£450	£550
1906	10,466,981	£350	£375	£450	£550
1907	18,458,663	£350	£375	£450	£550
1908	11,729,006	£350	£375	£450	£550
1909	12,157,099	£350	£375	£450	£550
1910	22,379,624	£350	£375	£450	£550
C on ground on reverse (Ottawa Mint)					
1908 Satin finish Proof only	633			Extremely rare	
1909	16,300	£350	£375	£500	£800
1910	28,020	£350	£375	£500	£700

THE BRITANNIA
COIN COMPANY
OF ROYAL WOOTTON BASSETT

DATE	MINTAGE	F	VF	EF	UNC
M on ground on reverse (Melbourne Mint)					
1902	4,267,157	£350	£375	£450	£550
1903	3,521,780	£350	£375	£450	£550
1904	3,743,897	£350	£375	£450	£550
1905	3,633,838	£350	£375	£450	£550
1906	3,657,853	£350	£375	£450	£550
1907	3,332,691	£350	£375	£450	£550
1908	3,080,148	£350	£375	£450	£550
1909	3,029,538	£350	£375	£450	£550
1910	3,054,547	£350	£375	£450	£550
P on ground on reverse (Perth Mint)					
1902	3,289,122	£350	£375	£450	£550
1903	4,674,783	£350	£375	£450	£550
1904	4,506,756	£350	£375	£450	£550
1905	4,876,193	£350	£375	£450	£550
1906	4,829,817	£350	£375	£450	£550
1907	4,972,289	£350	£375	£450	£550
1908	4,875,617	£350	£375	£450	£550
1909	4,524,241	£350	£375	£450	£550
1910	4,690,625	£350	£375	£450	£550
S on ground on reverse (Sydney Mint)					
1902	2,813,000	£350	£375	£450	£550
1902 Proof	incl. above		Extremely rare		
1903	2,806,000	£350	£375	£450	£550
1904	2,986,000	£350	£375	£450	£550
1905	2,778,000	£350	£375	£450	£550
1906	2,792,000	£350	£375	£450	£550
1907	2,539,000	£350	£375	£450	£550
1908	2,017,000	£350	£375	£450	£550
1909	2,057,000	£350	£375	£450	£550
1910	2,135,000	£350	£375	£450	£550

> **IMPORTANT NOTE:** The prices quoted in this guide are set at August 2022 with the price of gold at £1,500 per ounce and silver £15.80 per ounce— market fluctuations can have a marked effect on the values of modern precious metal coins.

GEORGE V (1911–36)

(Extra care should be exercised when purchasing as good quality forgeries exist of virtually all dates and mintmarks)

DATE	MINTAGE	F	VF	EF	UNC
1911	30,044,105	£350	£375	£450	£550
1911 Proof	3,764	—	—	—	£1600
1912	30,317,921	£350	£375	£450	£550
1913	24,539,672	£350	£375	£450	£550
1914	11,501,117	£350	£375	£450	£550
1915	20,295,280	£350	£375	£450	£550
1916	1,554,120	£350	£375	£500	£750
1917	1,014,714	£1500	£5500	£20,000	—
1925	4,406,431	£350	£375	£450	£550
C on ground on reverse (Ottawa Mint)					
1911	256,946	£350	£375	£500	£750
1913	3,715	£350	£500	£1750	—
1914	14,891	£350	£450	£1500	—
1916	6,111		Extremely rare		
1917	58,845	£350	£375	£600	£850
1918	106,516	£350	£375	£500	£650
1919	135,889	£350	£375	£500	£650
I on ground on reverse (Bombay Mint)					
1918	1,295,372	£350	£375	£400	—
M on ground on reverse (Melbourne Mint)					
1911	2,851,451	£350	£375	£450	£550
1912	2,469,257	£350	£375	£450	£550
1913	2,323,180	£350	£375	£450	£550
1914	2,012,029	£350	£375	£450	£550
1915	1,637,839	£350	£375	£450	£550
1916	1,273,643	£350	£375	£450	£550
1917	934,469	£350	£375	£500	£550
1918	4,969,493	£350	£375	£450	£550

"I" on reverse ground for the Bombay Mint

DATE	MINTAGE	F	VF	EF	UNC
1919	514,257	£350	£375	£450	£550
1920	530,266	£1350	£2500	£4000	£6500
1921	240,121	£4000	£7000	£8000	£24,000
1922	608,306	£4000	£7000	£8000	£25,000
1923	510,870	£350	£375	£500	£750
1924	278,140	£350	£375	£500	£750
1925	3,311,622	£350	£375	£450	£550
1926	211,107	£350	£375	£450	£550
1928	413,208	£500	£900	£1700	£4000
1929	436,719	£900	£1000	£1700	£5000
1930	77,547	£350	£375	£500	£800
1931	57,779	£350	£375	£650	£750

P on ground on reverse (Perth Mint)

1911	4,373,165	£350	£375	£450	£550
1912	4,278,144	£350	£375	£450	£550
1913	4,635,287	£350	£375	£450	£550
1914	4,815,996	£350	£375	£450	£550
1915	4,373,596	£350	£375	£450	£550
1916	4,096,771	£350	£375	£450	£550
1917	4,110,286	£350	£375	£450	£550
1918	3,812,884	£350	£375	£450	£550
1919	2,995,216	£350	£375	£450	£550
1920	2,421,196	£350	£375	£450	£550
1921	2,134,360	£350	£375	£450	£550
1922	2,298,884	£350	£375	£450	£550
1923	2,124,154	£350	£375	£450	£550
1924	1,464,416	£350	£375	£450	£550
1925	1,837,901	£350	£375	£500	£650
1926	1,313,578	£500	£850	£1500	£3500
1927	1,383,544	£350	£375	£500	£750
1928	1,333,417	£350	£375	£450	£600
1929	1,606,625	£350	£375	£450	£550
1930	1,915,352	£350	£375	£500	£675
1931	1,173,568	£350	£375	£450	£550

S on ground on reverse (Sydney Mint)

1911	2,519,000	£350	£375	£450	£550
1912	2,227,000	£350	£375	£450	£550
1913	2,249,000	£350	£375	£450	£550
1914	1,774,000	£350	£375	£450	£550
1915	1,346,000	£350	£375	£450	£550
1916	1,242,000	£350	£375	£450	£550
1917	1,666,000	£350	£375	£450	£550
1918	3,716,000	£350	£375	£450	£550
1919	1,835,000	£350	£375	£450	£550

Melbourne Mint (M on ground)

Perth Mint (P on ground)

DATE	MINTAGE	F	VF	EF	UNC
1920	—		Excessively rare		
1921	839,000	£600	£900	£1750	£2750
1922	578,000		Extremely rare		
1923	416,000		Extremely rare		
1924	394,000	£600	£1100	£1500	£2750
1925	5,632,000	£350	£375	£450	£550
1926	1,031,050		Extremely rare		

SA on ground on reverse (Pretoria Mint)

DATE	MINTAGE	F	VF	EF	UNC
1923	719	£1000	£2500	£7500	—
1923 Proof	655		Extremely rare		
1924	3,184	—	£3000	£6000	—
1925	6,086,264	£350	£400	£450	£550
1926	11,107,611	£350	£400	£450	£550
1927	16,379,704	£350	£400	£450	£550
1928	18,235,057	£350	£400	£450	£550
1929	12,024,107	£350	£400	£450	£550
1930	10,027,756	£350	£400	£450	£550
1931	8,511,792	£350	£400	£450	£550
1932	1,066,680	£350	£400	£450	£550

Pretoria Mint (SA on ground)

GEORGE VI (1937–52)

	MINTAGE	F	VF	EF	UNC
1937 Proof only	5,501	—	—	£3750	£5500

ELIZABETH II (1952–2022)

Pre Decimal Issues

DATE	MINTAGE	F	VF	EF	UNC
1957	2,072,000	£350	£375	£400	£450
1958	8,700,140	£350	£375	£400	£450
1959	1,358,228	£350	£375	£400	£450
1962	3,000,000	£350	£375	£400	£450
1963	7,400,000	£350	£375	£400	£450
1964	3,000,000	£350	£375	£400	£450
1965	3,800,000	£350	£375	£400	£450
1966	7,050,000	£350	£375	£400	£450
1967	5,000,000	£350	£375	£400	£450
1968	4,203,000	£350	£375	£400	£450

Later issues are included in the Decimal section.

HALF SOVEREIGNS

GEORGE III (1760–1820)

DATE	MINTAGE	F	VF	EF	UNC
1817	2,080,197	£250	£370	£1000	£2000
1818	1,030,286	£240	£450	£1000	£2000
1820	35,043	£240	£450	£1000	£1800

GEORGE IV (1820–30)

DATE	MINTAGE	F	VF	EF	UNC
1821 First bust, ornate shield reverse	231,288	£650	£1600	£3750	£5000
1821 — Proof	unrecorded	—	—	—	£8000
1823 First bust, Plain shield rev.	224,280	£250	£325	£1000	£2000
1824 —	591,538	£250	£325	£850	£1800
1825 —	761,150	£250	£325	£800	£1350
1826 bare head, shield with full legend reverse	344,830	£250	£360	£1000	£1600
1826 — Proof	unrecorded	—	—	—	£5500
1827 —	492,014	£250	£360	£1000	£1850
1828 —	1,224,754	£250	£375	£800	£1700

DATE	MINTAGE	F	VF	EF	UNC

WILLIAM IV (1830–37)

DATE	MINTAGE	F	VF	EF	UNC
1831 Proof only	unrecorded	—	—	—	£6000
1834..	133,899	£325	£700	£1500	£2750
1835..	772,554	£325	£700	£1000	£2400
1836..	146,865	£275	£600	£1250	£2400
1836 obverse from 6d die	incl. above	£2500	£5000	£10,000	—
1837..	160,207	£325	£550	£1700	£3250

VICTORIA (1837–1901)

YOUNG HEAD ISSUES

Shield reverse

DATE	MINTAGE	F	VF	EF	UNC
1838	273,341	£200	£270	£1000	£1800
1839 Proof only	1,230	—	—	—	£6500
1841..	508,835	£220	£280	£1400	£3000
1842..	2,223,352	£200	£270	£1000	£1600
1843..	1,251,762	£200	£270	£1000	£1750
1844..	1,127,007	£200	£250	£850	£1250
1845..	887,526	£320	£800	£3000	£5000
1846..	1,063,928	£175	£250	£850	£1300
1847..	982,636	£175	£250	£750	£1250
1848..	410,595	£175	£250	£850	£1300
1849..	845,112	£175	£250	£750	£1200
1850..	179,595	£240	£620	£2500	£3500
1851..	773,573	£175	£250	£700	£1200
1852..	1,377,671	£175	£250	£700	£1200
1853..	2,708,796	£175	£250	£700	£1200
1853 Proof....................................	unrecorded	—	—	—	£12,500
1855..	1,120,362	£175	£250	£700	£1200
1856..	2,391,909	£175	£250	£700	£1200
1857..	728,223	£175	£250	£700	£1200
1858..	855,578	£175	£250	£700	£1200
1859..	2,203,813	£175	£250	£700	£1200
1860..	1,131,500	£175	£250	£700	£1200
1861..	1,130,867	£175	£250	£700	£1200
1862..	unrecorded	£800	£2000	£10,000	—
1863..	1,571,574	£175	£250	£700	£1100
1863 with Die number	incl. above	£175	£250	£800	£1100
1864 —	1,758,490	£175	£250	£650	£1100
1865 —	1,834,750	£175	£250	£650	£1100
1866 —	2,058,776	£175	£250	£650	£1100
1867 —	992,795	£175	£250	£650	£1100
1869 —	1,861,764	£175	£250	£650	£1100
1870 —	1,159,544	£175	£250	£650	£1100
1871 —	2,062,970	£175	£250	£650	£1100
1872 —	3,248,627	£175	£250	£650	£1100
1873 —	1,927,050	£175	£250	£650	£1100
1874 —	1,884,432	£175	£250	£650	£1100
1875 —	516,240	£175	£250	£650	£1100
1876 —	2,785,187	£175	£250	£650	£1100
1877 —	2,197,482	£175	£250	£650	£1100
1878 —	2,081,941	£175	£250	£650	£1100
1879 —	35,201	£175	£250	£650	£1100
1880 —	1,009,049	£175	£250	£650	£1100
1880 no Die number	incl. above	£175	£250	£900	£1300
1883 —	2,870,457	£175	£250	£600	£1000
1884 —	1,113,756	£175	£250	£650	£1000
1885 —	4,468,871	£175	£250	£600	£1000

London Mint die number on reverse

M below shield (Melbourne Mint)

DATE	MINTAGE	F	VF	EF	UNC
1873..	165,034	£175	£400	£5000	—
1877..	80,016	£175	£400	£5000	—
1881..	42,009	£175	£500	£7000	—
1882..	107,522	£175	£500	£1200	—
1884..	48,009	£175	£250	£1750	—
1885..	11,003	£175	£600	£4000	—
1886..	38,008	£175	£600	£7000	—
1887..	64,013	£175	£750	£12,000	£20,000

Melbourne Mint (M below shield)

Date	Mintage	F	VF	EF	UNC
S below shield (Sydney Mint)					
1871	180,000 (?)	£175	£250	£750	—
1872	356,000	£175	£250	£750	—
1875	unrecorded	£175	£250	£750	—
1879	94,000	£175	£250	£650	—
1880	80,000	£175	£250	£850	—
1881	62,000	£175	£400	£1250	—
1882	52,000		Extremely rare		
1883	220,000	£175	£250	£900	—
1886	82,000	£175	£250	£600	—
1887	134,000	£175	£250	£800	£4500

JUBILEE HEAD ISSUES

Date	Mintage	F	VF	EF	UNC
1887	871,770	£175	£250	£500	£750
1887 Proof	797	£175	£250	—	£2250
1890	2.266,023	£175	£250	£500	£750
1891	1,079,286	£175	£250	£300	£475
1892	13,680,486	£175	£250	£300	£475
1893	4,426,625	£175	£250	£300	£475
M below shield (Melbourne Mint)					
1887	incl. above	£175	£250	£400	£700
1893	110,024	£175	£250	£450	£850
S below shield (Sydney Mint)					
1887	incl. above	£175	£250	£300	£600
1889	64,000	£175	£280	£1500	—
1891	154,000	£175	£250	£1000	—

OLD HEAD ISSUES

Date	Mintage	F	VF	EF	UNC
1893	incl. above	£175	£250	£300	£450
1893 Proof	773	—	—	—	£3250
1894	3,794,591	£175	£250	£300	£450
1895	2,869,183	£175	£250	£300	£450
1896	2,946,605	£175	£250	£300	£450
1897	3,568,156	£175	£250	£300	£450
1898	2,868,527	£175	£250	£300	£450
1899	3,361,881	£175	£250	£300	£450
1900	4,307,372	£175	£250	£300	£450
1901	2,037,664	£175	£250	£300	£450
M on ground on reverse (Melbourne Mint)					
1893	unrecorded		Extremely rare		
1896	218,946	£175	£250	£450	—
1899	97,221	£175	£250	£550	—
1900	112,920	£175	£250	£600	—
P on ground on reverse (Perth Mint)					
1900	119,376	£175	£330	£550	—
S on ground on reverse (Sydney Mint)					
1893	250,000	£175	£250	£800	—
1897	unrecorded	£175	£250	£700	—
1900	260,00	£175	£250	£650	—

EDWARD VII (1902–10)

Date	Mintage	F	VF	EF	UNC
1902	4,244,457	£175	£250	£300	£450
1902 Matt proof	15,123	—	—	—	£700
1903	2,522,057	£175	£250	£300	£450
1904	1,717,440	£175	£250	£300	£450
1905	3,023,993	£175	£250	£300	£450
1906	4,245,437	£175	£250	£300	£450
1907	4,233,421	£175	£250	£350	£475
1908	3,996,992	£175	£250	£350	£475
1909	4,010,715	£175	£250	£350	£475
1910	5,023,881	£175	£250	£300	£450
M on ground on reverse (Melbourne Mint)					
1906	82,042	£175	£250	£750	£1100
1907	405,034	£175	£250	£300	£450
1908	incl. above	£175	£250	£300	£450
1909	186,094	£175	£250	£600	£750

DATE		F	VF	EF	UNC

P on ground on reverse (Perth Mint)

1904..	60,030	£175	£250	£1000	—
1908..	24,668	£175	£250	£950	—
1909..	44,022	£175	£250	£500	—

S on ground on reverse (Sydney Mint)

1902	84,000	£175	£250	£300	£375
1902 Proof..................................				Extremely rare	
1903..	231,000	£175	£250	£300	£400
1906..	308,000	£175	£250	£300	£400
1908..	538,000	£175	£250	£300	£400
1910..	474,000	£175	£250	£300	£425

GEORGE V (1911–36)

1911..	6,104,106	£175	£250	£300	£375
1911 Proof..................................	3,764	—	—	—	£1100
1912..	6,224,316	£175	£250	£300	£375
1913..	6,094,290	£175	£250	£300	£375
1914..	7,251,124	£175	£250	£300	£375
1915..	2,042,747	£175	£250	£300	£375

M on ground on reverse (Melbourne Mint)

1915..	125,664	£175	£250	£300	£375

P on ground on reverse (Perth Mint)

1911	130,373	£175	£250	£300	£375
1915..	136,219	£175	£250	£300	£375
1918..	unrecorded	£205	£600	£2000	£3750
1919..	56,786				Rare
1920..	53,208				Rare

S on ground on reverse (Sydney Mint)

1911	252,000	£175	£250	£300	£375
1912..	278,000	£175	£250	£300	£375
1914..	322,000	£175	£250	£300	£375
1915..	892,000	£175	£250	£300	£375
1916..	448,000	£175	£250	£300	£375

SA on ground on reverse (Pretoria Mint)

1923 Proof only	655	—	—	—	£1500
1925..	946,615	£175	£250	£300	£375
1926..	806,540	£175	£250	£300	£375

GEORGE VI (1937–52)

1937 Proof only	5,501	—	—	—	£1000

Later issues are included in the Decimal section.

CROWNS

DATE	F	VF	EF	UNC

OLIVER CROMWELL

1658 8 over 7 (always)..............................	£2000	£4500	£10,000	—
1658 Dutch Copy			Extremely rare	
1658 Patterns. In Various Metals..............			Extremely rare	

CHARLES II (1660–85)

1662 First bust, rose (2 varieties)	£250	£900	£7000	—
1662 — no rose (2 varieties).....................	£250	£900	£7000	—
1663 —	£250	£900	£7000	—
1664 Second bust...................................	£200	£900	£7500	—
1665 —	£1500	£5000	—	—
1666 —	£300	£1100	£8000	—
1666 — error RE.X for REX			Extremely rare	
1666 — Elephant below bust	£1000	£4000	£20,000	—
1667 —	£190	£600	£5000	—
1668/7 — 8 over 7...................................	£200	£600	—	—
1668 —	£200	£600	£6000	—
1669/8 — 9 over 8...................................	£350	£800	—	—
1669 —	£325	£1200	£7000	—
1670/69 — 70 over 69	£250	£1000	—	—
1670 —	£220	£750	£6000	—
1671..	£220	£750	£5000	—
1671 Third bust	£220	£750	£5000	—
1672 —	£220	£600	£5000	—
1673 —	£220	£600	£5000	—
1674 —			Extremely rare	
1675 —	£800	£3250	—	—
1675/3 —	£700	£3000	—	—
1676 —	£180	£650	£6000	—
1677 —	£200	£650	£5500	—
1677/6 — 7 over 6...................................	£200	£900	—	—
1678/7 —	£200	£900	—	—
1678/7 — 8 over 7...................................	£275	£900	—	—
1679 —	£190	£750	£5000	—
1679 Fourth bust	£190	£750	£4500	—
1680 Third bust	£190	£1000	£5500	—
1680/79 — 80 over 79.............................	£225	£850	—	—
1680 Fourth bust	£200	£900	£6500	—
1680/79 — 80 over 79.............................	£240	£1100	—	—
1681 —	£200	£800	£6500	—
1681 — Elephant & Castle below bust......	£5500	£15000	—	—
1682/1 —	£225	£900	£6000	—
1682 — edge error QVRRTO for QVARTO	£400	—	—	—
1683 —	£400	£1150	£7000	—
1684 —	£400	£1300	—	—

JAMES II (1685–88)

1686 First bust	£325	£1200	£8000	—
1686 — No stops on obv	£425	£1800	—	—
1687 Second bust...................................	£300	£700	£6000	—
1688/7 — 8 over 7...................................	£350	£950	—	—
1688 —	£280	£900	£6000	—

WILLIAM AND MARY (1688–94)

1691	£850	£2000	£8500	—
1692	£850	£2200	£8000	—
1692 2 over upside down 2	£850	£2200	£8000	—

DATE	F	VF	EF	UNC

WILLIAM III (1694–1702)

	F	VF	EF	UNC
1695 First bust	£100	£380	£2750	—
1696 —	£100	£300	£2600	—
1696 — no stops on obv.	£225	£500	—	—
1996 — no stops obv./rev.	£250	£550	—	—
1696 — GEI for DEI	£750	£1800	—	—
1696 — Last 6 over 5	£200	£550	—	—
1696 Second bust				Unique
1696 Third bust	£100	£300	£2500	—
1697 —	£2800	£10,000	£40,000	—
1700 Third bust variety edge year DUODECIMO	£150	£550	£3250	—
1700 — edge year DUODECIMO TERTIO..	£150	£550	£3250	—

ANNE (1702–14)

	F	VF	EF	UNC
1703 First bust, VIGO	£500	£1600	£10,000	—
1705 — Plumes in angles on rev.	£800	£2500	£10,000	—
1706 — Roses & Plumes in angles on rev...	£300	£800	£4000	—
1707 — ..	£300	£800	£4000	—
1707 Second bust, E below	£250	£700	£3800	—
1707 — Plain	£250	£700	£3800	—
1708 — E below	£250	£700	£3800	—
1708/7 — 8 over 7	£250	£800	—	—
1708 — Plain	£250	£700	£3500	—
1708 — — error BR for BRI			Extremely rare	
1708 — Plumes in angles on rev.	£250	£800	£3800	—
1713 Third bust, Roses & Plumes in angles on rev.	£230	£800	£5000	—

GEORGE I (1714–27)

	F	VF	EF	UNC
1716	£750	£1800	£7250	—
1718 8 over 6	£750	£1800	£7000	—
1720 20 over 18	£750	£1800	£7250	—
1723 SSC in angles on rev. (South Sea Co.)	£750	£1800	£7000	—
1726	£750	£2000	£8000	—

GEORGE II (1727–60)

	F	VF	EF	UNC
1732 Young head, Plain, Proof	—	—	£27,500	
1732 — Roses & Plumes in angles on rev ..	£400	£1000	£5000	—
1734 — —	£400	£1000	£5000	—
1735 — —	£400	£1000	£5000	—
1736 — —	£400	£1000	£5000	—
1739 — Roses in angles on rev	£400	£750	£4500	—
1741 — —	£400	£750	£4500	—
1743 Old head, Roses in angles on rev	£400	£750	£3500	—
1746 — — LIMA below bust	£400	£750	£3500	—
1746 — Plain, Proof	—	—	£18,000	—
1750 — —	£550	£1400	£5500	—
1751 — —	£600	£1700	£6000	—

GEORGE III (1760–1820)

	F	VF	EF	UNC
Dollar with oval counterstamp	£175	£650	£1000	—
Dollar with octagonal counterstamp	£225	£700	£950	—
1804 Bank of England Dollar, Britannia rev.	£120	£275	£550	—
1818 LVIII	£50	£120	£550	£1500
1818 LIX	£50	£120	£550	£1500
1819 LIX	£50	£120	£550	£1500
1819 LIX 9 over 8	£55	£160	£700	—
1819 LIX no stops on edge	£65	£170	£500	£1500
1819 LX	£50	£140	£500	£1500
1820 LX	£45	£140	£500	£1250
1820 LX 20 over 19	£45	£220	£650	—

DATE	MINTAGE	F	VF	EF	UNC

GEORGE IV (1820–30)

1821 First bust, St George rev.
SECUNDO on edge	437,976	£55	£210	£750	£2000
1821 — — Proof	—	—	—	£6500
1821 — — Proof TERTIO (error edge)	—	—	—	£8000
1822 — — SECUNDO	124,929	£50	£220	£800	£2000
1822 — — TERTIO	Incl above	£50	£220	£800	£2000
1823 — — Proof only				Extremely rare	

1826 Second bust, shield rev, SEPTIMO
| Proof only | — | — | —£20,000 | |

WILLIAM IV (1830–37)

					UNC
1831 Proof only W.W. on truncation	—	—	—	£35,000
1831 Proof only W. WYON on truncation	—	—	—	£35,000
1834 Proof only	—	—	—	£50,000

VICTORIA (1837–1901)

YOUNG HEAD ISSUES
1839 Proof only	—	—	—	—	£30,000
1844 Star stops on edge	94,248	£80	£350	£1500	£4000
1844 Cinquefoil stops on edge	incl. above	£80	£350	£1500	£4000
1845 Star stops on edge	159,192	£80	£350	£1500	£4000
1845 Cinquefoil stops on edge	ncl. above	£80	£350	£1500	£4000
1847	140,976	£90	£400	£1750	£6000

GOTHIC HEAD ISSUES (Proof only)
1847 mdcccxlvii UNDECIMO on edge	8,000	£1200	£2200	£4000	£10,000
1847 — Plain edge	—	—	—	—	£15,000
1853 mdcccliii SEPTIMO on edge	460	—	—	—	£32,000
1853 — Plain edge	—	—	—	—	Very rare

JUBILEE HEAD ISSUES
1887	173,581	£25	£40	£75	£220
1887 Proof	1,084	—	—	—	£3200
1888 Narrow date	131,899	£25	£40	£100	£325
1888 Wide date	incl above	£35	£80	£400	—
1889	1,807,224	£25	£40	£75	£200
1890	997,862	£25	£40	£85	£325
1891	556,394	£25	£40	£85	£350
1892	451,334	£25	£40	£90	£375

OLD HEAD ISSUES (Regnal date on edge in Roman numerals)
1893 LVI	497,845	£26	£55	£160	£500
1893 LVII	incl. above	£26	£55	£250	£550
1893 Proof	1,312	—	—	—	£3500
1894 LVII	144,906	£26	£55	£225	£600
1894 LVIII	incl. above	£26	£55	£225	£600
1895 LVIII	252,862	£26	£55	£200	£600
1895 LIX	incl. above	£26	£55	£200	£600
1896 LIX	317,599	£26	£55	£200	£600
1896 LX	incl. above	£26	£55	£200	£600
1897 LX	262,118	£26	£55	£200	£600
1897 LXI	incl. above	£26	£55	£200	£600
1898 LXI	166,150	£26	£55	£200	£800
1898 LXII	incl. above	£26	£55	£200	£600
1899 LXII	166,300	£26	£55	£200	£600
1899 LXIII	incl. above	£26	£55	£200	£600
1900 LXIII	353,356	£26	£55	£200	£600
1900 LXIV	incl. above	£26	£55	£200	£600

Victoria, Jubilee head

DATE	MINTAGE	F	VF	EF	UNC

EDWARD VII (1901–10)

DATE	MINTAGE	F	VF	EF	UNC
1902..	256,020	£85	£150	£250	£350
1902 "Matt Proof"	15,123	—	—	—	£400

GEORGE V (1910–36)

	MINTAGE	F	VF	EF	UNC
1927 Proof only	15,030	—	£100	£180	£350
1928..	9,034	£110	£170	£300	£500
1929..	4,994	£110	£170	£300	£500
1930..	4,847	£110	£170	£300	£550
1931..	4,056	£110	£170	£300	£500
1932..	2,395	£200	£400	£800	£1400
1933..	7,132	£110	£175	£300	£550
1934..	932	£800	£1600	£3500	£5500
1935 Jubilee issue. Incuse edge inscription	714,769	£15	£20	£30	£45
1935 — — error edge inscription	incl. above	—	—	—	£1500
1935 — Specimen in box	incl. above	—	—	—	£60
1935 — Proof	incl. above	—	—	—	£200
1935 — Proof. Raised edge inscription	2,500	—	—	£275	£600
1935 — — fine lettering..............	incl. above	—	—	—	£1000
1935 — — error edge inscription	incl. above	—	—	—	£1500
1935 — Gold proof.....................	30	—	—	Extremely rare	
1936..	2,473	£200	£375	£650	£1000

GEORGE VI (1936–52)

	MINTAGE	F	VF	EF	UNC
1937 Coronation..........................	418,699	£18	£24	£35	£55
1937 Proof...................................	26,402	—	—	—	£70
1951 Festival of Britain, Proof-like	1,983,540	—	£3	£6	£8

ELIZABETH II (1952–2022)

Pre-Decimal issues (Five Shillings)

	MINTAGE	F	VF	EF	UNC
1953	5,962,621	—	—	£3	£6
1953 Proof..................................	40,000	—	—	—	£25
1960..	1,024,038	—	—	£3	£6
1960 Polished dies......................	70,000	—	—	—	£9
1965 Churchill	19,640,000	—	—	—	£1

Later issues are listed in the Decimal section.

DOUBLE FLORINS

VICTORIA (1837–1901)

	MINTAGE	F	VF	EF	UNC
1887 Roman I	483,347	£18	£35	£60	£150
1887 Roman I Proof	incl. above	—	—	—	£1100
1887 Arabic 1	incl. above	£18	£35	£60	£150
1887 Arabic 1 Proof....................	incl. above	—	—	—	£1100
1888..	243,340	£18	£45	£90	£200
1888 Second I in VICTORIA an inverted 1	incl. above	£30	£60	£110	£400
1889..	1,185,111	£20	£35	£65	£175
1889 inverted 1...........................	incl. above	£30	£60	£110	£450
1890..	782,146	£18	£45	£65	£175

Patterns were also produced in 1911, 1914 and 1950 and are all extremely rare.

HALFCROWNS

DATE	MINTAGE	F	VF	EF	UNC

OLIVER CROMWELL

DATE	MINTAGE	F	VF	EF	UNC
1656				Extremely rare	
1658		£2200	£3000	£6500	—
1658 Proof in Gold				Extremely rare	

CHARLES II (1660–85)

DATE	MINTAGE	F	VF	EF	UNC
1663 First bust		£180	£700	£4500	—
1663 — no stops on obv.		£200	£800	—	—
1664 Second bust		£250	£1200	£6000	—
1666 Third bust		£900	—	—	—
1666 — Elephant		£900	£3500	—	—
1667/4 — 7 over 4				Extremely rare	
1668/4 — 8 over 4		£300	£1500	—	—
1669 —		£400	£1600	—	—
1669/4 — 9 over 4		£275	£1000	—	—
1670 —		£160	£600	£3250	—
1670 — MRG for MAG		£300	£1000	—	—
1671 —		£160	£600	£3000	—
1671/0 — 1 over 0		£160	£600	£3500	—
1672 — Third bust				Extremely rare	
1672 Fourth bust		£160	£550	£3500	—
1673 —		£160	£550	£3250	—
1673 — Plumes both sides				Extremely rare	
1673 — Plume below bust		£8000	£22,000	—	—
1674 —		£160	£700	—	—
1675 —		£160	£500	£3000	—
1676 —		£150	£500	£3000	—
1676 — inverted 1 in date		£150	£500	£3000	—
1677 —		£150	£500	£2750	—
1678 —		£220	£900	—	—
1679 — GRATTA error				Extremely rare	
1679 —		£160	£500	£2650	—
1680 —		£175	£800	—	—
1681/0 — 1 over 0		£300	—	—	—
1681 —		£200	£675	£3500	—
1681 — Elephant & Castle		£3750	£12000	—	—
1682 —		£170	£550	£4000	—
1683 —		£170	£550	£3750	—
1683 — Plume below bust				Extremely rare	
1684/3 — 4 over 3		£350	£1200	£6000	—

JAMES II (1685–88)

DATE	MINTAGE	F	VF	EF	UNC
1685 First bust		£250	£700	£4500	—
1686 —		£240	£675	£4200	—
1686/5 — 6 over 5		£260	£800	—	—
1686 — V over S		£240	£800	—	—
1687 —		£240	£675	£4000	—
1687/6 — 7 over 6		£325	£850	—	—
1687 Second bust		£240	£600	£3750	—
1688 —		£240	£600	£3600	—

WILLIAM AND MARY (1688–94)

DATE	MINTAGE	F	VF	EF	UNC
1689 First busts; first shield		£120	£350	£2000	—
1689 — — no pearls in crown		£120	£350	£2000	—
1689 — — FRA for FR		£170	£600	£2400	—
1689 — — No stop on obv		£120	£550	£2350	—
1689 — Second shield		£120	£400	£2000	—
1689 — — no pearls in crown		£130	£400	£2000	—
1690 — —		£180	£700	£3250	—
1690 — — error GRETIA for GRATIA		£600	£1600	£6000	—
1691 Second busts		£160	£500	£2500	—
1692 —		£160	£500	£2500	—

DATE	MINTAGE	F	VF	EF	UNC
1693 —		£170	£500	£2800	—
1693 — 3 over inverted 3		£220	£800	£3500	—

WILLIAM III (1694–1702)

		F	VF	EF	UNC
1696 First bust, large shields, early harp		£80	£260	£1400	—
1696 — — — B (Bristol) below bust		£80	£270	£1500	—
1696 — — — C (Chester)		£90	£400	£1600	—
1696 — — — E (Exeter)		£120	£500	£1800	—
1696 — — — N (Norwich)		£100	£500	£1800	—
1696 — — — y (York)		£90	£400	£2350	—
1696 — — — — Scottish arms at date			Extremely rare		
1696 — — ordinary harp		£90	£325	£1800	—
1696 — — — C		£110	£500	£1750	—
1696 — — — E		£100	£500	£1750	—
1696 — — — N		£170	£700	£3000	—
1696 — Small shields, ordinary harp		£70	£300	£1500	—
1696 — — — B		£100	£350	£1600	—
1696 — — — C		£100	£350	£1850	—
1696 — — — E		£120	£600	£2600	—
1696 — — — N		£110	£500	£2200	—
1696 — — — y		£100	£600	£2200	—
1696 Second bust			Only one known		
1697 First bust, large shields, ordinary harp		£80	£325	£1500	—
1697 — — — GRR for GRA			Extremely rare		
1697 — — — B		£90	£350	£1800	—
1697 — — — C		£90	£375	£2000	—
1697 — — — E		£100	£375	£2000	—
1697 — — — N		£100	£375	£2000	—
1697 — — — y		£90	£375	£2100	—
1698 — —		£100	£375	£1850	—
1698/7 — — 8 over 7			Extremely rare		
1699 — —		£160	£500	£3700	—
1699 — — Scottish arms at date			Extremely rare		
1700 — —		£140	£400	£2400	—
1701 — —		£150	£450	£2500	—
1701 — — No stops on rev		£160	£650	—	—
1701 — — Elephant & Castle below	Fair £2500				
1701 — — Plumes in angles on rev.		£275	£800	£4750	—

ANNE (1702–14)

		F	VF	EF	UNC
1703 Plain (pre-Union)		£750	£2500	—	—
1703 VIGO below bust		£150	£500	£2200	—
1704 Plumes in angles on rev.		£200	£600	£2400	—
1705 —		£180	£700	£2400	—
1706 Roses & Plumes in angles on rev.		£100	£450	£2000	—
1707 —		£90	£325	£1600	—
1707 Plain (post-Union)		£90	£270	£1250	—
1707 E below bust		£90	£270	£1250	—
1707 — SEPTIMO edge			Extremely rare		
1708 Plain		£100	£300	£1500	—
1708 E below bust		£100	£300	£1650	—
1708 Plumes in angles on rev.		£110	£350	£1800	—
1709 Plain		£90	£350	£1250	—
1709 E below bust		£275	£1250	—	—
1710 Roses & Plumes in angles on rev.		£90	£370	£1600	—
1712 —		£90	£370	£1600	—
1713 Plain		£90	£370	£1600	—
1713 Roses & Plumes in angles on rev.		£90	£370	£1500	—
1714 —		£90	£370	£1500	—
1714/3 4 over 3		£125	£500	—	—

GEORGE I (1714–27)

		F	VF	EF	UNC
1715 Roses & Plumes in angles on rev.		£500	£1000	£3700	—
1715 Plain edge			Extremely rare		
1717 —		£500	£1100	£4000	—
1720 —		£500	£1100	£4000	—
1720/17 20 over 17		£475	£1100	£3800	—
1723 SSC in angles on rev.		£475	£1100	£3700	—
1726 Small Roses & Plumes in angles on rev...		£5000	£15,000	—	—

147

DATE	MINTAGE	F	VF	EF	UNC

GEORGE II (1727–60)

1731 Young head, Plain, proof only..................	—	—	£12000	—	
1731 — Roses & Plumes in angles on rev........	£180	£475	£2350	—	
1732 — —	£180	£475	£2350	—	
1734 — —	£180	£475	£2300	—	
1735 — —	£180	£475	£2300	—	
1736 — —	£180	£475	£2200	—	
1739 — Roses in angles on rev.	£170	£475	£2000	—	
1741/39 — — 41 over 30	£170	£600	—	—	
1741 — —	£170	£475	£2000	—	
1743 Old head, Roses in angles on rev.	£85	£225	£1200	—	
1745 — —	£85	£225	£1200	—	
1745 — LIMA below bust...............................	£80	£200	£750	—	
1746 — —	£80	£200	£750	—	
1746/5 — — 6 over 5	£90	£275	£950	—	
1746 — Plain, Proof	—	—	£6500	—	
1750 — —	£225	£600	£2800	—	
1751 — —	£250	£750	£3000	—	

GEORGE III (1760–1820)

1816 "Bull head"	—	£30	£90	£300	£650
1817 —	8,092,656	£30	£90	£300	£650
1817 "Small head".......................	incl. above	£30	£90	£300	£650
1818 —	2,905,056	£30	£90	£300	£650
1819/8 — 9 over 8.......................	incl. above		Extremely rare		
1819 —	4,790,016	£30	£90	£275	£600
1820 —	2,396,592	£55	£150	£500	£1000

GEORGE IV (1820–30)

1820 First bust, first reverse........	incl. above	£30	£80	£400	£800
1821 — —	1,435,104	£30	£80	£400	£800
1821 — — Proof..........................	incl. above	—	—	—	£4500
1823 — —	2,003,760	£1300	£4500	—	
1823 — Second reverse.............	incl. above	£30	£80	£350	£325
1824 — —	465,696	£35	£90	£300	£800
1824 Second bust, third reverse .	incl. above		Extremely rare		
1825 — —	2,258,784	£30	£80	£200	£525
1826 — —	2,189,088	£30	£80	£200	£525
1826 — — Proof..........................	incl. above	—	—	—	£2500
1828 — —	49,890	£110	£300	£900	£2650
1829 — —	508,464	£75	£175	£550	£1100

WILLIAM IV (1830–37)

1831 Plain edge...........................	—		Extremely rare		
1831 Proof (W.W. in script & block)	—	—	—	—	£4000
1834 W.W. in block....................	993,168	£35	£85	£375	£1200
1834 W.W. in script....................	incl. above	£35	£85	£375	£1200
1835...	281,952	£40	£100	£375	£1150
1836...	1,588,752	£35	£75	£375	£1150
1836/5 6 over 5	incl. above	£60	£125	£650	—
1837...	150,526	£50	£170	£750	£1700

VICTORIA (1837–1901)

YOUNG HEAD ISSUES

1839 (two varieties)	—	£1300	£4250	£11000	—
1839 Proof....................................	—	—	—	—	£6750
1840...	386,496	£60	£200	£900	£2400
1841...	42,768	£1000	£2000	£4500	£8000
1842...	486,288	£55	£150	£700	£1700
1843...	454,608	£150	£450	£1800	£4000
1844...	1,999,008	£50	£110	£550	£1750
1845...	2,231,856	£50	£110	£550	£1750
1846...	1,539,668	£55	£140	£600	£1800
1848 Plain 8...............................	367,488	£175	£450	£1650	£5000
1848/6	incl. above	£150	£400	£1250	£3500
1849...	261,360	£70	£160	£600	£2200
1849 Small date	incl. above	£100	£275	£1000	£2750

DATE	MINTAGE	F	VF	EF	UNC
1850............................	484,613	£75	£260	£1000	£2800
1853 Proof only	—	—	—	—	£7500
1874............................	2,188,599	£25	£70	£350	£750
1875............................	1,113,483	£25	£70	£350	£700
1876............................	633,221	£35	£90	£350	£850
1876/5 6 over 5	incl. above	£35	£80	£280	£800
1876/6 6 over 6	incl. above	£75	£150	£450	—
1877............................	447,059	£25	£70	£250	£700
1878............................	1,466,323	£25	£70	£250	£700
1879............................	901,356	£35	£90	£300	£900
1880............................	1,346,350	£25	£70	£250	£650
1881............................	2,301,495	£25	£70	£250	£600
1882............................	808,227	£30	£75	£270	£650
1883............................	2,982,779	£25	£70	£250	£550
1884............................	1,569,175	£25	£70	£250	£550
1885............................	1,628,438	£25	£70	£250	£550
1886............................	891,767	£25	£70	£250	£550
1887............................	1,438,046	£25	£65	£275	£600
JUBILEE HEAD ISSUES					
1887	incl. above	£10	£16	£32	£80
1887 Proof....................	1,084	—	—	—	£675
1888............................	1,428,787	£12	£25	£60	£240
1889............................	4,811,954	£10	£20	£55	£175
1890............................	3,228,111	£12	£25	£80	£230
1891............................	2,284,632	£12	£25	£80	£230
1892............................	1,710,946	£12	£25	£80	£250
OLD HEAD ISSUES					
1893............................	1,792,600	£12	£25	£60	£140
1893 Proof....................	1,312	—	—	—	£1200
1894............................	1,524,960	£16	£40	£100	£300
1895............................	1,772,662	£14	£35	£80	£275
1896............................	2,148,505	£12	£25	£70	£240
1897............................	1,678,643	£12	£25	£70	£240
1898............................	1,870,055	£12	£25	£70	£240
1899............................	2,865,872	£12	£25	£70	£240
1900............................	4,479,128	£12	£25	£70	£240
1901............................	1,516,570	£12	£25	£70	£240

Victoria, Young head type

DATE	MINTAGE	F	VF	EF	UNC

EDWARD VII (1901–10)

DATE	MINTAGE	F	VF	EF	UNC
1902	1,316,008	£12	£30	£80	£170
1902 "Matt Proof"	15,123	—	—	—	£300
1903	274,840	£175	£550	£2200	£4500
1904	709,652	£60	£225	£500	£1500
1905	166,008	£500	£1400	£5000	£9000
1906	2,886,206	£12	£50	£200	£900
1907	3,693,930	£12	£50	£200	£900
1908	1,758,889	£20	£90	£400	£1400
1909	3,051,592	£12	£60	£350	£900
1910	2,557,685	£12	£45	£130	£500

GEORGE V (1910–36)

First issue

DATE	MINTAGE	F	VF	EF	UNC
1911	2,914,573	£15	£35	£90	£275
1911 Proof	6,007	—	—	—	£375
1912	4,700,789	£12	£25	£50	£220
1913	4,090,169	£12	£28	£75	£240
1914	18,333,003	£7	£12	£40	£70
1915	32,433,066	£7	£12	£35	£65
1916	29,530,020	£7	£12	£35	£65
1917	11,172,052	£8	£15	£45	£100
1918	29,079,592	£7	£12	£35	£70
1919	10,266,737	£7	£15	£45	£100

Second issue—debased silver

1920	17,982,077	£4	£8	£22	£70
1921	23,677,889	£4	£8	£30	£65
1922	16,396,724	£5	£9	£24	£70
1923	26,308,526	£6	£8	£20	£45
1924	5,866,294	£15	£35	£90	£230
1925	1,413,461	£30	£75	£300	£1000
1926	4,473,516	£12	£28	£50	£200

Third issue —Modified effigy

1926	incl. above	£6	£14	£40	£120
1927	6,837,872	£6	£12	£35	£80

Fourth issue—New shield reverse

1927 Proof	15,000	—	—	—	£100
1928	18,762,727	£5	£8	£20	£35
1929	17,632,636	£5	£8	£20	£35
1930	809,051	£15	£60	£325	£900
1931	11,264,468	£5	£8	£20	£35
1932	4,793,643	£6	£10	£25	£90
1933	10,311,494	£5	£8	£20	£40
1934	2,422,399	£7	£12	£65	£200
1935	7,022,216	£5	£8	£18	£30
1936	7,039,423	£5	£8	£18	£20

George V, fourth issue, new shield reverse

GEORGE VI (1936–52)

DATE	MINTAGE	F	VF	EF	UNC
1937	9,106,440	—	£6	£9	£15
1937 Proof	26,402	—	—	—	£25
1938	6,426,478	£5	£6	£15	£25
1939	15,478,635	£5	£6	£9	£12
1940	17,948,439	£5	£6	£9	£12
1941	15,773,984	£5	£6	£9	£12
1942	31,220,090	£5	£6	£9	£10
1943	15,462,875	£5	£6	£9	£10
1944	15,255,165	£5	£6	£9	£10
1945	19,849,242	£5	£6	£9	£10
1946	22,724,873	£5	£6	£9	£10

Cupro-nickel

1947	21,911,484	—	£1	£2	£4
1948	71,164,703	—	£1	£2	£4
1949	28,272,512	—	£1	£2	£6
1950	28,335,500	—	£1	£2	£6
1950 Proof	17,513	—	—	—	£35
1951	9,003,520	—	£1	£2	£6
1951 Proof	20,000	—	—	—	£10
1952	Unknown		Only one known		

DATE	MINTAGE	F	VF	EF	UNC

ELIZABETH II (1952–2022)

DATE	MINTAGE	F	VF	EF	UNC
1953	4,333,214	—	—	£1	£3
1953 Proof	40,000	—	—	—	£8
1954	11,614,953	—	£1	£6	£40
1955	23,628,726	—	—	£1	£6
1956	33,934,909	—	—	£1	£6
1957	34,200,563	—	—	£1	£6
1958	15,745,668	—	£1	£6	£40
1959	9,028,844	—	£1	£9	£35
1960	19,929,191	—	—	£1	£3
1961	25,887,897	—	—	—	£2
1961 Polished dies	incl. above	—	—	£1	£2
1962	24,013,312	—	—	—	£1
1963	17,625,200	—	—	—	£1
1964	5,973,600	—	—	—	£2
1965	9,778,440	—	—	—	£1
1966	13,375,200	—	—	—	£1
1967	33,058,400	—	—	—	£1
1970 Proof	—	—	—	—	£8

FLORINS

VICTORIA (1837–1901)

YOUNG (CROWNED) HEAD ISSUES

"Godless" type (without D.G.—"Dei Gratia")

	MINTAGE	F	VF	EF	UNC
1848 "Godless" Pattern only plain edge	—			Very rare	
1848 "Godless" Pattern only milled edge	—			Extremely rare	
1849	413,820	£30	£75	£260	£525

(Beware of recent forgeries)

"Gothic" type, i.e. date in Roman numerals in obverse legend

"brit." in legend. No die no.

	MINTAGE	F	VF	EF	UNC
1851 mdcccli Proof	1,540			Extremely rare	
1852 mdccclii	1,014,552	£30	£65	£280	£700
1853 mdcccliii	3,919,950	£30	£65	£280	£700
1853 — Proof	incl. above			—	£7000
1854 mdcccliv	550,413	£800	£2000	—	—
1855 mdccclv	831,017	£30	£75	£320	£850
1856 mdccclvi	2,201,760	£30	£75	£320	£850
1857 mdccclvii	1,671,120	£30	£70	£300	£900
1858 mdccclviii	2,239,380	£30	£70	£300	£875
1859 mdccclix	2,568,060	£30	£70	£300	£800
1860 mdccclx	1,475,100	£35	£90	£325	£1000
1862 mdccclxii	594,000	£300	£800	£1800	£5000
1862 plain edge Proof				Very rare	
1863 mdccclxiii	938,520	£1300	£2500	£6500	£14000
1863 plain edge Proof				Very rare	

"Godless" florin

"brit" in legend. Die no. below bust

	MINTAGE	F	VF	EF	UNC
1864 mdccclxiv	1,861,200	£30	£65	£325	£800
1864 Gothic Piedfort flan	incl. above			Extremely rare	
1865 mdccclxv	1,580,044	£40	£100	£400	£750
1866 mdccclxvi	914,760	£35	£90	£400	£750
1867 mdccclxvii	423,720	£50	£170	£500	£1200
1867—only 42 arcs in border	incl. above			Extremely rare	

"britt" in legend. Die no. below bust

	MINTAGE	F	VF	EF	UNC
1868 mdccclxviii	896,940	£30	£80	£350	£850
1869 mdccclxix	297,000	£35	£100	£450	£1100
1870 mdccclxx	1,080,648	£30	£80	£350	£700
1871 mdccclxxi	3,425,605	£30	£80	£350	£675
1872 mdccclxxii	7,199,690	£30	£70	£270	£550
1873 mdccclxxiii	5,921,839	£30	£70	£270	£575
1874 mdccclxxiv	1,642,630	£30	£70	£270	£600
1874 — iv over iii in date	incl. above	£35	£80	£400	£800
1875 mdccclxxv	1,117,030	£35	£85	£275	£700
1876 mdccclxxvi	580,034	£50	£130	£550	£1200
1877 mdccclxxvii	682,292	£30	£70	£250	£600
1877 — 48 arcs in border no W.W.	incl. above	£30	£70	£250	£600

"Gothic" florin

DATE	MINTAGE	F	VF	EF	UNC
1877 — 42 arcs	incl. above	£30	£70	£250	£600
1877 — — no die number	incl. above			Extremely rare	
1878 mdccclxxviii with die number	1,786,680	£35	£70	£250	£600
1879 mdcccixxix no die no	1,512,247			Extremely rare	
1879 — 48 arcs in border	incl. above	£30	£60	£300	£700
1879 — no die number	incl. above			Extremely rare	
1879 — 38 arcs, no W.W..	incl. above	£30	£60	£300	£675
1880 mdccclxxx Younger portrait	—			Extremely rare	
1880 — 34 arcs, Older portrait....	2,167,170	£30	£60	£260	£600
1881 mdccclxxxi — —	2,570,337	£28	£60	£260	£600
1881 — xxΓi broken puncheon ...	incl. above	£35	£70	£260	£700
1883 mdccclxxxiii — —	3,555,667	£30	£70	£260	£650
1884 mdccclxxxiv — —	1,447,379	£30	£70	£260	£650
1885 mdccclxxxv — —	1,758,210	£30	£70	£260	£650
1886 mdccclxxxvi — —	591,773	£30	£70	£260	£650
1887 mdccclxxxvii — —	1,776,903	£50	£120	£325	£800
1887 — 46 arcs	incl. above	£50	£120	£350	£1000

JUBILEE HEAD ISSUES

1887	incl. above	£8	£16	£35	£70
1887 Proof	1,084	—	—	—	£550
1888	1,547,540	£8	£16	£45	£140
1889	2,973,561	£9	£20	£50	£150
1890	1,684,737	£10	£25	£100	£325
1891	836,438	£25	£80	£300	£600
1892	283,401	£40	£140	£400	£950

VICTORIA—OLD HEAD ISSUES

1893	1,666,103	£10	£20	£50	£125
1893 Proof	1,312	—	—	—	£800
1894	1,952,842	£15	£30	£110	£300
1895	2,182,968	£12	£32	£100	£300
1896	2,944,416	£10	£30	£80	£220
1897	1,699,921	£10	£30	£80	£200
1898	3,061,343	£10	£30	£80	£200
1899	3,966,953	£10	£30	£80	£220
1900	5,528,630	£10	£30	£80	£200
1901	2,648,870	£10	£30	£80	£200

EDWARD VII (1901–10)

1902	2,189,575	£10	£25	£70	£140
1902 "Matt Proof"	15,123	—	—	—	£250
1903	1,995,298	£12	£35	£140	£600
1904	2,769,932	£15	£45	£160	£550
1905	1,187,596	£65	£200	£700	£1800
1906	6,910,128	£12	£40	£140	£600
1907	5,947,895	£12	£35	£140	£600
1908	3,280,010	£20	£60	£350	£900
1909	3,482,829	£15	£50	£250	£700
1910	5,650,713	£15	£40	£120	£350

GEORGE V (1910–36)

First issue

1911	5,951,284	£7	£12	£40	£100
1911 Proof	6,007	—	—	—	£275
1912	8,571,731	£8	£18	£35	£140
1913	4,545,278	£10	£25	£50	£190
1914	21,252,701	£7	£18	£30	£80
1915	12,367,939	£7	£18	£30	£80
1916	21,064,337	£7	£18	£30	£80
1917	11,181,617	£7	£22	£40	£80
1918	29,211,792	£7	£18	£30	£100
1919	9,469,292	£9	£20	£45	£125

Second issue —*debased silver*

1920	15,387,833	£4	£12	£40	£90
1921	34,863,895	£4	£12	£40	£70
1922	23,861,044	£4	£12	£40	£70
1923	21,546,533	£4	£10	£30	£65
1924	4,582,312	£12	£35	£95	£275
1925	1,404,136	£30	£75	£300	£1000
1926	5,125,410	£10	£25	£60	£200

George V first type

DATE	MINTAGE	F	VF	EF	UNC
Fourth issue—*new reverse*					
1927 Proof only	101,497	—	—	—	£110
1928..............................	11,087,186	£4	£8	£15	£40
1929..............................	16,397,279	£4	£8	£18	£35
1930..............................	5,753,568	£4	£8	£22	£50
1931..............................	6,556,331	£4	£8	£20	£35
1932..............................	717,041	£15	£40	£300	£700
1933..............................	8,685,303	£4	£8	£18	£40
1935..............................	7,540,546	£4	£8	£15	£35
1936..............................	9,897,448	£4	£8	£15	£35

George V new reverse

GEORGE VI (1936–52)

1937..............................	13,006,781	£4	£5	£7	£12
1937 Proof.....................	26,402	—	—	—	£25
1938..............................	7,909,388	£6	£8	£15	£30
1939..............................	20,850,607	£4	£5	£8	£10
1940..............................	18,700,338	£4	£5	£7	£12
1941..............................	24,451,079	£4	£5	£7	£9
1942..............................	39,895,243	£4	£5	£7	£9
1943..............................	26,711,987	£4	£5	£7	£9
1944..............................	27,560,005	£4	£5	£7	£9
1945..............................	25,858,049	£4	£5	£7	£9
1946..............................	22,300,254	£4	£5	£7	£9
Cupro-nickel					
1947..............................	22,910,085	—	—	£1	£3
1948..............................	67,553,636	—	—	£1	£3
1949..............................	28,614,939	—	—	£1	£5
1950..............................	24,357,490	—	—	£2	£7
1950 Proof.....................	17,513	—	—	£1	£9
1951..............................	27,411,747	—	—	£2	£8
1951 Proof.....................	20,000	—	—	—	£9

ELIZABETH II (1952–2022)

1953	11,958,710	—	—	—	£2
1953 Proof.....................	40,000	—	—	—	£7
1954..............................	13,085,422	—	—	£6	£45
1955..............................	25,887,253	—	—	£1	£3
1956..............................	47,824,500	—	—	£1	£3
1957..............................	33,071,282	—	—	£4	£25
1958..............................	9,564,580	—	—	£4	£45
1959..............................	14,080,319	—	—	£4	£35
1960..............................	13,831,782	—	—	£1	£4
1961..............................	37,735,315	—	—	£1	£2
1962..............................	35,147,903	—	—	£1	£2
1963..............................	26,471,000	—	—	£1	£2
1964..............................	16,539,000	—	—	£1	£2
1965..............................	48,163,000	—	—	—	£1.50
1966..............................	83,999,000	—	—	—	£1.50
1967..............................	39,718,000	—	—	—	£1.50
1970 Proof.....................	—	—	—	—	£8

SHILLINGS

OLIVER CROMWELL

1658	£1100	£2250	£5000	—
1658 Dutch Copy			Extremely rare	

CHARLES II (1660–85)

1663 First bust	£140	£600	£1800	—
1663 — GARTIA error..............................			Extremely rare	
1663 — Irish & Scottish shields transposed	£300	£800	—	—
1666 — Elephant below bust	£650	£2500	£8500	—
1666 "Guinea" head, elephant	£3000	£6000	—	—
1666 Second bust			Extremely rare	
1668 —	£140	£400	£1850	—
1668/7 — 8 over 7..	£160	£600	—	—
1668 Second bust	£140	£450	£1800	—
1669/6 First bust variety..................................			Extremely rare	
1669...			Extremely rare	

DATE	F	VF	EF	UNC
1669 Second bust			Extremely rare	
1670 —	£150	£550	£2500	—
1671 —	£150	£550	£2500	—
1671 — Plume below, plume in centre rev.	£550	£1500	£5250	—
1672 —	£170	£600	£2500	—
1673 —	£170	£600	£2500	—
1673 — Plume below, plume in centre rev.	£600	£1500	£6500	—
1673/2 — 3 over 2	£200	£700	—	—
1674/3 — 4 over 3	£180	£600	—	—
1674 —	£180	£600	£2500	—
1674 — Plume below bust, plume in centre rev.	£550	£1800	£6250	—
1674 — Plume rev. only	£1000	£2700	£8000	—
1674 Third bust	£550	£2000	—	—
1675 Second bust	£220	£900	—	—
1675/4 — 5 over 4	£240	£850	—	—
1675 — Plume below bust, plume in centre rev.	£600	£1800	£6500	—
1675 Third bust	£350	£1500	—	—
1675/4 — 5 over 4	£300	£1250	—	—
1676 Second bust	£150	£650	£2000	—
1676/5 — 6 over 5	£160	£600	—	—
1676 — Plume below bust, plume in centre rev.	£600	£2000	£6500	—
1677 —	£150	£600	£2500	—
1677 — Plume below bust	£1200	£4000	£10,000	—
1678 —	£170	£600	£2500	—
1678/7 — 8 over 7	£200	£800	—	—
1679 —	£150	£600	£2750	—
1679 — Plume below bust, plume in centre rev.	£550	£1700	£7000	—
1679 — Plume below bust	£1000	£3500	£7000	—
1679 — 9 over 7	£200	£700	—	—
1680 —			Extremely rare	
1680 — Plume below bust, plume in centre rev.	£1300	£4000	£8500	—
1680/79 — — 80 over 79	£1100	£3250	—	—
1681 —	£400	£1200	£3500	—
1681 — 1 over 0	£400	£1000	£3750	—
1681/0 Elephant & Castle below bust	£4000	£11000	—	—
1682/1 — 2 over 1	£1200	£3500	—	—
1683 —			Extremely rare	
1683 Fourth (Larger) bust	£275	£1000	£3400	—
1684 —	£275	£1000	£3400	—

Charles II

JAMES II (1685–88)

	F	VF	EF	UNC
1685	£225	£600	£2750	—
1685 Plume in centre rev. rev			Extremely rare	
1685 No stops on rev.	£250	£700	—	—
1686	£240	£650	£2800	—
1686/5 6 over 5	£250	£700	£3000	—
1687	£250	£700	£3000	—
1687/6 7 over 6	£250	£650	£2800	—
1688	£270	£700	£3000	—
1688/7 last 8 over 7	£260	£675	£2900	—

James II

WILLIAM & MARY (1688–94)

	F	VF	EF	UNC
1692	£225	£600	£2800	—
1692 inverted 1	£225	£650	£2900	—
1693	£200	£600	£2800	—
1690 9 over 0	£275	£700	£3000	—

WILLIAM III (1694–1702)

Provincially produced shillings carry privy marks or initials below the bust:
B: Bristol. C: Chester. E: Exeter. N: Norwich. Y or y: York.

	F	VF	EF	UNC
1695 First bust	£40	£120	£650	—
1696 —	£40	£100	£550	—
1696 — no stops on rev.	£60	£140	£800	—
1696 — MAB for MAG			Extremely rare	
1696 — 1669 error			Extremely rare	
1696 — 1669 various GVLELMVS errors			Extremely rare	
1696 — B below bust	£60	£180	£1000	—
1696 — C	£70	£200	£1000	—
1696 — E	£75	£200	£1100	—

William & Mary

DATE	F	VF	EF	UNC
1696 — N	£80	£250	£1100	—
1696 — y	£70	£200	£1100	—
1696 — Y	£70	£200	£1100	—
1696 Second bust			Only one known	
1696 Third bust C below	£160	£500	£1600	—
1696 — Y			Extremely rare	
1697 First bust	£55	£120	£450	—
1697 — GRI for GRA error			Extremely rare	
1697 — Scottish & Irish shields transposed			Extremely rare	
1697 — Irish arms at date			Extremely rare	
1697 — no stops on rev	£80	£220	£900	—
1697 — GVLELMVS error			Extremely rare	
1697 — B	£90	£200	£1100	—
1697 — C	£80	£200	£1100	—
1697 — E	£90	£220	£1150	—
1697 — N	£75	£200	£1100	—
1697 — — no stops on obv.			Extremely rare	
1697 — y	£80	£180	£1100	—
1697 — — arms of France & Ireland transposed			Extremely rare	
1697 — Y	£80	£180	£900	—
1697 Third bust	£50	£125	£550	—
1697 — B	£100	£225	£1100	—
1697 — C	£110	£220	£1100	—
1697 — — Fr.a error	£150	£500	—	—
1697 — — no stops on obv.	£100	£325	—	—
1697 — — arms of Scotland at date			Extremely rare	
1697 — E	£85	£200	£1050	—
1697 — N	£100	£250	£1200	—
1697 — y	£90	£275	£1250	—
1697 Third bust variety	£65	£150	£650	—
1697 — B	£80	£200	£1250	—
1697 — C	£140	£800	—	—
1698 —	£110	£300	£1300	—
1698 — Plumes in angles of rev.	£275	£700	£2500	—
1698 Fourth bust "Flaming hair"	£200	£675	£2800	—
1698 Plain Edge Proof			Extremely rare	
1699 —	£200	£625	£2700	—
1699 Fifth bust	£120	£350	£1500	—
1699 — Plumes in angles on rev.	£240	£800	£2600	—
1699 — Roses in angles on rev.	£250	£900	£2800	—
1700 —	£70	£150	£650	—
1700 — Small round oo in date	£70	£150	£650	—
1700 — no stop after DEI	£60	£160	£700	—
1700 — Plume below bust	£3500	£11000	—	—
1701 — Plumes in angles on rev.	£200	£750	£2500	—

William III First bust

William III Fifth bust

ANNE (1702–14)

DATE	F	VF	EF	UNC
1702 First bust (pre-Union with Scotland)	£100	£325	£1250	—
1702 — Plumes in angles on rev.	£120	£400	£1600	—
1702 — VIGO below bust	£100	£300	£1300	—
1702 — — colon before ANNA			Extremely rare	
1703 Second bust, VIGO below	£80	£275	£1100	—
1704 — Plain	£600	£2000	—	—
1704 — Plumes in angles on rev.	£100	£350	£1500	—
1705 — Plain	£150	£600	£2000	—
1705 — Plumes in angles on rev.	£100	£400	£1400	—
1705 — Roses & Plumes in angles on rev.	£120	£400	£1200	—
1707 — —	£110	£350	£1500	—
1707 Second bust (post-Union) E below bust	£80	£300	£1200	—
1707 — E* below bust	£90	£350	£1300	—
1707 Third bust, Plain	£35	£120	£650	—
1707 — Plumes in angles on rev.	£50	£180	£800	—
1707 — E below bust	£40	£100	£550	—
1707 2nd "E" bust Plain Edge Proof			Extremely rare	
1708 Second bust, E below	£100	£250	£1000	—
1708 — E* below bust	£120	£400	£1100	—
1708/7 — — 8 over 7			Extremely rare	

Anne, first bust, VIGO below

DATE	MINTAGE	F	VF	EF	UNC
1708 — Roses & Plumes in angles on rev.........		£100	£450	£800	—
1708 Third bust, Plain		£45	£160	£525	—
1708 — Plumes in angles on rev......................		£80	£250	£800	—
1708 Third bust, E below bust		£80	£200	£750	—
1708/7 — — 8 over 7		£200	£450	—	—
1708 — Roses & Plumes in angles on rev.........		£80	£220	£750	—
1708 "Edinburgh" bust, E* below......................		£80	£220	£700	—
1709 Third bust, Plain		£50	£160	£500	—
1709 "Edinburgh" bust, E* below......................		£50	£170	£700	—
1710 Third bust, Roses & Plumes in angles......		£75	£180	£800	—
1710 Fourth bust, Roses & Plumes in angles ...		£80	£200	£850	—
1711 Third bust, Plain		£70	£160	£550	—
1711 Fourth bust, Plain		£35	£80	£260	—
1712 — Roses & Plumes in angles on rev.........		£70	£180	£700	—
1713 — —		£70	£180	£650	—
1713/2 — 3 over 2..		£90	£250	—	—
1714 — —		£70	£160	£500	—
1714/3 —		£120	£300	£1000	—

Anne, Fourth bust, roses and plumes reverse type

GEORGE I (1714–27)

DATE	MINTAGE	F	VF	EF	UNC
1715 First bust, Roses & Plumes in angles on rev.		£80	£250	£1000	—
1716 — —		£150	£500	£2000	—
1717 — —		£120	£350	£1600	—
1718 — —		£75	£250	£950	—
1719 — —		£140	£600	£2350	—
1720 — —		£100	£275	£900	—
1720/18 — —		£150	£500	£1500	—
1720 — Plain		£50	£150	£650	—
1721 — Roses & Plumes in angles on rev.........		£130	£400	£2000	—
1721/0 — — 1 over 0		£100	£400	£1200	—
1721 — Plain		£200	£650	£2000	—
1721/19 — — 21 over 19		£125	£400	—	—
1721/18 21 over 18 error, Plumes & Roses.......		£500	£1800	—	—
1722 — Roses & Plumes in angles on rev.........		£100	£320	£1350	—
1723 — —		£120	£350	£1500	—
1723 — SSC rev., Arms of France at date		£100	£325	£1000	—
1723 — SSC in angles on rev		£35	£110	£400	—
1723 Second bust, SSC in angles on rev..........		£50	£170	£600	—
1723 — Roses & Plumes in angles		£110	£350	£1300	—
1723 — WCC (Welsh Copper Co) below bust ..		£1000	£2500	£8500	—
1724 — Roses & Plumes in angles on rev.........		£110	£350	£1200	—
1724 — WCC below bust.....................................		£1000	£2500	£9000	—
1725 — Roses & Plumes in angles on rev.........		£110	£300	£1300	—
1725 — — no stops on obv.................................		£120	£300	£1300	—
1725 — WCC below bust.....................................		£1100	£2800	£9500	—
1726 — Roses & Plumes		£700	£2500	£7500	—
1726 — WCC below bust.....................................		£1200	£2750	£9500	—
1727 — —				Extremely rare	
1727 — — no stops on obv.................................				Extremely rare	

George I First bust with SSC in angles on reverse

George I Second bust, roses and plumes reverse type

GEORGE II (1727–60)

DATE	MINTAGE	F	VF	EF	UNC
1727 Young head, Plumes in angles on rev.......		£125	£500	£2350	—
1727 — Roses & Plumes in angles on rev.........		£100	£325	£900	—
1728 — —		£120	£400	£1250	—
1728 — Plain		£110	£300	£1250	—
1729 — Roses & Plumes in angles on rev.........		£110	£325	£1500	—
1731 — —		£115	£325	£1250	—
1731 — Plumes in angles on rev......................		£150	£600	£1800	—
1732 — Roses & Plumes in angles on rev.........		£110	£350	£1500	—
1734 — —		£70	£250	£800	—
1735 — —		£70	£250	£800	—
1736 — —		£70	£250	£775	—
1736/5 — — 6 over 5		£70	£250	£900	—
1737 — —		£65	£225	£700	—
1739 — Roses in angles on rev.........................		£60	£220	£700	—
1739/7 — — 9 over 7					Rare
1741 — —		£50	£200	£700	—
1741/39 — — 41 over 39					Rare
1743 Old head, Roses in angles on rev.............		£35	£130	£450	—
1745 — —		£35	£130	£450	—
1745 — — LIMA below bust		£35	£120	£500	—

George II Young head, roses and plumes reverse type

157

DATE	MINTAGE	F	VF	EF	UNC
1745/3 — — 5 over 3		£60	£175	£600	—
1746 — —		£60	£220	£750	—
1746/5 — — 6 over 5		£100	£300	—	—
1746 — Plain, Proof	—	—	£4000	—
1747 — Roses in angles on rev.		£50	£150	£700	—
1750 — Plain		£50	£170	£700	—
1750/46 — — 50 over 46		£75	£170	£650	—
1751 — —		£140	£600	£1750	—
1758 — —		£25	£60	£175	—

George II Old head, plain reverse

GEORGE III (1760–1820)

DATE	MINTAGE	F	VF	EF	UNC
1763 "Northumberland" bust (Beware of counterfeits)		£450	£800	£1600	—
First type,					
1787 rev. no semée of hearts in 4th shield		£25	£45	£125	—
1787 — No stop over head		£30	£50	£140	—
1787 — No stop at date		£50	£90	£175	—
1787 — No stops on obv		£400	£800	£2500	—
1787 rev. with semée of hearts in shield		£35	£65	£140	—
1798 "Dorrien Magens" bust	—	—	£30,000+	

NEW COINAGE—shield in garter reverse

DATE	MINTAGE	F	VF	EF	UNC
1816	—	£12	£25	£75	£175
1817	3,031,360	£12	£35	£85	£200
1817 GEOE for GEOR	incl. above	£120	£250	£700	—
1818	1,342,440	£25	£45	£150	£450
1819	7,595,280	£15	£35	£100	£230
1819/8 9 over 8	incl. above	£20	£50	£160	—
1820	7,975,440	£15	£30	£100	£230

George III First type

GEORGE IV (1820–30)

DATE	MINTAGE	F	VF	EF	UNC
1821 First bust, first reverse	2,463,120	£18	£55	£240	£650
1821 — — Proof	incl. above	—	—	—	£2000
1823 — Second reverse	693,000	£55	£95	£275	£700
1824 — —	4,158,000	£18	£55	£225	£475
1825 — —	2,459,160	£20	£55	£225	£650
1825/3 — — 5 over 3	incl. above			Extremely rare	
1825 Second bust, third reverse .	incl. above	£10	£35	£100	£375
1825 — — Roman I	incl. above			Extremely rare	
1826 — —	6,351,840	£10	£30	£80	£225
1826 6 over 2				Does this exist?	
1826 — — Proof	incl. above	—	—	—	£1500
1827 — —	574,200	£40	£100	£340	£800
1829 — —	879,120	£30	£70	£250	£650

George III New coinage Shield reverse type

WILLIAM IV (1830–37)

DATE	MINTAGE	F	VF	EF	UNC
1831 Proof only, Plain Edge	—	—	—	—	£1800
1834	3,223,440	£15	£40	£225	£500
1835	1,449,360	£20	£60	£250	£550
1836	3,567,960	£18	£45	£200	£500
1837	478,160	£25	£80	£300	£725

George IV second bust second reverse type

VICTORIA (1837–1901)

YOUNG HEAD ISSUES
First head

DATE	MINTAGE	F	VF	EF	UNC
1838 WW on truncation	1,956,240	£20	£50	£220	£500
1839 —	5,666,760	£30	£70	£250	£650
Second head					
1839 — Proof only, Plain Edge	incl. above	—	—	—	£2000
1839 no WW	incl. above	£20	£50	£180	£500
(Rare Proofs exist)					
1840	1,639,440	£20	£60	£200	£550
1841	875,160	£25	£65	£300	£600
1842	2,094,840	£20	£50	£200	£550
1843	1,465,200	£25	£65	£200	£600
1844	4,466,880	£18	£50	£160	£475
1845	4,082,760	£18	£50	£160	£500
1846	4,031,280	£18	£50	£160	£475
1848 last 8 of date over 6	1,041,480	£90	£225	£800	£1800

Victoria Second head type

DATE	MINTAGE	F	VF	EF	UNC
1849	845,480	£30	£75	£250	£700
1850	685,080	£800	£2200	£6000	£9000
1850/49	incl. above	£850	£1800	£5250	—
1851	470,071	£50	£120	£500	£1250
1852	1,306,574	£15	£35	£150	£425
1853	4,256,188	£15	£35	£150	£425
1853 Proof...............................	incl. above	—	—	—	£3000
1854	552,414	£250	£650	£2000	£5000
1854/1 4 over 1	incl. above	£300	£900	—	—
1855	1,368,400	£12	£30	£140	£375
1856	3,168,000	£12	£30	£140	£375
1857	2,562,120	£12	£30	£140	£375
1857 error F:G with inverted G ...	incl. above	£220	£600	—	—
1858	3,108,600	£15	£35	£140	£350
1859	4,561,920	£12	£30	£140	£350
1860	1,671,120	£12	£35	£160	£450
1861	1,382,040	£15	£40	£180	£600
1862	954,360	£70	£180	£500	£1600
1863	859,320	£140	£400	£1000	£2400
1863/1 3 over 1				Extremely rare	

Die no. added above date up to 1879

1864	4,518,360	£10	£30	£135	£340
1865	5,619,240	£10	£30	£135	£340
1866	4,984,600	£10	£30	£135	£340
1866 error BBITANNIAR	incl. above	£80	£300	£1000	—
1867	2,166,120	£15	£35	£140	£350

Third head—with die no

1867	incl. above	£175	£500	—	—
1868	3,330,360	£12	£40	£125	£350
1869	736,560	£20	£55	£170	£450
1870	1,467,471	£15	£40	£120	£325
1871	4,910,010	£12	£40	£120	£320
1872	8,897,781	£12	£40	£120	£320
1873	6,489,598	£12	£40	£120	£320
1874	5,503,747	£15	£40	£130	£340
1875	4,353,983	£12	£40	£120	£325
1876	1,057,487	£18	£60	£170	£600
1877	2,989,703	£12	£40	£120	£320
1878	3,127,131	£12	£40	£120	£320
1879	3,611,507	£20	£70	£220	£600

Fourth head—no die no

1879 no Die no.	incl. above	£10	£28	£100	£250
1880	4,842,786	£10	£28	£100	£250
1881	5,255,332	£10	£28	£100	£250
1882	1,611,786	£25	£80	£200	£600
1883	7,281,450	£10	£28	£80	£230
1884	3,923,993	£10	£28	£80	£230
1885	3,336,526	£10	£28	£80	£230
1886	2,086,819	£10	£28	£80	£230
1887	4,034,133	£10	£28	£80	£230

JUBILEE HEAD ISSUES

1887	incl. above	£4	£9	£18	£45
1887 Proof...............................	1,084	—	—	—	£500
1888	4,526,856	£6	£10	£25	£70
1889	7,039,628	£45	£100	£325	—
1889 Large bust (until 1892)........	incl. above	£6	£12	£50	£95
1890	8,794,042	£6	£12	£50	£95
1891	5,665,348	£6	£12	£50	£100
1892	4,591,622	£6	£12	£50	£125

OLD HEAD ISSUES

1893	7,039,074	£7	£14	£45	£100
1893 small lettering	incl. above	£7	£14	£45	£100
1893 Proof...............................	1,312	—	—	—	£450
1894	5,953,152	£10	£28	£75	£200
1895	8,880,651	£9	£25	£60	£180
1896	9,264,551	£7	£15	£45	£110
1897	6,270,364	£7	£12	£45	£100
1898	9,768,703	£7	£12	£45	£100
1899	10,965,382	£7	£12	£45	£100
1900	10,937,590	£7	£12	£45	£110
1901	3,426,294	£7	£12	£45	£100

Victoria Third head, with die no.

Victoria Fourth head, no die no.

Victoria Jubilee head

Victoria Old or Veiled head

DATE	MINTAGE	F	VF	EF	UNC

EDWARD VII (1901–10)

1902............................	7,809,481	£6	£15	£50	£100
1902 Proof matt......................	13,123	—	—	—	£175
1903............................	2,061,823	£10	£35	£160	£550
1904............................	2,040,161	£8	£35	£150	£525
1905............................	488,390	£110	£325	£1500	£4000
1906	10,791,025	£5	£12	£50	£140
1907............................	14,083,418	£5	£12	£50	£150
1908............................	3,806,969	£12	£30	£170	£600
1909............................	5,664,982	£9	£25	£125	£425
1910............................	26,547,236	£5	£10	£45	£100

GEORGE V (1910–36)

First issue

1911............................	20,065,901	£5	£9	£24	£60
1911 Proof............................	6,007	—	—	—	£160
1912............................	15,594,009	£6	£12	£28	£90
1913............................	9,011,509	£7	£20	£50	£150
1914............................	23,415,843	£4	£7	£30	£60
1915............................	39,279,024	£4	£7	£30	£60
1916............................	35,862,015	£4	£7	£30	£60
1917............................	22,202,608	£4	£7	£30	£70
1918............................	34,915,934	£4	£7	£30	£60
1919............................	10,823,824	£5	£8	£30	£70

Second issue—debased silver

1920	22,825,142	£2	£4	£25	£55
1921............................	22,648,763	£2	£4	£25	£55
1922............................	27,215,738	£2	£4	£25	£60
1923............................	14,575,243	£2	£4	£25	£55
1924............................	9,250,095	£7	£18	£65	£170
1925............................	5,418,764	£6	£10	£50	£140
1926............................	22,516,453	£3	£8	£30	£120

(Trial Proofs of 1923 and 1924 were struck in cupro nickel—both Rare)

Third issue—Modified bust

1926	incl. above	£2	£4	£30	£60
1927 —	9,247,344	£2	£4	£30	£60

Fourth issue— new reverse: large lion and crown on rev., date in legend

1927	incl. above	£2	£4	£20	£45
1927 Proof....................	15,000	—	—	—	£70
1928............................	18,136,778	£2	£4	£15	£45
1929............................	19,343,006	£2	£4	£15	£45
1930............................	3,172,092	£2	£4	£20	£55
1931............................	6,993,926	£2	£4	£15	£45
1932............................	12,168,101	£2	£4	£15	£50
1933............................	11,511,624	£2	£4	£15	£40
1934............................	6,138,463	£2	£4	£18	£50
1935............................	9,183,462	—	£4	£12	£25
1936............................	11,910,613	—	£4	£12	£25

George V First reverse

George V Fourth issue, Second reverse

GEORGE VI (1936–52)

E = England rev. (lion standing on large crown). S = Scotland rev. (lion seated on small crown holding sword and mace)

1937 E	8,359,122	—	£2	£4	£6
1937 E Proof............................	26,402	—	—	—	£25
1937 S	6,748,875	—	£2	£4	£6
1937 S Proof....................	26,402	—	—	—	£25
1938 E	4,833,436	—	£3	£10	£20
1938 S	4,797,852	—	£3	£10	£20
1939 E	11,052,677	—	£2	£4	£6
1939 S	10,263,892	—	£2	£4	£6
1940 E	11,099,126	—	—	£4	£7
1940 S	9,913,089	—	—	£4	£7
1941 E	11,391,883	—	—	£4	£6
1941 S	8,086,030	—	—	£4	£5
1942 E	17,453,643	—	—	£4	£5
1942 S	13,676,759	—	—	£4	£5

DATE	MINTAGE	F	VF	EF	UNC
1943 E	11,404,213	—	—	£4	£6
1943 S	9,824,214	—	—	£4	£5
1944 E	11,586,751	—	—	£4	£5
1944 S	10,990,167	—	—	£4	£5
1945 E	15,143,404	—	—	£4	£6
1945 S	15,106,270	—	—	£4	£5
1946 E	16,663,797	—	—	£4	£5
1946 S	16,381,501	—	—	£4	£5
Cupro-nickel					
1947 E	12,120,611	—	—	—	£2
1947 S	12,283,223	—	—	—	£2
1948 E	45,576,923	—	—	—	£2
1948 S	45,351,937	—	—	—	£2
1949 E	19,328,405	—	—	—	£5
1949 S	21,243,074	—	—	—	£5
1950 E	19,243,872	—	—	—	£5
1950 E Proof	17,513	—	—	—	£20
1950 S	14,299,601	—	—	—	£5
1950 S Proof	17,513	—	—	—	£20
1951 E	9,956,930	—	—	—	£5
1951 E Proof	20,000	—	—	—	£20
1951 S	10,961,174	—	—	—	£6
1951 S Proof	20,000	—	—	—	£20

English reverse

Scottish reverse

ELIZABETH II (1952–2022)

E = England rev. (shield with three lions). S = Scotland rev. (shield with one lion).

DATE	MINTAGE	F	VF	EF	UNC
1953 E	41,942,894	—	—	—	£1
1953 E Proof	40,000	—	—	—	£4
1953 S	20,663,528	—	—	—	£1
1953 S Proof	40,000	—	—	—	£4
1954 E	30,262,032	—	—	—	£2
1954 S	26,771,735	—	—	—	£2
1955 E	45,259,908	—	—	—	£2
1955 S	27,950,906	—	—	—	£2
1956 E	44,907,008	—	—	—	£10
1956 S	42,853,639	—	—	—	£10
1957 E	42,774,217	—	—	—	£1
1957 S	17,959,988	—	—	—	£10
1958 E	14,392,305	—	—	—	£10
1958 S	40,822,557	—	—	—	£1
1959 E	19,442,778	—	—	—	£1
1959 S	1,012,988	£1	£3	£10	£70
1960 E	27,027,914	—	—	—	£1
1960 S	14,376,932	—	—	—	£1
1961 E	39,816,907	—	—	—	£1
1961 S	2,762,558	—	—	—	£3
1962 E	36,704,379	—	—	—	£1
1962 S	17,475,310	—	—	—	£1
1963 E	49,433,607	—	—	—	£1
1963 S	32,300,000	—	—	—	£1
1964 E	8,590,900	—	—	—	£1
1964 S	5,239,100	—	—	—	£1
1965 E	9,216,000	—	—	—	£1
1965 S	2,774,000	—	—	—	£2
1966 E	15,002,000	—	—	—	£1
1966 S	15,604,000	—	—	—	£1
1970 E Proof	—				£10
1970 S Proof	—				£10

English reverse

Scottish reverse

SIXPENCES

DATE	F	VF	EF	UNC

OLIVER CROMWELL

1658 Patterns by Thos. Simon & Tanner
Four varieties .... Extremely rare

CHARLES II (1660–85)

	F	VF	EF	UNC
1674..	£75	£300	£1000	—
1675..	£75	£300	£1100	—
1675/4 5 over 4	£85	£300	£1100	—
1676..	£85	£300	£1000	—
1676/5 6 over 5	£90	£300	£1000	—
1677..	£80	£300	£1000	—
1678/7	£80	£300	£1100	—
1679..	£80	£300	£1000	—
1680..	£100	£500	£1300	—
1681..	£85	£300	£1100	—
1682/1	£85	£300	£1100	—
1682..	£110	£350	£1350	—
1683..	£85	£300	£1000	—
1684..	£90	£300	£1000	—

Charles II

JAMES II (1685–88)

	F	VF	EF	UNC
1686 Early shields	£150	£450	£1300	—
1687 Ealy Shields	£160	£500	£1550	—
1687/6 — 7 over 6............................	£160	£500	£1200	—
1687 Late shields	£160	£500	£1600	—
1687/6 — 7 over 6	£160	£500	£1450	—
1688 —	£160	£500	£1500	—

James II

WILLIAM & MARY (1688–94)

	F	VF	EF	UNC
1693	£130	£450	£1300	—
1693 error inverted 3	£240	£550	£1650	—
1694...	£130	£475	£1400	—

WILLIAM III (1694–1702)

Provincially produced sixpences carry privy marks or initials below the bust:
B: Bristol. C: Chester. E: Exeter. N: Norwich. Y or y: York.

	F	VF	EF	UNC
1695 First bust, early harp in 4th shield on rev.	£35	£110	£425	—
1696 — —	£35	£110	£350	—
1696 — — French arms at date		Extremely rare		
1696 — — Scottish arms at date...................		Extremely rare		
1696 — — DFI for DEI...................................		Extremely rare		
1696 — — No stops on obv.	£50	£150	£525	—
1696 — — B..	£40	£110	£450	—
1696 — — — B over E		Extremely rare		
1696 — — C..	£40	£100	£500	—
1696 — — E..	£50	£110	£500	—
1696 — — N..	£50	£100	£550	—
1696 — — y...	£50	£120	£625	—
1696 — — Y..	£50	£200	£650	—
1696 — Later harp	£50	£175	£475	—
1696 — — B..	£70	£225	£750	—
1696 — — — no stops on obv..........................	£80	£275	£625	—
1696 — — C..	£100	£400	£1000	—
1696 — — N..	£70	£325	—	—
1696 Second bust...	£300	£800	£2400	—
1697 First bust, later harp	£30	£75	£325	—
1697 — — Arms of France & Ireland transposed		Extremely rare		

William and Mary

William III first bust

DATE	MINTAGE	F	VF	EF	UNC
1697 — — B		£55	£120	£500	—
1697 — — C		£70	£200	£525	—
1697 — — Irish shield at date				Extremely rare	
1697 — — E		£70	£200	£550	—
1697 — — — error GVLIEMVS				Extremely rare	
1697 — — y		£65	£150	£550	—
1697 — — Irish shield at date				Extremely rare	
1697 Second bust		£220	£550	£1800	—
1697 Third bust		£35	£75	£300	—
1697 — error GVLIEIMVS				Extremely rare	
1697 — B		£55	£150	£500	—
1697 — IRA for FRA				Extremely rare	
1697 — C		£80	£250	£600	—
1697 — E		£80	£250	£600	—
1697 — Y		£60	£220	£600	—
1698 —		£60	£200	£575	—
1698 — Plumes in angles on rev.		£100	£250	£900	—
1699 —		£110	£275	£950	—
1699 — Plumes in angles on rev.		£80	£275	£950	—
1699 — Roses in angles on rev.		£75	£260	£900	—
1699 — — error GⅤLIELMVS				Extremely rare	
1700 —		£45	£110	£425	—
1700 — Plume below bust		£2500	—	—	—
1701 —		£70	£175	£550	—

William III third bust

ANNE (1702–14)

1703 VIGO below bust Before Union with Scotland	£40	£150	£550	—	
1705 Plain		£60	£170	£575	—
1705 Plumes in angles on rev.		£60	£175	£600	—
1705 Roses & Plumes in angles on rev.		£70	£180	£600	—
1707 Roses & Plumes in angles on rev.		£50	£160	£500	—
1707 (Post-Union), Plain		£40	£90	£400	—
1707 E (Edinburgh) below bust		£40	£90	£380	—
1707 Plumes in angles on rev.		£50	£150	£400	—
1708 Plain		£45	£100	£425	—
1708 E below bust		£50	£100	£375	—
1708 E* below bust		£60	£140	£450	—
1708 "Edinburgh" bust E* below		£50	£140	£450	—
1708 Plumes in angles on rev.		£60	£160	£600	—
1710 Roses & Plumes in angles on rev.		£40	£125	£550	—
1711 Plain		£25	£70	£300	—

Queen Anne

GEORGE I (1714–27)

1717 Roses & Plumes in angles on rev.		£90	£300	£900	—
1717 Plain edge				Extremely rare	
1720 —		£90	£300	£850	—
1723 SSC in angles on rev.		£30	£70	£220	—
1723 Larger lettering		£30	£70	£220	—
1726 Small Roses & Plumes in angles on rev.		£80	£240	£700	—

George I

GEORGE II (1727–60)

1728 Young head, Plain		£70	£240	£550	—
1728 — Proof		—	—	£4000	—
1728 — Plumes in angles on rev.		£40	£140	£450	—
1728 — Roses & Plumes in angles on rev.		£35	£125	£400	—
1731 — —		£40	£140	£425	—
1732 — —		£40	£140	£425	—
1734 — —		£40	£140	£425	—
1735 — —		£40	£150	£425	—
1735/4 5 over 4		£45	£150	£425	—
1736 — —		£45	£150	£425	—
1739 — Roses in angles on rev.		£30	£110	£350	—
1741 —		£30	£110	£340	—
1743 Old head, Roses in angles on rev.		£25	£75	£250	—
1745 — —		£25	£75	£250	—
1745 — — 5 over 3		£30	£85	£275	—

George II, young head

DATE	MINTAGE	F	VF	EF	UNC
1745 — Plain, LIMA below bust		£30	£80	£275	—
1746 — — —		£30	£80	£300	—
1746 — — Proof..		—	—	£1800	—
1750 — —		£35	£140	£350	—
1751 — —		£35	£150	£400	—
1757 — —		£18	£35	£95	—
1758 — —		£18	£35	£95	—

George II, old head

GEORGE III (1760–1820)

1787 rev. no semée of hearts on 4th shield		£15	£35	£80	£120
1787 rev. with semée of hearts.........................		£15	£35	£80	£120

NEW COINAGE

1816	—	£7	£15	£45	£125
1817	10,921,680	£7	£15	£45	£125
1818...	4,284,720	£10	£25	£90	£180
1819...	4,712,400	£8	£15	£45	£120
1819 very small 8 in date.............	incl. above	£12	£22	£70	£160
1820...	1,488,960	£8	£15	£60	£140

George III new coinage

GEORGE IV (1820–30)

1821 First bust, first reverse	863,280	£12	£30	£120	£350
1821 error BBRITANNIAR............		£100	£300	£950	—
1821 — — Proof.........................	incl. above	—	—	—	£1300
1824 — Second (garter) reverse..	633,600	£10	£30	£100	£340
1825 — —	483,120	£12	£30	£100	£320
1826 — —	689,040	£40	£100	£250	£600
1826 Second bust, third (lion on crown) reverse	incl. above	£10	£30	£100	£220
1826 — — Proof.........................	incl. above	—	—	—	£1100
1827 — —	166,320	£40	£110	£300	£700
1828 — —	15,840	£20	£50	£150	£350
1829 — —	403,290	£15	£45	£125	£350

George IV second reverse

WILLIAM IV (1830–37)

1831...	1,340,195	£15	£40	£125	£350
1831 Proof, milled edge	incl. above	—	—	—	£1000
1834...	5,892,480	£15	£40	£125	£350
1835...	1,552,320	£15	£40	£125	£350
1836...	1,987,920	£15	£45	£150	£380
1837...	506,880	£25	£50	£250	£600

William IV

VICTORIA (1837–1901)

YOUNG HEAD ISSUES
First head

1838...	1,607,760	£15	£40	£130	£350
1839	3,310,560	£15	£40	£130	£350
1839 Proof................................	incl. above	—	—	—	£1600
1840...	2,098,800	£15	£40	£130	£350
1841...	1,386,000	£18	£45	£150	£425
1842...	601,920	£15	£40	£130	£350
1843...	3,160,080	£15	£40	£130	£350
1844...	3,975,840	£15	£30	£140	£375
1844 Large 44 in date................	incl. above	£18	£40	£130	£425
1845...	3,714,480	£15	£35	£110	£375
1846...	4,226,880	£15	£35	£110	£375
1847...	—	£1000	—	—	—
1848...	586,080	£50	£125	£375	£600
1848/6 final 8 over 6...................	incl. above	£50	£120	£400	—
1850...	498,960	£15	£40	£120	£450
1850/3 0 over 3	incl. above	£18	£40	£110	£400
1851...	2,288,107	£10	£30	£100	£400
1852...	904,586	£10	£30	£150	£380
1853...	3,837,930	£10	£30	£150	£380
1853 Proof................................	incl above	—	—	—	£1800

DATE	MINTAGE	F	VF	EF	UNC
1854..	840,116	£200	£600	£1500	3500
1855..	1,129,684	£10	£30	£120	£300
1855/3 last 5 over 3....................	incl. above	£15	£45	£150	£350
1856..	2,779,920	£10	£40	£120	£320
1857..	2,233,440	£10	£40	£120	£300
1858..	1,932,480	£10	£40	£120	£300
1859..	4,688,640	£10	£40	£120	£300
1859/8 9 over 8	incl. above	£12	£40	£120	£420
1860..	1,100,880	£10	£35	£120	£380
1862..	990,000	£100	£240	£600	£2000
1863..	491,040	£80	£170	£500	£1400

Victoria first young head

Die no. added above date from 1864 to 1879

1864..	4,253,040	£10	£25	£110	£275
1865..	1,631,520	£10	£25	£100	£275
1866..	4,140,080	£10	£25	£100	£275
1866 no Die no.	incl. above			Extremely Rare	

Second head

1867..	1,362,240	£10	£30	£130	£300
1868..	1,069,200	£10	£30	£120	£300
1869..	388,080	£10	£30	£120	£340
1870..	479,613	£10	£30	£120	£300
1871..	3,662,684	£8	£30	£85	£300
1871 no Die no.	incl. above	£8	£30	£85	£260
1872..	3,382,048	£8	£30	£85	£260
1873..	4,594,733	£8	£30	£85	£260
1874..	4,225,726	£8	£30	£100	£250
1875..	3,256,545	£8	£30	£85	£275
1876	841,435	£8	£30	£85	£275
1877..	4,066,486	£8	£30	£85	£275
1877 no Die no	incl. above	£8	£30	£85	£275
1878..	2,624,525	£8	£30	£85	£300
1878/7 8 struck over 7 Error.......	incl. above	£45	£200	£750	—
1878 Dritanniar Error	incl. above	£125	£300	£1000	—
1879..	3,326,313	£8	£25	£90	£275
1879 no Die no	incl. above	£8	£25	£90	£275
1880 no Die no	3,892,501	£8	£25	£80	£275

Victoria Jubilee head, shield reverse

Third head

1880	incl above	£8	£20	£80	£220
1881..	6,239,447	£8	£20	£80	£220
1882..	759,809	£15	£50	£150	£500
1883..	4,986,558	£8	£20	£70	£200
1884..	3,422,565	£8	£20	£70	£200
1885..	4,652,771	£8	£20	£70	£200
1886..	2,728,249	£8	£20	£70	£200
1887..	3,675,607	£8	£20	£70	£200

Jubilee head, wreath reverse

JUBILEE HEAD ISSUES

1887 Shield reverse	incl. above	£6	£10	£15	£30
1887 — Proof	incl. above	—	—	—	£1500
1887 Six Pence in wreath reverse	incl. above	£6	£8	£18	£35
1888 —	4,197,698	£8	£12	£35	£60
1889 —	8,738,928	£8	£12	£35	£70
1890 —	9,386,955	£8	£12	£35	£70
1891 —	7,022,734	£8	£12	£35	£90
1892 —	6,245,746	£8	£12	£35	£100
1893 —	7,350,619	£800	£1500	£4000	—

Victoria Old Head

OLD HEAD ISSUES

1893..	incl. above	£7	£12	£22	£50
1893 Proof..................................	1,312	—	—	—	£400
1894..	3,467,704	£8	£18	£55	£160
1895..	7,024,631	£8	£18	£50	£125
1896..	6,651,699	£7	£15	£40	£80
1897..	5,031,498	£7	£15	£40	£80
1898..	5,914,100	£7	£15	£40	£80
1899..	7,996,80	£7	£15	£40	£75
1900..	8,984,354	£7	£15	£40	£75
1901..	5,108,757	£7	£15	£40	£75

DATE	MINTAGE	F	VF	EF	UNC

EDWARD VII (1901–10)

DATE	MINTAGE	F	VF	EF	UNC
1902	6,367,378	£5	£12	£35	£70
1902 "Matt Proof"	15,123	—	—	—	£150
1903	5,410,096	£7	£20	£50	£170
1904	4,487,098	£15	£50	£175	£500
1905	4,235,556	£8	£20	£70	£220
1906	7,641,146	£7	£12	£40	£120
1907	8,733,673	£7	£12	£45	£130
1908	6,739,491	£10	£30	£110	£350
1909	6,584,017	£8	£18	£50	£175
1910	12,490,724	£5	£8	£25	£65

Edward VII

GEORGE V (1910–36)

First issue

DATE	MINTAGE	F	VF	EF	UNC
1911	9,155,310	£3	£7	£15	£40
1911 Proof	6,007	—	—	—	£150
1912	10,984,129	£3	£7	£20	£65
1913	7,499,833	£3	£8	£22	£80
1914	22,714,602	£3	£7	£10	£35
1915	15,694,597	£3	£7	£12	£45
1916	22,207,178	£3	£7	£10	£35
1917	7,725,475	£8	£25	£60	£150
1918	27,553,743	£3	£7	£12	£30
1919	13,375,447	£3	£7	£12	£40
1920	14,136,287	£3	£7	£10	£35

Second issue—debased silver

DATE	MINTAGE	F	VF	EF	UNC
1920	incl. above	£1	£3	£10	£40
1921	30,339,741	£1	£3	£10	£40
1922	16,878,890	£1	£3	£10	£30
1923	6,382,793	£4	£10	£45	£110
1924	17,444,218	£1	£5	£10	£35
1925	12,720,558	£1	£3	£10	£35
1925 Broad rim	incl. above	£1	£3	£10	£35
1926 —	21,809,621	£1	£3	£10	£35

Third issue—Modified bust

DATE	MINTAGE	F	VF	EF	UNC
1926	incl. above	£1	£2	£10	£35
1927	8,924,873	—	£2	£10	£35

George V first reverse

Fourth issue—New design (oakleaves)

DATE	MINTAGE	F	VF	EF	UNC
1927 Proof only	15,000	—	—	—	£75
1928	23,123,384	£1	£2	£8	£25
1929	28,319,326	£1	£2	£8	£25
1930	16,990,289	£1	£2	£8	£30
1931	16,873,268	£1	£2	£8	£30
1932	9,406,117	£1	£2	£8	£40
1933	22,185,083	£1	£2	£8	£25
1934	9,304,009	£1	£2	£12	£35
1935	13,995,621	£1	£2	£6	£15
1936	24,380,171	£1	£2	£6	£15

George V second reverse (fourth issue)

GEORGE VI (1936–52)

First type

DATE	MINTAGE	F	VF	EF	UNC
1937	22,302,524	—	—	£1	£5
1937 Proof	26,402	—	—	—	£15
1938	13,402,701	—	£2	£5	£18
1939	28,670,304	—	—	£1	£5
1940	20,875,196	—	—	£1	£5
1941	23,086,616	—	—	£1	£5
1942	44,942,785	—	—	£1	£4
1943	46,927,111	—	—	£1	£4
1944	36,952,600	—	—	£1	£4
1945	39,939,259	—	—	£1	£3
1946	43,466,407	—	—	£1	£3

Cupro-nickel

DATE	MINTAGE	F	VF	EF	UNC
1947	29,993,263	—	—	£1	£3
1948	88,323,540	—	—	£1	£3

George VI first reverse

Second type—new cypher on rev.

DATE	MINTAGE	F	VF	EF	UNC
1949	41,335,515	—	—	£1	£3
1950	32,741,955	—	—	£1	£3
1950 Proof	17,513	—	—	—	£8
1951	40,399,491	—	—	£1	£3

George VI second reverse

DATE	MINTAGE	F	VF	EF	UNC
1951 Proof	20,000	—	—	—	£8
1952	1,013,477	£12	£30	£60	£175

ELIZABETH II (1952–2022)

DATE	MINTAGE	F	VF	EF	UNC
1953	70,323,876	—	—	—	£2
1953 Proof	40,000	—	—	—	£4
1954	105,241,150	—	—	—	£3
1955	109,929,554	—	—	—	£1
1956	109,841,555	—	—	—	£1
1957	105,654,290	—	—	—	£1
1958	123,518,527	—	—	—	£3
1959	93,089,441	—	—	—	£1
1960	103,283,346	—	—	—	£3
1961	115,052,017	—	—	—	£3
1962	166,483,637	—	—	—	25p
1963	120,056,000	—	—	—	25p
1964	152,336,000	—	—	—	25p
1965	129,644,000	—	—	—	25p
1966	175,676,000	—	—	—	25p
1967	240,788,000	—	—	—	25p
1970 Proof	—				£8

GROATS OR FOURPENCES

DATE	MINTAGE	F	VF	EF	UNC

The earlier fourpences are included in the Maundy oddments section as they are generally considered to have been issued for the Maundy ceremony.

WILLIAM IV (1831–37)

	MINTAGE	F	VF	EF	UNC
1836	—	£8	£20	£45	£95
1837	962,280	£8	£20	£45	£100

VICTORIA (1838–1901)

	MINTAGE	F	VF	EF	UNC
1837	Extremely Rare Proofs or Patterns only				
1838	2,150,280	£7	£15	£40	£100
1838 over last 8 on its side		£10	£20	£60	£140
1839	1,461,240	£7	£16	£50	£120
1839 Proof	incl. above				Rare
1840	1,496,880	£7	£15	£50	£120
1840 Small 0 in date	incl. above	£7	£15	£50	£120
1841	344,520	£7	£15	£50	£120
1842/1 2 over 1	incl. above	£7	£15	£50	£120
1842	724,680	£7	£15	£45	£120
1843	1,817640	£8	£18	£50	£150
1843 4 over 5	incl. above	£7	£15	£50	£140
1844	855,360	£7	£15	£50	£125
1845	914,760	£7	£15	£50	£125
1846	1,366,200	£7	£15	£50	£120
1847 7 over 6	225,720	£15	£35	£125	—
1848	712,800	£7	£15	£50	£110
1848/6 8 over 6	incl. above	£30	£110	—	—
1848/7 8 over 7	incl. above	£8	£20	£60	£120
1849	380,160	£8	£18	£60	£120
1849/8 9 over 8	incl. above	£8	£20	£70	£150
1851	594,000	£40	£90	£275	£475
1852	31,300	£55	£130	£425	—
1853	11,880	£80	£170	£600	—
1853 Proof Milled Rim	incl. above	—	—	—	£1300
1853 Plain edge Proof		Extremely rare			
1854	1,096,613	£7	£15	£40	£110
1855	646,041	£7	£15	£40	£110
1855/3 Last 5 over 3	—	£12	£25	£75	£200
1857 Proofs only		Extremely rare			
1862 Proofs only		Extremely rare			
1888 Jubilee Head	—	£15	£30	£60	£140

THREEPENCES

DATE	MINTAGE	F	VF	EF	UNC

The earlier threepences are included in the Maundy oddments section.

WILLIAM IV (1830–37)

(issued for use in the West Indies)

1834		£12	£25	£100	£250
1835		£10	£20	£80	£240
1836		£10	£20	£85	£240
1837		£15	£35	£130	£320

Wiliam IV

VICTORIA (1837–1901)

1838 BRITANNIAB error			Extremely rare		
1838	—	£15	£30	£80	£250
1839	—	£15	£30	£90	£260
1840	—	£15	£30	£90	£260
1841	—	£18	£32	£100	£300
1842	—	£15	£30	£90	£270
1843	—	£15	£30	£70	£220
1843/34 43 over 34	—	£15	£30	£90	£250
1844	—	£16	£30	£90	£240
1845	1,319,208	£16	£30	£70	£240
1846	52,008	£25	£70	£275	£550
1847	4,488		Extremely rare		
1848	incl. above		Extremely rare		
1849	131,208	£12	£28	£80	£250
1850	954,888	£12	£25	£60	£225
1851	479,065	£12	£30	£70	£230
1851 reads 1551			Very rare		
1851 5 over 8	incl. above	£25	£50	£220	—
1852	4,488	£80	£220	£700	£1100
1853	36,168	£60	£140	£300	£700
1854	1,467,246	£8	£25	£75	£220
1855	383,350	£12	£30	£90	£275
1856	1,013,760	£10	£25	£90	£225
1857	1,758,240	£10	£25	£80	£250
1858	1,441,440	£10	£25	£70	£225
1858 BRITANNIAB error	incl. above		Extremely rare		
1858/6 final 8 over 6	incl. above	£15	£30	£200	—
1858/5 final 8 over 5	incl. above	£10	£30	£150	—
1859	3,579,840	£8	£20	£60	£200
1860	3,405,600	£12	£28	£75	£260
1861	3,294,720	£10	£25	£70	£200
1862	1,156,320	£10	£28	£70	£200
1863	950,400	£30	£70	£125	£350
1864	1,330,560	£7	£22	£50	£170
1865	1,742,400	£7	£22	£60	£190
1866	1,900,800	£7	£22	£60	£180
1867	712,800	£7	£22	£60	£180
1868	1,457,280	£7	£22	£60	£190
1868 RRITANNIAR error	incl. above		Extremely rare		
1869	—	£25	£175	£300	£650
1870	1,283,218	£6	£18	£60	£160
1871	999,633	£6	£18	£50	£140
1872	1,293,271	£5	£16	£50	£120
1873	4,055,550	£5	£16	£50	£120
1874	4,427,031	£5	£16	£50	£130
1875	3,306,500	£5	£16	£50	£120
1876	1,834,389	£5	£16	£50	£120
1877	2,622,393	£5	£16	£50	£120
1878	2,419,975	£6	£18	£55	£160
1879	3,140,265	£5	£16	£40	£110

Victoria Young head type

DATE	MINTAGE	F	VF	EF	UNC
1880	1,610,069	£5	£16	£40	£100
1881	3,248,265	£5	£16	£40	£95
1882	472,965	£8	£25	£70	£200
1883	4,369,971	£5	£10	£30	£65
1884	3,322,424	£5	£12	£35	£75
1885	5,183,653	£5	£12	£35	£80
1886	6,152,669	£5	£12	£30	£60
1887	2,780,761	£5	£12	£30	£65

Dates of 1838, 1839, 1840, 1841, 1842, 1843, 1844, 1847, 1848 and 1853 were issued for colonial use.

JUBILEE HEAD ISSUES

1887	incl. above	£2	£4	£15	£30
1887 Proof	incl. above	—	—	—	£250
1888	518,199	£2	£5	£20	£45
1889	4,587,010	£2	£5	£20	£50
1890	4,465,834	£2	£5	£20	£50
1891	6,323,027	£2	£5	£20	£50
1892	2,578,226	£2	£5	£20	£55
1893	3,067,243	£20	£60	£180	£425

Victoria Jubilee head

OLD HEAD ISSUES

1893	incl. above	£2	£5	£16	£35
1893 Proof	incl. above	—	—	—	£275
1894	1,608,603	£4	£7	£25	£70
1895	4,788,609	£2	£5	£22	£60
1896	4,598,442	£2	£5	£18	£40
1897	4,541,294	£2	£5	£18	£40
1898	4,567,177	£2	£5	£18	£40
1899	6,246,281	£2	£5	£18	£40
1900	10,644,480	£2	£5	£18	£40
1901	6,098,400	£2	£5	£15	£30

Victoria Old or Veiled head

EDWARD VII (1901–10)

1902	8,268,480	£2	£3	£10	£20
1902 "Matt Proof"	incl. above	—	—	—	£60
1903	5,227,200	£2	£5	£20	£55
1904	3,627,360	£4	£12	£50	£120
1905	3,548,160	£2	£5	£25	£65
1906	3,152,160	£3	£9	£40	£90
1907	4,831,200	£2	£4	£20	£60
1908	8,157,600	£2	£3	£20	£55
1909	4,055,040	£2	£4	£20	£60
1910	4,563,380	£2	£4	£18	£45

Edward VII

GEORGE V (1910–36)

First issue

1911	5,841,084	—	—	£3	£12
1911 Proof	incl. above	—	—	—	£70
1912	8,932,825	—	—	£3	£15
1913	7,143,242	—	—	£3	£15
1914	6,733,584	—	—	£3	£14
1915	5,450,617	—	—	£3	£16
1916	18,555,201	—	—	£3	£12
1917	21,662,490	—	—	£3	£12
1918	20,630,909	—	—	£3	£10
1919	16,845,687	—	—	£3	£10
1920	16,703,597	—	—	£3	£10

George V second issue

Second issue—debased silver

1920	incl. above	—	—	£3	£14
1921	8,749,301	—	—	£3	£14
1922	7,979,998	—	—	£5	£40
1925	3,731,859	—	—	£4	£28
1926	4,107,910	—	—	£4	£35

Third issue—Modified bust

1926	incl. above	—	—	£8	£25

169

DATE	MINTAGE	F	VF	EF	UNC
Fourth issue—new design (oakleaves)					
1927 Proof only	15,022	—	—	—	£140
1928..	1,302,106	£4	£10	£30	£65
1930..	1,319,412	£2	£4	£10	£40
1931..	6,251,936	—	—	£2	£7
1932..	5,887,325	—	—	£2	£7
1933..	5,578,541	—	—	£2	£7
1934..	7,405,954	—	—	£2	£7
1935..	7,027,654	—	—	£2	£7
1936..	3,328,670	—	—	£2	£7

George V, fourth issue oak leaves design reverse

GEORGE VI (1936–52)

Silver

1937..	8,148,156	—	—	£1	£5
1937 Proof...................................	26,402	—	—	—	£20
1938..	6,402,473	—	—	£1	£5
1939..	1,355,860	—	—	£4	£15
1940..	7,914,401	—	—	£1	£4
1941..	7,979,411	—	—	£1	£4
1942..	4,144,051	£2	£5	£12	£35
1943..	1,397,220	£3	£8	£15	£40
1944..	2,005,553	£10	£25	£50	£100
1945..			Only one known		

1942, 1943, 1944, 1945 were for colonial issue only.

George VI small silver 3d

Nickel brass

1937..	45,707,957	—	—	£1	£4
1937 Proof...................................	26,402	—	—	—	£20
1938..	14,532,332	—	—	£1	£25
1939..	5,603,021	—	—	£5	£50
1940..	12,636,018	—	—	£4	£35
1941..	60,239,489	—	—	£1	£10
1942..	103,214,400	—	—	£1	£10
1943..	101,702,400	—	—	£1	£10
1944..	69,760,000	—	—	£1	£12
1945..	33,942,466	—	—	£5	£25
1946..	620,734	£6	£25	£240	£900
1948..	4,230,400	—	—	£7	£60
1949..	464,000	£6	£28	£250	£950
1950..	1,600,000	—	£2	£20	£140
1950 Proof	17,513	—	—	—	£25
1951..	1,184,000	—	£4	£35	£170
1951 Proof...................................	20,000	—	—	—	£25
1952..	25,494,400	—	—	—	£12

George VI "Thrift" design of the nickel brass 3d

ELIZABETH II (1952–2022)

1953..	30,618,000	—	—	—	£1
1953 Proof	40,000	—	—	—	£12
1954..	41,720,000	—	—	—	£5
1955..	41,075,200	—	—	—	£5
1956..	36,801,600	—	—	—	£6
1957..	24,294,500	—	—	—	£6
1958..	20,504,000	—	—	—	£9
1959..	28,499,200	—	—	—	£6
1960..	83,078,400	—	—	—	£2
1961..	41,102,400	—	—	—	£1
1962..	51,545,600	—	—	—	£1
1963..	39,482,866	—	—	—	£1
1964..	44,867,200	—	—	—	—
1965..	27,160,000	—	—	—	—
1966..	53,160,000	—	—	—	—
1967..	151,780,800	—	—	—	—
1970 Proof...................................	—				£6

TWO PENCES

DATE		F	VF	EF	UNC

GEORGE III (1760–1820)

		F	VF	EF	UNC
1797 "Cartwheel"	722,972	£35	£90	£450	£1200
1797 — Copper Proofs		Many types from £1000+			

VICTORIA (1837–1901)

For use in the Colonies
Small silver

		F	VF	EF	UNC
1838		£4	£10	£20	£45
1848		£4	£12	£20	£50

Earlier issues of the small silver two pences are listed in the Maundy section.

THREE-HALFPENCES

WILLIAM IV (1830–37)

For use in the Colonies

	F	VF	EF	UNC
1834	£6	£18	£40	£100
1835	£10	£25	£75	£210
1835 over 4	£6	£16	£40	£115
1836	£8	£18	£50	£125
1837	£15	£40	£120	£350

VICTORIA (1837–1901)

For use in the Colonies

	F	VF	EF	UNC
1838	£6	£15	£35	£100
1839	£6	£15	£35	£100
1840	£8	£20	£60	£160
1841	£6	£15	£40	£90
1842	£6	£18	£50	£115
1843	£6	£15	£40	£90
1860	£12	£30	£100	£225
1862	£18	£40	£110	£275

PENNIES

The earlier small silver pennies are included in the Maundy oddments section.

GEORGE III (1760–1820)

Note: Mintage figures are from an on-line thesis by Sue Tungate, Birmingham University, October 2011 (information supplied by Dennis Onions).

Soho Mint
1797 "Cartwheel" type,

		F	VF	EF	UNC
10 laurel leaves	43,969,204	£25	£60	£320	£1000
Numerous proofs in different metals are known for this issue—all are rare.					
1797 — 11 laurel leaves	incl. above	£25	£60	£320	£1000
1806 (34mm)	19,355,480	£7	£20	£85	£300
1807	11,290,168	£7	£20	£85	£300
1808	—				Unique

GEORGE IV (1820–30)

		F	VF	EF	UNC
1825	1,075,200	£18	£45	£275	£700
1826 (varieties)	5,913,600	£18	£45	£275	£700
1826 Proof	—	—	—	—	£1200
1827	1,451,520	£300	£1000	£5000	—

George III "Cartwheel" penny reverse. The obverse is as the two pence above.

DATE	MINTAGE	F	VF	EF	UNC

WILLIAM IV (1830–37)

DATE	MINTAGE	F	VF	EF	UNC
1831 (varieties)	806,400	£30	£75	£425	£1250
1831 Proof	—	—	—	—	£1500
1834	322,560	£32	£75	£425	£1350
1837	174,720	£70	£210	£800	£3000

VICTORIA (1837–1901)

YOUNG HEAD ISSUES
Copper

DATE	MINTAGE	F	VF	EF	UNC
1839 Proof	unrecorded	—	—	—	£3500
1841	913,920	£10	£50	£300	£875
1841 No colon after REG	incl. above	£8	£20	£175	£550
1843	483,840	£100	£375	£2000	£5000
1844	215,040	£12	£30	£200	£625
1844 Proofs exist	—		Extremely rare		
1845	322,560	£15	£35	£270	£800
1846	483,840	£15	£25	£240	£750
1846 FID: DEF colon spaced	incl. above	£15	£25	£240	£750
1846 FID:DEF colon close	incl. above	£16	£30	£240	£800
1847	430,080	£12	£25	£200	£600
1848	161,280	£12	£25	£175	£575
1848/7 final 8 over 7	incl. above	£9	£22	£160	£500
1848/6 final 8 over 6	incl. above	£20	£120	£525	—
1849	268,800	£225	£600	£2500	—
1851	268,800	£15	£45	£220	£800
1853	1,021,440	£7	£15	£100	£200
1853 Proof	—	—	—	—	£3500
1854	6,720,000	£8	£22	£120	£260
1854/3 4 over 3	incl. above	£15	£50	£200	—
1855	5,273,856	£8	£20	£120	£300
1856 Plain trident close colon DEF:	1,212,288	£110	£250	£1100	£3000
1856 Orn trident far colon DEF:	—	£120	£270	£1100	£3200
1856 Proofs exists	—		Extremely rare		
1857 Plain trident	752,640	£7	£18	£100	£330
1857 Ornamental trident	incl. above	£6	£18	£90	£350
1858/7 final 8 over 7	incl. above	£7	£18	£90	£350
1858/6 final 8 over 6	—	£40	£120	£550	—
1858/3 final 8 over 3	incl. above	£25	£90	£400	—
1858	1,599,040	£7	£16	£100	£375
1859	1,075,200	£10	£28	£180	£525
1860/59	32,256	£900	£2200	£4000	£7000

Note all are 60/59. All have a prominent die flan under Victoria's chin.

Victoria copper penny

Bronze
Prices of bronze Victoria Young "bun" head pennies are for the common types. There are many known varieties which are listed in detail in other more specialised publications. Prices for coins in mint with full lustre will be considerably higher.

DATE	MINTAGE	F	VF	EF	UNC
1860 Beaded border	5,053,440	£40	£100	£250	£1000
1860 Toothed border	incl. above	£10	£30	£80	£400
1860 — Piedfort flan	—		Extremely rare		
1861	36,449,280	£8	£15	£55	£375
1862	50,534,400	£8	£15	£55	£350
1862 8 over 6	incl. above		Extremely rare		
1863	28,062,720	£8	£15	£55	£325
1863 Die no below date	incl. above		Extremely rare		
1864 Plain 4	3,440,640	£30	£175	£700	£3500
1864 Crosslet 4	incl. above	£35	£185	£800	£4000
1865	8,601,600	£8	£20	£60	£400
1865/3 5 over 3	incl. above	£50	£160	£600	—
1866	9,999,360	£8	£25	£80	£500
1867	5,483,520	£8	£25	£150	£900
1868	1,182,720	£20	£80	£300	£2400
1869	2,580,480	£150	£500	£2000	£6000
1870	5,695,022	£18	£50	£200	£800
1871	1,290,318	£45	£150	£500	£2500
1872	8,494,572	£8	£25	£80	£325

Victoria Young or "Bun" head bronze penny

DATE	MINTAGE	F	VF	EF	UNC
1873	8,494,200	£8	£25	£80	£325
1874	5,621,865	£8	£25	£80	£325
1874 H	6,666,240	£8	£25	£80	£380
1874 Later (older) bust	incl. above	£18	£50	£130	£575
1875	10,691,040	£8	£25	£75	£350
1875 H	752,640	£35	£125	£950	£2500
1876 H	11,074,560	£8	£15	£65	£375
1877	9,624,747	£8	£15	£65	£375
1878	2,764,470	£8	£15	£65	£375
1879	7,666,476	£6	£18	£60	£375
1880	3,000,831	£6	£18	£60	£360
1881	2,302,362	£8	£18	£60	£325
1881 H	3,763,200	£12	£20	£65	£350
1882 H	7,526,400	£8	£18	£60	£325
1882 no H	—		Extremely Rare		
1883	6,237,438	£8	£18	£65	£275
1884	11,702,802	£8	£20	£65	£275
1885	7,145,862	£8	£18	£60	£275
1886	6,087,759	£8	£18	£60	£275
1887	5,315,085	£8	£18	£60	£275
1888	5,125,020	£8	£18	£65	£300
1889	12,559,737	£8	£18	£55	£400
1890	15,330,840	£8	£18	£55	£275
1891	17,885,961	£8	£15	£55	£275
1892	10,501,671	£10	£20	£100	£300
1893	8,161,737	£8	£15	£55	£275
1893 3 over 2	—	£90	£250	£375	£600
1894	3,883,452	£15	£45	£160	£550

Victoria Old head

OLD HEAD ISSUES

1895 Trident 2mm from P(ENNY)	5,395,830	£20	£90	£300	£850
1895 Trident 1mm from P	incl. above	—	£2	£18	£75
1896	24,147,156	—	£2	£18	£65
1897	20,756,620	—	£2	£15	£60
1897 Raised dot after O of ONE (O·NE)		£150	£275	£900	—
1898	14,296,836	—	£3	£18	£65
1899	26,441,069	—	£3	£16	£60
1900	31,778,109	—	£3	£16	£45
1901	22,205,568	—	£3	£10	£30

EDWARD VII (1901–10)

1902	26,976,768	—	£1	£8	£30
1902 "Low tide" to sea line	incl. above	£4	£15	£75	£250
1903	21,415,296	—	£3	£15	£90
1904	12,913,152	—	£4	£25	£200
1905	17,783,808	—	£3	£15	£85
1906	37,989,504	—	£3	£15	£75
1907	47,322,240	—	£3	£15	£75
1908	31,506,048	—	£3	£18	£140
1909	19,617,024	—	£3	£20	£175
1910	29,549,184	—	£3	£15	£65

Edward VII

GEORGE V (1910–36)

1911	23,079,168	—	£3	£12	£65
1912	48,306,048	—	£3	£12	£65
1912 H next to date	16,800,000	—	£4	£40	£250
1913	65,497,812	—	£3	£15	£80
1914	50,820,997	—	£3	£18	£85
1915	47,310,807	—	£3	£20	£90
1916	86,411,165	—	£3	£15	£65
1917	107,905,436	—	£3	£15	£60
1918	84,227,372	—	£3	£12	£55
1918 H	3,660,800	£1	£15	£150	£700
1918 KN	incl. above	£8	£80	£600	£2500
1919	113,761,090	—	£2	£15	£55
1919 H	5,209,600	£1	£20	£275	£1100
1919 KN	incl. above	£15	£120	£800	£3200
1920	124,693,485	—	£2	£12	£30
1921	129,717,693	—	£2	£12	£40
1922	16,346,711	—	£3	£28	£160
1922 with reverse of 1927	Unknown			Very rare	

George V

173

DATE	MINTAGE	F	VF	EF	UNC
1926	4,498,519	—	£6	£25	£150
1926 Modified effigy	incl above	£25	£150	£800	£2700
1927	60,989,561	—	£2	£10	£45
1928	50,178,00	—	£2	£10	£40
1929	49,132,800	—	£2	£10	£45
1930	29,097,600	—	£2	£20	£80
1931	19,843,200	—	£2	£10	£55
1932	8,277,600	—	£2	£15	£110
1933			Only 7 examples known		
1934	13,965,600	—	£2	£25	£110
1935	56,070,000	—		£2	£15
1936	154,296,000			£2	£12

George VI

GEORGE VI (1936–52)

	MINTAGE	F	VF	EF	UNC
1937	88,896,000	—	—	—	£4
1937 Proof	26,402	—	—	—	£15
1938	121,560,000	—	—	—	£6
1939	55,560,000	—	—	—	£15
1940	42,284,400	—	—	£8	£25
1944 Mint Dark	42,600,000	—	—	—	£8
1945 Mint Dark	79,531,200	—	—	—	£8
1946 Mint Dark	66,855,600	—	—	—	£8
1947	52,220,400	—	—	—	£5
1948	63,961,200	—	—	—	£5
1949	14,324,400	—	—	—	£8
1950	240,000	£8	£16	£30	£50
1950 Proof	17,513	—	—	—	£25
1951	120,000	£20	£28	£50	£75
1951 Proof	20,000	—	—	—	£40

ELIZABETH II (1952–2022)

	MINTAGE	F	VF	EF	UNC
1953	1,308,400	—	—	£2	£5
1953 Proof	40,000	—	—	—	£10
1954			Only one known		
1961	48,313,400	—	—	—	£2
1962	143,308,600	—	—	—	50p
1963	125,235,600	—	—	—	50p
1964	153,294,000	—	—	—	50p
1965	121,310,400	—	—	—	50p
1966	165,739,200	—	—	—	50p
1967	654,564,000	—	—	—	—
1970 Proof	—				£8

Later issues are included in the Decimal section.

Elizabeth II

HALFPENNIES

CHARLES II (1660–85)

		F	VF	EF	UNC
1672		£70	£300	£1400	—
1672 CRAOLVS error			Extremely rare		
1673		£70	£300	£1350	—
1673 CRAOLVS error			Extremely rare		
1673 No rev. stop		£100	£600	—	—
1673 No stops on obv.			Extremely rare		
1675		£65	£500	£1500	—
1675 No stops on obv.		£80	£550	—	—
1675/3 5 over 3		£175	£650	—	—

JAMES II (1685–88)

Tin (with copper plug)

		F	VF	EF	UNC
1685		£250	£750	£4000	—
1686		£300	£750	£4200	—
1687		£325	£800	£4000	—

Charles II

DATE	F	VF	EF	UNC

WILLIAM & MARY (1688–94)

Tin (with copper plug)

	F	VF	EF	UNC
1689 Small draped busts, edge dated.............		Extremely rare		
1690 Large cuirassed busts, edge dated.........	£200	£750	£3500	—
1691 — date on edge and in exergue..............	£180	£700	£3200	—
1692 — —	£200	£750	£3400	—

Copper

	F	VF	EF	UNC
1694 Large cuirassed busts, date in exergue	£80	£300	£1300	—
1694 — — GVLIEMVS error		Extremely rare		
1694 — — MΛRIΛ error		Extremely rare		
1694 — — No stops on rev.		Extremely rare		

Copper halfpenny of William & Mary

WILLIAM III (1694–1702)

	F	VF	EF	UNC
1695 *First issue* (date in exergue).....................	£50	£220	£1200	—
1695 — No stop after BRITANNIA on rev.		Extremely rare		
1696 —	£40	£180	£1000	—
1696 — TERTVS error		Extremely rare		
1697 —	£50	£180	£1000	—
1697 — No stop after TERTIVS on obv.	£55	£325	—	—
1698 —	£50	£220	£1100	—
1698 *Second issue* (date in legend)	£55	£200	—	—
1698 — No stop after date................................	£50	£200	—	—
1699 —	£55	£220	£1100	—
1699 — No stop after date................................	£250	—	—	—
1699 *Third issue* (date in exergue) (Britannia with right hand on knee)......................................	£40	£200	£900	—
1699 — No stop after date................................		Extremely rare		
1699 — BRITΛNNIΛ error	£225	—	—	—
1699 — TERTVS error		Extremely rare		
1699 — No stop on rev....................................		Extremely rare		
1699 — No stops on obv..................................	£90	£375	—	—
1700 —	£50	£200	£1000	—
1700 — No stops on obv..................................	£100	£375	—	—
1700 — No stops after GVLIELMUS	£100	£375	—	—
1700 — BRITVANNIA error..............................		Extremely rare		
1700 — GVIELMS error..................................	£100	£350	—	—
1700 — GVLIEEMVS error..............................	£100	£350	—	—
1701 —	£50	£200	£1000	—
1701 — BRITΛNNIΛ error	£80	£300	—	—
1701 — No stops on obv..................................		Extremely rare		
1701 — inverted As for Vs...............................	£90	£350	—	—

William III first issue

GEORGE I (1714–27)

	F	VF	EF	UNC
1717 *"Dump" issue*...	£50	£250	£850	—
1718 —	£40	£225	£800	—
1719 — Patterns			Rare	
1719 *Second issue*	£40	£200	£850	—
1720 —	£35	£160	£700	—
1721 —	£35	£150	£700	—
1721 — Stop after date....................................	£45	£160	—	—
1722 —	£35	£140	£650	—
1722 — inverted A for V on obv.		Extremely rare		
1723 —	£35	£160	£650	—
1723 — No stop on rev....................................	£110	£500	—	—
1724 —	£40	£160	£650	—

GEORGE II (1727–60)

	F	VF	EF	UNC
1729 *Young head*..	£30	£100	£470	—
1729 — No stop on rev....................................	£30	£100	£470	—
1730 —	£22	£100	£475	—
1730 — GEOGIVS error..................................	£80	£250	£850	—
1730 — Stop after date....................................	£30	£130	£475	—
1730 — No stop after REX on obv.	£35	£160	£500	—
1731 —	£25	£120	£450	—

George I "Dump" type

DATE	MINTAGE	F	VF	EF	UNC
1731 — No rev. stop		£28	£125	£450	—
1732 —		£25	£110	£450	—
1732 — No rev. stop		£28	£140	£500	—
1733 —		£25	£100	£475	—
1734/3 — 4 over 3		£35	£220	—	—
1734 — No stop on obv.		£35	£220	—	—
1735 —		£24	£90	£450	—
1736 —		£24	£90	£450	—
1737 —		£24	£95	£500	—
1738 —		£24	£90	£400	—
1739 —		£20	£70	£375	—
1740 Old head		£20	£75	£350	—
1742 —		£20	£75	£350	—
1742/0 — 2 over 0		£25	£150	£500	—
1743 —		£18	£75	£380	—
1744 —		£18	£75	£390	—
1745 —		£18	£75	£400	—
1746 —		£18	£75	£350	—
1747 —		£18	£75	£350	—
1748 —		£18	£75	£350	—
1749 —		£18	£75	£350	—
1750 —		£18	£75	£350	—
1751 —		£18	£75	£350	—
1752 —		£18	£75	£350	—
1753 —		£18	£75	£350	—
1754 —		£18	£75	£350	—

George II "Old" head

GEORGE III (1760–1820)

First type—Royal Mint

1770		£18	£50	£300	—
1770 No stop on rev.		£25	£70	£350	—
1771		£12	£50	£300	—
1771 No stop on rev.		£20	£65	£300	—
1772 Error GEORIVS		£80	£250	£850	—
1772		£12	£50	£250	—
1772 No stop on rev		£20	£65	£280	—
1773		£10	£45	£280	—
1773 No stop after REX		£35	£100	£425	—
1773 No stop on rev.		£20	£70	£300	—
1774		£12	£40	£230	—
1775		£12	£40	£230	—

Second type—Soho Mint

1799	42,481,116	£5	£12	£55	£120

Third type

1806	87,993,526	£5	£12	£60	£110
1807	41,394,384	£5	£12	£60	£110

George III second "Soho" type

GEORGE IV (1820–30)

1825	215,040	£12	£45	£190	£400
1826 (varieties)	9,031,630	£12	£45	£190	£400
1826 Proof	—	—	—	—	£800
1827	5,376,000	£12	£45	£160	£375

WILLIAM IV (1830–37)

1831	806,400	£12	£30	£130	£325
1831 Proof	—	—	—	—	£850
1834	537,600	£12	£30	£130	£325
1837	349,440	£12	£30	£130	£325

VICTORIA (1837–1901)

Copper

1838	456,960	£8	£20	£80	£320

William IV

DATE	MINTAGE	F	VF	EF	UNC
1839 Proof	268,800	—	—	—	£1100
1841	1,075,200	£6	£18	£70	£275
1843	967,680	£50	£100	£300	£1100
1844	1,075,200	£12	£40	£180	£400
1845	1,075,200	£275	£600	£2300	—
1846	860,160	£12	25	£85	£280
1847	725,640	£12	22	£85	£280
1848	322,560	£12	25	£80	£280
1848/7 final 8 OVER 7	incl. above	£15	£35	£110	£300
1851	215,040	£7	£18	£80	£300
1852	637,056	£10	22	£90	£300
1853	1,559,040	£5	£10	£40	£120
1853/2 3 over 2	incl. above	£15	£30	£60	£275
1853 Proof	—	—	—	—	£1300
1854	12,354,048	£5	£9	£40	£160
1855	1,455,837	£5	£9	£40	£160
1856	1,942,080	£12	28	£90	£350
1857	1,820,720	£6	£18	£50	£175
1858	2,472,960	£5	£12	£50	£160
1858/7 final 8 over 7	incl. above	£5	£12	£50	£160
1858/6 final 8 over 6	incl. above	£5	£12	£50	£175
1859	1,290,240	£8	25	£80	£300
1859/8 9 over 8	incl. above	£8	25	£70	£325
1860	unrecorded	£1800	£3500	£7000	£12500

Victoria copper halfpenny

Bronze

1860 Beaded border	6,630,400	£3	£10	£50	£200
1860 Toothed border		£4	£12	£70	£300
1861	54,118,400	£4	£10	£60	£200
1862 Die letter A, B or C to left of lighthouse				Extremely rare	
1862	61,107,200	£3	£9	£55	£180
1863	15,948,800	£3	£9	£75	£175
1864	537,600	£3	£12	£70	£250
1865	8,064,000	£4	£18	£80	£325
1865/3 5 over 3	incl. above	£50	£120	£450	—
1866	2,508,800	£5	£15	£70	£300
1867	2,508,800	£5	£15	£65	£280
1868	3,046,400	£5	£15	£75	£320
1869	3,225,600	£30	£100	£400	£1200
1870	4,350,739	£5	£15	£60	£260
1871	1,075,280	£60	£100	£500	£1600
1872	4,659,410	£4	£10	£50	£220
1873	3,404,880	£4	£10	£50	£220
1874	1,347,655	£6	25	£110	£350
1874 H	5,017,600	£3	£10	£60	£270
1875	5,430,815	£3	£8	£60	£220
1875 H	1,254,400	£5	£12	£60	£240
1876 H	5,809,600	£5	£12	£75	£300
1877	5,209,505	£3	£10	£60	£200
1878	1,425,535	£6	£20	£100	£375
1878 Wide date		£100	£200	£550	—
1879	3,582,545	£3	£10	£40	£200
1880	2,423,465	£4	£12	£60	£210
1881	2,007,515	£4	£12	£50	£180
1881 H	1,792,000	£3	£10	£50	£220
1882 H	4,480,000	£3	£10	£50	£240
1883	3,000,725	£3	£12	£60	£260
1884	6,989,580	£3	£10	£45	£175
1885	8,600,574	£3	£10	£45	£175
1886	8,586,155	£3	£10	£45	£175
1887	10,701,305	£3	£10	£45	£175
1888	6,814,670	£3	£10	£45	£175
1889	7,748,234	£3	£10	£45	£175

Victoria bronze halfpenny

DATE	MINTAGE	F	VF	EF	UNC
1889/8 9 over 8	incl. above	£30	£60	£250	—
1890...................................	11,254,235	£3	£10	£45	£130
1891...................................	13,192,260	£3	£10	£40	£130
1892...................................	2,478,335	£3	£10	£50	£160
1893...................................	7,229,344	£3	£10	£40	£150
1894...................................	1,767,635	£6	£14	£85	£200
OLD HEAD ISSUES					
1895	3,032,154	£2	£8	£25	£85
1896...................................	9,142,500	£1	£4	£10	£55
1897...................................	8,690,315	£1	£4	£10	£55
1898...................................	8,595,180	£1	£5	£12	£65
1899...................................	12,108,001	£1	£4	£10	£50
1900...................................	13,805,190	£1	£4	£10	£40
1901...................................	11,127,360	£1	£3	£8	£35

Victoria bronze
Old head
halfpenny

EDWARD VII (1901–10)

1902...................................	13,672,960	£2	£4	£8	£30
1902 "Low tide"...................	incl. above	£22	£90	£180	£450
1903...................................	11,450,880	£2	£5	£20	£80
1904...................................	8,131,200	£2	£6	£25	£110
1905...................................	10,124,800	£2	£5	£20	£80
1906...................................	16,849,280	£2	£5	£25	£90
1907...................................	16,849,280	£2	£5	£20	£90
1908...................................	16,620,800	£2	£5	£20	£90
1909...................................	8,279,040	£2	£5	£20	£90
1910...................................	10,769,920	£2	£5	£20	£90

GEORGE V (1910–36)

1911...................................	12,570,880	£1	£4	£15	£40
1912...................................	21,185,920	£1	£3	£15	£35
1913...................................	17,476,480	£1	£3	£15	£40
1914...................................	20,289,111	£1	£3	£15	£40
1915...................................	21,563,040	£2	£3	£20	£55
1916...................................	39,386,143	£1	£2	£15	£40
1917...................................	38,245,436	£1	£2	£15	£35
1918...................................	22,321,072	£1	£2	£15	£35
1919...................................	28,104,001	£1	£2	£15	£35
1920...................................	35,146,793	£1	£2	£15	£40
1921...................................	28,027,293	£1	£2	£15	£40
1922...................................	10,734,964	£1	£4	£25	£45
1923...................................	12,266,282	£1	£2	£15	£35
1924...................................	13,971,038	£1	£2	£15	£30
1925...................................	12,216,123	—	£2	£15	£30
1925 Modified effigy................	incl. above	£4	£10	£50	£90
1926...................................	6,172,306	—	£2	£10	£40
1927...................................	15,589,622	—	£2	£10	£40
1928...................................	20,935,200	—	£2	£8	£35
1929...................................	25,680,000	—	£2	£8	£35
1930...................................	12,532,800	—	£2	£8	£35
1931...................................	16,137,600	—	£2	£8	£35
1932...................................	14,448,000	—	£2	£8	£35
1933...................................	10,560,000	—	£2	£8	£35
1934...................................	7,704,000	—	£2	£12	£50
1935...................................	12,180,000	—	£1	£6	£20
1936...................................	23,008,800	—	£1	£5	£15

Edward VII

George V

GEORGE VI (1936–52)

1937...................................	24,504,000	—	—	£1	£5
1937 Proof.............................	26,402	—	—	—	£25
1938...................................	40,320,000	—	—	£1	£6
1939...................................	28,924,800	—	—	£1	£5
1940...................................	32,162,400	—	—	£4	£15

DATE	MINTAGE	F	VF	EF	UNC
1941	45,120,000	—	—	£1	£8
1942	71,908,800	—	—	£1	£5
1943	76,200,000	—	—	£1	£5
1944	81,840,000	—	—	£1	£5
1945	57,000,000	—	—	£1	£5
1946	22,725,600	—	—	£1	£6
1947	21,266,400	—	—	£1	£6
1948	26,947,200	—	—	£1	£4
1949	24,744,000	—	—	£1	£4
1950	24,153,600	—	—	£1	£5
1950 Proof	17,513	—	—	—	£18
1951	14,868,000	—	—	£1	£6
1951 Proof	20,000	—	—	—	£18
1952	33,784,000	—	—	£1	£4

George VI

ELIZABETH II (1952–2022)

DATE	MINTAGE	F	VF	EF	UNC
1953	8,926,366	—	—	—	£1
1953 Proof	40,000	—	—	—	£4
1954	19,375,000	—	—	—	£3
1955	18,799,200	—	—	—	£3
1956	21,799,200	—	—	—	£3
1957	43,684,800	—	—	—	£1
1957 Calm sea	incl. above	—	—	£10	£30
1958	62,318,400	—	—	—	£1
1959	79,176,000	—	—	—	£1
1960	41,340,000	—	—	—	£1
1962	41,779,200	—	—	—	£1
1963	45,036,000	—	—	—	20p
1964	78,583,200	—	—	—	20p
1965	98,083,200	—	—	—	20p
1966	95,289,600	—	—	—	20p
1967	146,491,200	—	—	—	10p
1970 Proof	—				£5

Elizabeth II

Later issues are included in the Decimal section.

FARTHINGS

DATE		F	VF	EF	UNC

OLIVER CROMWELL

Undated (copper) Draped bust, shield rev. Variations   Extremely rare

CHARLES II (1660–85)

Copper

	F	VF	EF	UNC
1672	£45	£240	£800	—
1672 No stops on obv.	£70	£300	£900	
1673	£50	£260	£900	—
1673 CAROLA for CAROLO error	£150	£550		
1673 No stops on obv.			Extremely rare	
1673 No stop on rev.			Extremely rare	
1674	£55	£300	£900	—
1675	£50	£250	£875	—
1675 No stop after CAROLVS			Extremely rare	
1679	£60	£300	£1000	—
1679 No stop on rev.	£70	£350	—	—
Tin (with copper plug)				
1684 with date on edge	£250	£900	—	—
1685 —			Extremely rare	

Charles II copper issue

DATE	F	VF	EF	UNC

JAMES II (1685–88)

Tin (with copper plug)

	F	VF	EF	UNC
1684 Cuirassed bust			Extremely rare	
1685 —	£180	£700	£3000	—
1686 —	£190	£700	£3000	—
1687 —			Extremely rare	
1687 Draped bust..	£250	£1000	—	—

WILLIAM & MARY (1688–94)

Tin (with copper plug)

	F	VF	EF	UNC
1689 Small draped busts	£300	£700	—	—
1689) — with edge date 1690			Extremely rare	
1690 Large cuirassed busts	£170	£650	£3000	—
1690 — with edge date 1689			Extremely rare	
1691 —	£200	£700	—	—
1692 —	£200	£700	£3000	—

Copper

	F	VF	EF	UNC
1694 —	£70	£275	£1000	—
1694 — No stop after MARIΛ...........................			Extremely rare	
1694 — No stop on obv....................................			Extremely rare	
1694 — No stop on rev.....................................			Extremely rare	
1694 — Unbarred As in BRITANNIA.................			Extremely rare	

WILLIAM III (1694–1702)

	F	VF	EF	UNC
1695 *First issue* (date in exergue).....................	£45	£250	£900	—
1695 — GVLIELMV error			Extremely rare	
1696 —	£45	£225	£900	—
1697 —	£45	£225	£900	—
1697 — GVLIELMS error			Extremely rare	
1698 —	£220	£800	—	—
1698 *Second issue* (date in legend)	£50	£275	£950	—
1699 *First issue*	£40	£250	£900	—
1699 *Second issue*	£40	£250	£900	—
1699 — No stop after date...............................	£50	£350	—	—
1700 *First issue*	£35	£150	£750	—
1700 — error RRITANNIA			Extremely rare	

ANNE (1702–14)

	F	VF	EF	UNC
1714 pattern	£425	£700	£1500	—

GEORGE I (1714–27)

	F	VF	EF	UNC
1717 First small "Dump" issue	£200	£650	£1250	—
1718 1 Known				—
1719 Second issue..	£40	£175	£600	—
1719 — No stop on rev.....................................	£70	£375	—	—
1719 — No stops on obv..................................	£70	£325	—	—
1720 —	£30	£170	£600	—
1721 —	£25	£170	£600	—
1721/0 — Last 1 over 0	£40	£180	—	—
1722 —	£35	£150	£575	—
1723 —	£35	£150	£600	—
1723 — R over sideways R in REX			Extremely rare	
1724 —	£35	£160	£600	—

GEORGE II (1727–60)

	F	VF	EF	UNC
1730 Young head	£15	£60	£350	—
1731 —	£15	£60	£350	—
1732 —	£15	£75	£400	—
1733 —	£15	£80	£425	—
1734 —	£15	£65	£400	—
1734 — No stop on obv.	£30	£110	£450	—

James II tin issue with central copper plug

William III

Queen Anne

George I, first "Dump" type

George I second type

DATE	MINTAGE	F	VF	EF	UNC
1735 —		£15	£70	£400	—
1735 — 3 over 5		£25	£120	£450	—
1736 —		£15	£60	£400	—
1737 —		£15	£60	£370	—
1739 —		£15	£60	£370	—
1741 Old Head		£15	£50	£350	—
1744 —		£15	£50	£350	—
1746 —		£15	£50	£330	—
1746 — V over LL in GEORGIVS			Extremely rare		
1749 —		£16	£65	£340	—
1750 —		£15	£55	£290	—
1754 —		£10	£30	£200	—
1754 — 4 over 0		£28	£120	£350	—

*George II
Young head*

GEORGE III (1760–1820)

DATE	MINTAGE	F	VF	EF	UNC
1771 *First* (London) issue		£20	£65	£300	—
1773 —		£12	£40	£220	—
1773 — No stop on rev		£20	£60	£250	—
1773 — No stop after REX		£25	£80	£320	—
1774 —		£12	£40	£220	—
1775 —		£12	£40	£220	—
1797 *Second* (Soho Mint) issue			Patterns only		
1799 *Third* (Soho Mint) issue	4,225,428	£2	£8	£40	£100
1806 *Fourth* (Soho Mint) issue	4,833,768	£2	£8	£40	£100
1807 —	1,075,200	£2	£8	£40	£100

*George III,
third (Soho
Mint) issue*

GEORGE IV (1820–30)

DATE	MINTAGE	F	VF	EF	UNC
1821 *First bust* (laureate, draped), first reverse (date in exergue)	2,688,000	£4	£12	£60	£140
1822 —	5,924,350	£4	£12	£60	£140
1823 —	2,365,440	£4	£12	£60	£140
1823 I for 1 in date	incl. above	£25	£75	£300	£600
1825 —	4,300,800	£4	£12	£60	£150
1826 —	6,666,240	£4	£12	£60	£140
1826 *Second bust* (couped, date below), second reverse (ornament in exergue)	incl. above	£4	£12	£60	£140
1826 — Proof	—	—	—	—	£750
1827 —	2,365,440	£4	£12	£60	£170
1828 —	2,365,440	£4	£12	£60	£170
1829 —	1,505,280	£4	£12	£60	£170
1830 —	2,365,440	£4	£12	£60	£170

*George III,
fourth (Soho
Mint) issue*

WILLIAM IV (1830–37)

DATE	MINTAGE	F	VF	EF	UNC
1831	2,688,000	£5	£12	£50	£150
1831 Proof	—	—	—	—	£800
1834	1,935,360	£5	£12	£50	£160
1835	1.720,320	£5	£15	£55	£170
1836	1,290.240	£5	£12	£55	£160
1837	3.010,560	£5	£12	£55	£200

William IV

VICTORIA (1837–1901)

FIRST YOUNG HEAD (COPPER) ISSUES

DATE	MINTAGE	F	VF	EF	UNC
1838	591,360	£5	£15	£60	£200
1839	4,300,800	£5	£15	£60	£200
1839 Proof	—	—	—	—	£900
1840	3,010,560	£4	£15	£50	£180
1841	1,720,320	£4	£15	£50	£190
1841 Proof			Extremely rare		
1842	1,290,240	£12	£40	£140	£400
1843	4,085,760	£5	£14	£40	£190

George IV

DATE	MINTAGE	F	VF	EF	UNC
1843 I for 1 in date		£90	£425	£900	—
1844...	430,080	£80	£220	£800	£2200
1845...	3,225,600	£6	£10	£50	£175
1846...	2,580,480	£7	£20	£55	£220
1847...	3,879,720	£5	£12	£50	£175
1848...	1,290,240	£5	£12	£50	£175
1849...	645,120	£50	£100	£375	£900
1850...	430,080	£5	£10	£40	£170
1851...	1,935,360	£8	£20	£80	£250
1851 D over sideways D in DEI ...	incl. above	£80	£110	£450	—
1852...	822,528	£10	£20	£80	£275
1853...	1,028,628	£4	£7	£30	£70
1853 Proof..................................	—	—	—	—	£1400
1854...	6,504,960	£4	£10	£35	£110
1855...	3,440,640	£4	£10	£35	£120
1856...	1,771,392	£10	£25	£80	£300
1856 R over E in VICTORIA.........	incl. above	£20	£50	£300	—
1857...	1,075,200	£4	£10	£40	£110
1858...	1,720,320	£4	£10	£40	£110
1859...	1,290,240	£12	£25	£90	£350
1860...	unrecorded	£1600	£3750	£7000	—

Victoria Young Head first (copper) issue

SECOND YOUNG OR "BUN" HEAD (BRONZE) ISSUES

DATE	MINTAGE	F	VF	EF	UNC
1860 Toothed border...................	2,867,200	£2	£5	£40	£120
1860 Beaded border	incl. above	£3	£7	£40	£130
1860 Toothed/Beaded border mule	incl. above			Extremely rare	
1861...	8,601,600	£2	£5	£35	£120
1862...	14,336,000	£1	£5	£35	£120
1862 Large 8 in date...................	incl. above			Extremely rare	
1863...	1,433,600	£45	£90	£300	£725
1864...	2,508,800	£1	£5	£30	£110
1865...	4,659,200	£1	£5	£30	£110
1865 5 over 2.............................	incl. above	£10	£20	£70	—
1866...	3,584,000	£1	£5	£25	£120
1867...	5,017,600	£1	£5	£25	£120
1868...	4,851,210	£1	£5	£25	£135
1869...	3,225,600	£3	£10	£55	£200
1872...	2,150,400	£1	£5	£25	£110
1873...	3,225,620	£1	£5	£25	£110
1874 H.......................................	3,584,000	£1	£5	£25	£130
1874 H both Gs over sideways G	incl. above	£150	£350	£1000	—
1875...	712,760	£4	£12	£40	£150
1875 H.......................................	6,092,800	£1	£5	£20	£85
1876 H.......................................	1,175,200	£5	£18	£70	£240
1878...	4,008,540	£1	£4	£20	£80
1879...	3,977,180	£1	£4	£20	£80
1880...	1,842,710	£1	£4	£20	£80
1881...	3,494,670	£1	£4	£20	£80
1881 H.......................................	1,792,000	£1	£4	£20	£80
1882 H.......................................	1,792,000	£1	£5	£25	£100
1883...	1,128,680	£5	£20	£70	£170
1884...	5,782,000	£1	£4	£20	£60
1885...	5,442,308	£1	£4	£20	£60
1886...	7.707,790	£1	£4	£20	£60
1887...	1,340,800	£1	£4	£20	£60
1888...	1,887,250	£1	£4	£20	£60
1890...	2,133,070	£1	£4	£20	£60
1891...	4,959,690	£1	£4	£20	£60
1892...	887,240	£4	£15	£60	£170
1893...	3,904,320	£1	£4	£20	£60
1894...	2,396,770	£1	£4	£25	£70
1895...	2,852,852	£10	£30	£90	£300

Victoria Young Head second (bronze) issue

DATE	MINTAGE	F	VF	EF	UNC
OLD HEAD ISSUES					
1895 Bright finish	incl. above	£1	£2	£16	£40
1896 —	3,668,610	£1	£2	£16	£30
1897 —	4,579,800	£1	£2	£16	£30
1897 Dark finish	incl. above	£1	£2	£16	£30
1898 —	4,010,080	£1	£2	£16	£30
1899 —	3,864,616	£1	£2	£16	£30
1900 —	5,969,317	£1	£2	£16	£30
1901 —	8,016,460	£1	£2	£10	£28

Victoria
Old head

EDWARD VII (1901–10)

DATE	MINTAGE	F	VF	EF	UNC
1902	5,125,120	50p	£1	£10	£16
1903	5,331,200	50p	£1	£12	£20
1904	3,628,800	£2	£5	£20	£45
1905	4,076,800	£1	£2	£12	£40
1906	5,340,160	50p	£1	£12	£30
1907	4,399,360	50p	£1	£10	£25
1908	4,264,960	50p	£1	£10	£25
1909	8,852,480	50p	£1	£10	£25
1910	2,298,400	£5	£10	£30	£80

Edward VII

GEORGE V (1910–36)

DATE	MINTAGE	F	VF	EF	UNC
1911	5,196,800	50p	£1	£6	£14
1912	7,669,760	50p	£1	£8	£14
1913	4,184,320	50p	£1	£6	£14
1914	6,126,988	50p	£1	£5	£14
1915	7,129,255	50p	£1	£5	£16
1916	10,993,325	50p	£1	£5	£14
1917	21,434,844	25p	50p	£4	£10
1918	19,362,818	25p	50p	£4	£10
1919	15,089,425	25p	50p	£4	£10
1920	11,480,536	25p	50p	£4	£8
1921	9,469,097	25p	50p	£4	£8
1922	9,956,983	25p	50p	£4	£8
1923	8,034,457	25p	50p	£4	£8
1924	8,733,414	25p	50p	£4	£8
1925	12,634,697	25p	50p	£4	£8
1926 Modified effigy	9,792,397	25p	50p	£4	£8
1927	7,868,355	25p	50p	£4	£8
1928	11,625,600	25p	50p	£4	£8
1929	8,419,200	25p	50p	£4	£8
1930	4,195,200	25p	50p	£4	£8
1931	6,595,200	25p	50p	£4	£8
1932	9,292,800	25p	50p	£4	£8
1933	4,560,000	25p	50p	£4	£8
1934	3,052,800	25p	50p	£4	£8
1935	2.227,200	£1	£3	£12	£28
1936	9,734,400	25p	50p	£3	£6

George V

GEORGE VI (1936–52)

DATE	MINTAGE	F	VF	EF	UNC
1937	8,131,200	—	—	50p	£1
1937 Proof	26,402	—	—	—	£8
1938	7,449,600	—	—	£1	£6
1939	31,440,000	—	—	50p	£1
1940	18,360,000	—	—	50p	£1
1941	27,312,000	—	—	50p	£1
1942	28,857,600	—	—	50p	£1
1943	33,345,600	—	—	50p	£1
1944	25,137,600	—	—	50p	£1

George VI

DATE	MINTAGE	F	VF	EF	UNC
1945	23,736,000	—	—	50p	£1
1946	24,364,800	—	—	50p	£1
1947	14,745,600	—	—	50p	£1
1948	16,622,400	—	—	50p	£1
1949	8,424,000	—	—	50p	£1
1950	10,324,800	—	—	50p	£1
1950 Proof	17,513	—	—	50p	£8
1951	14,016,000	—	—	50p	£1
1951 Proof	20,000	—	—	50p	£8
1952	5,251,200	—	—	50p	£1

ELIZABETH II (1952–2022)

1953	6,131,037	—	—	—	£1
1953 Proof	40,000	—	—	—	£8
1954	6,566,400	—	—	—	£2
1955	5,779,200	—	—	—	£2
1956	1,996,800	—	£1	£2	£6

Elizabeth II

HALF FARTHINGS

DATE	MINTAGE	F	VF	EF	UNC

GEORGE IV (1820–30)

1828 (two different obverses) (issued for Ceylon)	7,680,000	£10	£22	£60	£225
1830 (large or small date) (issued for Ceylon)	8,766,320	£10	£22	£60	£225

WILLIAM IV (1830–37)

1837 (issued for Ceylon)	1,935,360	£25	£75	£200	£400

William IV

VICTORIA (1837–1901)

1839	2,042,880	£5	£10	£35	£100
1842	unrecorded	£4	£8	£30	£100
1843	3,440,640	£3	£6	£25	£70
1844	6,451,200	£3	£6	£15	£55
1844 E over N in REGINA	incl. above	£10	£45	£100	—
1847	3,010,560	£6	£12	£40	£130
1851	unrecorded	£6	£12	£40	£150
1851 5 over 0	unrecorded	£8	£20	£60	£180
1852	989,184	£6	£12	£45	£160
1853	955,224	£6	£15	£50	£200
1853 Proof	incl. above	—	—	—	£850
1854	677,376	£9	£30	£80	£220
1856	913,920	£9	£30	£80	£220
1868 Proof	unrecorded			Very Rare	

Victoria

THIRD FARTHINGS

DATE	MINTAGE	F	VF	EF	UNC

GEORGE IV (1820–30)

| 1827 (issued for Malta) | unrecorded | £8 | £20 | £50 | £125 |

WILLIAM IV (1830–37)

| 1835 (issued for Malta) | unrecorded | £8 | £24 | £55 | £160 |

George IV

VICTORIA (1837–1901)

1844 (issued for Malta)	1,301,040	£15	£35	£110	£250
1844 RE for REG	incl. above	£30	£70	£275	—
1866	576,000	£6	£15	£35	£75
1868	144,000	£6	£15	£35	£70
1876	162,000	£6	£15	£35	£90
1878	288,000	£6	£15	£35	£80
1881	144,000	£6	£15	£35	£80
1884	144,000	£6	£15	£35	£80
1885	288,000	£6	£15	£35	£80

EDWARD VII (1902–10)

| 1902 (issued for Malta) | 288,000 | £5 | £10 | £25 | £45 |

Victoria

GEORGE V (1911–36)

| 1913 (issued for Malta) | 288,000 | £5 | £10 | £25 | £45 |

QUARTER FARTHINGS

DATE	MINTAGE	F	VF	EF	UNC

VICTORIA (1837–1901)

1839 (issued for Ceylon)	3,840,000	£50	£80	£150	£300
1851 (issued for Ceylon)	2,215,680	£50	£80	£150	£300
1852 (issued for Ceylon)	unknown	£50	£80	£150	£300
1853 (issued for Ceylon)	unknown	£50	£80	£150	£325
1853 Proof	unknown	—	—	—	£1500

EMERGENCY ISSUES

DATE   F   VF   EF   UNC

GEORGE III (1760–1820)

To alleviate the shortage of circulating coinage during the Napoleonic Wars the Bank of England firstly authorised the countermarking of other countries' coins, enabling them to pass as English currency. The coins, countermarked with punches depicting the head of George III, were mostly Spanish American 8 reales of Charles III. Although this had limited success it was later decided to completely overstrike the coins with a new English design on both sides— specimens that still show traces of the original host coin's date are avidly sought after by collectors. This overstriking continued for a number of years although all the known coins are dated 1804. Finally, in 1811 the Bank of England issued silver tokens which continued up to 1816 when a completely new regal coinage was introduced.

DOLLAR
Oval countermark of George III

	F	VF	EF	UNC
On "Pillar" type 8 reales	£200	£850	£1500	—
°On "Portrait" type.............	£200	£400	£1250	—

Octagonal countermark of George III

	F	VF	EF	UNC
On "Portrait" type..............	£200	£750	£1400	—

HALF DOLLAR
Oval countermark of George III

	F	VF	EF	UNC
On "Portrait" type 4 reales	£200	£500	£1250	—

FIVE SHILLINGS OR ONE DOLLAR
These coins were overstruck on Spanish-American coins

	F	VF	EF
1804..................................	£150	£350	£750

— *With details of original coin still visible add from 10%.*

BANK OF ENGLAND TOKENS

THREE SHILLINGS

	F	VF	EF	UNC
1811 Draped bust..............	£35	£75	£275	—
1812 —	£35	£75	£300	—
1812 Laureate bust	£35	£65	£200	—
1813 —	£35	£65	£200	—
1814 —	£35	£65	£200	—
1815 —	£35	£65	£200	—
1816 —	£250	£600	£1850	—

ONE SHILLING AND SIXPENCE

	F	VF	EF	UNC
1811 Draped bust..............	£20	£50	£100	£250
1812 —	£20	£50	£100	£250
1812 Laureate bust	£20	£50	£100	£250
1812 Proof in platinum				Unique
1813 —	£20	£45	£75	£250
1813 Proof in platinum				Unique
1814 —	£20	£55	£75	£250
1815 —	£20	£55	£75	£250
1816 —	£20	£55	£75	£250

NINEPENCE
1812 Pattern (three types)   from £3000

MAUNDY SETS

DATE	F	VF	EF	UNC

CHARLES II (1660–85)

DATE	F	VF	EF	UNC
Undated	£250	£375	£825	—
1670	£250	£370	£800	—
1671	£270	£450	£850	—
1672	£245	£380	£750	—
1673	£225	£350	£720	—
1674	£225	£340	£735	—
1675	£220	£325	£715	—
1676	£240	£375	£770	—
1677	£195	£310	£690	—
1678	£295	£460	£840	—
1679	£225	£360	£775	—
1680	£225	£345	£730	—
1681	£255	£380	£775	—
1682	£230	£360	£725	—
1683	£230	£360	£750	—
1684	£255	£385	£780	—

JAMES II (1685–88)

DATE	F	VF	EF	UNC
1686	£240	£375	£760	—
1687	£235	£370	£750	—
1688	£265	£410	£780	—

WILLIAM & MARY (1688–94)

DATE	F	VF	EF	UNC
1689	£850	£1250	£1850	—
1691	£650	£900	£1500	—
1692	£700	£925	£1600	—
1693	£650	£900	£1750	—
1694	£470	£735	£1300	—

WILLIAM III (1694–1702)

DATE	F	VF	EF	UNC
1698	£245	£480	£850	—
1699	£495	£700	£1575	—
1700	£270	£490	£925	—
1701	£245	£450	£875	—

ANNE (1702–14)

DATE	F	VF	EF	UNC
1703	£230	£440	£775	—
1705	£250	£450	£775	—
1706	£200	£375	£680	—
1708	£625	£1000	£1825	—
1709	£250	£475	£850	—
1710	£280	£500	£825	—
1713	£250	£435	£750	—

Sets in contemporary dated boxes are usually worth a higher premium. For example approximately £30 can be added to sets from Victoria to George VI in contemporary undated boxes and above £40 for dated boxes.

GEORGE I (1714–27)

DATE	F	VF	EF	UNC
1723	£270	£460	£775	—
1727	£260	£4505	£760	—

GEORGE II (1727–60)

DATE	F	VF	EF	UNC
1729	£210	£325	£675	—
1731	£210	£335	£675	—
1732	£200	£320	£660	—
1735	£200	£320	£660	—
1737	£190	£325	£640	—
1739	£190	£320	£625	—
1740	£175	£300	£585	—
1743	£310	£445	£850	—
1746	£170	£300	£565	—
1760	£185	£325	£605	—

GEORGE III (1760–1820)

DATE	F	VF	EF	UNC
1763	£170	£290	£465	—
1763 Proof	—			£20000
1766	£215	£350	£550	—
1772	£185	£300	£525	—
1780	£235	£350	£650	—
1784	£190	£320	£500	—
1786	£195	£310	£515	—
1792 Wire	£275	£450	£650	£875
1795	£115	£200	£325	£405
1800	£115	£200	£300	£375
New Coinage				
1817	£150	£260	£305	£475
1818	£150	£245	£290	£465
1820	£145	£255	£300	£455

GEORGE IV (1820–30)

DATE	F	VF	EF	UNC
1822	—	£170	£245	£450
1823	—	£160	£255	£425
1824	—	£165	£260	£425
1825	—	£150	£250	£400
1826	—	£145	£245	£400
1827	—	£145	£255	£405
1828	—	£150	£250	£415
1828 Proof	—	—		£4100
1829	—	£150	£250	£395
1830	—	£150	£240	£390

WILLIAM IV (1830–37)

DATE	F	VF	EF	UNC
1831	—	£170	£280	£460
1831 Proof	—	—		£1800
1831 Proof Gold	—	—		£41000
1832	—	£205	£315	£480
1833	—	£170	£275	£425
1834	—	£175	£280	£450
1835	—	£160	£265	£415
1836	—	£175	£285	£440
1837	—	£200	£325	£485

DATE	MINTAGE	EF	UNC

VICTORIA (1837–1901)

YOUNG HEAD ISSUES

DATE	MINTAGE	EF	UNC
1838	4,158	£260	£435
1838 Proof	unrecorded		£3400
1838 Proof Gold			£40000
1839	4,125	£325	£575
1839 Proof	unrecorded	£700	£1900
1840	4,125	£300	£445
1841	2,574	£395	£680
1842	4,125	£425	£625
1843	4,158	£260	£425
1844	4,158	£345	£575
1845	4,158	£225	£415
1846	4,158	£495	£780
1847	4,158	£575	£1100
1848	4,158	£525	£1100
1849	4,158	£365	£550
1850	4,158	£250	£425
1851	4,158	£305	£475
1852	4,158	£600	£1150
1853	4,158	£625	£1100
1853 Proof	unrecorded		£2100
1854	4,158	£260	£400
1855	4,158	£300	£500
1856	4,158	£235	£375
1857	4,158	£265	£425
1858	4,158	£240	£375
1859	4,158	£215	£325
1860	4,158	£240	£375
1861	4,158	£205	£385
1862	4,158	£250	£425
1863	4,158	£270	£450
1864	4,158	£240	£345
1865	4,158	£240	£355
1866	4,158	£225	£340
1867	4,158	£220	£350
1867 Proof	unrecorded	—	£3100
1868	4,158	£200	£315
1869	4,158	£240	£395
1870	4,458	£190	£290
1871	4,488	£185	£280
1871 Proof	unrecorded	—	£3000
1872	4,328	£180	£280
1873	4,162	£180	£275
1874	4,488	£185	£275
1875	4,154	£180	£270
1876	4,488	£190	£275
1877	4,488	£180	£265
1878	4,488	£185	£265
1878 Proof	unrecorded	—	£2750
1879	4,488	£190	£245
1879 Proof	unrecorded	—	£2850
1880	4,488	£185	£250
1881	4,488	£180	£250
1881 Proof	unrecorded	—	£2500
1882	4,146	£215	£285
1882 Proof	unrecorded	—	£2650
1883	4,488	£160	£225
1884	4,488	£160	£225
1885	4,488	£160	£225
1886	4,488	£165	£225
1887	4,488	£180	£265

JUBILEE HEAD ISSUES

DATE	MINTAGE	EF	UNC
1888	4,488	£160	£235
1888 Proof	unrecorded	—	£2400
1889	4,488	£155	£245
1890	4,488	£160	£230
1891	4,488	£160	£230
1892	4,488	£170	£245

OLD HEAD ISSUES

DATE	MINTAGE	EF	UNC
1893	8,976	£115	£190
1894	8,976	£130	£225
1895	8,976	£120	£195
1896	8,976	£120	£195
1897	8,976	£120	£190
1898	8,976	£120	£195
1899	8,976	£125	£200
1900	8,976	£110	£185
1901	8,976	£110	£180

EDWARD VII (1902–10)

DATE	MINTAGE	EF	UNC
1902	8,976	£95	£175
1902 Matt proof	15,123	—	£215
1903	8,976	£100	£170
1904	8,976	£110	£180
1905	8,976	£110	£180
1906	8,800	£100	£170
1907	8,760	£100	£175
1908	8,769	£90	£165
1909	1,983	£175	£280
1910	1,440	£195	£290

GEORGE V (1911–36)

DATE	MINTAGE	EF	UNC
1911	1,786	£150	£250
1911 Proof	6,007	—	£425
1912	1,246	£160	£260
1913	1,228	£155	£260
1914	982	£205	£290
1915	1,293	£165	£270
1916	1,128	£160	£250
1917	1,237	£160	£250
1918	1,375	£165	£260
1919	1,258	£160	£260
1920	1,399	£160	£250
1921	1,386	£160	£255
1922	1,373	£165	£260
1923	1,430	£165	£270
1924	1,515	£165	£270
1925	1,438	£150	£245
1926	1,504	£150	£245
1927	1,647	£155	£255
1928	1,642	£165	£270
1929	1,761	£170	£270
1930	1,724	£150	£240
1931	1,759	£150	£240
1932	1,835	£145	£250
1933	1,872	£140	£240
1934	1,887	£140	£240
1935	1,928	£170	£255
1936	1,323	£225	£310

GEORGE VI (1936–52)

DATE	MINTAGE	EF	UNC
1937	1,325	£140	£175
1937 Proof	20,900	£140	£210
1938	1,275	£175	£255
1939	1,234	£180	£265
1940	1,277	£175	£255
1941	1,253	£180	£260
1942	1,231	£175	£255
1943	1,239	£175	£260
1944	1,259	£175	£260

DATE	MINTAGE	EF	UNC
1945	1,355	£170	£255
1946	1,365	£175	£255
1947	1,375	£185	£275
1948	1,385	£185	£280
1949	1,395	£190	£280
1950	1,405	£195	£285
1951	1,468	£195	£290
1952	1,012	£205	£305
1952 Proof (copper)			£17,000

ELIZABETH II (1952–2022)

DATE AND PLACE OF ISSUE	MINTAGE	UNC
1953 St. Paul's Cathedral	1,025	£1050
1953 Proof in gold	unrecorded	Ex. rare
1953 Proof Matt		Very rare
1954 Westminster Abbey	1,020	£200
1955 Southwark Cathedral	1,036	£200
1955 Proof Matt		£3300
1956 Westminster Abbey	1,088	£205
1957 St. Albans Cathedral	1,094	£205
1958 Westminster Abbey	1,100	£205
1959 St. George's Chapel, Windsor	1,106	£205
1960 Westminster Abbey	1,112	£205
1961 Rochester Cathedral	1,118	£205
1962 Westminster Abbey	1,125	£200
1963 Chelmsford Cathedral	1,131	£200
1964 Westminster Abbey	1,137	£200
1965 Canterbury Cathedral	1,143	£200
1966 Westminster Abbey	1,206	£205
1967 Durham Cathedral	986	£230
1968 Westminster Abbey	964	£240
1969 Selby Cathedral	1,002	£220
1970 Westminster Abbey	980	£235
1971 Tewkesbury Abbey	1,018	£215
1972 York Minster	1,026	£220
1973 Westminster Abbey	1,004	£215
1974 Salisbury Cathedral	1,042	£215
1975 Peterborough Cathedral	1,050	£215
1976 Hereford Cathedral	1,158	220
1977 Westminster Abbey	1,138	£240
1978 Carlisle Cathedral	1,178	£215
1979 Winchester Cathedral	1,188	£215
1980 Worcester Cathedral	1,198	£215
1981 Westminster Abbey	1,178	£215
1982 St David's Cathedral	1,218	£220

DATE AND PLACE OF ISSUE	MINTAGE	UNC
1983 Exeter Cathedral	1,228	£215
1984 Southwell Minster	1,238	£215
1985 Ripon Cathedral	1,248	£215
1986 Chichester Cathedral	1,378	£225
1987 Ely Cathedral	1,390	£225
1988 Lichfield Cathedral	1,402	£220
1989 Birmingham Cathedral	1,353	£220
1990 Newcastle Cathedral	1,523	£220
1991 Westminster Abbey	1,384	£220
1992 Chester Cathedral	1,424	£225
1993 Wells Cathedral	1,440	£225
1994 Truro Cathedral	1,433	£225
1995 Coventry Cathedral	1,466	£225
1996 Norwich Cathedral	1,629	£230
1997 Birmingham Cathedral	1,786	£230
1998 Portsmouth Cathedral	1,654	£230
1999 Bristol Cathedral	1,676	£235
2000 Lincoln Cathedral	1,686	£220
2000 Silver Proof	13,180	£195
2001 Westminster Abbey	1,132	£250
2002 Canterbury Cathedral	1,681	£215
2002 Gold Proof	2,002	£2350
2003 Gloucester Cathedral	1,608	£235
2004 Liverpool Cathedral	1,613	£240
2005 Wakefield Cathedral	1,685	£240
2006 Guildford Cathedral	1,937	£240
2006 Silver Proof	6,394	£195
2007 Manchester Cathedral	1,822	£295
2008 St Patrick's Cathedral (Armagh)	1,833	£685
2009 St. Edmundsbury Cathedral	1,602	£600
2010 Derby Cathedral	1,617	£550
2011 Westminster Abbey	1,734	£525
2012 York Minster	1,633	£600
2013 Christ Church Cathedral Oxford.	1,627	£640
2014 Blackburn Cathedral	1,693	£750
2015 Sheffield Cathedral	1,721	£650
2016 St. George's Chapel, Windsor	1,940	£625
2017 Leicester Cathedral	1,919	£700
2018 St. George's Chapel, Windsor	1,993	£725
2019 St. George's Chapel, Windsor	1,997	£750
2020 Service cancelled due to the Pandemic. Recipients received the coins in the post	2,010	£800
2021 Service cancelled. Recipients received the coins in the post	1,995	£800
2022 St. George's Chapel, Windsor	1,920	£850

Despite the decimalisation of the coinage in 1971, in keeping with ancient tradition the Royal Maundy sets are still made up of four silver coins (4p, 3p, 2p and 1p). The designs for the reverse of the coins are a crowned numeral in a wreath of oak leaves—basically the same design that has been used for Maundy coins since George IV.

MAUNDY ODDMENTS
SINGLE COINS

DATE	F	VF	EF

FOUR PENCE

CHARLES II (1660–85)

It is nowadays considered that the early small denomination silver coins 4d–1d were originally struck for the Maundy ceremony although undoubtedly many subsequently circulated as small change—therefore they are listed here under "Maundy silver single coins".

DATE	F	VF	EF
Undated..	£70	£130	£195
1670...	£70	£145	£235
1671...	£100	£200	£285
1672/1	£80	£125	£185
1673...	£75	£120	£180
1674...	£70	£115	£175
1674 7 over 6..................................	£75	£130	£205
1675...	£60	£110	£165
1675/4...	£75	£115	£190
1676...	£70	£100	£190
1676 7 over 6..................................	£80	£125	£205
1677...	£55	£95	£160
1678...	£55	£95	£160
1678 8 over 6..................................	£60	£100	£165
1678 8 over 7..................................	£65	£115	£175
1679...	£55	£95	£150
1680...	£55	£100	£160
1681...	£55	£110	£170
1681 B over R in HIB......................	£65	£130	£200
1682...	£60	£90	£180
1682/1...	£70	£100	£195
1683...	£60	£90	£180
1684...	£70	£120	£200
1684 4 over 3..................................	£85	£130	£215

Charles II

JAMES II (1685–88)

	F	VF	EF
1686...	£75	£120	£205
1686 Date over crown	£80	£130	£225
1687...	£70	£115	£185
1687 7 over 6..................................	£80	£115	£190
1687 8 over 7..................................	£75	£115	£200
1688...	£85	£125	£220
1688 1 over 8..................................	£110	£150	£230
1688/7	£85	£130	£225

WILLIAM & MARY (1688–94)

	F	VF	EF
1689...	£75	£135	£200
1689 GV below bust.........................	£80	£130	£210
1689 GVLEELMVS...........................	£140	£260	£335
1690...	£80	£135	£225
1690 6 over 5..................................	£95	£135	£230
1691...	£100	£145	£235
1691 1 over 0..................................	£90	£150	£230
1692...	£135	£195	£285
1692 MAR·IA	£215	£310	£400
1692 2 over 1..................................	£130	£160	£260
1693...	£135	£245	£360
1693 3 over 2..................................	£140	£255	£385
1694...	£95	£150	£225
1694 small lettering	£100	£160	£230

William & Mary

WILLIAM III (1694–1702)

	F	VF	EF
1697—Reported................................	—	—	—
1698...	£85	£150	£225
1699...	£75	£130	£210
1700...	£95	£160	£250
1701...	£90	£155	£235
1702...	£85	£140	£225

Queen Anne

DATE	F	VF	EF	UNC
ANNE (1702–14)				
1703	£90	£135	£225	—
1704	£70	£120	£185	—
1705	£145	£210	£295	—
1706	£80	£130	£185	—
1708	£80	£135	£210	—
1709	£80	£130	£205	—
1710	£60	£115	£165	—
1713	£80	£130	£195	—
GEORGE I (1714–27)				
1717	£80	£130	£190	—
1721	£80	£130	£185	—
1723	£95	£145	£220	—
1727	£95	£140	£230	—
GEORGE II (1727–60)				
1729	£75	£120	£180	—
1731	£70	£120	£170	—
1732	£70	£110	£170	—
1735	£65	£100	£165	—
1737	£70	£115	£170	—
1739	£60	£105	£160	—
1740	£55	£95	£145	—
1743	£140	£200	£310	—
1743 3 over 0	£150	£230	£330	—
1746	£55	£85	£140	—
1760	£65	£115	£160	—
GEORGE III (1760–1820)				
1763 Young head	£60	£95	£145	—
1763 Proof	—	—	Extremely rare	
1765	£450	£800	£1100	—
1766	£70	£115	£160	—
1770	£170	£270	£375	—
1772	£80	£130	£200	—
1776	£70	£130	£180	—
1780	£55	£100	£140	—
1784	£50	£95	£130	—
1786	£70	£120	£170	—
1792 Older head, Thin 4	£100	£180	£235	£325
1795	—	£55	£100	£140
1800	—	£50	£90	£130
1817 New coinage	—	£60	£100	£145
1818	—	£60	£95	£140
1820	—	£55	£95	£145
GEORGE IV (1820–30)				
1822	—	—	£95	£160
1823	—	—	£90	£150
1824	—	—	£80	£150
1826	—	—	£80	£140
1827	—	—	£80	£145
1828	—	—	£85	£140
1829	—	—	£80	£135
1830	—	—	£85	£140
WILLIAM IV (1830–37)				
1831–37	—	—	£80	£155
1831 Proof	—	—	£325	£495
VICTORIA (1837–1901)				
1838 Proof	—	—	—	£1000
1839 Proof	—	—	—	£525
1853 Proof	—	—	—	£725
1838–87 (Young Head)	—	—	£40	£60
1841	—	—	£50	£75
1888–92 (Jubilee Head)	—	—	£35	£55
1893–1901 (Old Head)	—	—	£30	£50

George I

George II

George III

George IV

Victoria

DATE	F	VF	EF	UNC

EDWARD VII (1901–10)

1902–08	–	–	£30	£45
1902 Proof	–	–	£35	£50
1909 & 1910	–	–	£60	£100

GEORGE V (1910–36)

1911–36	–	–	£45	£65
1911 Proof	–	–	£60	£85

GEORGE VI (1936–52)

1937–52	–	–	£50	£70
1937 Proof	–	–	£40	£60

ELIZABETH II (1952–2022)

1953	–	–	£210	£270
1954–85	–	–	£45	£75
1986–2007	–	–	£65	£85
2002 in Gold Proof	–	–	£525	£800
2008	–	–	–	£190
2009	–	–	–	£180
2010	–	–	–	£160
2011	–	–	–	£150
2012	–	–	–	£160
2013	–	–	–	£165
2014	–	–	–	£210
2015	–	–	–	£165
2016	–	–	–	£170
2017	–	–	–	£200
2018	–	–	–	£210
2019	–	–	–	£210
2020	–	–	–	£220
2021	–	–	–	£225
2022	–	–	–	£250

Elizabeth II

THREEPENCE

CHARLES II (1660–85)

Undated	£65	£120	£200	–
1670	£75	£125	£185	–
1671	£65	£125	£180	–
1671 GRVTIA	£80	£150	£245	–
1672	£80	£130	£195	–
1673	£70	£110	£175	–
1674	£70	£110	£175	–
1675	£70	£110	£180	–
1676	£75	£125	£220	–
1676 6 over 5	£85	£135	£235	–
1676 ERA for FRA	£110	£165	£250	–
1677	£65	£90	£165	–
1678	£55	£85	£135	–
1679	£50	£80	£135	–
1679 O/A in CAROLVS	£120	£170	£265	–
1680	£65	£100	£175	–
1681	£70	£110	£190	–
1682/1	£65	£110	£175	–
1682	£65	£115	£175	–
1683	£65	£110	£170	–
1684	£65	£110	£175	–
1684/3	£75	£115	£180	–

Charles II

JAMES II (1685–88)

1685	£80	£125	£200	–
1685 Struck on fourpence flan	£145	£220	£325	–
1686	£80	£110	£175	–
1687	£80	£110	£170	–
1687 7 over 6	£85	£115	£175	–
1688	£85	£130	£215	–
1688 8 over 7	£85	£135	£225	–

James II

William & Mary

DATE	F	VF	EF	UNC

WILLIAM & MARY (1688–94)

DATE	F	VF	EF	UNC
1689	£80	£125	£190	—
1689 No stop on reverse	£85	£135	£200	—
1689 LMV over MVS (obverse)	£120	£160	£240	—
1690	£90	£135	£195	—
1690 9 over 6	£95	£145	£215	—
1690 6 over 5	£90	£140	£210	—
1691 First bust	£390	£590	£850	—
1691 Second bust	£250	£375	£525	—
1692	£120	£170	£265	—
1692 G below bust	£115	£175	£270	—
1692 GV below bust	£115	£170	£270	—
1692 GVL below bust	£115	£170	£275	—
1693	£150	£220	£300	—
1693 3 over 2	£155	£245	£310	—
1694	£95	£120	£200	—
1694 MARIΛ	£140	£180	£265	—
1694 GV below bust	£100	£135	£210	—
1694 GVL below bust	£100	£140	£220	—

William III

WILLIAM III (1694–1702)

DATE	F	VF	EF	UNC
1698	£80	£145	£225	—
1699	£70	£130	£195	—
1700	£80	£145	£220	—
1701 Small lettering	£80	£140	£215	—
1701 GBA instead of GRA	£90	£150	£225	—
1701 Large lettering	£90	£145	£210	—

ANNE (1702–14)

DATE	F	VF	EF	UNC
1703	£80	£125	£205	—
1703 7 of date above crown	£90	£150	£225	—
1704	£65	£95	£170	—
1705	£85	£140	£220	—
1706	£65	£100	£170	—
1707	£60	£100	£155	—
1708	£70	£125	£185	—
1708 8 over 7	£70	£110	£190	—
1709	£70	£145	£195	—
1710	£55	£105	£150	—
1713	£75	£135	£190	—

Queen Anne

GEORGE I (1714–27)

DATE	F	VF	EF	UNC
1717	£70	£115	£170	—
1721	£70	£115	£170	—
1723	£80	£135	£200	—
1727	£75	£130	£195	—

George I

GEORGE II (1727–60)

DATE	F	VF	EF	UNC
1729	£60	£105	£150	—
1731	£60	£105	£155	—
1731 Small lettering	£70	£115	£175	—
1732	£55	£100	£155	—
1732 Stop over head	£65	£110	£170	—
1735	£70	£110	£175	—
1737	£65	£100	£165	—
1739	£65	£100	£175	—
1740	£55	£95	£145	—
1743 Small and large lettering	£65	£95	£160	—
1743 Stop over head	£65	£95	£165	—
1746	£45	£80	£135	—
1746 6 over 3	£55	£85	£150	—
1760	£60	£90	£155	—

George II

GEORGE III (1760–1820)

DATE	F	VF	EF	UNC
1762	£30	£50	£70	—
1763	£30	£50	£75	—
1763 Proof	—	—	Extremely rare	

DATE	F	VF	EF	UNC
1765	£375	£550	£825	—
1766	£70	£110	£185	—
1770	£85	£130	£210	—
1772	£60	£90	£120	—
1780	£60	£90	£125	—
1784	£80	£115	£195	—
1786	£80	£110	£190	—
1792	£105	£160	£245	£340
1795	—	£40	£80	£120
1800	—	£45	£85	£130
1817	—	£55	£95	£170
1818	—	£55	£95	£170
1820	—	£55	£95	£170

GEORGE IV (1820–30)

1822	—	—	£85	£170
1823	—	—	£75	£160
1824	—	—	£75	£170
1825–30	—	—	£75	£165

WILLIAM IV (1830–37)

1831 Proof	—	—	£380	£650
1831	—	—	£110	£175
1832	—	—	£120	£215
1833–1836	—	—	£85	£170
1837	—	—	£105	£195

VICTORIA (1837–1901)

1838	—	—	£120	£225
1838 Proof	—	—	—	£1700
1839	—	—	£225	£400
1839 Proof	—	—	—	£585
1840	—	—	£160	£275
1841	—	—	£315	£550
1842	—	—	£290	£455
1843	—	—	£130	£235
1844	—	—	£215	£365
1845	—	—	£85	£165
1846	—	—	£415	£725
1847	—	—	£475	£875
1848	—	—	£450	£850
1849	—	—	£215	£350
1850	—	—	£115	£225
1851	—	—	£175	£325
1852	—	—	£475	£875
1853	—	—	£475	£875
1853 Proof	—	—	—	£1100
1854	—	—	£155	£300
1855	—	—	£180	£365
1856	—	—	£100	£220
1857	—	—	£150	£285
1858	—	—	£120	£235
1859	—	—	£100	£195
1860	—	—	£135	£250
1861	—	—	£140	£245
1862	—	—	£155	£275
1863	—	—	£190	£305
1864	—	—	£135	£245
1865	—	—	£135	£260
1866	—	—	£125	£250
1867	—	—	£125	£235
1868	—	—	£115	£215
1869	—	—	£170	£290
1870	—	—	£105	£195
1871	—	—	£100	£185
1872	—	—	£95	£180
1873	—	—	£90	£170
1874	—	—	£90	£185

George III

George IV

William IV

Victoria

DATE	F	VF	EF	UNC
1875	—	—	£85	£175
1876	—	—	£85	£175
1877	—	—	£80	£170
1878	—	—	£85	£175
1879	—	—	£85	£170
1880	—	—	£80	£160
1881	—	—	£80	£160
1882	—	—	£145	£230
1883	—	—	£75	£155
1884	—	—	£75	£155
1885	—	—	£70	£140
1886	—	—	£70	£135
1887	—	—	£85	£170
1888–1892 (Jubilee Head)	—	—	£60	£115
1893–1901 (Old Head)	—	—	£45	£70

Edward VII

EDWARD VII (1901–10)

	F	VF	EF	UNC
1902	—	—	£30	£50
1902 Proof	—	—	—	£60
1903	—	—	£40	£80
1904	—	—	£55	£100
1905	—	—	£55	£90
1906	—	—	£45	£85
1907	—	—	£45	£85
1908	—	—	£40	£75
1909	—	—	£80	£130
1910	—	—	£90	£145

GEORGE V (1910–36)

	F	VF	EF	UNC
1911–34	—	—	£60	£85
1911 Proof	—	—	—	£125
1935	—	—	£70	£110
1936	—	—	£80	£140

George V

GEORGE VI (1936–52)

	F	VF	EF	UNC
1937–52	—	—	£55	£85
1937 Proof	—	—	—	£70

ELIZABETH II (1952–2022)

	F	VF	EF	UNC
1953	—	—	£200	£305
1954–85	—	—	£45	£75
1986–2007	—	—	£55	£80
2002 In gold (proof)	—	—	—	£625
2008	—	—	—	£155
2009	—	—	—	£145
2010	—	—	—	£150
2011	—	—	—	£130
2012	—	—	—	£140
2013	—	—	—	£140
2014	—	—	—	£170
2015	—	—	—	£155
2016	—	—	—	£150
2017	—	—	—	£170
2018	—	—	—	£180
2019	—	—	—	£190
2020	—	—	—	£200
2021	—	—	—	£210
2022	—	—	—	£215

Elizabeth

TWOPENCE

CHARLES II (1660–85)

	F	VF	EF	UNC
Undated	£60	£95	£155	—
1668	£65	£100	£170	—
1670	£55	£80	£150	—
1671	£55	£90	£150	—
1672	£55	£90	£150	—
1672/1	£65	£110	£160	—
1673	£55	£85	£155	—
1674	£60	£95	£150	—

Charles II

DATE	F	VF	EF	UNC
1675..	£50	£90	£140	—
1676..	£55	£95	£155	—
1677..	£45	£85	£135	—
1678..	£40	£80	£130	—
1679..	£45	£75	£125	—
1679 HIB over FRA.................	£50	£90	£140	—
1680..	£50	£85	£135	—
1680 over 79.........................	£45	£80	£130	—
1681..	£55	£80	£135	—
1682..	£65	£90	£165	—
1682/1 ERA for FRA.............	£80	£125	£225	—
1683..	£60	£100	£160	—
1683 over 2...........................	£60	£110	£180	—
1684..	£55	£95	£155	—

James II

JAMES II (1685–88)

	F	VF	EF	UNC
1686..	£60	£100	£160	—
1686 reads IACOBVS............	£90	£135	£230	—
1687..	£65	£100	£165	—
1687 ERA for FRA	£80	£130	£225	—
1688..	£55	£90	£155	—
1688/7	£65	£90	£170	—

WILLIAM & MARY (1688–94)

	F	VF	EF	UNC
1689..	£70	£105	£180	—
1691..	£65	£95	£150	—
1692..	£80	£135	£205	—
1693..	£75	£120	£195	—
1693 GV below bust..............	£85	£125	£195	—
1693/2	£70	£110	£180	—
1694..	£55	£90	£150	—
1694 MARLA error.................	£90	£150	£255	—
1694 GVLI under bust	£70	£110	£195	—
1694 GVL under bust	£65	£110	£190	—
1694/3	£65	£115	£200	—

William & Mary

WILLIAM III (1694–1702)

	F	VF	EF	UNC
1698..	£70	£120	£185	—
1699..	£55	£100	£150	—
1700..	£75	£120	£190	—
1701..	£70	£115	£175	—

William III

ANNE (1702–14)

	F	VF	EF	UNC
1703..	£70	£115	£190	—
1704..	£50	£80	£135	—
1704 No stops on obverse	£60	£90	£170	—
1705..	£65	£105	£165	—
1706..	£80	£130	£195	—
1707..	£50	£85	£150	—
1708..	£75	£110	£180	—
1709..	£85	£145	£225	—
1710..	£50	£80	£115	—
1713..	£75	£120	£200	—

Queen Anne

GEORGE I (1714–27)

	F	VF	EF	UNC
1717..	£50	£85	£135	—
1721..	£50	£90	£130	—
1723..	£70	£105	£170	—
1726..	£55	£85	£135	—
1727..	£65	£100	£155	—

GEORGE II (1727–60)

	F	VF	EF	UNC
1729..	£50	£90	£125	—
1731..	£50	£90	£125	—
1732..	£50	£90	£120	—
1735..	£55	£85	£120	—

George II

DATE	F	VF	EF	UNC
1737	£45	£85	£120	—
1739	£45	£80	£120	—
1740	£45	£75	£115	—
1743	£40	£70	£110	—
1743/0	£45	£80	£115	—
1746	£40	£70	£95	—
1756	£35	£65	£95	—
1759	£35	£70	£95	—
1760	£50	£75	£100	—

George III

GEORGE III (1760–1820)

	F	VF	EF	UNC
1763	£45	£70	£95	—
1763 Proof			Extremely rare	
1765	£370	£475	£675	—
1766	£45	£75	£95	—
1772	£40	£70	£95	—
1772 second 7 over 6	£40	£80	£105	—
1780	£40	£70	£95	—
1784	£40	£70	£90	—
1786	£50	£80	£95	—
1792	—	£90	£140	£200
1795	—	£35	£60	£85
1800	—	£35	£70	£85
1817	—	£40	£70	£90
1818	—	£40	£70	£90
1820	—	£45	£80	£100

George IV

GEORGE IV (1820–30)

	F	VF	EF	UNC
1822–30	—	—	£40	£70
1825 TRITANNIAR	—	—	£65	£125
1826 TRITANNIAR	—	—	£65	£125

WILLIAM IV (1830–37)

	F	VF	EF	UNC
1831–37	—	—	£45	£80
1831 Proof	—	—	£140	£250

VICTORIA (1837–1901)

William IV

	F	VF	EF	UNC
1838–87 (Young Head)	—	—	£30	£55
1859 BEITANNIAR	—	—	£80	£135
1861 6 over 1	—	—	£40	£80
1888–92 (Jubilee Head)	—	—	£35	£55
1893–1901 (Old Head)	—	—	£30	£45
1838 Proof	—	—	—	£475
1839 Proof	—	—	—	£325
1853 Proof	—	—	—	£350

EDWARD VII (1901–10)

	F	VF	EF	UNC
1902–08	—	—	£25	£35
1902 Proof	—	—	£30	£55
1909	—	—	£45	£80
1910	—	—	£50	£90

Victoria

GEORGE V (1910–36)

	F	VF	EF	UNC
1911–34	—	—	£35	£60
1911 Proof	—	—	£45	£80
1935	—	—	£40	£65
1936	—	—	£50	£80

GEORGE VI (1936–52)

	F	VF	EF	UNC
1937–47	—	—	£40	£65
1937 Proof	—	—	£35	£60
1948–52	—	—	£45	£70

DATE	F	VF	EF	UNC

ELIZABETH II (1952–2022)

DATE	F	VF	EF	UNC
1953	—	—	£145	£215
1954–85	—	—	£40	£55
1986–2007	—	—	£40	£70
2002 Gold Proof	—	—	—	£425
2008	—	—	—	£125
2009	—	—	—	£115
2010	—	—	—	£110
2011	—	—	—	£90
2012	—	—	—	£115
2013	—	—	—	£120
2014	—	—	—	£140
2015	—	—	—	£115
2016	—	—	—	£135
2017	—	—	—	£170
2018	—	—	—	£170
2019	—	—	—	£175
2020	—	—	—	£185
2021	—	—	—	£175
2022	—	—	—	£180

Elizabeth

PENNY

CHARLES II (1660–85)

DATE	F	VF	EF	UNC
Undated	£80	£125	£200	—
1670	£75	£120	£180	—
1671	£75	£120	£175	—
1672/1	£70	£120	£175	—
1673	£70	£120	£170	—
1674	£70	£120	£175	—
1674 Ɔratia (error)	£105	£160	£250	—
1675	£70	£120	£170	—
1675 Ɔratia (error)	£105	£165	£260	—
1676	£85	£125	£190	—
1676 Ɔratia (error)	£115	£170	£275	—
1677	£60	£110	£165	—
1677 Ɔratia (error)	£95	£140	£230	—
1678	£150	£255	£365	—
1678 Ɔratia (error)	£175	£280	£380	—
1679	£85	£125	£210	—
1680	£85	£120	£200	—
1680 on 2d flan	£130	£250	£300	—
1681	£110	£155	£230	—
1682	£75	£125	£195	—
1682 ERA for FRA	£90	£150	£245	—
1683	£85	£120	£195	—
1683/1	£85	£150	£225	—
1684	£130	£220	£270	—
1684/3	£135	£225	£280	—

Charles II

JAMES II (1685–88)

DATE	F	VF	EF	UNC
1685	£75	£120	£180	—
1686	£80	£120	£180	—
1687	£80	£130	£185	—
1687 7 over 6	£90	£135	£195	—
1687/8	£85	£130	£190	—
1688	£65	£115	£170	—
1688/7	£75	£115	£190	—

James II

WILLIAM & MARY (1688–94)

DATE	F	VF	EF	UNC
1689	£450	£680	£950	—
1689 MΛRIΛ	£470	£690	£925	—
1689 GVIELMVS (Error)	£450	£700	£950	—
1690	£85	£155	£235	—
1691	£85	£160	£230	—
1691/0	£85	£165	£250	—

William & Mary

DATE	F	VF	EF	UNC
1692	£230	£325	£515	—
1692/1	£240	£345	£540	—
1693	£115	£185	£270	—
1694	£80	£140	£230	—
1694 HI for HIB	£125	£180	£275	—
1694 No stops on obverse	£100	£160	£240	—

WILLIAM III (1694–1702)

1698	£90	£150	£200	—
1698 HI. BREX (Error)	£110	£165	£270	—
1698 IRA for FRA	£100	£160	£210	—
1699	£250	£390	£525	—
1700	£95	£165	£225	—
1701	£90	£140	£210	—

William III

ANNE (1702–14)

1703	£85	£130	£195	—
1705	£75	£115	£180	—
1706	£70	£95	£165	—
1708	£425	£525	£750	—
1709	£60	£95	£150	—
1710	£140	£200	£295	—
1713/0	£85	£135	£190	—

Anne

GEORGE I (1714–27)

1716	£50	£90	£115	—
1718	£50	£90	£115	—
1720	£55	£95	£125	—
1720 HIPEX (Error)	£75	£120	£205	—
1723	£75	£125	£180	—
1725	£50	£85	£130	—
1726	£50	£85	£125	—
1727	£70	£120	£170	—

George I

GEORGE II (1727–60)

1729	£45	£85	£125	—
1731	£50	£85	£125	—
1732	£50	£80	£120	—
1735	£40	£70	£100	—
1737	£40	£70	£105	—
1739	£40	£70	£100	—
1740	£45	£70	£100	—
1743	£40	£65	£95	—
1746	£45	£80	£115	—
1746/3	£50	£80	£120	—
1750	£30	£55	£85	—
1752	£30	£55	£85	—
1752/0	£35	£60	£90	—
1753	£30	£55	£85	—
1754	£30	£55	£85	—
1755	£30	£55	£85	—
1756	£30	£55	£80	—
1757	£30	£55	£80	—
1757 No colon after Gratia	£45	£75	£90	—
1758	£30	£60	£85	—
1759	£35	£60	£80	—
1760	£40	£75	£95	—

GEORGE III (1760–1820)

1763	£55	£75	£115	—
1763 Proof	—	—	Extremely rare	
1766	£40	£70	£90	—
1770	£60	£95	£120	—
1772	£40	£70	£85	—
1780	£115	£160	£220	—
1781	£35	£60	£85	—

George III

DATE	F	VF	EF	UNC
1784	£45	£65	£90	—
1786	£40	£60	£90	—
1792	£40	£70	£105	£140
1795	—	£25	£50	£70
1800	—	£25	£45	£70
1817	—	£30	£45	£70
1818	—	£30	£45	£70
1820	—	£35	£50	£75

George IV

GEORGE IV (1820–30)

	F	VF	EF	UNC
1822–30	—	—	£40	£60

William IV

WILLIAM IV (1830–37)

	F	VF	EF	UNC
1831–37	—	—	£45	£65
1831 Proof	—	—	£175	£250

VICTORIA (1837–1901)

	F	VF	EF	UNC
1838–87 (Young Head)	—	—	£30	£45
1888–92 (Jubilee Head)	—	—	£30	£40
1893–1901 (Old Head)	—	—	£25	£30
1838 Proof	—	—	—	£270
1839 Proof	—	—	—	£190
1853 Proof	—	—	—	£225

Victoria

EDWARD VII (1901–10)

	F	VF	EF	UNC
1902–08	—	—	£20	£30
1902 Proof	—	—	£30	£40
1909	—	—	£45	£75
1910	—	—	£55	£90

Edward VII

GEORGE V (1910–36)

	F	VF	EF	UNC
1911–14	—	—	£45	£75
1911 Proof	—	—	£50	£100
1915	—	—	£50	£85
1916–19	—	—	£45	£80
1920	—	—	£45	£80
1921–28	—	—	£45	£75
1929	—	—	£45	£80
1930–34	—	—	£40	£75
1935	—	—	£45	£80
1936	—	—	£55	£85

George V

GEORGE VI (1936–52)

	F	VF	EF	UNC
1937–40	—	—	£50	£75
1937 Proof	—	—	£45	£80
1941	—	—	£55	£85
1942–47	—	—	£50	£85
1948–52	—	—	£60	£90

ELIZABETH II (1952–2022)

	F	VF	EF	UNC
1953	—	—	£300	£450
1965–85	—	—	£45	£75
1986–2007	—	—	£50	£80
2002 Proof in gold	—	—	—	£425
2008	—	—	—	£145
2009	—	—	—	£140
2010	—	—	—	£120
2011	—	—	—	£110
2012	—	—	—	£130
2013	—	—	—	£125
2014	—	—	—	£150
2015	—	—	—	£120
2016	—	—	—	£135
2017	—	—	—	£150
2018	—	—	—	£155
2019	—	—	—	£160
2020	—	—	—	£170
2021	—	—	—	£180
2022	—	—	—	£190

Elizabeth II

DECIMAL COINAGE

Since the introduction of the Decimal system in the UK, many coins have been issued for circulation purposes in vast quantities. In addition, from 1982 sets of coins to non-proof standard, and including examples of each denomination found in circulation, have been issued each year. For 1982 and 1983 they were to "circulation" standard and described as "Uncirculated". Individual coins from these sets are annotated "Unc" on the lists that follow. From 1984 to the present day they were described as "Brilliant Uncirculated" (BU on the lists), and from around 1986 these coins are generally distinguishable from coins intended for circulation. They were from then produced by the Proof Coin Division of the Royal Mint (rather than by the Coin Production Room which produces circulation-standard coins). For completeness however, we have included the annotations Unc and BU back to 1982, the start year for these sets.

It is emphasised that the abbreviations Unc and BU in the left-hand columns adjacent to the date refer to an advertising description or to an engineering production standard, not the preservation condition or grade of the coin concerned. Where no such annotation appears adjacent to the date, the coin is circulation-standard for issue as such.

We have included the "mintage" figures for circulation coins down to Half Penny where known. The figure given for the 1997 Two Pounds, is considerably less than the actual quantity struck, because many were scrapped before issue due to failing an electrical conductivity test. Where a coin is available in uncirculated grade at, or just above, face value no price has been quoted. NOTE: *For many of the later issues, especially the latest issue precious metal coins, the price quoted is the issue price.*

Base metal Proof issues of circulation coinage (£2 or £1 to one or half penny) of the decimal series were only issued, as with Unc or BU, as part of Year Sets, but many of these sets have been broken down into individual coins, hence the appearance of the latter on the market.

The lists do not attempt to give details of die varieties, except where there was an obvious intention to change the appearance of a coin, e.g. 1992 20p.

2008 saw new reverses and modified obverses for all circulation denominations from the One Pound to the One Penny. All seven denominations were put into circulation dated 2008, all with both the old and the new reverses.

The circulation standard mintage figures have mainly been kindly supplied by courtesy of the Head of Historical Services and the Department of UK Circulation Coin Sales, both at the Royal Mint.

KILO COINS
(gold and silver)

The UK's first-ever Kilo coins were struck to commemorate the 2012 Olympic Games in 0.999 fine gold and 0.999 fine silver. These and subsequent issues are listed in detail below, and all were struck to proof standard and to similar metallic standards. They are also listed under their relevant "series" where appropriate. In addition some issues were struck in 2, 5 or 10 kilos but these are not specifically listed here.

DATE	FACE VALUE	AUTHORISED ISSUE QTY.	NO. ISSUED	ISSUE PRICE
2012 Olympic Gold;				
obverse: 1998 Ian Rank-Broadley's Royal Portrait				
reverse: Sir Anthony Caro's "Individual Endeavour" £1,000		60	20	£100,000
2012 Olympic Silver;				
obverse: 1998 Rank-Broadley Royal Portrait				
reverse: Tom Phillip's "Team Endeavour".. £500		2,912	910	£3,000
2012 Diamond Jubilee Gold;				
obverse: Queen in Garter Robes (Rank-Broadley)				
reverse: Royal Arms (Buckingham Palace Gates) £1,000		21	21	£60,000
2012 Diamond Jubilee Silver;				
obverse: Queen in Garter Robes (Rank-Broadley)				
reverse: Royal Arms (Buckingham Palace Gates) £500		1,250	206	£2,600
2013 Coronation Anniversary Gold;				
obverse: 1998 Rank-Broadley Royal Portrait				
reverse: John Bergdahl's Coronation Regalia £1,000		27	13	£50,000
2013 Coronation Anniversary Silver;				
obverse: 1998 Rank-Broadley Royal Portrait				
reverse: John Bergdahl's Coronation Regalia £500		400	301	£2,600
2013 Royal Christening Gold;				
obverse: 1998 Rank-Broadley Royal Portrait				
reverse: John Bergdahl's Lily Font £1,000		22	19	£48,000
2013 Royal Christening Silver;				
obverse: 1998 Rank-Broadley Royal Portrait				
reverse: John Bergdahl's Lily Font £500		500	194	£2,600
2014 First World War Outbreak Gold;				
obverse: 1998 Rank-Broadley Royal Portrait				
reverse: Sandle's Hostile Environment.. £1,000		25	10	£45,000
2014 First World War Outbreak Silver;				
obverse: 1998 Rank-Broadley Royal Portrait				
reverse: Sandle's Hostile Environment... £500		430	165	£2,000
2015 50th Anniversary of Death of Sir Winston Churchill Gold;				
obverse: 1998 Rank-Broadley Royal Portrait				
reverse: Millner's image of Churchill... £1,000		15	9	£45,000
2015 50th Anniversary of Death of Sir Winston Churchill Silver;				
obverse: 1998 Rank-Broadley Royal Portrait				
reverse: Milner's image of Churchill £500		170	117	£2,000
2015 The Longest Reign Gold;				
obverse: Butler Royal Portrait				
reverse: Stephen Taylor Queen's Portraits £1,000		15	15	£42,500
2016 The Longest Reign Silver;				
obverse: Butler Royal Portrait				
reverse: Stephen Taylor Queen's Portraits £500		320	278	£2,000
2016 Year of the Monkey Gold;				
obverse: Clark Royal Portrait				
reverse: Wuon-Gean Ho's Rhesus monkey £1,000		8	—	£42,500
2016 Year of the Monkey Silver;				
obverse: Butler Royal Portrait				
everse: Wuon-Gean Ho's Rhesus monkey.. £500		88	—	£2,000
2016 Queen's 90th Birthday Gold;				
obverse: Clark Royal Portrait				
reverse: Christopher Hobbs Floral design..................................... £1,000		25	15	—
2016 Queen's 90th Birthday Silver;				
obverse: Clark Royal Portrait				
reverse: Christopher Hobbs Floral design.. £500		450	447	£2,000

DATE	FACE VALUE	AUTHORISED ISSUE QTY.	NO. ISSUED	ISSUE PRICE
2017 The Queen's Sapphire Accession Jubilee Silver; obverse: Clark Royal Portrait reverse: Gregory Cameron's design of Crowned Coat of Arms....... £500		300	225	£2,050
2017 Lunar Year of the Rooster Gold; obverse: Clark Royal Portrait reverse: Wuon-Gean Ho's Rooster.. £1,000		8	8	£42,500
2017 Lunar Year of the Rooster Silver; obverse: Clark Royal Portrait reverse: Wuon-Gean Ho's Rooster.. £500		68	—	£2,050
2017 Platinum Wedding Gold; obverse: Etienne Millner Double Royal Portrait reverse: Heraldic shields by John Bergdahl £1,000		31	15	£49,950
2017 Platinum Wedding Silver; obverse: Etienne Millner Double Royal Portrait reverse: Heraldic shields by John Bergdahl £500		550	—	£2,025
2018 Anniversary of the Armistice Gold; obverse: Clark Royal Portrait reverse: Kneeling soldier by Paul Day £1,000		10	—	£49,995
2018 Anniversary of the Armistice Silver; obverse: Clark Royal Portrait reverse: Kneeling soldier by Paul Day £500		100	—	£2,025
2018 Lunar Year of the Dog Gold; obverse: Clark Royal Portrait reverse: Wuon-Gean Ho's Dog.. £1,000		8	—	£42,500
2018 Lunar Year of the Dog Silver; obverse: Clark Royal Portrait reverse: Wuon-Gean Ho's Dog.. £500		108	—	£2,025
2018 Britannia Silver; obverse: Clark Royal Portrait reverse: David Lawrence Stylised bust of Britannia £500		250	—	£2,025
2018 Sapphire Coronation Jubilee Gold; obverse: Jody Clark Royal Portrait reverse: Dominique Evans The Queen in the Royal Coach........... £1,000		15	—	£49,950
2018 Sapphire Coronation Jubilee Silver; obverse: Jody Clark Royal Portrait reverse: Dominique Evans The Queen in the Royal Coach.............. £500		250	—	£2,025

2015 50th Anniversary of Death of Sir Winston Churchill Silver

2021 Lunar— Year of the Ox

2017 Platinum Wedding Gold

2021 White Greyhound of Richmond

Illustrations on this page are not shown to scale.

DATE	FACE VALUE	AUTHORISED ISSUE QTY.	NO. ISSUED	ISSUE. PRICE
2019 Britannia Silver;				
obverse: Clark Royal Portrait				
reverse: David Lawrence's portrait of Britannia beside a lion £500		115	—	£2,025
2019 Queen Victoria Silver;				
obverse: Clark Royal Portrait				
reverse: William Wyon portrait of Queen Victoria and Prince Albert £500		125	—	£2,025
2019 Lunar Year of the Pig Gold;				
obverse: Clark Royal Portrait				
reverse: Harry Brockway's Pig.. £1000		8	—	—
2019 Lunar Year of the Pig Silver;				
obverse: Clark Royal Portrait				
reverse: Harry Brockway's Pig.. £500		38	—	£2,025
2019 The Falcon of the Plantagenets Gold;				
obverse: Clark Royal Portrait				
reverse: by Jody Clark.. £1000		10	—	£59,995
2019 The Falcon of the Plantagenets Silver;				
obverse: Clark Royal Portrait				
reverse: by Jody Clark... £500		125	—	£2,050
2019 The Yale of Beaufort Gold;				
obverse: Clark Royal Portrait				
reverse: by Jody Clark.. £1000		13	—	—
2019 The Yale of Beaufort Silver;				
obverse: Clark Royal Portrait				
reverse: by Jody Clark.. £500		120	—	£2,025
2019 Great Engraver Series: Una & the Lion Silver (also in 2 and 5 kilos);				
obverse: Clark Royal Portrait				
reverse: William Wyon's Una.. £5000		12	—	£59,995
2020 White Lion of Mortimer Gold;				
obverse: Clark Royal Portrait				
reverse: by Jody Clark.. £1000		10	—	£59,995
2020 White Lion of Mortimer Silver;				
obverse: Clark Royal Portrait				
reverse: by Jody Clark.. £500		90	—	£2,025
2020 White Horse of Hanover Gold;				
obverse: Clark Royal Portrait				
reverse: by Jody Clark.. £1000		13	—	£57,750
2020 White Horse of Hanover Silver;				
obverse: Clark Royal Portrait				
reverse: by Jody Clark.. £500		115	—	£2,050
2020 Lunar Year of the Rat Gold;				
obverse: Clark Royal Portrait				
reverse: P. J. Lynch's Rat.. £1000		8	—	£59,995
2020 Lunar Year of the Rat Silver;				
obverse: Clark Royal Portrait				
reverse: P. J. Lynch's Rat... £500		28	—	£2,050
2021 Lunar Year of the Ox Gold;				
obverse: Clark Royal Portrait				
reverse: Harry Brockway £1000		10	—	£63,865
2021 Lunar Year of the Ox Silver,				
obverse: Clark Royal Portrait				
reverse: Harry Brockway £500		38	—	£2,050
2021 White Greyhound of Richmond Gold,				
obverse: Clark Royal Portrait				
reverse: Jody Clark £1000		10	—	£63,865
2021 White Greyhound of Richmond Silver;				
obverse: Clark Royal Portrait				
reverse: Jody Clark £500		80	—	£2,050

As the issuing of one kilo coins as part of a collection or series of coins has become a more regular occurrence for the Royal Mint, it has been decided to ONLY list later issues under their themes. Therefore for other 1 kilo coins see Precious Metal Bullion and Collector Coins (Series) for these and a more in-depth listing of the latest bullion coin releases.

FIVE-OUNCE COINS
(gold and silver)

Appearing for the first time in 2012 were Five-Ounce coins, minted in the same metals and standards as the Kilo Coins. The Five-Ounce Britannia coins, both gold (50mm) and silver (65mm) proofs, which appeared first in 2013 are listed in the Britannia section.

DATE	FACE VALUE	AUTHORISED ISSUE QTY.	NO ISSUED	ISSUE PRICE
2012 Olympic Gold;				
obverse: 1998 Rank-Broadley Royal Portrait				
reverse: Pegasus (C. Le Brun) £10		500	193	£11,500
2012 Olympic Silver;				
obverse: 1998 Rank-Broadley Royal Portrait				
reverse: Pegasus (C. Le Brun) £10		7,500	5,056	£525
2012 Diamond Jubilee Gold;				
obverse: Queen in Garter Robes (Rank-Broadley)				
reverse: Queen seated (facing).......................£10		250	140	£9,500
2012 Diamond Jubilee Silver;				
obverse: Queen in Garter Robes (Rank-Broadley)				
reverse: Queen seated (facing).......................£10		1,952	1,933	£450
2013 Coronation Anniversary Gold;				
obverse: 1998 Rank-Broadley Royal Portrait				
reverse: Regalia in Westminster Abbey (J. Olliffe) £10		129	74	£9,500
2013 Coronation Anniversary Silver;				
obverse: 1998 Rank-Broadley Royal Portrait				
reverse: Regalia in Westminster Abbey (J. Olliffe) £10		1,953	1,604	£450
2013 Royal Christening Gold;				
obverse: 1998 Rank-Broadley Royal Portrait				
reverse: Bergdahl's Lily Font £10		150	48	£8,200
2013 Royal Christening Silver;				
obverse: 1998 Rank-Broadley Royal Portrait				
reverse: Bergdahl's Lily Font £10		1,660	912	£450
2014 First World War Outbreak Gold;				
obverse: 1998 Rank-Broadley Royal Portrait				
reverse: Bergdahl's Britannia...........................£10		110	36	£7,500
2014 First World War Outbreak Silver;				
obverse: 1998 Rank-Broadley Royal Portrait				
reverse: Bergdahl's Britannia...........................£10		1,300	606	£395

DATE	FACE VALUE	AUTHORISED ISSUE QTY.	NO. ISSUED	ISSUE PRICE
2014 Lunar Year of the Horse Gold; obverse: 1998 Rank-Broadley Royal Portrait reverse: Wuon-Gean Ho's Horse £500		—	—	£7,500
2014 Lunar Year of the Horse Silver; obverse: 1998 Rank-Broadley Royal Portrait reverse: Wuon-Gean Ho's Horse £10		799	799	£395
2015 Year of the Sheep Gold; obverse: 1998 Rank-Broadley Royal Portrait reverse: Wuon-Gean Ho's Swaledale Sheep £500		38	26	£7,500
2015 Year of the Sheep Silver; obverse: 1998 Rank-Broadley Royal Portrait reverse: Wuon-Gean Ho's Swaledale Sheep £10		1,088	331	£395
2015 50th Anniversary of Death of Sir Winston Churchill Gold; obverse: Clark Royal Portrait reverse: Millner's image of Churchill £10		60	58	£7,500
2015 50th Anniversary of Death of Sir Winston Churchill Silver; obverse: Clark Royal Portrait reverse: Millner's image of Churchill £10		500	855 (?)	£450
2015 First World War Gold; obverse: Clark Royal Portrait reverse: James Butler Devastation of War £500		50	17	£6,950
2015 First World War Silver; obverse: Clark Royal Portrait reverse: James Butler Devastation of War £10		500	355	£395
2015 The Longest Reign Gold; obverse: Butler Royal Portrait reverse: Stephen Taylor Queen's Portraits £500		180	180	£6,950
2015 The Longest Reign Silver; obverse: Butler Royal Portrait reverse: Stephen Taylor Queen's Portraits £10		1,500	1499	£395
2015 Christening of Princess Charlotte; obverse: Clark Royal Portrait reverse: John Bergdahl Baroque design £10		500	500	£400
2016 Year of the Monkey Gold; obverse: Clark Royal Portrait reverse: Wuon-Gean Ho's Rhesus monkey £500		38	—	£7,500
2016 Year of the Monkey Silver; obverse: Butler Royal Portrait reverse: Wuon-Gean Ho's Rhesus monkey £10		588	—	£395
2016 Queen's 90th Birthday Gold; obverse: Clark Royal Portrait reverse: Christopher Hobbs Floral design £500		170	170	£7,500
2016 Queen's 90th Birthday Silver; obverse: Clark Royal Portrait reverse: Christopher Hobbs Floral design £10		1,750	1727	£395
2016 First World War Gold; obverse: Clark Royal Portrait reverse: David Lawrence Four Soldiers walking £500		30	—	£7,500
2016 First World War Silver; obverse: Clark Royal Portrait reverse: David Lawrence Four Soldiers walking £10		500	—	£395
2016 2016 Shakespeare Gold; obverse: Clark Royal Portrait; reverse: Tom Phillips Shakespeare Portrait £500		—	50	—
2016 Shakespeare Silver; obverse: Clark Royal Portrait; reverse: Tom Phillips Shakespeare Portrait £10		750	343	£395
2017 Lunar Year of the Rooster Gold; obverse: Clark Royal Portrait reverse: Wuon-Gean Ho's Rooster £500		38	35	£8,250
2017 Lunar Year of the Rooster Gold; obverse: Clark Royal Portrait reverse: Wuon-Gean Ho's Rooster £10		388	369	£415
2017 The Queen's Sapphire Jubilee Gold; obverse: Clark Royal Portrait reverse: Gregory Cameron's Crowned Coat of Arms £500		110	110	£8,250

DATE	FACE VALUE	AUTHORISED ISSUE QTY.	NO. ISSUED	ISSUE PRICE
2017 The Queen's Sapphire Jubilee Silver; obverse: Clark Royal Portrait reverse: Gregory Cameron's Crowned Coat of Arms....£10		1,500	1,445	£415
2017 First World War Gold; obverse: Clark Royal Portrait reverse: Philip Jackson Soldier £500		50	—	£8,250
2017 First World War Silver; obverse: Clark Royal Portrait reverse: Philip Jackson Soldier £10		450	—	£415
2017 Royal Platinum Wedding Gold; obverse: Royal Portraits by Etienne Millner reverse: John Bergdahl Heraldic design....£500		450	86	£415
2018 Lunar Year of the Dog Gold; obverse: Clark Royal Portrait reverse: Wuon-Gean Ho's Dog....£500		58	—	£8,565
2018 Lunar Year of the Dog Silver; obverse: Clark Royal Portrait reverse: Wuon-Gean Ho's Dog....£10		388	—	£420
2018 Four Generations of Royalty Gold; obverse: Clark Royal Portrait reverse: Timothy Noad Initials of the Royal succession....£500		100	—	£8,565
2018 Four Generations of Royalty Silver; obverse: Clark Royal Portrait reverse: Timothy Noad Initials of the Royal succession....£10		1,000	—	£420
2018 Sapphire Coronation Gold; obverse: Clark Royal Portrait reverse: Dominique Evans Queen in Coronation Coach £500		85	—	£8,565
2018 Sapphire Coronation Silver; obverse: Clark Royal Portrait reverse: Dominique Evans Queen in Coronation Coach £10		1,050	—	£420
2018 Anniversary of the Armistice Gold; obverse: Clark Royal Portrait reverse: Paul Day Lone Soldier £500		50	—	£8,565
2018 Anniversary of the Armistice Silver; obverse: Clark Royal Portrait reverse: Paul Day Lone Soldier £10		525	—	£420
2019 Queen Victoria Gold; obverse: Clark Royal Portrait reverse: W. Wyon's portrait of Queen Victoria and Prince Albert £500		70	—	£8,645
2019 Queen Victoria Silver; obverse: Clark Royal Portrait reverse: W. Wyon's portrait of Queen Victoria and Prince Albert £10		800	—	£420
2019 The Tower of London Gold; obverse: Clark Royal Portrait reverse: Glyn Davis Yeoman Warder £500		45	—	£8,645
2019 The Tower of London Silver; obverse: Clark Royal Portrait reverse: Glyn Davis Yeoman Warder £10		585	—	£420
2019 The Tower of London Gold; obverse: Clark Royal Portrait reverse: Glyn Davis Ceremony of the Keys £500		45	—	£8,645
2019 The Tower of London Silver; obverse: Clark Royal Portrait reverse: Glyn Davis Ceremony of the Keys £10		585	—	£420
2019 The Falcon of the Plantagenets Gold; obverse: Clark Royal Portrait reverse: Clark's Falcon £500		85	—	£8,645
2019 The Falcon of the Plantagenets Silver; obverse: Clark Royal Portrait reverse: Clark's Falcon £10		550	—	£420
2019 The Tower of London Gold; obverse: Clark Royal Portrait reverse: Glyn Davis Crown Jewels £500		45	—	£8,645
2019 The Tower of London Silver; obverse: Clark Royal Portrait reverse: Glyn Davis Crown Jewels £10		585	—	£420

DATE	FACE VALUE	AUTHORISED ISSUE QTY.	NO. ISSUED	ISSUE PRICE
2019 Lunar Year of the Pig Gold; obverse: Clark Royal Portrait reverse: Harry Brockway's Pig	£500	38	—	£8,645
2019 Lunar Year of the Pig Silver; obverse: Clark Royal Portrait reverse: Harry Brockway's Pig	£10	288	—	£420
2019 The Tower of London Gold; obverse: Clark Royal Portrait reverse: Glyn Davies Legend of the Ravens	£500	45	—	£8,645
2019 The Tower of London Silver; obverse: Clark Royal Portrait reverse: Glyn Davies Legend of the Ravens	£10	585	—	£420
2019 The Yale of Beaufort Gold; obverse: Clark Royal Portrait reverse: by Jody Clark	£500	70	—	£8,645
2019 The Yale of Beaufort Silver; obverse: Clark Royal Portrait reverse: by Jody Clark	£10	335	—	£420
2019 Great Engraver Series: Una & the Lion Gold; obverse: Clark Royal Portrait reverse: William Wyon	£500	65	—	£9,995
2020 White Lion of Mortimer Gold; obverse: Clark Royal Portrait reverse: by Jody Clark	£500	55	—	£9,995
2020 White Lion of Mortimer Silver; obverse: Clark Royal Portrait reverse: by Jody Clark	£10	250	—	£420
2020 White Horse of Hanover Gold; obverse: Clark Royal Portrait reverse: by Jody Clark	£500	69	—	£9,595
2020 White Horse of Hanover Silver; obverse: Clark Royal Portrait reverse: by Jody Clark	£10	315	—	£420
2020 Lunar Year of the Rat Gold; obverse: Clark Royal Portrait reverse: P. J. Lynch	£500	28	—	£9,995
2020 Lunar Year of the Rat Silver; obverse: Clark Royal Portrait reverse: P. J. Lynch	£10	188	—	£420
2021 Lunar Year of the Ox Gold; obverse: Clark Royal Portrait reverse: Harry Brockway	£500	38	—	£10,605
2021 Lunar Year of the Ox Silver; obverse: Clark Royal Portrait reverse: Harry Brockway	£10	198	—	£420
2022 Lunar Year of the Tiger Gold; obverse: Clark Royal Portrait reverse: David Lawrence	£500	128	—	£11,125

FIVE POUNDS (Sovereign series)

This series is all minted in gold, and, except where stated, have the Pistrucci St George and Dragon reverse. BU coins up to 2001 bear a U in a circle. From 2009 the initials B.P. in the exergue are replaced by PISTRUCCI in small letters on the left. From 2014 the denomination is called the "Five-Sovereign" piece by the Royal Mint in their marketing publications.

> **NOTE: The prices quoted in this guide are set at August 2022 with the price of gold at £1,500 per ounce and silver £15.80 per ounce—market fluctuations will have a marked effect on the values of modern precious metal coins. Many of the prices given for recent gold coins are the Royal Mint issue price.**

DATE	Mintage	UNC
1980 Proof	10,000	£2000
1981 Proof	5,400	£2000
1982 Proof	2,500	£2000
1984 BU	15,104	£1750
1984 Proof	8,000	£2000
1985 New portrait BU	13,626	£1750
1985 — Proof	6,130	£2000
1986 BU	7,723	£1500
1987 Uncouped portrait BU	5,694	£1750
1988 BU	3,315	£1750
1989 500th Anniversary of the Sovereign. Enthroned portrayal obverse and Crowned shield reverse BU	2,937	£2000
1989 — Proof	5,000	£2000
1990 Reverts to couped portrait BU	1,226	£1750
1990 Proof	1,721	£2000
1991 BU	976	£1750
1991 Proof	1,336	£2000
1992 BU	797	£1750
1992 Proof	1,165	£2000
1993 BU	906	£1750
1993 Proof	1,078	£2000
1994 BU	1,000	£1750
1994 Proof	918	£2000
1995 BU	1,000	£1750
1995 Proof	1,250	£2000
1996 BU	901	£1750
1996 Proof	742	£2000
1997 BU	802	£1750
1997 Proof	860	£2000
1998 New portrait BU	825	£1750
1998 Proof	789	£2000
1999 BU	970	£1750
1999 Proof	1,000	£2000
2000 ("Bullion")	10,000	£1750
2000 BU	994	£1750
2000 Proof	3,000	£2000
2001 BU	1,000	£1750
2001 Proof	3,500	£2000
2002 Shield rev. ("Bullion")	—	£1750
2002 BU	—	£1750
2002 Proof	3,000	£2000
2003 BU	812	£1750
2003 Proof	—	£2000
2004 BU	1,000	£1750
2004 Proof	—	£2000
2005 Noad's heraldic St George and Dragon BU	936	£2000
2005 — Proof	—	£2200
2006 BU	731	£1750
2006 Proof	—	£2000
2007 BU	768	£1750
2007 Proof		£2000
2008 BU	750	£1750
2008 Proof	—	£2000
2009 BU	1,000	£1750
2009 Proof	—	£2000
2010 BU	1,000	£1750
2010 Proof	—	£2000

Pistrucci's famous rendering of St George and the Dragon which appears on all except special commemorative five pound coins.

The obverse of the 1989 500th Anniversary of the original Sovereign coin portrays HM the Queen enthroned.

DATE	Mintage	UNC
2011 BU	657	£1750
2011 Proof	—	£2000
2012 Day's St George and Dragon BU	496	£1750
2012 — Proof	—	£1850
2013 BU	262	£1750
2013 Proof	—	£2000
2014 BU	645	£1750
2014 Proof	—	£2000
2015 Proof	—	£2000
2015 Jody Clark Portrait BU	609	£2000
2015 — Proof	—	£1750
2016 BU	498	£1750
2016 James Butler Portrait Proof	575	£2250
2017 200th Anniversary of the Sovereign (Clark portrait) BU ...	992	£2000
2017 — Proof	750	£2250
2018 BU	1,500	£1750
2018 Proof	850	£2000
2019 BU Matt finish	550	£2000
2020 200th Anniversary of death of George III With GR cypher privy mark	—	£2250
2021 BU	350	£2420
2022 Platinum Jubilee—Timothy Noad coat of arms BU	750	£2635

2017 200th Anniversary reverse design as the original issue.

FIVE POUNDS (Crown series)

This series commenced in 1990 when the "Crown" was declared legal tender at £5, instead of 25p as all previous issues continued to be. Mintage is in cupro-nickel unless otherwise stated. BU includes those in individual presentation folders, and those in sets sold with stamp covers and/or banknotes.

DATE	Mintage	UNC
1990 Queen Mother's 90th Birthday.	2,761,431	£6
1990 — BU	48,477	£10
1990 — Silver Proof	56,800	£35
1990 — Gold Proof	2,500	£2000
1993 Coronation 40th Anniversary	1,834,655	£6
1993 — BU	—	£10
1993 — Proof	—	£15
1993 — Silver Proof	58,877	£35
1993 — Gold Proof	2,500	£2000
1996 HM the Queen's 70th Birthday	2,396,100	£6
1996 — BU	—	£10
1996 — Proof	—	£15
1996 — Silver Proof	39,336	£35
1996 — Gold Proof	2,127	£2000
1997 Royal Golden Wedding	1,733,000	£8
1997 — BU	—	£10
1997 — — with £5 note	5,000	£60
1997 — Proof	—	£15
1997 — Silver Proof	33,689	£35
1997 — Gold Proof	2,750	£2000
1998 Prince of Wales 50th Birthday	1,407,300	£9
1998 — BU	—	£10
1998 — Proof	—	£20
1998 — Silver Proof	13,379	£45
1998 — Gold Proof	—	£2500
1999 Princess of Wales Memorial.	1,600,000	£10
1999 — BU	—	£14
1999 — Proof	—	£20
1999 — Silver Proof	49,545	£60
1999 — Gold Proof	7,500	£3000
1999 Millennium	3,796,300	£8
1999 — BU	—	£12
1999 — Proof	—	£15
1999 — Silver Proof	49,057	£35

DATE	Mintage	UNC
1999 — Gold Proof..	2,500	£2000
2000 —...3,147,092*		£10
2000 — BU...	—	£18
2000 — — with special Millennium Dome mintmark	—	£25
2000 — Proof...	—	£20
2000 — Silver Proof with gold highlight..............................	14,255	£50
2000 — Gold Proof...	2,500	£2000
2000 Queen Mother's 100th Birthday	—	£8
2000 — BU...	—	£12
2000 — Silver Proof	31,316	£40
2000 — — — Piedfort..	14,850	£65
2000 — Gold Proof...	3,000	£2000
2001 Victorian Era..	851,491	£10
2001 — BU...	—	£12
2001 — Proof...	—	£20
2001 — Silver Proof	19,216	£45
2001 — — with frosted relief..	596	£150
2001 — Gold Proof...	3,000	£2000
2001 — — with frosted relief..	733	£2750
2002 Golden Jubilee 3,469,243*		£8
2002 — BU...	—	£12
2002 — Proof...	—	£15
2002 — Silver Proof	54,012	£45
2002 — Gold Proof...	5,502	£2000
2002 Queen Mother Memorial.............................*incl. above**		£9
2002 — BU...	—	£12
2002 — Silver Proof	16,117	£40
2002 — Gold Proof...	3,000	£2000
2003 Coronation Jubilee 1,307,147		£10
2003 — BU...	100,481	£13
2003 — Proof...	—	£20
2003 — Silver Proof	28,758	£45
2003 — Gold Proof...	1,896	£2000
2004 Entente Cordiale Centenary 1,205,594		£10
2004 — Proof Reverse Frosting	6,065	£15
2004 — Silver Proof	11,295	£50
2004 — — — Piedfort..	2,500	£90
2004 — Gold Proof...	926	£2000
2004 — Platinum Proof Piedfort.......................................	501	£4250
2005 Trafalgar Bicentenary..1,075 516*		£12
2005 — BU...	—	£15
2005 — Proof...	—	£20
2005 — Silver Proof	21,448	£45
2005 — — — Piedfort..	2,818	£65
2005 — Gold Proof...	1,805	£2000
2005 Bicentenary of the Death of Nelson ....*incl. above**		£12
2005 — BU...	—	£15
2005 — Proof...	—	£20
2005 — Silver Proof	12,852	£45
2005 — — — Piedfort..	2,818	£65
2005 — Gold Proof...	1,760	£2000
2005 — Platinum Proof Piedfort.......................................	200	£4000
2006 Queen's 80th Birthday..	52,267	£10
2006 — BU...	—	£12
2006 — Proof...	—	£15
2006 — Silver Proof	20,790	£45
2006 — — — Piedfort, selective gold plating on reverse	5,000	£60
2006 — Gold Proof...	2,750	£2000
2006 — Platinum Proof Piedfort.......................................	250	£4000
2007 Queen's Diamond Wedding	30,561	£10
2007 — BU...	—	£12
2007 — Proof...	—	£15
2007 — Silver Proof	15,186	£45
2007 — — — Piedfort..	2,000	£65
2007 — Gold Proof...	2,380	£2000
2007 — Platinum Proof Piedfort.......................................	250	£4000
2008 Prince of Wales 60th Birthday	14,088	£12
2008 — BU...	54,746	£15
2008 — Proof...	—	£20

DATE	Mintage	UNC
2008 — Silver Proof	6,264	£55
2008 — — Piedfort	1,088	£75
2008 — Gold Proof	867	£2000
2008 Elizabeth I 450th Anniversary of Accession	20,047	£12
2008 — BU	26,700	£15
2008 — Proof	—	£20
2008 — Silver Proof	9,216	£50
2008 — — Piedfort	1,602	£75
2008 — Gold Proof	1,500	£2000
2008 — Platinum Proof Piedfort	125	£4000
2009 500th Anniversary of Henry VIII Accession	30,000	£12
2009 — BU	69,119	£15
2009 — Proof	—	£25
2009 — Silver Proof	10,419	£50
2009 — — Piedfort	3,580	£75
2009 — Gold Proof	1,130	£2000
2009 — Platinum Proof Piedfort	100	£4250
2009 Olympic Countdown (3 years) BU	184,921	£12
2009 — Silver Proof	26,645	£55
2009 — — Piedfort	4,874	£75
2009 — Gold Proof	1,860	£2000
2009 Olympic Celebration of Britain "The Mind" series (incl. green logo):		
Stonehenge Silver Proof	—	£60
Palace of Westminster/Big Ben Silver Proof	—	£60
— Cu Ni Proof	—	£20
Angel of the North Silver Proof	—	£60
Flying Scotsman Silver Proof	—	£60
Globe Theatre Silver Proof	—	£60
Sir Isaac Newton Silver Proof	—	£60
2010 350th Anniversary of the Restoration of the Monarchy	15,000	£15
2010 — BU	30,247	£20
2010 — Proof	—	£25
2010 — Silver Proof	6,518	£50
2010 — — Piedfort	4,435	£90
2010 — Gold Proof	1,182	£2000
2010 — Platinum Proof Piedfort	—	£4000
2010 Olympic Countdown (2 years) BU	153,080	£12
2010 — Silver Proof	20,159	£55
2010 — — Piedfort	2,197	£120
2010 — Gold Proof	1,562	£2000
2010 Olympic Celebration of Britain, "The Body" series (incl. red logo):		
Coastline of Britain (Rhossili Bay) Silver Proof	—	£65
Giants Causeway Silver Proof	—	£65
River Thames Silver Proof	—	£65
British Fauna (Barn Owl) Silver Proof	—	£65
British Flora (Oak Leaves and Acorn) Silver Proof	—	£65
Weather Vane Silver Proof	—	£65
2010 Olympic Celebration of Britain "The Spirit" series (incl. blue logo):		
Churchill Silver Proof	—	£75
— CuNi Proof	—	£20
Spirit of London (Kind Hearts etc.) Silver Proof	—	£75
— CuNi Proof	—	£20
Humour Silver Proof	—	£75
Unity (Floral emblems of Britain) Silver Proof	—	£75
Music Silver Proof	—	£75
Anti-slavery Silver Proof	—	£75
2011 90th Birthday of the Duke of Edinburgh BU	18,730	£35
2011 — Proof	—	£35
2011 — Silver Proof	4,599	£75
2011 — — Piedfort	2,659	£90
2011 — Gold Proof	636	£2000
2011 — Platinum Proof Piedfort	—	£7500
2011 Royal Wedding of William and Catherine BU	250,000	£15
2011 — Silver Proof	26,069	£60
2011 — Gold-plated Silver Proof	7,451	£80
2011 — Silver Proof Piedfort	2,991	£100
2011 — Gold Proof	2,066	£2000
2011 — Platinum Proof Piedfort	—	£5500

DATE	Mintage	UNC
2011 Olympic Countdown (1 year) BU	163,235	£12
2011 — Silver Proof	25,877	£55
2011 — — Piedfort	4,000	£75
2011 — Gold Proof	1,300	£2000
2012 Diamond Jubilee BU	484,775	£15
2012 — Proof	—	£20
2012 — Silver Proof	16,370	£50
2012 — — Piedfort	3,187	£90
2012 — Gold-plated silver proof	12,112	£60
2012 — Gold proof	1,025	£2000
2012 — Platinum Piedfort Proof	20	£5500
2012 Olympic Countdown (Games Time) BU	52,261	£13
2012 — Silver Proof	12,670	£65
2012 — — Piedfort	2,324	£85
2012 — Gold proof	1,007	£2000
2012 Official Olympic BU	315,983	£15
2012 — Silver Proof	20,810	£55
2012 — — Piedfort	5,946	£85
2012 — Gold-plated silver proof	12,112	£60
2012 — Gold proof	1,045	£2000
2012 Official Paralympic BU	—	£15
2012 — Silver Proof	—	£55
2012 — — Piedfort	—	£85
2012 — Gold proof	—	£2000
2013 60th Anniversary of the Queen's Coronation BU	57,262	£12
2013 — Proof	—	£35
2013 — Silver Proof	4,050	£80
2013 — — Piedfort	2,626	£95
2013 — Gold-plated silver proof	2,547	£80
2013 — Gold proof	418	£2000
2013 — Platinum Piedfort Proof	106	£7500
2013 Queen's Portraits, 4 coins each with one of the four portraits, paired with James Butler's Royal Arms. Issued only as sets of 4 in precious metals (see under Proof and Specimen Set section)	—	—
2013 Royal Birth of Prince George (St George & Dragon), Silver Proof	7,460	£150
2013 Christening of Prince George BU	56,014	£20
2013 — Silver Proof	7,264	£80
2013 — — Piedfort	2,251	£160
2013 — Gold Proof	486	£2000
2013 — Platinum Proof Piedfort	38	£7500
2014 300th Anniversary of the death of Queen Anne BU	12,181	£60
2014 — Proof	—	£60
2014 — Silver Proof	2,212	£80
2014 — — Piedfort	636	£160
2014 — Gold-plated Silver Proof	627	£100
2014 — Gold Proof	253	£2000
2014 First Birthday of Prince George Silver Proof	7,451	£85
2014 100th Anniversary of the First World War Outbreak, issued only as set of 6 coins (see under Proof and Specimen Sets)	—	—
2014 Portrait of Britain, issued only as set of 4 coins, with trichromatic colour-printing (see under Proof and Specimen Sets section)	—	—
2015 50th Anniversary of death of Sir Winston Churchill BU	—	£15
2015 — Silver Proof	4,238	£60
2015 — — Piedfort	1,800	£100
2015 — Gold Proof	325	£2000
2015 — Platinum Proof Piedfort	90	£5000
2015 200th Anniversary of the Battle of Waterloo, BU	24,554	£15
2015 — Silver Proof	2,523	£80
2015 — — Piedfort	896	£140
2015 — Gold Proof	273	£2000
2015 First World War 100th Anniversary, continued, issued only as set of 6 coins	807	—
New Portrait		
2015 2nd Birthday of Prince George, Silver Proof	4,009	£85

DATE	Mintage	UNC
2015 Birth of Princess Charlotte, BU	—	£20
2015 — Silver Proof	—	£80
2015 — Gold Proof	500	£2000
2015 Christening of Princess Charlotte, Silver Proof	4,842	£2000
2015 — Gold Proof	350	£80
2015 The Longest Reign, BU	48,848	£18
2015 — Silver Proof	10,249	£60
2015 — — Piedfort	3,171	£95
2015 — Gold Proof	899	£2000
2015 — Platinum Proof Piedfort	88	£5000
2016 Queen's 90th Birthday, BU	74,195	£15
2016 — Proof	—	£25
2016 — Silver Proof	8,947	£60
2016 — — Piedfort	3,099	£95
2016 — Gold Proof	906	£2000
2016 — Platinum Proof Piedfort	81	£4500
2016 Portraits of Britain, issued only as set of 4 coins, with trichromatic colour-printing (see under Proof and Specimen Sets section)	1,098	—
2016 First World War Centenary, continued, issued only as a set of 6 Silver Proof coins	1,916	—
2016 Battle of the Somme, Silver Proof	3,678	£75
2017 Portraits of Britain, issued only as set of 4 coins, with trichromatic colour-printing (see under Proof and Specimen Sets section)	1,500	—
2017 1000th Anniversary of Coronation of King Canute, BU	26,567	£15
2017 — Proof	—	£30
2017 — Silver Proof	2,925	£60
2017 — — Piedfort	1,069	£100
2017 — Gold Proof	150	£2000
2017 Prince Philip, Celebrating a Life of Service, BU	29,097	£20
2017 — Silver Proof	2,574	£85
2017 — — Piedfort	1,250	£155
2017 — Gold Proof	299	£2000
2017 Remembrance Day Poppy	—	£15
2017 — Silver Proof	5,000	£100
2017 — — Piedfort	1,500	£200
2017 First World War Centenary, continued, issued only as set of 6 Silver Proof coins	1,917	—
2017 House of Windsor Centenary, BU	—	£15
2017 — — in pack for Engagement of Prince Harry	5,000	£20
2017 — Proof	—	£30
2017 — Silver Proof	13,000	£85
2017 — — Piedfort	5,500	£185
2017 — Gold Proof	884	£2000
2017 Christmas Tree BU	—	£13
2018 Her Majesty's Sapphire Jubilee, BU	—	£15
2018 — Proof	—	£30
2018 — Silver Proof	8,260	£85
2018 — — Piedfort	2,471	£155
2018 — Gold Proof	648	£2000
2018 70th Birthday of the Prince of Wales BU	—	£15
2018 — Silver Proof	3,500	£85
2018 — — Piedfort	1,000	£155
2018 — Gold Proof	50	£2,500
2018 — Platinum Proof	525	£650
2018 — Platinum Proof Piedfort	70	£5,500
2018 Prince George's 5th Birthday	—	£15
2018 — Proof	—	£18
2018 — Silver Proof	—	£85
2018 — — Piedfort	—	£165
2018 — Gold Proof	650	£2000
2018 Four generations of the Royal Family	—	£15
2018 — Proof	—	£20
2018 — Silver Proof	5,000	£100

2017 Portrait of Britain, issued only as set of 4 coins, with trichromatic colour-printing.

DATE	Mintage	UNC
2018 — — Piedfort..	2,000	£175
2018 — Gold Proof..	500	£2000
2018 250 years of the Royal Academy	—	£15
2018 — Silver Proof	2,750	£100
2018 Royal Wedding of Prince Harry	12,000	£20
2018 — Proof	—	£25
2018 — Silver Proof	15,000	£100
2018 — — Piedfort..	2,220	£175
2018 — Gold Proof..	500	£2000
2018 Portraits of Britain, issued only as set of 4 coins, with trichromatic colour-printing (see under Proof and Specimen Sets section)	2,016	—
2018 Stories of War set of six coins (see under Proof and Specimen Sets section)...	—	—
2019 The Ceremony of the Keys BU...	—	£15
2019 — Silver Proof	4,000	£85
2019 — — Piedfort..	1,160	£175
2019 — Gold	385	£2000
2019 The Tower of London 4 coin set BU.................................	—	£85
2019 — Silver Proof	4,000	£350
2019 — — Piedfort..	1,160	£650
2019 — Gold	385	£8000
2019 200th Anniversary of the Birth of Queen Victoria BU	—	£15
2019 —Silver Proof	7,500	£85
2019 — — Piedfort..	2,750	£175
2019 — Gold	725	£2000
2019 Pride of England BU...	—	£13
2019 Centenary of Remembrance BU	—	£17
2019 — Silver Proof	3,240	£100
2019 — — Piedfort..	775	£185
2019 — Gold	240	£2500
2020 The Tower of London series—The White Tower BU........	—	£13
2020 —Silver Proof	2,500	£85
2020 — — Piedfort..	450	£175
2020 — Gold Proof..	125	£2500
2020 Reign of George III BU	—	£15
2020 — Silver Proof	2,500	£85
2020 — — Piedfort..	550	£175
2020 — Gold Proof..	250	£2500
2020 250th Anniversary of William Wordsworth BU.................	—	£15
2020 — Silver Proof	3,000	£85
2020 — Gold Proof..	300	£2500
2020 Tower of London Collection—the Royal Menagerie BU...	—	£15
2020 — Silver Proof	1,510	£85
2020 — — Piedfort..	410	£175
2020 — Gold Proof..	135	£2500
2020 Remembrance Day BU...	—	£15
2020 — Silver Proof	1920	£85
2020 — — Piedfort..	700	£185
2020 75th Anniversary of the end of World War II BU..............	—	£15
2020 — Silver Proof	2575	£85
2020 — — Piedfort..	565	£175
2020 — Gold Proof..	225	£2500
2020 150th Anniversary of the British Red Cross BU	—	£18
2020 — Silver Proof	4000	£850
2020 — — Piedfort..	1150	£175
2020 — Gold Proof..	250	£2500
2021 Alfred the Great BU	—	£13
2021 — Silver Proof	2,250	£90
2021 — — Piedfort..	900	£167.50
2021 — Gold Proof..	160	£2590

DATE	Mintage	UNC
2021 Remembrance Day 2021 BU....................	—	£17
2021 — Silver Proof	2021	£100
2021 — — Piedfort	600	£187.50
2022 The Platinum Jubilee of Her Majesty the Queen BU.....	—	£10
2022 — Premium Exclusive....................................	10,010	£18
2022 — Silver Proof	6,905	£92.50
2022 — — Piedfort	2,162	£172.50
2022 — Gold Proof....................................	550	£2725
2022 — Platinum Piedfort	82	£5495
2022 The 40th Birthday of HRH The Duke of Cambridge BU	—	£13
2022 — Silver Proof	3,500	£29.50
2022 — — Piedfort....................................	1,500	£172.50
2022 — Gold Proof....................................	300	£2725
2022 The Queen's Reign with Signature—Honours and Investitures		
BU	—	£13
2022 — Silver Proof	4,000	£92.50
2022 — — Piedfort....................................	1500	£172.50
2022 — Gold Proof....................................	250	£2725

The Royal Mint also issue other coins of a specific theme in various denominations. To help the collector identify these special issues it has been decided to list them with their appropriate headings under "Precious Metal Bullion and Collector Coins" (series). For example, "The Queen's Beasts", "Music Legends" and other series as appropriate.

DOUBLE SOVEREIGN

As with the Sovereign series Five Pound coins, those listed under this heading bear the Pistrucci St George and Dragon reverse, except where otherwise stated, and are minted in gold. They are, and always have been, legal tender at £2, and have a diameter identical to that of the base metal Two Pound coins listed further below under a different heading. The denomination does not appear on Double Sovereigns. Most were originally issued as part of Royal Mint sets.

DATE	Mintage	UNC
1980 Proof	10,000	£750
1982 Proof	2,500	£750
1983 Proof	12,500	£750
1985 New Portrait Proof	5,849	£750
1987 Proof	14,301	£750
1988 Proof	12,743	£750
1989 500th Anniversary of the Sovereign. Enthroned portrayal obverse and		
Crowned shield reverse Proof	2,000	£1200
1990 Proof	4,374	£750
1991 Proof	3,108	£750
1992 Proof	2,608	£750
1993 Proof	2,155	£750
1996 Proof	3,167	£750
1998 New Portrait Proof	4,500	£750
2000 Proof	2,250	£750
2002 Shield reverse Proof	8,000	£750
2003 Proof	2,250	£750
2004 Proof	2,500	£750
2005 Noad's heraldic St George and Dragon reverse Proof	—	£800
2006 Proof	—	£750
2007 Proof	—	£750
2008 Proof	—	£750
2009 Proof	—	£750
2010 Proof	2,750	£750
2011 Proof	2,950	£750
2012 Day's stylised St George and Dragon reverse, BU	60	£1000
2012 — Proof	1,945	£1200
2013 BU	—	£800
2013 Proof	1,895	£800
2014 BU	1,300	£750
2014 Proof	—	£800
2015 Proof	1,100	£700
2015 New Portrait by Jody Clark Proof	1,100	£900
2016 Butler Portrait Proof	925	£900
2017 200th Anniv. of the Sovereign design as 1817 issue	1,200	£1000
2018 Proof	1,600	£1200
2019 BU	—	—
2020 BU	—	£850
2020 200th Anniversary of death of George III		
With GR cypher privy mark Proof	1,100	£1200
2021 BU	—	—
2022 Platinum Jubilee. Noad's reverse coat of arms BU	—	—

Standard reverse

Reverse by Timothy Noad

Reverse by Paul Day

IMPORTANT NOTE:
The prices quoted in this guide are set at August 2022 with the price of gold at £1,500 per ounce and silver £15.80 per ounce—market fluctuations can have a marked effect on the values of modern precious metal coins.
Note: most of the prices given for recent gold issues are the Royal Mint issue price

TWO POUNDS

This series commenced in 1986 with nickel-brass commemorative coins, with their associated base metal and precious metal BU and proof coins. From 1997 (actually issued in 1998) a thinner bi-metal version commenced with a reverse theme of the advance of technology, and from this date the coin was specifically intended to circulate. This is true also for the parallel issues of anniversary and commemorative Two Pound issues in 1999 and onwards. All have their BU and proof versions, as listed below.

In the case of Gold Proofs, a few have Certificates of Authenticity and/or green boxes of issue describing the coin as a Double Sovereign. All Gold Proofs since 1997 are of bi-metallic gold except for 2001 (red gold with the inner circle coated in yellow gold) and 2002 (Technology issue, uncoated red gold). After 2008 all RM boxes were black for all denominations.

A new definitive design was introduced during 2015 incorporating the Jody Clark portrait and Britannia by Antony Dufort but to date the mintage each year has been relatively low.

NOTE: The counterfeiting of circulation £2 coins has been around for several years but 2015 saw several proof-like base metal designs. Five types are known at present: 2011 (Mary Rose) and 2015 (all four designs).

DATE	Mintage	UNC
1986 Commonwealth Games.....................................	8,212,184	£5
1986 — BU...	—	£8
1986 — Proof..	59,779	£15
1986 — Silver BU..	—	£35
1986 — — Proof..	—	£45
1986 — Gold Proof..	—	£1000
1989 Tercentenary of Bill of Rights.	4,392,825	£10
1989 — BU (issued in folder with Claim of Right)	—	£25
1989 — BU folder..	—	£8
1989 — Proof..	—	£15
1989 — Silver Proof	—	£35
1989 — — — Piedfort..	—	£60
1989 Tercentenary of Claim of Right (issued in Scotland)	381,400	£30
1989 — BU (see above)..	—	£35
1989 — Proof..	—	£35
1989 — Silver Proof	—	£45
1989 — — Piedfort..	—	£65
1994 Tercentenary of the Bank of England	1,443,116	£10
1994 — BU...	—	£12
1994 — Proof..	—	£30
1994 — Silver Proof	27,957	£35
1994 — — — Piedfort..	9,569	£65
1994 — Gold Proof..	—	£1000
1994 — — — with Double Sovereign obverse (no denomination) —		£1200
1995 50th Anniversary of End of WWII.	4,394,566	£10
1995 — BU...	—	£12
1995 — Proof..	—	£15
1995 — Silver Proof	35,751	£35
1995 — — — Piedfort..	—	£65
1995 — Gold Proof..	—	£1000
1995 50th Anniversary of The United Nations.............	1,668,575	£10
1995 — BU...	—	£12
1995 — Proof..	—	£15
1995 — Silver Proof	—	£40
1995 — — — Piedfort..	—	£65
1995 — Gold Proof..	—	£1000
1996 European Football Championships.	5,195,350	£10
1996 — BU	—	£12
1996 — Proof..	—	£15
1996 — Silver Proof	25,163	£40
1996 — — — Piedfort..	7,634	£65
1996 — Gold Proof..	—	£1000
1997 Technology Standard rev. **First Bi-metallic issue**	13,734,625	£5
1997 — BU...	—	£8
1997 — Proof..	—	£12
1997 — Silver Proof	29,910	£35
1997 — — — Piedfort..	16,000	£65
1997 — Gold Proof (red (outer) and yellow (inner) 22ct)	—	£1000

First bi-metal standard reverse

DATE	Mintage	UNC
1998 *New Portrait by Ian Rank-Broadley*	91,110,375	£4
1998 BU	—	£8
1998 Proof	—	£12
1998 Silver Proof	19,978	£35
1998 — — Piedfort	7,646	£60
1999 Technology Standard rev.	33,719,000	£4
1999 Rugby World Cup	4,933,000	£6
1999 — BU	—	£10
1999 — Silver Proof (gold plated ring)	9,665	£45
1999 — — Piedfort (Hologram)	10,000	£85
1999 — Gold Proof	—	£1000
2000 Technology Standard rev.	25,770,000	£4
2000 — BU	—	£6
2000 — Proof	—	£10
2000 — Silver Proof	—	£40
2001 Technology Standard rev.	34,984,750	£4
2001 — BU	—	£5
2001 — Proof	—	£10
2001 Marconi	4,558,000	£5
2001 — BU	—	£8
2001 — Proof	—	£10
2001 — Silver Proof (gold plated ring)	11,488	£40
2001 — — Reverse Frosting (issued in set with Canada $5)	—	£65
2001 — — — Piedfort	6,759	£65
2001 — Gold Proof	—	£1000
2002 Technology Standard rev.	13,024,750	£4
2002 — BU	—	£6
2002 — Proof	—	£10
2002 — Gold Proof (red 22ct)	—	£1000
2002 Commonwealth Games, Scotland	771,750	£15
2002 — Wales	558,500	£15
2002 — Northern Ireland	485,500	£30
2002 — England	650,500	£15
2002 — BU (issued in set of 4)	—	£60
2002 — Proof (issued in set of 4)	—	£75
2002 — Silver Proof (issued in set of 4)	—	£250
2002 — — — Piedfort (painted) (issued in set of 4)	—	£350
2002 — Gold Proof (issued in set of 4)	—	£3500
2003 Technology Standard rev.	17,531,250	£4
2003 — BU	—	£8
2003 — Proof	—	£12
2003 DNA Double Helix	4,299,000	£5
2003 — BU	41,568	£8
2003 — Proof	—	£10
2003 — Silver Proof (Gold-plated ring)	11,204	£40
2003 — — Piedfort	8,728	£65
2003 — Gold Proof	3,237	£1000
2004 Technology Standard rev.	11,981,500	£4
2004 — BU	—	£6
2004 — Proof	—	£12
2004 Trevithick Steam Locomotive	5,004,500	£5
2004 — BU	56,871	£8
2004 — Proof	—	£10
2004 — Silver BU	1,923	£25
2004 — — Proof (Gold-plated ring)	10,233	£45
2004 — — — Piedfort	5,303	£65
2004 — Gold Proof	1,500	£1000
2005 Technology Standard rev.	3,837,250	£4
2005 — BU	—	£6
2005 — Proof	—	£8
2005 Gunpowder Plot	5,140,500	£5
2005 — BU	—	£8
2005 — Proof	—	£10
2005 — Silver Proof	4,394	£40
2005 — — — Piedfort	4,585	£65
2005 — Gold Proof	914	£750

DATE	Mintage	UNC
2005 End of World War II......	10,191,000	£5
2005 — BU......	—	£8
2005 — Silver Proof......	21,734	£40
2005 — — Piedfort......	4,798	£65
2005 — Gold Proof......	2,924	£1000
2006 Technology Standard rev.......	16,715,000	£4
2006 — Proof......	—	£6
2006 Brunel, The Man (Portrait)	7,928,250	£5
2006 — BU......	—	£6
2006 — Proof......	—	£10
2006 — Silver Proof......	7,251	£40
2006 — — Piedfort......	3,199	£65
2006 —Gold Proof......	1,071	£1000
2006 Brunel, His Achievements (Paddington Station)	7,452,250	£5
2006 — BU......	—	£6
2006 — Proof......	—	£10
2006 — Silver Proof......	5,375	£40
2006 — — Piedfort......	3,018	£65
2006 — Gold Proof......	746	£1000
2007 Technology Standard rev.......	10,270,000	£4
2007 — Proof......	—	£8
2007 Tercentenary of the Act of Union......	7,545,000	£5
2007 BU......	—	£6
2007 — Proof......	—	£8
2007 — Silver Proof......	8,310	£40
2007 — — Piedfort......	4,000	£65
2007 — Gold Proof......	750	£1000
2007 Bicentenary of the Abolition of the Slave Trade .	8,445,000	£8
2007 — BU......	—	£10
2007 — Proof......	—	£12
2007 — Silver Proof......	7,095	£40
2007 — — Piedfort......	3,990	£65
2007 — Gold Proof......	1,000	£1000
2008 Technology Standard rev.......	15,346,000	£4
2008 — BU......	—	£6
2008 — Proof......	—	£12
2008 Centenary of 4th Olympiad, London	910,000	£12
2008 — BU......	—	£15
2008 — Proof......	—	£20
2008 — Silver Proof......	6,841	£40
2008 — — Piedfort......	1,619	£70
2008 — Gold Proof......	1,908	£1000
2008 Olympic Games Handover Ceremony......	853,000	£14
2008 — BU......	47,765	£18
2008 — Silver Proof......	30,000	£45
2008 — — Piedfort......	3,000	£75
2008 — Gold Proof......	3,250	£1000
2009 Technology Standard rev.......	8,775,000	£4
2009 — BU......	—	£5
2009 — Proof......	—	£10
2009 — Silver Proof......	—	£40
2009 250th Anniversary of birth of Robert Burns......	3,253,000	£5
2009 — BU......	120,223	£8
2009 — Proof......	—	£12
2009 — Silver Proof......	9,188	£40
2009 — — Piedfort......	3,500	£70
2009 — Gold Proof......	1,000	£1000
2009 200th Anniversary of birth of Charles Darwin......	3,903,000	£5
2009 — BU......	119,713	£8
2009 — Proof......	—	£12
2009 — Silver Proof......	9,357	£40
2009 — — Piedfort......	3,282	£70
2009 — Gold Proof......	1,000	£1000
2010 Technology Standard rev.......	6,890,000	£4
2010 — BU......	—	£8
2010 — Proof......	—	£12

DATE	Mintage	UNC
2010 — Silver Proof	—	£40
2010 Florence Nightingale 150 Years of Nursing	6,175,000	£4
2010 — BU	73,160	£10
2010 — Proof	—	£12
2010 — Silver Proof	5,117	£40
2010 — — Piedfort	2,770	£75
2010 — Gold Proof	472	£1000
2011 Technology Standard rev.	24,375,000	£4
2011 — BU	—	£5
2011 — Proof	—	£12
2011 — Silver Proof	—	£35
2011 500th Anniversary of the Mary Rose	1,040,000	£10
2011 — BU	53,013	£12
2011 — Proof	—	£15
2011 — Silver Proof	6,618	£40
2011 — — Piedfort	2,680	£75
2011 — Gold Proof	692	£1000
2011 400th Anniversary of the King James Bible	975,000	£10
2011 — BU	56,268	£12
2011 — Proof	—	£15
2011 — Silver Proof	4,494	£40
2011 — — Piedfort	2,394	£75
2011 — Gold Proof	355	£1000
2012 Technology Standard rev.	3,900,000	£3
2012 — BU	—	£6
2012 — Proof	—	£12
2012 — Silver Proof	—	£40
2012 — Gold Proof	—	£1000
2012 200th Anniversary of birth of Charles Dickens	8,190,000	£4
2012 — BU	15,035	£11
2012 — Proof	—	£12
2012 — Silver Proof	2,631	£40
2012 — — Piedfort	1,279	£75
2012 — Gold Proof	202	£1000
2012 Olympic Handover to Rio	845,000	£14
2012 — BU	28,356	£20
2012 Proof	—	£25
2012 — Silver Proof	3,781	£40
2012 — — Piedfort	2,000	£120
2012 — Gold Proof	771	£1000
2013 Technology Standard rev.	15,860,250	£4
2013 — BU	—	£6
2013 — Proof	—	£12
2013 — Silver Proof	—	£65
2013 — Gold Proof	—	£1000
2013 150th Anniversary of the London Underground, Roundel design	1,560,000	£6
2013 — BU	11,647	£12
2013 — Proof	—	£18
2013 — Silver Proof	3,389	£40
2013 — — Piedfort	162	£100
2013 — Gold Proof	132	£1000
2013 150th Anniversary of the London Underground, Train design	1,690,000	£6
2013 — BU	11,647	£12
2013 — Proof	—	£18
2013 — Silver Proof	4,246	£40
2013 — — Piedfort	186	£100
2013 — Gold Proof	140	£1000
2013 350th Anniversary of the Guinea	2,990,000	£5
2013 — BU	10,340	£12
2013 — Proof	—	£18
2013 — Silver Proof	1,640	£40
2013 — — Piedfort	969	£100
2013 — Gold Proof	284	£1000

DATE	Mintage	UNC
2014 Technology Standard rev.	18,200,000	£4
2014 — BU	—	£10
2014 — Proof	—	£25
2014 — Silver Proof	—	£40
2014 100th Anniversary of First World War Outbreak	5,720,000	£4
2014 — BU	40,557	£10
2014 — Proof	—	£20
2014 — Silver Proof	4,983	£40
2014 — — — Piedfort	2,496	£100
2014 — Gold Proof	—	£1000
2014 500th Anniversary of Trinity House	3,705,000	£4
2014 — BU	10,521	£12
2014 — Proof	—	£20
2014 — Silver Proof	1,285	£40
2014 — — — Piedfort	652	£100
2014 — Gold Proof	204	£1000
2015 Technology Standard rev.	35,360,058	£4
2015 — BU	39,009	£10
2015 — Proof	3,930	£20
2015 — Silver Proof	1,512	£40
2015 — Gold Proof	406	£1000
2015 Anniversary of First World War—Royal Navy	650,000	£10
2015 — BU	39,009	£12
2015 — Proof	—	£20
2015 — Silver Proof	3,030	£40
2015 — — — Piedfort	1,512	£100
2015 — Gold Proof	406	£1000
2015 800th Anniversary of Magna Carta	1,495,000	£15
2015 — BU	32,818	£20
2015 — Proof	—	£25
2015 — Silver Proof	2,995	£40
2015 — — — Piedfort	1,988	£100
2015 — Gold Proof	399	£1000

New Portrait by Jody Clark

DATE	Mintage	UNC
2015 — Silver Proof	—	£40
2015 — — — Piedfort	—	£100
2015 — Gold Proof	—	£1000
2015 Britannia—**the new standard reverse design**	650,000	£8
2015 — BU	—	£10
2015 — Proof	—	£20
2015 — Silver Proof	—	£40
2015 — Gold Proof	—	£1000
2015 — Platinum Proof	—	£900
2016 Britannia Standard rev.	2,925,000	£5
2016 — BU	—	£10
2016 — Proof	—	£20
2016 — Silver Proof	—	£40
2016 400th Anniversary Shakespeare's death, Comedies	4,355,000	£4
2016 — — BU	—	£10
2016 — — Proof	—	£20
2016 — — Silver Proof	951	£40
2016 — — — — Piedfort	533	£125
2016 — — Gold Proof	152	£1000
2016 — Tragedies	5,695,000	£4
2016 — — BU	—	£10
2016 — — Proof	—	£20
2016 — — Silver Proof	1,004	£40
2016 — — — — Piedfort	679	£125
2016 — — Gold Proof	209	£1000
2016 — Histories	4,615,000	£4
2016 — — BU	—	£10
2016 — — Proof	—	£20
2016 — — Silver Proof	965	£40

Britannia standard reverse

DATE	Mintage	UNC
2016 — — — Piedfort....................................	624	£125
2016 — — Gold Proof..................................	156	£1000
2016 350th Anniversary of Great Fire of London	5,135,000	£4
2016 — BU..	23,215	£10
2016 — Proof	—	£20
2016 — Silver Proof	1,649	£50
2016 — — — Piedfort....................................	1,356	£125
2016 — Gold Proof......................................	259	£1000
2016 Anniversary of First World War—Army	9,550,000	£4
2016 — BU..	19,066	£10
2016 — Proof	—	£20
2016 — Silver Proof	1,703	£50
2016 — — — Piedfort....................................	931	£125
2016 — Gold Proof......................................	279	£1000
2017 Britannia Standard rev. BU	—	£5
2017 — Proof	—	£20
2017 — Silver Proof	—	£50
2017 — Gold Proof......................................	—	£1000
2017 Anniversary of First World War—Aviation BU.....	55,840	£10
2017 — Proof	—	£20
2017 — Silver Proof	7,000	£75
2017 — — — Piedfort....................................	1,528	£125
2017 — Gold Proof......................................	634	£1000
2017 Jane Austen BU....................................	54,729	£10
2017 — Proof	—	£20
2017 — Silver Proof	7,498	£75
2017 — — — Piedfort....................................	2,125	£125
2017 — Gold Proof......................................	884	£1000
2018 Britannia Standard rev.	—	£3
2018 —BU..	—	£10
2018 — Proof	—	£20
2018 — Silver Proof	—	£40
2018 — Gold Proof......................................	—	£1000
2018 Bicentenary of Mary Shelley's "Frankenstein" BU	—	£12
2018 — Proof	—	£25
2018 — Silver Proof	—	£70
2018 — Gold Proof......................................	—	£1000
2018 Journey to Armistice BU	—	£10
2018 — Proof	—	£20
2018 — Silver Proof	5,000	£50
2018 — — — Piedfort....................................	2,500	£125
2018 — Gold Proof......................................	750	£1000
2018 Centenary of the RAF BU	—	£10
2018 — Proof	—	£25
2018 — Silver Proof	7,500	£50
2018 — — — Piedfort....................................	3,000	£125
2018 — Gold Proof......................................	1,000	£1000
2018 250th Anniversary of Captain Cook's "Voyage of Discovery"—I BU	—	£10
2018 — Proof	—	£25
2018 — Silver Proof	4,795	£70
2018 — — — Piedfort....................................	4,000	£125
2018 —Gold Proof.......................................	340	£1000
2019 Britannia Standard rev. BU	—	£10
2019 — Proof	—	£20
2019 — Silver Proof	—	£50
2019 D-Day: 75th Anniversary BU	—	£10
2019 — Proof	—	£25
2019 — Silver Proof	8,750	£75
2019 — — Piedfort.......................................	3,010	£125
2019 — Gold Proof......................................	750	£1000
2019 Captain Cook II BU...............................	—	£10
2019 — Proof	—	£25
2019 — Silver Proof	5,000	£85
2019 — — — Piedfort....................................	4,000	£125
2019 — Gold Proof......................................	350	£1100

DATE	Mintage	UNC
2019 Samuel Pepys BU	—	£10
2019 — Proof	—	£25
2019 — Silver Proof	3,500	£85
2019 — — Piedfort	2,019	£125
2019 — Gold Proof...	350	£1100
2019 260th Anniversary of Wedgwood BU	—	£10
2019 — Proof	—	£25
2019 — Silver Proof	4,500	£100
2019 — — Piedfort	2,250	£125
2019 — Gold Proof...	350	£1100
2020 Britannia Standard rev. BU..............................	—	£10
2020 — Proof	—	£20
2020 — Silver Proof	—	£85
2020 Captain Cook III BU..	—	£10
2020 — Proof	—	£25
2020 — Silver Proof	4,795	£85
2019 — — Piedfort	2,250	£125
2020 — Gold Proof...	340	£1000
2020 VE Day Anniversary BU	—	£
2020 — Proof	—	£25
2020 — Silver Proof	—	£85
2020 — — — Piedfort	—	£150
2020 — Gold Proof...	—	£1100
2020 100 years of Agatha Christie BU	—	£10
2020 — Proof	—	£25
2020 — Silver Proof	—	£85
2020 — — — Piedfort	—	£150
2020 — Gold Proof...	—	£1100
2020 Anniversary of the sailing of the "Mayflower" BU.	—	£10
2020 — Proof	—	£25
2020 — Silver Proof	—	£85
2020 — — — Piedfort	—	£150
2020 — Gold Proof...	—	£1155
2021 Britannia Standard rev. BU..............................	—	£10
2021 — Proof	—	£20
2021 — Silver Proof	—	£85
2021 Celebrating the life and work of H. G. Wells BU	—	£10
2021 — Proof	—	£25
2021 — Silver Proof	3135	£72.50
2021 — — Piedfort	985	£117.50
2021 — Gold Proof...	330	£1095
2021 250th Anniversary of the birth of Sir. Walter Scott BU..	—	£10
2021 — Proof	—	£25
2021 — Silver Proof	1771	£72.50
2021 — — Piedfort	771	£117.50
2021 — Gold Proof...	175	£1095
2022 Britannia Standard rev. BU..............................	—	£10
2022 — Proof	—	£20
2022 — Silver Proof	—	£85
2022 150 Years of the FA Cup BU.............................	—	£12
2022 — Silver Proof	5,660	£72.50
2022 — — Piedfort	1,160	£117.50
2022 — Gold Proof...	360	£1,125
2022 Alexander Graham Bell BU...............................	—	£10
2022 — Silver Proof	2,500	£72.50
2022 — — Piedfort	1,000	£117.50
2022 — Gold Proof...	125	£1,180

Note: The silver editions are silver centres with silver outers plated with gold. The gold issues are 22ct yellow gold centres with 22ct red gold outers.

SOVEREIGN

All are minted in gold, bear the Pistrucci St George and Dragon reverse except where stated, and are legal tender at one pound. From 2009 there is no streamer behind St George's Helmet in the Pistrucci design.

DATE	Mintage	UNC
1974	5,002,566	£360
1976	4,150,000	£360
1976 Brilliant Proof	—	£10000
1978	6,550,000	£360
1979	9,100,000	£360
1979 Proof	50,000	£400
1980	5,100,000	£360
1980 Proof	91,200	£400
1981	5,000,000	£360
1981 Proof	32,960	£425
1982	2,950,000	£360
1982 Proof	22,500	£425
1983 Proof	21,250	£500
1984 Proof	19,975	£500
1985 **New portrait** Proof	17,242	£625
1986 Proof	17,579	£600
1987 Proof	22,479	£600
1988 Proof	18,862	£600
1989 500th Anniversary of the Sovereign—details as Five Pounds (Sov. Series). Proof	23,471	£1850
1990 Proof	8,425	£600
1991 Proof	7,201	£600
1992 Proof	6,854	£600
1993 Proof	6,090	£600
1994 Proof	7,165	£600
1995 Proof	9,500	£600
1996 Proof	9,110	£600
1997 Proof	9,177	£600
1998 **New Portrait** Proof	11,349	£550
1999 Proof	11,903	£500
2000 (first Unc issue since 1982)	129,069	£375
2000 Proof	12,159	£550
2001	49,462	£360
2001 Proof	10,000	£500
2002 Golden Jubilee Shield Rev. ("bullion")	74,263	£400
2002 Proof	20,500	£750
2003 ("bullion")	43,208	£375
2003 Proof	12,433	£500
2004 ("bullion")	30,688	£375
2004 Proof	10,175	£475
2005 Timothy Noad's heraldic St George and Dragon	75,542	£550
2005 — Proof	12,500	£700
2006 ("bullion")	—	£375
2006 Proof	9,195	£450
2007 ("bullion")	75,000	£360
2007 Proof	8,199	£500
2008 ("bullion")	35,000	£375
2008 Proof	12,500	£475
2009 ("bullion")	75,000	£375
2009 Proof	9,770	£500
2010 ("bullion")	243,986	£360
2010 Proof	8,828	£525
2011 ("bullion")	250,000	£325
2011 Proof	15,000	£500

Standard reverse

500th Anniversary reverse

Golden Jubilee Shield reverse

Noad modern reverse

DATE	Mintage	UNC
2012 Paul Day's St George and Dragon BU "bullion".	250,000	£425
2012 — Proof	5,501	£1250
2013 BU ("bullion")...	2,695	£375
2013 Proof...	8,243	£475
2013 With "I" mintmark, minted by MMTC-PAMP, Haryana, India, under Licence from, and supervision of, the Royal Mint	—	£450
2014 BU ("bullion"	15,000	£375
2014 Proof)...	9,725	£550
2014 BU ("bullion") with "I" mintmark	—	£450
2015 BU ("bullion")...	10,000	£375
2015 Proof...	4,456	£475
2015 **New Portrait** by Jody Clark BU........................	10,000	£400
2015— Proof	7,494	£475
2016 BU ("bullion")...	1,251	£400
2016 Queen's 90th Birthday, Butler portrait. Proof.....	7,995	£800
2017 200th Anniversary of the Sovereign. Original 1817 "Garter" design. Proof-like...........................	13,500	£895
2017 — Piedfort	3,750	£1250
2017 BU with 200 Privy mark......................................	—	£850
2017 Royal Platinum Wedding Strike on the day (no privy mark)	1,793	£850
2017 BU ("bullion")...	—	£375
2018 BU ("bullion")...	—	£375
2018 Proof...	10,500	£500
2018 — Piedfort	2,675	£900
2019 BU Matt finish..	20,500	£475
2019 Proof...	9,500	£550
2019 — Piedfort	—	£850
2020 BU ("bullion")...	—	£375
2020 200th Anniversary of death of George III With GR cypher privy mark....................................	9,845	£650
2020 Matt finish, plain edge	—	£750
2021 BU ("bullion")..	—	£375
2021 Proof Queen's 95th Birthday (95 millings on edge). Unique privy mark (Royal crown with the number 95 entwined)	9,850	£600
2022 Proof Platinum Jubilee, Royal Coat of Arms reverse	10,500	£585

For coins struck on the day of a special event see the table opposite.

Note that coins struck on the actual day of the event are always accompanied by a certificate of authenticity from the Royal Mint. With many of these "Strike on the day" coins this is the only means of identification as they do not all carry special privy marks. Only those with these privy marks are listed here.

Day's stylised reverse

200th Anniversary reverse

2020 Withdrawal from the EU

2021 Proof Queen's 95th Birthday

2022 Proof Platinum Jubilee, Royal Coat of Arms

SOVEREIGNS STRUCK ON THE DAY

To commemorate certain special occasions the Royal Mint strike a limited number of sovereigns on the day of the event. Listed below are the events so marked and the quantities issued. Some are only identified by a special certificate issued with the coin, but the later issues are marked with a special privy mark appropriate to the occasion. The first strike on the day was to mark the Diamond Jubilee of Her Majesty the Queen on June 2, 2012, followed by the 60th anniversary of the Coronation the following year. Since then various occasions have been celebrated and this has generated a great deal of interest among collectors, with the generally low quantities struck reflected in their values if kept in their original box accompanied by the certificate.

Date	Occasion struck	Quantity	Type	Privy mark
June 2, 2012	Diamond Jubilee of Her Majesty the Queen	1,990	BU	—
June 2, 2013	60th anniversary of the Coronation	900	BU	—
July 22, 2013	Birth of Prince George	2,013	BU	—
July 22, 2014	First birthday of Prince George	398	BU	—
May 2, 2015	Birth of Princess Charlotte	743	BU	—
July 22, 2015	Second birthday of Prince George	301	BU (Jody Clark obv.)	—
June 11, 2016	90th birthday of Her Majesty the Queen	499	BU	—
June 2, 2017	65th anniversary of the accession of Her Majesty the Queen	739	BU	—
July 1, 2017	200th anniversary of the issue of the 1817 sovereign	1,793	BU, plain edge	—
November 20, 2017	Platinum Wedding of Her Majesty the Queen and Prince Philip	745	BU	—
June 2, 2018	65th anniversary of the Coronation	323	BU, plain edge	65
July 22, 2018	5th birthday of Prince George	457	BU, plain edge	—
May 24, 2019	200th anniversary of birth of Queen Victoria	Limit 650	Matt, plain edge	VR
August 26, 2019	200th anniversary of birth of Prince Albert	Limit 650	Matt, plain edge	VA
January 31, 2020	"Brexit" Day	Limit 1,500	Matt, plain edge	Crowned portcullis
May 8, 2020	75th anniversary of VE Day	Limit 750	Matt, plain edge	VE75
August 15, 2020	75th anniversary of the End of WWII	Limit 750	Matt, plain edge	VJ75
April 21, 2021*	The 95th birthday of Her Majesty the Queen	Limit 1,295	Matt, plain edge	95 in Crown
February 6, 2022	Platinum Jubilee of Her Majesty the Queen (Royal Arms reverse design by the heraldic artist Timothy Noad)	Limit 1,200	BU	—

* Owing to the death of HRH Prince Philip this occasion was postponed until June 12, Her Majesty's official birthday.

In addition to the above, the Royal Mint have also adopted the policy of striking other denominations on appropriate dates and these are offered as "Strike on the Day" coins. It has been decided that these are outside of the scope of this publication and are therefore not recorded. For more information visit the Royal Mint website at www.royalmint.com

---

IMPORTANT NOTE:
The prices quoted in this guide are set at August 2022 with the price of gold at £1,500 per ounce and silver £15.80 per ounce—market fluctuations can have a marked effect on the values of modern precious metal coins.

HALF SOVEREIGN

Legal Tender at 50 pence, otherwise the notes for the Sovereign apply. From 2009 the exergue in the Pistrucci design is larger in area, and the initials B.P. are absent. From 2011, however, the initials were restored.

DATE	Mintage	UNC
1980 Proof only	86,700	£225
1982	2,500,000	£180
1982 Proof	21,590	£220
1983 Proof	19,710	£275
1984 Proof	19,505	£275
1985 New portrait Proof	15,800	£275
1986 Proof	17,075	£250
1987 Proof	20,687	£275
1988 Proof	18,266	£250
1989 500th Anniversary of the Sovereign—details as Five Pounds (Sov. Series) Proof	21,824	£550
1990 Proof	7,889	£275
1991 Proof	6,076	£275
1992 Proof	5,915	£325
1993 Proof	4,651	£325
1994 Proof	7,167	£275
1995 Proof	7,500	£275
1996 New Portrait Proof	7,340	£275
1997 Proof	9,177	£275
1998 Proof	7,496	£275
1999 Proof	9,403	£275
2000	146,822	£180
2000 Proof	9,708	£260
2001	98,763	£180
2001 Proof	7,500	£250
2002 Golden Jubilee Shield reverse ("bullion")	61,347	£225
2002 Proof	—	£350
2003 ("bullion")	47,805	£180
2003 Proof	—	£250
2004 ("bullion")	32,479	£180
2004 Proof	—	£250
2005 Timothy Noad's heraldic St George and Dragon	—	£250
2005 — Proof	—	£325
2006 ("bullion")	—	£180
2006 Proof	—	£250
2006 ("bullion")	—	£180
2007 Proof	—	£250
2008 ("bullion")	—	£180
2008 Proof	—	£250
2009 ("bullion")	—	£180
2009 Proof	—	£250
2010 ("bullion")	16,485	£180
2010 Proof	—	£250
2011 ("bullion")	—	£180
2011 Proof	—	£250
2012 Paul Day's stylised reverse. Diamond Jubilee BU	—	£250
2012 — Proof	—	£425
2013 BU "bullion"	—	£225
2013 Proof	—	£300
2014 BU "bullion"	—	£225
2014 Proof	—	£300
2014 BU "bullion" with "I" mintmark	—	£200
2015 BU "bullion"	500	£300
2015 Proof	1,704	£300
2015 New Jody Clark portrait. Proof	—	£300
2016 BU "bullion"	472	£300
2016 Queen's 90th Birthday, Butler portrait. Proof	1,995	£400

Standard reverse

500th Anniversary reverse

Golden Jubilee Shield reverse

Timothy Noad's Heraldic reverse

Paul Day's Diamond Jubilee reverse

DATE	Mintage	UNC
2017 200th Anniversary of the Sovereign. Original 1817 "Garter" design. Proof-like...............	1,817	£500
2017 With 200 Privy mark	—	£300
2018 BU "bullion"	—	£180
2018 Proof with 65 privy mark	2,500	£260
2019 BU Matt finish..	4,620	£225
2019 Proof..	—	£260
2020 ("bullion")...	—	£180
2020 200th Anniversary of death of George III With GR cypher privy mark................	3,910	£280
2021 Proof with 95 privy mark	3,260	£315
2021 ("bullion")..	—	£180
2022 Platinum Jubilee, Royal Coat of Arms reverse ...	2,000	£315

200th Anniversary reverse

QUARTER SOVEREIGN

Minted in 22ct gold, this denomination was introduced in 2009 in the same style as the rest of the sovereign series.

DATE	Mintage	UNC
2009 ("bullion")..	50,000	£100
2009 Proof..	13,495	£150
2010 ("bullion")..	250,000	£100
2010 Proof..	6,007	£150
2011 ("bullion")..	50,000	£100
2011 Proof..	7,764	£150
2012 Paul Day's stylised reverse Diamond Jubilee.....	137	£175
2012 — Proof..	7,579	£200
2013 ("bullion")..	—	£100
2013 Proof..	1,729	£150
2014 Proof..	1,696	£150
2015 Proof..	1,808	£145
2015 Jody Clark portrait Proof	550	£155
2016 Butler portrait Proof...	1,727	£220
2017 200th Anniversary Proof	5,100	£200
2018 Proof with 65 privy mark	—	£175
2019 BU Matt finish..	1,750	£165
2019 Proof..	—	£200
2020 200th Anniversary of death of George III With GR cypher privy mark, proof	—	£200
2021 Proof with 95 privy mark	1,700	£200

ONE POUND

Introduced into circulation in 1983 to replace the £1 note, the original, £1 coins are minted in nickel-brass unless otherwise stated. The reverse changed yearly until 2008, and until 2008 the Royal Arms was the "definitive" version. 2008 also saw the introduction of the Matthew Dent Uncrowned Shield of the Royal Arms, a new "definitive", and this reverse appeared in 2008 and every year until 2017. A Capital Cities Series of two coins each year for two years commenced in 2010. From 2013 a further 4-coin series over two years was issued, portraying two floral emblems associated with each of the four countries making up the United Kingdom. Collectors and others should be aware of the many different counterfeit £1 coin versions that circulated up until 2017, a high proportion of which do not have matching obverses and reverses although many do. These original £1 coins have now been withdrawn from circulation. A 12-sided bi-metallic coin replaced the round £1 coin in 2017 which incorporates several security features to help defeat the counterfeiters.

DATE	Mintage	UNC
1983 Royal Arms	443,053,510	£3
1983 — BU	1,134,000	£8
1983 — Proof	107,800	£8
1983 — Silver Proof	50,000	£25
1983 — — — Piedfort	10,000	£85
1984 Scottish Thistle	146,256,501	£3
1984 — BU	199,430	£6
1984 — Proof	106,520	£8
1984 — Silver Proof	44,855	£25
1984 — — — Piedfort	15,000	£35
1985 **New portrait.** Welsh Leek	228,430,749	£3
1985 — BU	213,679	£5
1985 — Proof	102,015	£6
1985 — Silver Proof	50,000	£25
1985 — — — Piedfort	15,000	£35
1986 Northern Ireland Flax	10,409,501	£3
1986 — BU	—	£6
1986 — Proof	—	£7
1986 — Silver Proof	37,958	£25
1986 — — — Piedfort	15,000	£35
1987 English Oak	39,298,502	£3
1987 — BU	—	£5
1987 — Proof	—	£8
1987 — Silver Proof	50,000	£25
1987 — — — Piedfort	15,000	£35
1988 Crowned Shield Of The Royal Arms	7,118,825	£5
1988 — BU	—	£7
1988 — Proof	—	£8
1988 — Silver Proof	50,000	£25
1988 — — — Piedfort	10,000	£35
1989 Scottish Thistle	70,580,501	£4
1989 — BU	—	£6
1989 — Proof	—	£9
1989 — Silver Proof	22,275	£25
1989 — — — Piedfort	10,000	£35
1990 Welsh Leek	—	£4
1990 — BU	97,269,302	£6
1990 — Proof	—	£7
1990 — Silver Proof	23,277	£25
1991 Northern Ireland Flax	38,443,575	£3
1991 — BU	—	£6
1991 — Proof	—	£9
1991 — Silver Proof	22,922	£25

1983, 1993, 1998, 2003
EDGE: DECUS ET TUTAMEN

1984, 1989
NEMO ME IMPUNE LACESSIT

1985, 1990
PLEIDIOL WYF I'M GWLAD

1986, 1991
DECUS ET TUTAMEN

1987, 1992
DECUS ET TUTAMEN

DATE	Mintage	UNC
1992 English Oak	36,320,487	£3
1992 — BU	—	£6
1992 — Proof	—	£7
1992 — Silver Proof	13,065	£25
1993 Royal Arms	114,744,500	£3
1993 — BU	—	£6
1993 — Proof	—	£7
1993 — Silver Proof	16,526	£25
1993 — — Piedfort	12,500	£30
1994 Scottish Lion	29,752,525	£4
1994 — BU	—	£6
1994 — Proof	—	£8
1994 — Silver Proof	25,000	£25
1994 — — Piedfort	11,722	£30
1995 Welsh Dragon	34,503,501	£3
1995 — BU	—	£6
1995 — — (Welsh)	—	£7
1995 — Proof	—	£10
1995 — Silver Proof	27,445	£25
1995 — — Piedfort	8,458	£30
1996 Northern Ireland Celtic Cross	89,886,000	£4
1996 — BU	—	£6
1996 — Proof	—	£7
1996 — Silver Proof	25,000	£25
1996 — — Piedfort	10,000	£30
1997 English Lions	57,117,450	£4
1997 — BU	—	£6
1997 — Proof	—	£7
1997 — Silver Proof	20,137	£30
1997 — — Piedfort	10,000	£35
1998 **New portrait.** Royal Arms. BU	—	£15
1998 — Proof	—	£20
1998 — Silver Proof	13,863	£35
1998 — — Piedfort	7,894	£40
1999 Scottish Lion. BU	—	£15
1999 — Proof	—	£20
1999 — Silver Proof	16,328	£30
1999 — — Reverse Frosting	—	£45
1999 — — Piedfort	9,975	£35
2000 Welsh Dragon	109,496,500	£3
2000 — BU	—	£6
2000 — Proof	—	£8
2000 — Silver Proof	15,913	£25
2000 — — Reverse Frosting	—	£45
2000 — — Piedfort	9,994	£35
2001 Northern Ireland Celtic Cross.	63,968,065	£3
2001 — BU	58,093,731	£6
2001 — Proof	—	£8
2001 — Silver Proof	11,697	£25
2001 — — Reverse Frosting	—	£45
2001 — — Piedfort	8,464	£35
2002 English Lions	77,818,000	£3
2002 — BU	—	£5
2002 — Proof	—	£8
2002 — Silver Proof	17,693	£35
2002 — — Reverse Frosting	—	£45
2002 — — Piedfort	6,599	£50
2002 — Gold Proof	—	£450
2003 Royal Arms	61,596,500	£4
2003 — BU	23,760	£6
2003 — Proof	—	£8
2003 — Silver Proof	15,830	£30
2003 — — Piedfort	9,871	£35

1988
DECUS ET TUTAMEN

1994, 1999
NEMO ME IMPUNE LACESSIT

1995, 2000
PLEIDIOL WYF I'M GWLAD

1996, 2001
DECUS ET TUTAMEN

1997, 2002
DECUS ET TUTAMEN

2004
PATTERNED EDGE

DATE	Mintage	UNC
2004 Forth Railway Bridge	39,162,000	£4
2004 — BU	24,014	£6
2004 — Proof	—	£10
2004 — Silver Proof	11,470	£30
2004 — — Piedfort	7,013	£40
2004 — Gold Proof	—	£450
2005 Menai Bridge	99,429,500	£4
2005 — BU	—	£6
2005 — Proof	—	£10
2005 — Silver Proof	8,371	£35
2005 — — Piedfort	6,007	£40
2005 — Gold Proof	—	£450
2006 Egyptian Arch	38,938,000	£4
2006 — BU	—	£6
2006 — Proof	—	£10
2006 — Silver Proof	14,765	£30
2006 — — Piedfort	5,129	£40
2006 — Gold Proof	—	£450
2007 Gateshead Millennium Bridge	26,180,160	£4
2007 — BU	—	£6
2007 — Proof	—	£10
2007 — Silver Proof	10,110	£35
2007 — — Piedfort	5,739	£40
2007 — Gold Proof	—	£450
2008 Royal Arms	3,910,000	£3
2008 — BU	18,336	£6
2008 — Proof	—	£8
2008 — Silver Proof	8,441	£30
2008 — Gold Proof	674	£450
2008 — Platinum Proof	—	£500
2008 A series of 14 different reverses, the 25th Anniversary of the modern £1 coin, Silver Proof with selected gold highlighting on the reverses. the latter being all those used since 1983, the coins being with appropriate edge lettering	—	£450
2008 The same as above, Gold Proof (the 2008 Royal Arms being already listed above)	150	£6250
2008 **New Rev.,** Shield of the Royal Arms, no border beads on Obv.	29,518,000	£3
2008 BU	—	£5
2008 Proof	—	£6
2008 Silver Proof	5,000	£30
2008 Silver Proof Piedfort	2,456	£50
2008 Gold Proof	860	£475
2008 Platinum Proof	—	£600
2009	7,820,000	£2
2009 BU	130,644	£5
2009 Proof	—	£6
2009 Silver Proof	8,508	£30
2009 Gold Proof	540	£600
2010	38,505,000	£2
2010 BU	—	£8
2010 Proof	—	£6
2010 Silver BU	—	£30
2010 — Proof	—	£45
2010 City Series (London)	2,635,000	£3
2010 — BU	66,313	£10
2010 — Proof	—	£15
2010 — Silver Proof	7,693	£45
2010 — — Piedfort	3,682	£65
2010 — Gold Proof	950	£500
2010 City Series (Belfast)	6,205,000	£3
2010 — BU	64,461	£10

2005
PATTERNED EDGE

2006
PATTERNED EDGE

2007
PATTERNED EDGE

2008 (proof sets—silver and gold)
DECUS ET TUTAMEN

2008, 2009, 2010, 2011
DECUS ET TUTAMEN

2011
**Y DDRAIG GOCH
DDYRY CYCHWYN**

DATE	Mintage	UNC
2010 — Proof	—	£15
2010 — Silver Proof	5,805	£45
2010 — — Piedfort	3,503	£65
2010 — Gold Proof	585	£500
2011	25,415,000	£3
2011 BU	—	£10
2011 Proof	—	£15
2011 Silver BU (in 21st and 18th Birthday cards)	—	£30
2011 — Proof	—	£35
2011 City Series (Cardiff)	1,615,000	£5
2011 — BU	47,933	£10
2011 — Proof	—	£15
2011 — Silver Proof	5,553	£50
2011 — — Piedfort	1,615	£70
2011 — Gold Proof	524	£500
2011 City Series (Edinburgh)	935,000	£6
2011 — BU	47,896	£15
2011 — Proof	—	£20
2011 — Silver Proof	4,973	£60
2011 — — Piedfort	2,696	£90
2011 — Gold Proof	499	£500
2012	35,700,030	£3
2012 BU	—	£5
2012 Proof	—	£10
2012 Silver BU (in Silver Baby Gift)	—	£75
2012 Silver Proof	—	£45
2012 — with selective gold plating	—	£55
2012 Gold Proof	—	£500
2013	13,090,500	£3
2013 BU	—	£10
2013 Proof	—	£15
2013 Silver BU	—	£60
2013 Silver Proof	—	£45
2013 Gold Proof	—	£500
2013 Floral Series (England)	5,270,000	£2
2013 — BU	6112	£10
2013 — Proof	—	£15
2013 — Silver Proof	3,334	£60
2013 — — Piedfort	1,071	£80
2013 — Gold Proof	284	£750
2013 Floral Series (Wales)	5,270,000	£2
2013 — BU	6112	£15
2013 — Proof	—	£15
2013 — Silver Proof	3,094	£60
2013 — — Piedfort	860	£80
2013 — Gold Proof	274	£750
2013 Royal Coat of Arms (Sewell), Gold Proof	—	£550
2013 Crowned Royal Arms (Gorringe), Gold Proof	—	£550

(The above two coins are part of a set of three, along with the 2013 gold proof, with definitive reverse with Uncrowned Royal Arms (Dent)).

DATE	Mintage	UNC
2014	79,305,200	£3
2014 BU	—	£6
2014 Proof	—	£10
2014 Silver BU	—	£40
2014 Silver Proof	—	£45
2014 Floral Series (Scotland)	5,185,000	£2
2014 — BU	3,832	£6
2014 — Proof	—	£10
2014 — Silver Proof	1,540	£60
2014 — — Piedfort	—	£80
2014 — Gold Proof	154	£850

2011
NISI DOMINUS FRUSTRA

2013 Wales £1 Floral gold proof.

Most £1 coins are also available in precious metals.

2014 Scotland £1 Floral gold proof.

2015

DATE	Mintage	UNC
2014 Floral Series (Northern Ireland)	5,780,000	£2
2014 — BU	—	£10
2014 — Proof	—	£12
2014 — Silver Proof	1,502	£60
2014 — — — Piedfort	788	£80
2014 — Gold Proof	166	£850
2015	29,580,000	£3
2015 BU	—	£8
2015 Proof	—	£12
2015 Silver Proof	—	£45
2015 Gold Proof	—	£550
2015 Platinum Proof	—	—
2015 *New Portrait* BU	62,495,640	£3
2015 Proof	—	£10
2015 Silver Proof	7,500	£50
2015 Gold Proof	500	£550
2015 Heraldic Royal Arms	—	£3
2015 — BU	—	£6
2015 — Silver Proof	3,500	£50
2015 — — — Piedfort	2,000	£100
2015 — Gold Proof	500	£550
2016 BU	—	£20
2016 Proof	—	£25
2016 Silver Proof	—	£50
2016 The Last Round Pound		
2016 — BU	96,089	£15
2016 — Proof	—	£20
2016 — Silver Proof	7,491	£45
2016 — — — Piedfort	2,943	£125
2016 — Gold Proof	499	£650

2016 The last round pound

12-sided coin Nations of the Crown design

DATE	Mintage	UNC
2016	648,936,536	£3
2016 BU	—	£15
2016 BU cross crosslet mm in folder with Last Round £1	10,000	£75
2017	749,616,200	£3
2017 BU	—	£10
2017 Proof	—	£12
2017 Silver Proof	26,000	£50
2017 Silver Proof Piedfort	4,500	£250
2017 Gold Proof	2,008	£650
2017 Platinum Proof	232	£750
2018 BU	—	£10
2018 Proof	—	£12
2018 Silver Proof	—	£50
2019 BU	—	£12
2019 Proof	—	£15
2019 Silver Proof	—	£50
2020 BU	—	£12
2020 Proof	—	£15
2020 Silver Proof	—	£50
2021 BU	—	£12
2021 Proof	—	£15
2021 Silver Proof	—	£50
2022 BU	—	£12
2022 Proof	—	£15
2022 Silver Proof	—	£50

12-sided issue with Jody Clark portrait obverse and the reverse designed by 15-year-old David Pearce

FIFTY PENCE

Introduced as legal tender for 10 shillings to replace the banknote of that value prior to decimalisation, coins of the original size are no longer legal tender. Unless otherwise stated, i.e. for commemoratives, the reverse design is of Britannia. The reverse legend of NEW PENCE became FIFTY PENCE from 1982.

The description of "Unc" has been used against some 50 pence pieces dated 2009 and 2011 (for Olympic and Paralympic sports) to distinguish them from coins minted to circulation standard and BU standard, being a standard between the latter two. The uncirculated standard coins have a more even rim than the circulation standard examples, particularly observable on the obverse.

Since the surge of interest in collecting 50p coins prices have increased. The following values are for uncirculated coins. Any found in change will of course have been circulated and will not command such a high premium but the rarer ones will still be worth more than face value.

DATE	Mintage	UNC
1969	188,400,000	£2
1970	19,461,500	£5
1971 Proof	—	£10
1972 Proof	—	£12
1973 Accession to EEC	89,775,000	£3
1973 — Proof	—	£8
1973 — Silver Proof Piedfort	About 24	£3250
1974 Proof	—	£10
1975 Proof	—	£10
1976	43,746,500	£2
1976 Proof	—	£7
1977	49,536,000	£2
1977 Proof	—	£6
1978	72,005,000	£2
1978 Proof	—	£6
1979	58,680,000	£2
1979 Proof	—	£6
1980	89,086,000	£2
1980 Proof	—	£6
1981	74,002,000	£2
1981 Proof	—	£8
1982	51,312,000	£3
1982 Unc	—	£6
1982 Proof	—	£8
1983	62,824,000	£2
1983 Unc	—	£6
1983 Proof	—	£8
1984 BU (only issued in Year Sets)	158,820	£7
1984 Proof	—	£10
1985 **New portrait**	682,103	£2
1985 BU (only issued in Year Sets)	—	£7
1985 Proof	—	£8
1986 BU (only issued in Year Sets)	—	£7
1986 Proof	—	£12
1987 BU (only issued in Year Sets)	—	£7
1987 Proof	—	£12
1988 BU (only issued in Year Sets)	—	£7
1988 Proof	—	£12
1989 BU (only issued in Year Sets)	—	£7
1989 Proof	—	£12
1990 BU (only issued in Year Sets)	—	£7
1990 Proof	—	£12
1991 BU (only issued in Year Sets)	—	£7
1991 Proof	—	£12
1992 BU (only issued in Year Sets)	—	£10

Accession to the EEC 1973.

Presidency of the EC Council 1992.

1994

TE	Mintage	UNC
1992 Proof..	—	£12
1992 Presidency of EC Council and EC accession 20th anniversary		
(includes 1993 date).................................	109,000	£45
1992 — BU..	—	£50
1992 — Proof..	—	£55
1992 — Silver Proof	26,890	£70
1992 — — Piedfort......................................	10,993	£90
1992 — Gold Proof......................................	—	£550
1993 BU (only issued in Year Sets)................	—	£10
1993 Proof..	—	£12
1994 50th Anniversary of the Normandy Landings........	6,705,520	£3
1994 — BU (also in presentation folder)	—	£8
1994 — Proof..	—	£10
1994 — Silver Proof	40,000	£30
1994 — — Piedfort......................................	10,000	£50
1994 — Gold Proof......................................	—	£500
1995 BU (only issued in Year Sets)................	—	£9
1995 Proof..	—	£12
1996 BU (only issued in Year Sets)................	—	£9
1996 Proof..	—	£12
1996 Silver Proof	—	£25
1997 BU	—	£8
1997 Proof..	—	£10
1997 Silver Proof	—	£25
1997 **New reduced size**	456,364,100	£2
1997 BU	—	£5
1997 Proof..	—	£6
1997 Silver Proof	—	£20
1997 — — Piedfort......................................	—	£35
1998 **New portrait**	64,306,500	£2
1998 BU	—	£5
1998 Proof..	—	£8
1998 Presidency and 25th anniversary of EU entry	5,043,000	£3
1998 — BU..	—	£5
1998 — Proof..	—	£8
1998 — Silver Proof	8,859	£30
1998 — — Piedfort......................................	8,440	£40
1998 — Gold Proof......................................	—	£500
1998 50th Anniversary of the National Health Service ..	5,001,000	£3
1998 — BU..	—	£5
1998 — Silver Proof	9,032	£30
1998 — — Piedfort......................................	5,117	£40
1998 — Gold Proof......................................	—	£500
1999..	24,905,000	£2
1999 BU	—	£5
1999 Proof..	—	£10
2000..	27,915,500	£2
2000 BU	—	£5
2000 Proof..	—	£7
2000 150th Anniversary of Public Libraries	11,263,000	£2
2000 — BU..	—	£6
2000 — Proof	—	£9
2000 — Silver Proof	7,634	£30
2000 — — Piedfort......................................	5,721	£40
2000 — Gold proof......................................	—	£500
2001..	84,998,500	£2
2001 BU	—	£5
2001 Proof..	—	£7
2002..	23,907,500	£2
2002 BU	—	£5
2002 Proof..	—	£7
2002 Gold Proof	—	£475
2003..	23,583,000	£2
2003 BU	—	£5
2003 Proof..	—	£6
2003 Suffragette..	3,124,030	£6
2003 — BU..	9582	£9
2003 — Proof	—	£15
2003 — Silver Proof	6,267	£35

1998 EU Presidency

1998 NHS

2000 Public Libraries

2003 Suffragettes

DATE	Mintage	UNC
2003 — — — Piedfort	6,795	£45
2003 — Gold Proof	942	£450
2004	35,315,500	£2
2004 BU	—	£5
2004 Proof	—	£8
2004 Roger Bannister	9,032,500	£3
2004 — BU	10,371	£8
2004 — Proof	—	£10
2004 — Silver Proof	4,924	£35
2004 — — — Piedfort	4,054	£45
2004 — Gold Proof	644	£450
2005	25,363,500	£2
2005 BU	—	£6
2005 Proof	—	£8
2005 Samuel Johnson	17,649,000	£3
2005 — BU	—	£8
2005 — Proof	—	£10
2005 — Silver Proof	4,029	£35
2005 — — — Piedfort	3,808	£45
2005 — Gold Proof	—	£450
2006	24,567,000	£2
2006 Proof	—	£8
2006 Silver Proof	—	£25
2006 Victoria Cross, The Award	12,087,000	£3
2006 — BU	—	£6
2006 — Proof	—	£8
2006 — Silver Proof	6,310	£30
2006 — — — Piedfort	3,532	£50
2006 — Gold Proof	866	£450
2006 Victoria Cross, Heroic Acts	10,000,500	£3
2006 — BU	—	£6
2006 — Proof	—	£8
2006 — Silver Proof	6,872	£30
2006 — — — Piedfort	3,415	£50
2006 — Gold Proof	804	£450
2007	11,200,000	£2
2007 Proof	—	£8
2007 Centenary of Scout Movement	7,710,750	£3
2007 — BU	—	£8
2007 — Proof	—	£12
2007 — Silver Proof	10,895	£35
2007 — — Piedfort	1,555	£65
2007 — Gold Proof	1,250	£450
2008	3,500,000	£2
2008 — BU	—	£8
2008 — Proof	—	£10
2008 — Silver Proof	—	£25
2008 — Gold Proof	—	£450
2008 — Platinum Proof	—	£1550
2008 **New Shield Rev.** Obv. rotated by approx. 26⁰	22,747,000	£5
2008 BU	—	£8
2008 Proof	—	£10
2008 Silver Proof	—	£25
2008 Silver Proof Piedfort	—	£45
2008 Gold Proof	—	£450
2008 Platinum Proof	—	£1550

2004 Roger Bannister

2005 Samuel Johnson

2006 Victoria Cross—the Award

2006 Victoria Cross—Heroic Acts

The "Shield" design which replaced Britannia on the reverse of the circulating 50 pence coin was introduced in 2008 and continues in use as the standard reverse each year in addition to the many commemorative issues available.

2008 Shield design

2007 Centenary of Scouting

DATE	Mintage	UNC
2009 BU	—	£30
2009 Proof	—	£35
2009 Silver Proof	—	£35
2009 250th Anniversary of Kew Gardens	210,000	£150
2009 — BU	128,364	£175
2009 — Proof	—	£200
2009 — Silver Proof	7,575	£350
2009 — — — Piedfort	2,967	£425
2009 — Gold Proof	629	£750
2009 Olympic and Paralympic Sports (Track & Field Athletics) Unc (Blue Peter Pack)	19,751	£125
2009 16 different reverses from the past marking the 40th Anniversary of the 50p coin. Proof	1,039	£500
2009 — Silver Proof	1,163	£800
2009 — Gold Proof	70	£8250
2009 — — — Piedfort	40	£22,000
2010 BU	—	£25
2010 Proof	—	£30
2010 Silver Proof	—	£35
2010 100 years of Girl Guiding UK....................	7,410,090	£3
2010 — BU	99,075	£7
2010 — Proof	—	£12
2010 — Silver Proof	5,271	£30
2010 — — — Piedfort	2,879	£35
2010 — Gold Proof	355	£575
2011 BU	—	£30
2011 Proof	—	£40
2011 Silver Proof	—	£50
2011 50th Anniversary of the WWF....................	3,400,000	£4
2011 — BU	67,299	£10
2011 — Proof	—	£25
2011 — Silver Proof	24,870	£45
2011 — — — Piedfort	2,244	£80
2011 — Gold Proof	243	£675
2011 Olympic & Paralympic Sports Issues:		
Aquatics Unc, head clear of lines............................	2,179,000	£4
— Head with lines BU (as illustrated below)	—	£850
— Head clear of lines. BU.......................................	—	£5
— Silver BU..	30,000	£25
Archery Unc..	3,345,000	£3
— BU..	—	£4
— Silver BU..	30,000	£25
Athletics Unc	2,224,000	£3
— BU..	—	£4
— Silver BU..	30,000	£25
Badminton Unc	2,133,000	£3
— BU..	—	£4
— Silver BU..	30,000	£25
Basketball Unc	1,748,000	£3
— BU..	—	£5
— Silver BU..	30,000	£25
Boccia Unc	2,166,000	£3
— BU..	—	£4
— Silver BU..	30,000	£25
Boxing Unc	2,148,000	£3
— BU..	—	£4
— Silver BU..	30,000	£25

2009 Kew Gardens

2010 100 years of Guiding

2011 WWF Anniversary

Archery
by Piotr Powaga

Aquatics—the rare error coin
by Jonathan Olliffe

Badminton
by Emma Kelly

Basketball
by Sarah Payne

Athletics
by Florence Jackson

Boccia
by Justin Chung

Boxing
by Shane Abery

Canoeing
by Timothy Lees

Cycling
by Theo Crutchley-Mack

Equestrian
by Thomas Babbage

Fencing
by Ruth Summerfield

Football
by Neil Wolfson

Goalball
by Jonathan Wren

Gymnastics
by Jonathan Olliffe

Handball
by Natasha Ratcliffe

Hockey
by Robert Evans

Judo
by David Cornell

Modern Pentathlon
by Daniel Brittain

Rowing
by Davey Podmore

Sailing
by Bruce Rushin

Shooting
by Pravin Dewdhory

Table Tennis
by Alan Linsdell

Taekwando
by David Gibbons

Tennis
by Tracy Baines

Triathlon
by Sarah Harvey

DATE		Mintage	UNC
Canoeing Unc		2,166,000	£3
— BU		—	£4
— Silver BU		30,000	£25
Cycling Unc		2,090,000	£3
— BU		—	£4
— Silver BU		30,000	£25
Equestrian Unc		2,142,000	£3
— BU		—	£4
— Silver BU		30,000	£25
Fencing Unc		2,115,000	£3
— BU		—	£4
— Silver BU		30,000	£25
Football Unc		1,125,000	£10
— BU		—	£15
— Silver BU		30,000	£35
Goalball Unc		1,615,000	£4
— BU		—	£7
— Silver BU		30,000	£25
Gymnastics Unc		1,720,000	£3
— BU		—	£4
— Silver BU		30,000	£25
Handball Unc		1,676,000	£4
— BU		—	£7
— Silver BU		30,000	£30
Hockey Unc		1,773,000	£3
— BU		—	£4
— Silver BU		30,000	£25
Judo Unc		1,161,000	£10
— BU		—	£15
— Silver BU		30,000	£35
Modern Pentathlon Unc		1,689,000	£3
— BU		—	£5
— Silver BU		30,000	£25
Rowing Unc		1,717,000	£3
— BU		—	£4
— Silver BU		30,000	£25
Sailing Unc		1,749,000	£3
— BU		—	£4
— Silver BU		30,000	£25
Shooting Unc		1,656,000	£3
— BU		—	£4
— Silver BU		30,000	£25
Table Tennis Unc		1,737,000	£3
— BU		—	£4
— Silver BU		30,000	£25
Taekwondo Unc		1,664,000	£3
— BU		—	£4
— Silver BU		30,000	£25
Tennis Unc		1,454,000	£4
— BU		—	£7
— Silver BU		30,000	£25
Triathlon Unc		1,163,000	£10
— BU		—	£15
— Silver BU		30,000	£30
Volleyball Unc		2,133,000	£3
— BU		—	£4
— Silver BU		30,000	£25
Weightlifting Unc		1,879,000	£3
— BU		—	£4
— Silver BU		30,000	£25
Wheelchair Rugby Unc		1,765,000	£3
— BU		—	£4
— Silver BU		30,000	£25
Wrestling Unc		1,129,000	£10
— BU		—	£15
— Silver BU		30,000	£35

Volleyball
by Daniela Boothman

Weight Lifting
by Rob Shakespeare

Wheelchair Rugby
by Natasha Ratcliffe

Wrestling
by Roderick Enriquez

Note—*Each of the artists of the 29 Olympic sports above was presented with a gold proof coin with their own design. The Track & Field Athletics design coin was dated 2009, the Cycling was dated 2010, and the remaining issues 2011.*

DATE	Mintage	UNC
2012..	32,300,030	£2
2012 BU	—	£8
2012 Proof..	—	£10
2012 Silver Proof with selective gold plating	—	£50
2012 Gold Proof	—	£500
2012 Olympic Gold Proof Piedfort. *The 11 Olympic sports in which the United Kingdom Team GB achieved a Gold Medal was celebrated with an issue limit of only 27 Piedfort coins for each sport, some in sets, some as individual coins (see under Proof and Specimen sets)*	27	—
2013..	10,301,000	£2
2013 BU	—	£10
2013 Proof..	—	£15
2013 Silver Proof	2,013	£55
2013 Gold Proof	198	£450
2013 100th anniversary of Birth of Christopher Ironside	7,000,000	£8
2013 — BU...	4,403	£15
2013 — Proof...	—	£20
2013 — Silver Proof	1,823	£45
2013 — — Piedfort.......................................	816	£100
2013 — Gold Proof.......................................	198	£450
2013 Centenary of the Birth of Benjamin Britten	5,300,000	£8
2013 — BU...	—	£25
2013 — Silver Proof	717	£200
2013 — — Piedfort.......................................	515	£250
2013 — Gold Proof.......................................	70	£475
2014..	49,001,000	£2
2014 BU	—	£10
2014 Proof..	—	£15
2014 Silver Proof	—	£55
2014 XX Commonwealth Games	6,502,918	£8
2014 — BU...	14,581	£10
2014 — Proof...	—	£15
2014 — Silver Proof	2,610	£45
2014 — — Piedfort.......................................	792	£100
2014 — Gold Proof.......................................	—	£450
2015..	20,101,000	£2
2015 BU	—	£8
2015 Proof..	—	£10
2015 Silver Proof	—	£30
2015 Gold Proof	—	£450
2015 Platinum Proof	—	—
2015 Battle of Britain 75th Anniversary BU (no denomination)..	35,199	£5
2015 — Proof...	—	£15
2015 — Silver Proof	2,839	£30
2015 — — Piedfort.......................................	1,422	£80
2015 — Gold Proof.......................................	389	£450

New Portrait by Jody Clark

2015 Battle of Britain 75th Anniversary (with denomination) UNC................................	5,900,000	£3
2015 Standard Shield rev.	—	£2
2015 BU	—	£8
2015 Proof..	—	£12
2015 Silver Proof	—	£30
2015 Gold Proof	—	£450
2015 Platinum Proof	—	—
2016 BU	—	£20
2016 Proof..	—	£25
2016 Silver Proof	—	£35
2016 Battle of Hastings 950th Anniversary	6,700,000	£3
2016 — BU...	21,718	£7
2016 — Proof...	—	£15
2016 — Silver Proof	2,338	£35
2016 — — Piedfort.......................................	1,469	£155
2016 — Gold Proof.......................................	237	£450
2016 Beatrix Potter 150th Anniversary........................	6,900,000	£4
2016 — BU...	61,658	£7
2016 — Silver Proof	7,471	£150
2016 — — Piedfort.......................................	2,486	£200
2016 — Gold Proof.......................................	732	£550

2013 Christopher Ironside

2013 Benjamin Britten

2015 Battle of Britain

2016 Beatrix Potter

DATE	Mintage	UNC
2016 Beatrix Potter: Peter Rabbit	9,600,000	£4
2016 — BU	93,851	£7
2016 — Silver Proof with coloured highlights	15,245	£350
2016 Beatrix Potter: Jemima Puddle-Duck....................	2,100,000	£16
2016 — BU	54,929	£14
2016 — Silver Proof with coloured highlights	15,171	£85
2016 Beatrix Potter: Mrs. Tiggy-Winkle	8,800,000	£4
2016 — BU	47,597	£9
2016 — Silver Proof with coloured highlights	15,243	£50
2016 Beatrix Potter: Squirrel Nutkin.............................	5,000,000	£4
2016 — BU	45,884	£7
2016 — Silver Proof with coloured highlights	15,143	£50
2016 Team GB for Olympics	6,400,000	£3
2016 — BU	34,162	£10
2016 — Silver Proof	4,456	£35
2016 — — Piedfort	1,246	£95
2016 — Gold Proof	302	£450
2017 BU	—	£5
2017 Proof..	—	£12
2017 Silver Proof	—	£30
2017 375th anniversary of Sir Isaac Newton's birth.......	1,801,500	£5
2017 — BU	54,057	£10
2017 — Proof	—	£15
2017 — Silver Proof	3,875	£50
2017 — — Piedfort	1,935	£95
2017 — Gold Proof	282	£775
2017 Beatrix Potter: Peter Rabbit	19,900,000	£4
2017 — BU	221,866	£12
2017 — — Silver Proof with coloured highlights...........	40,000	£55
2017 — — Gold Proof	425	£1000
2017 Beatrix Potter: Mr. Jeremy Fisher	9,900,000	£4
2017 — BU	165,618	£8
2017 — Silver Proof with coloured highlights	40,000	£50
2017 Beatrix Potter: Tom Kitten	9,500,000	£4
2017 — BU	159,302	£8
2017 — Silver Proof with coloured highlights	34,140	£50
2017 Beatrix Potter: Benjamin Bunny	25,000,000	£4
2017 — BU	—	£8
2017 — Silver Proof with coloured highlights	35,821	£50
2018 BU (sets only)	—	£10
2018 Proof..	—	£12
2018 Silver Proof	—	£30
2018 375th anniversary of Sir Isaac Newton's birth (see above: 2018 only available from the Royal Mint Experience)		£75
2018 Anniversary of the Representation of the People Act	9,000,000	£3
2018 Beatrix Potter: Peter Rabbit	1,400,000	£10
2018 — BU	—	£5
2018 — Silver Proof with coloured highlights	—	£55
2018 — Gold Proof	450	£1000
2018 Beatrix Potter: Flopsy Bunny................................	1,400,000	£4
2018 — BU	—	£5
2018 — Silver Proof with coloured highlights	—	£55

2016 Peter Rabbit

2016 Team GB

2017 Isaac Newton

2018 Peter Rabbit

DATE	Mintage	UNC
2018 Beatrix Potter: The Tailor of Gloucester	3,900,000	£5
• 2018 — BU	—	£6
2018 —Silver Proof with coloured highlights	—	£55
2018 Beatrix Potter: Mrs Tittlemouse...........................	1,700,000	£5
● 2018 — BU	—	£6
2018 —Silver Proof with coloured highlights	—	£55
2018 Paddington Bear at Paddington Station	5,001,000	£5
• 2018 — BU	—	£10
2018.................— Silver Proof with coloured highlights	75,000	£60
2018 — Gold Proof..	1,250	£780
2018 Paddington Bear at Buckingham Palace	5,901,000	£5
✔ 2018 — BU	—	£10
2018 — Silver Proof with coloured highlights	75,000	£60
2018 — Gold Proof..	1,250	£780
● 2018 The Snowman BU	—	£10
2018 — Silver Proof	15,000	£60
2018 — Gold Proof..	400	£775
2019...	122,000,000	£2
2019 BU	—	£5
2019 Proof	—	£12
2019 Silver Proof	—	£30
• 2019 Stephen Hawking BU	—	£10
2019 — Silver Proof	7,000	£55
2019 — — Piedfort	2,500	£95
2019 — Gold Proof..	400	£795
2019 Sherlock Holmes BU	—	£10
2019 — Silver Proof	7,500	£55
2019 — — Piedfort	3,500	£95
2019 — Gold Proof..	600	£795
2019 The Gruffalo BU	—	£10
2019 — Silver Proof	30,000	£65
2019 — Gold Proof..	600	£795
2019 Peter Rabbit BU	—	£10
2019 — Silver Proof	30,000	£65
2019 — Gold Proof..	500	£795
2019 Paddington Bear at the Tower of London	—	£3
• 2019 — BU	—	£10
2019 — Silver Proof with coloured highlights	25,000	£65
2019 — Gold Proof..	600	£980
2019 Paddington Bear at St. Paul's	—	£3
• 2019 — BU	—	£10
2019 — Silver Proof with coloured highlights	25,000	£65
2019 — Gold Proof..	600	£980
2019 50 years of the 50p BU.......................................	—	£10
2019 — Silver Proof Piedfort	1,969	£95
2019 — Silver Proof	3,500	£55
2019 — Gold Proof..	300	£980
● 2019 20th Anniversary of the Gruffalo BU..................	—	£12
2019 — Silver Proof	25,000	£65
2019 — Gold (Red) Proof	600	£980
• 2019 The Snowman II BU	—	£10
2019 — Silver Proof	25,000	£65
2019 — Gold (Red) Proof	600	£980
2019 Wallace & Gromit BU	—	£18
2019 — Silver Proof	25,000	£65
2019 — Gold (Red) Proof	630	£980
2020...	46,540,375	£2
2020 BU	—	£5
2020 Proof	—	£12
2020 Silver Proof	—	£30
2020 Withdrawal from the EU (Brexit)	10,001,000	£2
2020 Withdrawal from the EU (Brexit) BU	—	£10
2020 — BU (EEC 1973 + EU Withdrawal, 2-coin set)....	5,000	£30
2020 — Silver Proof	47,000	£60
2020 — Gold (Red) Proof	1,500	£945
2020 Team GB BU...	—	£10
2020 — Proof	—	£12
2020 — Silver Proof	—	£55
2020 Rosalind Franklin BU...	—	£8
2020 — Proof	—	£15
2020 — Silver Proof	—	£55
2020 — Silver Proof Piedfort..	—	£99

*2018
Flopsy Bunny*

*Paddington at the Tower
of London*

2018 The Snowman

2019 Stephen Hawking

2019 Sherlock Holmes

*Note: the prices given for
recently-issued gold coins are
the Royal Mint issue prices.*

DATE	Mintage	UNC
2020 — Gold (Red) Proof	250	£1075
2020 Dinosauria (Megalosaurus) BU	—	£10
2020 — BU (coloured coin)	50,000	£20
2020 — Silver Proof	3,000	£65
2020 — — Proof (coloured coin)	7,000	£75
2020 — Gold Proof	350	£945
2020 Dinosauria (Iguanodon) BU	—	£10
2020 — BU (coloured coin)	50,000	£20
2020 — Silver Proof	14,500	£65
2020 — — Proof (coloured coin)	7,000	£75
2020 — Gold Proof	500	£1020
2020 Dinosauria (Hylaeosaurus) BU	—	£10
2020 — BU (coloured coin)	50,000	£20
2020 — Silver Proof	14,500	£65
2020 — — Proof (coloured coin)	7,000	£75
2020 — Gold Proof	500	£1020
2020 Winnie the Pooh—Christopher Robin BU		£9
2020 — BU (coloured coin)	45,000	£20
2020 — Silver Proof	18,000	£67.50
2020 — Gold Proof	525	£1,125
2020 — Winnie the Pooh and friends BU......................	—	£10
2020 — BU (coloured coin)	45,000	£20
2020 — Silver Proof (coloured coin)...........................	18,000	£67.50
2020 — Gold Proof	525	£1,125
2020 — Piglet BU	—	£9
2020 — BU (coloured coin)	45,000	£20
2020 — Silver Proof	18,000	£67.50
2020 — Gold Proof	525	£1,125
2020 The Snowman BU	—	£10
2020 — BU (coloured coin)	15,000	£20
2020 — Silver Proof	7,000	£67.50
2020 — Gold Proof	275	£1,125
2020 Diversity Built Britain	10,300,000	£2
2020 — BU	—	£6
2020 — Silver Proof	25,000	£57.50
2020 — — Piedfort	2,500	£100
2020 — Gold Proof	950	£1,125
2020 — — Piedfort	200	£2,225
2020 Peter Rabbit BU	—	£10
2020 — Silver Proof	15,000	£65
2020 — Gold Proof	500	£945
2021 50th Anniversay of Decimal Day BU	—	£10
2021 — Silver Proof	6,000	£57.50
2021 — — Piedfort	2,500	£100.00
2021— Gold Proof (coin struck on the day)	700	£1,250
2021 — —	450	£1,100
2021 — — Piedfort	200	£2,175
2021 Mary Anning Collection—Temnodantesaurus BU	—	£10
2021 — BU (coloured coin)	50,000	£20
2021 — Silver Proof	3,000	£62.50
2021 — — (coloured coin)	7,000	£67.50
2021 — Gold Proof	250	£1,100
2021 Mary Anning Collection—Plesiosaurus BU	—	£10
2021 — BU (coloured coin)	50,000	£20
2021 — Silver Proof	3,000	£62.50
2021 — — (coloured coin)	7,000	£67.50
2021 — Gold Proof	250	£1,100
2021 Mary Anning Collection—Dimporphodon BU	—	£10
2021 — BU (coloured coin)	50,000	£20
2021 — Silver Proof	3,000	£62.50
2021 — — (coloured coin)	7,000	£67.50
2021 — Gold Proof	250	£1,100
2021 John Logie Baird BU	—	£10
2021 — Silver Proof	5,010	£57.50
2021 — — Piedfort	2,200	£100
2021 — Gold Proof..	405	£1,005

2020
Dinosauria—Iguanodon

DATE	Mintage	UNC
2021 Olympic Games Team 2020 (GB) BU	—	£10
2021 — BU (coloured coin)	12,021	£20
2021 — Silver Proof (coloured coin)	5,510	£67.50
2021. — — Piedfort	1,510	£105
2021 — Gold Proof	260	£1,000
2021 Winnie the Pooh & Friends BU	—	£10
2021 — (coloured coin)	45,000	£20
2021 — Silver Proof (coloured coin)	19,095	£67.50
2021 — Gold Proof	630	£1,065
2021 Winnie the Pooh—Owl BU	—	£9
2021 — (coloured coin)	45,000	£20
2021 — Silver Proof	18,000	£67.50
2021 — Gold Proof	535	£1,065
2021 Winnie the Pooh—Tigger BU	—	£9
2021 — (coloured coin)	45,000	£20
2021 — Silver Proof	18,000	£67.50
2021 — Gold Proof	535	£1,065
2021 Charles Babbage BU	—	£8
2021 — Silver Proof	4,000	£57.50
2021 — Silver Proof Piedfort	1,510	£102.50
2021 — Gold Proof	260	£1,065
2021 100 Years of Insulin BU	—	£12
2021 — Silver Proof	3,710	£57.50
2021 — Silver Proof Piedfort	1,510	£102.50
2021 — Gold Proof	260	£1,065
2021 The Snowman BU	—	£10
2021 — BU (coloured coin)	10,000	£20
2021 — Silver Proof (coloured coin)	7,000	£67.50
2021 — Gold Proof	300	£1,065
2022 Winnie the Pooh—Eeyore BU	—	£8
2022 — (coloured coin)	12,500	£20
2022 — Silver Proof (coloured coin)	6,010	£67.50
2022 — Gold Proof	160	£1,095
2022 Her Majesty the Queen's Platinum Jubilee 50p (John Bergdhal obverse Queen on horseback) BU	—	£7
2022 — Silver Proof	7,605	£57.50
2022 — — Piedfort	2,510	£102.50
2022 — Gold Proof	580	£1,095
2022 — — Piedfort	80	£2185
2022 — Platinum Proof	150	£1,395
2022 Her Majesty the Queen's Platinum Jubilee 50p for circulation at 50p (Jody Clark Obverse)	—	£2
2022 50 Years of Pride BU	—	£10
2022 — (coloured coin)	10,000	£18
2022 — Silver Proof (coloured coin)	4,000	£67.50
2022 — — Piedfort (coloured coin)	1,500	£112.50
2022 — Gold Proof	200	£1,095
2022 — — Piedfort	50	£2,185
2022 Birmingham 2022 Commonwealth Games BU	—	£10
2022 — (coloured coin) Team England	7,510	£18
2022 — (coloured coin) Team Wales	5,010	£18
2022 — (coloured coin) Team N Ireland	5,010	£18
2022 — (coloured coin) Scotland	5,010	£18
2022 — Silver Proof (coloured coin)	4,760	£67.50
2022 — — Piedfort (coloured coin)	1,260	£112.50
2022 — Gold Proof	410	£1,095
2022 Kanga and Roo BU	—	£10
2022 — (coloured coin)	12,500	£20
2022 — Silver Proof (coloured coin)	6,010	£67.50
2022 — Gold Proof	160	£1,150
2022 Winnie the Pooh and Friends BU	—	£10
2022 — (coloured coin)	12,500	£20
2022 — Silver Proof (coloured coin)	6,510	£67.50
2022 — Gold Proof	210	£1,150

TWENTY-FIVE PENCE (CROWN)

This series is a continuation of the pre-decimal series, there having been four crowns to the pound. The coins below have a legal tender face value of 25p to this day, and are minted in cupro-nickel except where stated otherwise.

DATE	Mintage	UNC
1972 Royal Silver Wedding	7,452,100	£2
1972 — Proof	150,000	£8
1972 — Silver Proof	100,000	£36
1977 Silver Jubilee	37,061,160	£2
1977 — in Presentation folder	Incl. above	£3
1977 — Proof	193,000	£8
1977 — Silver Proof	377,000	£32
1980 Queen Mother 80th Birthday	9,306,000	£2
1980 — in Presentation folder	Incl. above	£3
1980 — Silver Proof	83,670	£32
1981 Royal Wedding	26,773,600	£2
1981 — in Presentation folder	Incl. above	£3
1981 — Silver Proof	218,140	£32

TWENTY PENCE

The series commenced in 1982, some 11 years after the introduction of decimal coinage. Its presence from introduction date meant that there was no requirement for ten pence circulation-standard coins until the latter's size was reduced in 1992. Its alloy is uniquely 84% copper and 16% nickel, unlike the 75/25 of the fifty pence.

DATE	Mintage	UNC	DATE	Mintage	UNC
1982	740,815,000	£2	1991 Proof	—	£8
1982 Proof	—	£7	1992	Est. approx. 1,500,000	£4
1982 Silver Proof Piedfort	25,000	£25	1992 BU	—	£5
1983	158,463,000	£3	***Enhanced effigy***		
1983 Proof	—	£6	1992	Est. approx. 29,705,000	£4
1984	65,350,000	£1	1992 — BU	—	£5
1984 BU	—	£3	1992 — Proof	—	£8
1984 Proof	—	£7	1993	123,123,750	£1
New portrait			1993 BU	—	£3
1985	74,273,699	£2	1993 Proof	—	£6
1985 BU	—	£4	1994	67,131,250	£1
1985 Proof	—	£6	1994 BU	—	£3
1986 BU	—	£7	1994 Proof	—	£5
1986 Proof	—	£10	1995	102,005,000	£1
1987	137,450,000	£1	1995 BU	—	£3
1987 BU	—	£3	1995 Proof	—	£5
1987 Proof	—	£6	1996	83,163,750	£2
1988	38,038,344	£1	1996 BU	—	£3
1988 BU	—	£3	1996 Proof	—	£5
1988 Proof	—	£5	1996 Silver Proof	—	£20
1989	132,013,890	£1	1997	89,518,750	£2
1989 BU	—	£3	1997 BU	—	£3
1989 Proof	—	£6	1997 Proof	—	£5
1990	88,097,500	£1	***New portrait***		
1990 BU	—	£3	1998	76,965,000	£2
1990 Proof	—	£6	1998 BU	—	£4
1991	35,901,250	£1	1998 Proof	—	£5
1991 BU	—	£4	1999	73,478,750	£2

DATE	Mintage	UNC	DATE	Mintage	UNC
1999 BU	—	£3	2011 BU	—	£5
1999 Proof	—	£5	2011 Proof	—	£8
2000	136,428,750	£2	2011 Silver Proof	—	£20
2000 BU	—	£3	2012	69,650,030	£2
2000 Proof	—	£5	2012 BU	—	£5
2000 Silver Proof	—	£20	2012 Proof	—	£8
2001	148,122,500	£2	2012 Silver Proof (issued in set with Victorian		
2001 BU	—	£3	4 Shilling piece)	—	£30
2001 Proof	—	£5	2012 — — with selective gold plating	—	£35
2002	93,360,000	£2	2012 Gold Proof	—	£375
2002 BU	—	£3	2013	66,325,000	£2
2002 Proof	—	£5	2013 BU	—	£5
2002 Gold Proof	—	£375	2013 Proof	—	£10
2003	153,383,750	£2	2013 Silver Proof	—	£25
2003 BU	—	£4	2013 Gold Proof	—	£375
2003 Proof	—	£6	2014	173,775,000	£2
2004	120,212,500	£2	2014 BU	—	£5
2004 BU	—	£4	2014 Proof	—	£10
2004 Proof	—	£6	2014 Silver Proof	—	£25
2005	124,488,750	£2	2015	63,175,000	£3
2005 BU	—	£4	2015 BU	—	£5
2005 Proof	—	£6	2015 Proof	—	£10
2006	114,800,000	£2	2015 Silver Proof	—	£25
2006 BU	—	£4	2015 Gold Proof	—	£375
2006 Proof	—	£6	2015 Platinum Proof	—	—
2006 Silver Proof	—	£20	**New Portrait**		
2007	117,075,000	£2	2015	131,250,000	£3
2007 BU	—	£4	2015 BU	—	£5
2007 Proof	—	£6	2015 Proof	—	£5
2008	11,900,000	£2	2015 Silver Proof	—	£25
2008 BU	—	£4	2015 Gold Proof	—	£375
2008 Proof	—	£7	2015 Platinum Proof	—	—
2008 Silver Proof	—	£20	2016	212,625,000	£3
2008 Gold Proof	—	£375	2016 BU	—	£5
2008 Platinum Proof	—	£750	2016 Proof	—	£10
New Reverse, date on Obverse			2016 Silver Proof	—	£25
2008	115,022,000	£2	2017 BU	—	£10
2008 Mule—paired with old Obv. (thus no date)			2017 Proof	—	£10
Est. approx. 120,000 (?)		£125	2017 Silver Proof	—	£25
2008 BU	—	£3	2018 BU	—	£10
2008 Proof	—	£6	2018 Proof	—	£10
2008 Silver Proof	—	£20	2018 Silver Proof	—	£25
2008 — — Piedfort	—	£25	2019 BU	—	£5
2008 Gold Proof	—	£375	2019 Proof	—	£10
2008 Platinum Proof	—	£750	2019 Silver Proof	—	£25
2009	121,625,300	£2	2020 BU	—	£5
2009 BU	—	£5	2020 Proof	—	£10
2009 Proof	—	£7	2020 Silver Proof	—	£25
2009 Silver Proof	—	£25	2021 BU	—	£5
2010	112,875,500	£2	2021 Proof	—	£10
2010 BU	—	£5	2021 Silver Proof	—	£25
2010 Proof	—	£7	2022 BU	—	£5
2010 Silver Proof	—	£20	2022 Proof	—	£10
2011	191,625,000	£2	2022 Silver Proof	—	£25

TEN PENCE

*The series commenced before decimalisation with the legend
NEW PENCE, this changed to TEN PENCE from 1982. These
"florin-sized" coins up to 1992 are no longer legal tender.
Cupro-nickel was replaced by nickel-plated steel from 2011.*

DATE	Mintage	UNC	DATE	Mintage	UNC
1968	336,143,250	£3	1994 Proof	—	£7
1969	314,008,000	£4	1995	43,259,000	£1
1970	133,571,000	£4	1995 BU	—	£5
1971	63,205,000	£3	1995 Proof	—	£7
1971 Proof	—	£4	1996	118,738,000	£2
1972 Proof only	—	£7	1996 BU	—	£4
1973	152,174,000	£3	1996 Proof	—	£7
1973 Proof	—	£4	1996 Silver Proof	—	£20
1974	92,741,000	£3	1997	99,196,000	£2
1974 Proof	—	£4	1997 BU	—	£4
1975	181,559,000	£3	1997 Proof	—	£4
1975 Proof	—	£4	*New portrait*		
1976	228,220,000	£3	1998 BU	—	£8
1976 Proof	—	£4	1998 Proof	—	£10
1977	59,323,000	£6	1999 BU	—	£4
1977 Proof	—	£8	1999 Proof	—	£11
1978 Proof	—	£10	2000	134,733,000	£1
1979	115,457,000	£2	2000 BU	—	£4
1979 Proof	—	£4	2000 Proof	—	£7
1980	88,650,000	£3	2000 Silver Proof	—	£20
1980 Proof	—	£4	2001	129,281,000	£1
1981	3,487,000	£10	2001 BU	—	£3
1981 Proof	—	£15	2001 Proof	—	£4
1982 BU	—	£4	2002	80,934,000	£2
1982 Proof	—	£6	2002 BU	—	£3
1983 BU	—	£3	2002 Proof	—	£5
1983 Proof	—	£4	2002 Gold Proof	—	£450
1984 BU	—	£4	2003	88,118,000	£2
1984 Proof	—	£6	2003 BU	—	£3
New portrait			2003 Proof	—	£5
1985 BU	—	£5	2004	99,602,000	£1
1985 Proof	—	£7	2004 BU	—	£3
1986 BU	—	£4	2004 Proof	—	£5
1986 Proof	—	£6	2005	69,604,000	£1
1987 BU	—	£4	2005 BU	—	£2
1987 Proof	—	£7	2005 Proof	—	£4
1988 BU	—	£5	2006	118,803,000	£1
1988 Proof	—	£7	2006 BU	—	£3
1989 BU	—	£6	2006 Proof	—	£7
1989 Proof	—	£9	2006 Silver Proof	—	£20
1990 BU	—	£6	2007	72,720,000	£1
1990 Proof	—	£9	2007 BU	—	£4
1991 BU	—	£6	2007 Proof	—	£7
1991 Proof	—	£9	2008	9,720,000	£2
1992 BU	—	£5	2008 BU	—	£5
1992 Proof	—	£7	2008 Proof	—	£8
1992 Silver Proof	—	£15	2008 Silver Proof	—	£20
Size reduced (24.5mm).			2008 Gold Proof	—	£450
1992	1,413,455,170	£3	2008 Platinum Proof	—	£500
1992 BU	—	£4	*New Reverse, no border beads on Obverse*		
1992 Proof	—	£5	2008	71,447,000	£1
1992 Silver Proof	—	£15	2008 BU	—	£4
1992 — — Piedfort	14,167	£25	2008 Proof	—	£5
1993 BU	—	£2	2008 Silver Proof	—	£20
1993 Proof	—	£7	2008 — — Piedfort	—	£25
1994 BU	—	£2	2008 Gold Proof	—	£450

Angel of the North	James Bond	Cricket	Double-decker bus	English breakfast
Fish and chips	Greenwich Mean Time	Houses of Parliament	Ice cream	Jubilee
King Arthur	Loch Ness	Mackintosh	NHS	Oak tree

Pillar box

Robin

Stonehenge

Tea

Union Flag   Village   World Wide Web   X marks the spot   Yeoman warder

Zebra crossing

In 2018 and 2019 a special series was introduced for the 10p denomination. There are 26 coins, each depicting a letter of the alphabet as shown above.

DATE	Mintage	UNC	DATE	Mintage	UNC
2008 Platinum Proof	—	£500	**New portrait**		
2009	84,360,000	£1	2015	91,900,000	£1
2009 BU	—	£3	2015 BU	—	£5
2009 Proof	—	£5	2015 Proof	—	£6
2009 Silver Proof	—	£30	2015 Silver Proof	—	£30
2010	96,600,500	£1	2015 Gold Proof	—	£450
2010 BU	—	£5	2016	135,380,000	£1
2010 Proof	—	£7	2016 BU	—	£8
2010 Silver Proof	—	£30	2016 Proof	—	£10
Nickel-plated steel			2016 Silver Proof	—	£30
2011	59,603,850	£1	2017	32,300,000	£1
2011 — BU	—	£5	2017 BU	—	£4
2011 — Proof	—	£10	2017 Proof	—	£10
2011 Silver Proof	—	£30	2017 Silver Proof	—	£30
2012	11,600,030	£1	2018 BU	—	£1
2012 BU	—	£5	2018 Proof	—	£4
2012 Proof	—	£10	2018 Silver Proof	—	£30
2012 Silver proof with selective gold plating	—	£35	2018 Alphabet series (26 different letters)		
2012 Gold Proof	—	£450		220,000 of each coin	£2 each
2013	320,200,750	£1	2018 — Silver Proof	—	£35 each
2013 BU	—	£5	2019 BU	—	£1
2013 Proof	—	£10	2019 Proof	—	£6
2013 Silver Proof	—	£30	2019 Silver Proof	—	£35
2013 Gold Proof	—	£450	2019 Alphabet series (26 different letters)	—	£2 each
2014	490,202,020	£1	2019 — Silver Proof	—	£35 each
2014 BU	—	£5	2020 BU	—	£1
2014 Proof	—	£12	2020 Proof	—	£6
2014 Silver Proof	—	£30	2020 Silver Proof	—	£35
2015	119,000,000	£1	2021 BU	—	£1
2015 BU	—	£4	2021 Proof	—	£6
2015 Proof	—	£5	2021 Silver Proof	—	£35
2015 Silver Proof	—	£30	2022 BU	—	£1
2015 Gold Proof	—	£450	2022 Proof	—	£6
2015 Platinum Proof	—	£500	2022 Silver Proof	—	£35

SIX PENCE

This "new" denomination has been struck, as part of the Royal Mint's gifting range (originally priced at £30). They are of sterling silver to BU standard and 19.41mm in diameter. Being similar in size to the pre-decimal 6d they have also been marketed as part of coin sets along with old sixpences. A recent initiative for Christmas is a sixpence for "Stir-up Sunday". This is the day, the Sunday before Advent, when traditionally families would make their Christmas puddings and stir in a sixpence for luck. The fortunate person who finds the coin in their serving of festive pudding, can look forward to good fortune in the year ahead.

The 2021 "Stir up Sunday" sixpence was issued in gold and silver versions. One would feel very lucky indeed to find a gold sixpence lurking in one's Christmas pudding!

FIVE PENCE

This series commenced simultaneously with the Ten Pence (qv). They were the same size and weight as their predecessor, the shilling, and such coins up to 1990 are no longer legal tender. As with the Ten Pence, cupro-nickel was replaced by nickel-plated steel from 2011.

DATE	Mintage	UNC	DATE	Mintage	UNC
1968	98,868,250	£3	1992 BU	—	£3
1969	120,270,000	£3	1992 Proof	—	£7
1970	225,948,525	£3	1993 BU	—	£5
1971	81,783,475	£3	1993 Proof	—	£9
1971 Proof	—	£3	1994	93,602,000	£1
1972 Proof	—	£7	1994 BU	—	£5
1973 Proof	—	£5	1994 Proof	—	£7
1974 Proof	—	£5	1995	183,384,000	£1
1975	141,539,000	£3	1995 BU	—	£5
1975 Proof	—	£4	1995 Proof	—	£7
1976 Proof	—	£8	1996	302,902,000	£1
1977	24,308,000	£8	1996 BU	—	£4
1977 Proof	—	£7	1996 Proof	—	£7
1978	61,094,000	£4	1996 Silver proof	—	£15
1978 Proof	—	£4	1997	236,596,000	£1
1979	155,456,000	£4	1997 BU	—	£4
1979 Proof	—	£4	1997 Proof	—	£7
1980	220,566,000	£3	***New portrait***		
1980 Proof	—	£4	1998	217,376,000	£1
1981 Proof	—	£7	1998 BU	—	£4
1982 BU Legend changed to FIVE PENCE.	—	£7	1998 Proof	—	£7
1982 Proof	—	£8	1999	195,490,000	£1
1983 BU	—	£5	1999 BU	—	£4
1983 Proof	—	£6	1999 Proof	—	£7
1984 BU	—	£4	2000	388,512,000	£1
1984 Proof	—	£5	2000 BU	—	£4
New Portrait.			2000 Proof	—	£7
1985 BU	—	£2	2000 Silver Proof	—	£15
1985 Proof	—	£7	2001	337,930,000	£1
1986 BU	—	£2	2001 BU	—	£3
1986 Proof	—	£7	2001 Proof	—	£5
1987	48,220,000	£1	2002	219,258,000	£1
1987 BU	—	£3	2002 BU	—	£3
1987 Proof	—	£5	2002 Proof	—	£5
1988	120,744,610	£1	2002 Gold Proof	—	£275
1988 BU	—	£3	2003	333,230,000	£1
1988 Proof		£5	2003 BU	—	£3
1989	101,406,000	£1	2003 Proof	—	£5
1989 BU	—	£4	2004	271,810,000	£1
1989 Proof	—	£5	2004 BU	—	£3
1990 BU	—	£2	2004 Proof	—	£5
1990 Proof	—	£5	2005	236,212,000	£1
1990 Silver Proof	—	£15	2005 BU	—	£3
Size reduced (18mm)			2005 Proof	—	£5
1990	1,634,976,005	£2	2006	317,697,000	£1
1990 BU	—	£3	2006 BU	—	£3
1990 Proof	—	£4	2006 Proof	—	£7
1990 Silver Proof	—	£15	2006 Silver Proof	—	£15
1990 — — Piedfort	—	£20	2007	246,720,000	£1
1991	724,979000	£1	2007 BU	—	£5
1991 BU	—	£3	2007 Proof	—	£7
1991 Proof	—	£5	2008	92,880,000	£1
1992	453,173,500	£1	2008 BU	—	£3

DATE	Mintage	UNC
2008 Proof	—	£5
2008 Silver Proof	—	£25
2008 Gold Proof	—	£275
2008 Platinum Proof	—	£300

New Reverse, no border beads on Obverse

DATE	Mintage	UNC
2008	155,172,000	£1
2008 BU	—	£4
2008	—	£5
2008 Silver Proof	—	£20
2008 — — Piedfort	—	£35
2008 Gold Proof	—	£275
2008 Platinum Proof	—	£300
2009	132,960,300	£1
2009 BU	—	£6
2009 Proof	—	£7
2009 Silver Proof	—	£15
2010	296,245,500	£1
2010 BU	—	£4
2010 Proof	—	£5
2010 Silver Proof	—	£15
2011 Nickel-plated steel	50,400,000	£1
2011 — BU	—	£4
2011 — Proof	—	£6
2011 Silver Proof	—	£15
2012	339,802,350	£1
2012 BU	—	£5
2012 Proof	—	£8
2012 Silver Proof with selective gold plating	—	£15
2012 Gold Proof	—	£275
2013	318,800,750	£1
2013 BU	—	£5
2013 Proof	—	£8
2013 Silver Proof	—	£25
2013 Gold Proof	—	£275

DATE	Mintage	UNC
2014	885,004,520	£1
2014 BU	—	£5
2014 Proof	—	£8
2014 Silver Proof	—	£20

New Portrait

DATE	Mintage	UNC
2015	536,600,000	£2
2015 BU	—	£4
2015 Proof	—	£6
2015 Silver Proof	—	£20
2015 Gold Proof	—	£275
2016	308,200,000	£2
2016 BU	—	£4
2016 Proof	—	£8
2016 Silver Proof	—	£20
2017	220,515,000	—
2017 BU	—	£4
2017 Proof	—	£6
2017 Silver Proof	—	£25
2017 Gold Proof	—	£275
2018 BU	—	£5
2018 Proof	—	£6
2018 Silver Proof	—	£25
2019 BU	—	£4
2019 Proof	—	£6
2019 Silver Proof	—	£25
2020 BU	—	£4
2020 Proof	—	£6
2020 Silver Proof	—	£25
2021 BU	—	£4
2021 Proof	—	£6
2021 Silver Proof	—	£25
2022 BU	—	£4
2022 Proof	—	£6
2022 Silver Proof	—	£25

TWO PENCE

Dated from 1971, and legal tender from Decimal Day that year, early examples are found in the blue Specimen decimal set wallets of 1968. They were minted in bronze up to 1991, and mainly in copper-plated steel from 1992. However details of where this rule does not totally apply (1992, 1996, 1998–2000 and 2002, 2006, 2008 and 2009) are given below. As with other denominations, "NEW" was replaced by "TWO" from 1982. Note that some years the 2p is only issued in the Year Sets

DATE	Mintage	UNC
1971	1,454,856,250	£3
1971 Proof	—	£5
1972 Proof	—	£8
1973 Proof	—	£10
1974 Proof	—	£8
1975	Est. approx. 273,145,000	£3
1975 Proof	—	£5
1976	Est. approx. 53,779,000	£3
1976 Proof	—	£5
1977	109,281,000	£3
1977 Proof	—	£5
1978	189,658,000	£3
1978 Proof	—	£5
1979	260,200,000	£2
1979 Proof	—	£5
1980	408,527,000	£2
1980 Proof	—	£4

DATE	Mintage	UNC
1981	353,191,000	£4
1981 Proof	—	£5

Legend changed to TWO PENCE

DATE	Mintage	UNC
1982	205,000	£4
1982 Proof	—	£6
1983	631,000	£2
1983 Error NEW instead of TWO	—	£1250
1983 Proof	—	£5
1984	158,820	£2
1984 Proof		£4

New portrait

DATE	Mintage	UNC
1985	107,113,000	£3
1985 BU	—	£2
1985 Proof	—	£4
1986	168,967,500	£2
1986 BU	—	£3
1986 Proof	—	£5

DATE	Mintage	UNC
1987	218,100,750	£2
1987 BU	—	£3
1987 Proof	—	£5
1988	419,889,000	£2
1988 BU	—	£3
1988 Proof	—	£5
1989	359,226,000	£2
1989 BU	—	£3
1989 Proof	—	£5
1990	204,499,700	£2
1990 BU	—	£3
1990 Proof	—	£5
1991	86,625,250	£2
1991 BU	—	£3
1991 Proof	—	£5
1992 Copper plated steel	102,247,000	£2
1992 Bronze BU	—	£3
1992 — Proof	—	£5
1993	235,674,000	£2
1993 BU	—	£3
1993 Proof	—	£4
1994	531,628,000	£2
1994 BU	—	£3
1994 Proof	—	£5
1995	124,482,000	£2
1995 BU	—	£3
1995 Proof	—	£5
1996	296,278,000	£2
1996 BU	—	£3
1996 Proof	—	£5
1996 Silver Proof	—	£15
1997	496,116,000	£2
1997 BU	—	£3
1997 Proof	—	£5
New Portrait		
1998	Est. approx. 120,243,000	£2
1998 BU	—	£3
1998 Proof	—	£5
1998 Bronze	Est. approx. 93,587,000	£2
1999	353,816,000	£2
1999 Bronze BU	—	£3
1999 — Proof	—	£5
2000	536,659,000	£2
2000 BU	—	£3
2000 Proof	—	£5
2000 Silver Proof	—	£15
2001	551,880,000	£2
2001 BU	—	£3
2001 Proof	—	£5
2002	168,556,000	£2
2002 BU	—	£3
2002 Proof	—	£5
2002 Gold Proof	—	£500
2003	260,225,000	£2
2003 BU	—	£3
2003 Proof	—	£5
2004	356,396,000	£2
2004 BU	—	£3
2004 Proof	—	£5
2005	280,396,000	£2
2005 BU	—	£3
2005 Proof	—	£5
2006	170,637,000	£2
2006 BU	—	£3
2006 Proof	—	£5
2006 Silver Proof	—	£15
2007	254,500,000	£2
2007 BU	—	£3

DATE	Mintage	UNC
2007 Proof	—	£5
2008	10,600,000	£2
2008 BU	—	£3
2008 Proof	—	£5
2008 Silver Proof	—	£15
2008 Gold Proof	—	£500
2008 Platinum Proof	—	£600
New Rev., no border beads on Obv.		
2008	241,679,000	£2
2008 — BU	—	£3
2008 — Proof	—	£5
2008 — Silver Proof	—	£15
2008 — Silver Proof Piedfort	—	£65
2008 — Gold Proof	—	£500
2008 — Platinum Proof	—	£600
2009	150,500,500	£2
2009 BU	—	£3
2009 Proof	—	£5
2009 Silver Proof	—	£15
2010	99,600,000	£2
2010 BU	—	£3
2010 Proof	—	£6
2010 Silver Proof	—	£15
2011	144,300,000	£2
2011 BU	—	£3
2011 Proof	—	£6
2011 Silver Proof	—	£15
2012	67,800,000	£2
2012 BU	—	£3
2012 Proof	—	£8
2012 Silver Proof with selective gold plating	—	£50
2012 Gold Proof	—	£500
2013	40,600,000	£2
2013 BU	—	£5
2013 Proof	—	£8
2013 Silver Proof	—	£35
2013 Gold Proof	—	£500
2014	247,600,020	£2
2014 BU	—	£3
2014 Proof	—	£8
2014 Silver Proof	—	£45
New Portrait		
2015	139,200,000	£2
2015 BU	—	£3
2015 Proof	—	£5
2015 Silver Proof	—	£35
2015 Gold Proof	—	£500
2015 Platinum Proof	—	£550
2016	185,200,000	£2
2016 BU	—	£5
2016 Proof	—	£8
2016 Silver Proof	—	£35
2017	16,600,000	£2
2017 BU	—	£3
2017 Proof	—	£5
2017 Silver Proof	—	£35
2018 BU	—	£5
2018 Proof	—	£8
2018 Silver Proof	—	£35
2019 BU	—	£5
2019 Proof	—	£8
2019 Silver Proof	—	£35
2020 BU	—	£5
2020 Proof	—	£8
2020 Silver Proof	—	£35
2021 BU	—	£5
2021 Proof	—	£8
2021 Silver Proof	—	£35

ONE PENNY

The history of this coin is very similar to that of the Two Pence coin (qv) except that all 1998 examples were of copper-plated steel.

DATE	Mintage	UNC
1971	1,521,666,250	£1
1971 Proof	—	£2
1972 Proof	—	£10
1973	280,196,000	£2
1973 Proof	—	£4
1974	330,892,000	£2
1974 Proof	—	£3
1975	221,604,000	£2
1975 Proof	—	£4
1976	300,160,000	£2
1976 Proof	—	£3
1977	285,430,000	£2
1977 Proof	—	£3
1978	292,770,000	£3
1978 Proof	—	£3
1979	459,000,000	£3
1979 Proof	—	£3
1980	416,304,000	£2
1980 Proof	—	£3
1981	301,800,000	£2
1981 Proof	—	£3

Legend changed to ONE PENNY

1982	100,292,000	£2
1982 Unc	—	£3
1982 Proof	—	£5
1983	243,002,000	£1
1983 Unc	—	£2
1983 Proof	—	£4
1984	154,759,625	£1
1984 BU	—	£2
1984 Proof	—	£3

New portrait

1985	200,605,245	£1
1985 BU	—	£2
1985 Proof	—	£3
1986	369,989,130	£1
1986 BU	—	£2
1986 Proof	—	£3
1987	4999,946,000	£1
1987 BU	—	£2
1987 Proof	—	£3
1988	793,492,000	£1
1988 BU	—	£2
1988 Proof	—	£3
1989	658,142,000	£1
1989 BU	—	£2
1989 Proof	—	£3
1990	529,047,500	£2
1990 BU	—	£3
1990 Proof	—	£4
1991	206,457,000	£1
1991 BU	—	£2
1991 Proof	—	£4
1992 Copper-plated steel	253,867,000	£3

DATE	Mintage	UNC
1992 Bronze BU	—	£6
1992 — Proof	—	£4
1993	602,590,000	£1
1993 BU	—	£2
1993 Proof	—	£5
1994	843,834,000	£1
1994 BU	—	£2
1994 Proof	—	£5
1995	303,314,000	£1
1995 BU	—	£3
1995 Proof	—	£5
1996	723,840,060	£1
1996 BU	—	£2
1996 Proof	—	£5
1996 Silver Proof	—	£30
1997	396,874,000	£1
1997 BU	—	£2
1997 Proof	—	£4

New portrait

1998	739,770,000	£1
1998 — BU	—	£3
1998 Proof	—	£4
1999	891,392,000	£2
1999 Bronze BU	—	£4
1999 Bronze Proof	—	£8
2000	1,060,420,000	£1
2000 BU	—	£2
2000 Proof	—	£4
2000 Silver Proof	—	£25
2001	928,698,000	£1
2001 BU	—	£2
2001 Proof	—	£4
2002	601,446,000	£1
2002 BU	—	£2
2002 Proof	—	£4
2002 Gold Proof	—	£200
2003	539,436,000	£1
2003 BU	—	£2
2003 Proof	—	£3
2004	739,764,000	£1
2004 BU	—	£2
2004 Proof	—	£4
2005	536,318,000	£1
2005 BU	—	£2
2005 Proof	—	£3
2006	524,605,000	£1
2006 BU	—	£2
2006 Proof	—	£4
2006 Silver Proof	—	£20
2007	548,002,000	£1
2007 BU	—	£4
2007 Proof	—	£7
2008	180,600,000	£1
2008 BU	—	£3
2008 Proof	—	£5

DATE	Mintage	UNC
2008 Silver Proof	—	£25
2008 Gold Proof	—	£200
2008 Platinum Proof	—	£250
New Rev, no border beads		
2008	507,952,000	£1
2008 — BU	—	£2
2008 — Proof	—	£3
2008 — Silver Proof	—	£25
2008 Silver Proof Piedfort	—	£35
2008 Gold Proof	—	£200
2008 Platinum Proof	—	£250
2009	556,412,800	£1
2009 BU	—	£3
2009 Proof	—	£4
2009 Silver BU, in "Lucky Baby Gift Pack"	—	£25
2009 — Proof	—	£35
2010	609,603,000	£1
2010 BU	—	£3
2010 Proof	—	£4
2010 Silver BU, in "Lucky Baby Gift Card"	9,701	£25
2010 — Proof	—	£35
2011	431,004,000	£1
2011 BU	—	£2
2011 Proof	—	£3
2011 Silver BU in "Lucky Baby Pack"	—	£25
2011 – Proof	—	£35
2012	227,201,000	£1
2012 BU	—	£2
2012 Proof	—	£4
2012 Silver BU (three different packagings)	—	£25
2012 Silver Proof with selective gold plating	—	£35
2012 Gold Proof	—	£200
2013	260,900,000	£1
2013 BU	—	£4
2013 Proof	—	£5
2013 Silver BU	—	£25
2013 — Proof	—	£30
2013 Gold Proof	—	£200
2014	464,801,520	£1
2014 BU	—	£2
2014 Proof	—	£5
2014 Silver BU	—	£25
2014 Silver Proof	—	£35
2015	154,600,000	£1
2015 BU	—	£2
2015 Proof	—	£5
2015 Silver BU	—	£25
2015 — Proof	—	£35
2015 Gold Proof	—	£200
2015 Platinum Proof	—	£250
New Portrait		
2015	418,201,016	£2
2015 BU	—	£3
2015 Proof	—	£6
2015 Silver Proof	—	£25
2015 Gold Proof	—	£200
2015 Platinum Proof	—	£250
2016	371,002,000	£1
2016 BU	—	£4
2016 Proof	—	£7
2016 Silver BU	2,842	£20
2016 Silver Proof	—	£25
2017	240,999,600	£1
2017 BU	—	£2
2017 Proof	—	£5
2017 Silver BU	—	£20
2017 Silver Proof	—	£25
2018 BU	—	£4
2018 Proof	—	£7
2018 Silver BU	—	£20
2018 Silver Proof	—	£25
2019 BU (only issued in year sets)	—	£5
2019 Proof	—	£8
2019 Silver BU	—	£20
2019 Silver Proof	—	£30
2020 BU	—	£5
2020 Proof	—	£8
2020 Silver BU	—	£25
2020 Silver Proof	—	£35
2021 BU	—	£5
2021 Proof	—	£8
2021 Silver BU	—	£25
2021 Silver Proof	—	£35

HALF PENNY

No longer legal tender, its history tracks that of the Two Pence and One Penny.

DATE	Mintage	UNC
1971	1,394,188,250	£2
1971 Proof	—	£3
1972 Proof	—	£15
1973	365,680,000	£2
1973 Proof	—	£3
1974	365,448,000	£2
1974 Proof	—	£3
1975	197,600,000	£2
1975 Proof	—	£3
1976	412,172,000	£2
1976 Proof	—	£3
1977	66,368,000	£1
1977 Proof	—	£3
1978	59,532,000	£1
1978 Proof	—	£4
1979	219,1322,000	£2
1979 Proof	—	£4
1980	202,788,000	£2
1980 Proof	—	£3
1981	46,748,000	£2
1981 Proof	—	£4
Legend changed to HALF PENNY		
1982	190,752,000	£1
1982 Unc	—	£2
1982 Proof	—	£3
1983	7,600,000	£1
1983 Unc	—	£1
1983 Proof	—	£6
1984	40,000	£4
1984 BU	—	£6
1984 Proof	—	£8

THE BRITANNIA SERIES

In addition to the large Britannia coin issues already listed, the series has grown to include many denominations and strikes in silver, gold and platinum. The coins are essentially bullion pieces and their values are usually related to the current price of precious metals, although the increasing popularity of the series in recent years has seen examples changing hands for figures well in excess of their bullion values, this is so especially with proof and other special strikes or the occasional mule or error. To ascertain the value of a piece it is usually only necessary to check with the prevailing price of precious metals. Hopefully this guide will give an indication of the recent market prices

SILVER

The silver Britannia series commenced in 1997, and, as with the Gold Britannia series, sets of the coins are listed in the "Proof and Specimen Sets" section. Coins contain one Troy ounce of fine silver (£2) alloyed to Britannia standard, i.e. 95.8 per cent fine silver, or fractions of one ounce as follows: half ounce (£1), quarter ounce (50 pence) and one tenth of an ounce (20 pence). Reverses change annually, all four coins of any particular date being of the same design. The reverses by Philip Nathan appear as follows:

1997 Chariot, 1998 Standing Britannia, 1999 Chariot, 2000 Standing Britannia, 2001 Una and the Lion, 2002 Standing Britannia, 2003 Britannia's Helmeted Head, 2004 Standing Britannia, 2005 Britannia Seated, 2006 Standing Britannia, 2009 Chariot.

The 2007 design is by Christopher Le Brun, and features a seated Britannia with Lion at her feet. The 2008 is by John Bergdahl, and features a standing Britannia facing left.

Two pounds Britannia coins to BU or "bullion" standard have been issued as individual coins for each year from 1998 onwards. 2010 features Suzie Zamit's Britannia with a portrait in a Corinthian style helmet.

The 2011 coins feature a seated Britannia and Union Flag, as described in the Britannia gold series below.

2012 saw the 15th anniversary of the Silver Series, but the reverse chosen was that of the Standing Britannia by Philip Nathan, which also marked the 25th Gold series. In addition, there is a 9-coin proof set of Half-Ounce silver coins dated 2012 featuring each of the Reverses used in the past, a 25th Anniversary collection. The story of the 2013 silver Britannia coins closely parallels that of the gold coins. The silver one-twentieth of an ounce has the logical face value of 10 pence.

The 2014 Silver Britannias closely follow the pattern of the three designs of 2014 Gold. This included the introduction of the silver one-fortieth of an ounce, with a face value of 5 pence. The Nathan Britannia has crenellated borders on both the obverse and the reverse, while the Year of the Horse has plain borders on both. Examples exist, however, of both One ounce silver bullion coins having the Other's obverse, thus producing two error coins, or "mules". 2014 also saw the SS *Gairsoppa* Quarter-ounce silver Britannia bullion coin with the edge inscription SS GAIRSOPPA. These coins have the Nathan Britannia reverse, and are struck from metal recovered from the vessel which was sunk by enemy action in 1941.

Both 2013 and 2014 one-ounce BU bullion Nathan Britannia coins exist with snakes or horses (respectively) on a plain edge. These were the result of a contract between the Royal Mint and the bullion dealers A-mark of Santa Monica,

California, and commemorate Chinese Lunar years. In 2015 Designer Jody Clark scored a first when his portrayal of Britannia was used on the £50 coin which also carried his new portrait of the Queen.

GOLD

In 1987 the gold Britannia £100 coin was introduced. It contained one Troy ounce of fine gold, alloyed to 22 carat, and this has continued to the present day. At the same time, and also continuing, gold coins of face value £50, £25 and £10 appeared, containing a half ounce, quarter ounce and one tenth of an ounce of fine gold respectively. From 1987 to 1989 the alloy was of copper (Red Gold), whereas from 1990 to the present day the alloy has been of silver and copper (yellow gold).

Proof sets of these coins are listed in the "Proof and Specimen Sets" section. In addition, non-proof coins have been minted, it is believed for each of the four coins for every year. The one ounce £100 Britannia is primarily issued as a bullion coin in the non-proof standard, originally in competition with the South African Krugerrand. Its price is quoted daily on the financial pages of some newspapers.

There are five reverse designs by Philip Nathan: 1987–96 Standing Britannia, 1997 Chariot, 1998–2000 Standing Britannia, 2001 Una and the Lion, 2002 Standing Britannia, 2003 Britannia's Helmeted Head, 2004 Standing Britannia, 2005 Britannia seated, 2006 Standing Britannia. For 2007 the design is a Seated Britannia with lion at her feet, by Christopher Le Brun. The 2008 design is of Britannia standing and facing left, by John Bergdahl. The 2009 reverse is similar to that of 1997, Britannia on a chariot, while 2010 has Suzie Zamit's Britannia potrait with a Corinthian style helmet. The 2011 design is by David Mach, and portrays a seated Britannia with trident and shield, replicating the design on a 1937 penny, superimposed on a Union Flag. The rotation of the coin from left to right, or vice-versa, creates an illusion of Britannia moving with the ripple of the flag.

In general the proof coins have reverse features frosted. The proofs with Standing Britannia and Una and the Lion reverses include P NATHAN on the reverse, whereas the equivalent bullion coins have NATHAN. The other three reverses have PN on both proofs and bullion coins.

2012 was the 25th anniversary of the Gold Britannia coin series, and the reverse design chosen was that of the 1987 coins, standing Britannia, by Philip Nathan. This was repeated in 2013, but only for Brilliant Uncirculated "Bullion" coins. A separate new series was introduced for Proof coins, a seated Britannia with an owl was featured, the artist being Robert Hunt. The range of Britannia Proofs was increased from 4 to 6, with the addition of a Five-ounce coin (qv) and a one-twentieth of an ounce, curiously denominated at One Pound and with a diameter of 12mm, just larger than a Maundy One Penny. All 2013 Gold Britannias are minted in 0.999 Au alloy.

2014 and 2015 each saw three Reverse designs. The Nathan outstretched arm of Britannia continued as the bullion coin. The series by new artists were of a standing Britannia facing left with lion (2014) by Jody Clark, and a "head and shoulders" Britannia holding the trident on her right shoulder, by Antony Dufont, the latter coin included the Clark portrayal of the Queen on the obverse.

The 2016 series Reverse was designed by Suzie Zamit and depicts Britannia as the Warrior Queen. The 2017 series celebrating the 30th anniversary of the gold Britannia used a design by Louis Tamlin which depicts a helmeted outline of Britain .

A further new denomination appeared in 2014, the gold one-fortieth of an ounce, diameter 8mm and face value 50 pence.

In 2018 David Lawrence chose to portray a beautiful head and shoulders of Britannia wearing a Corinthian helmet, returning to her classical roots. However, for 2019 David once again had her standing in a warlike pose with a lion at her feet and pointing her trident towards the sun. As David Lawrence himself explained: "My initial thoughts were influenced by the great engravers of the past. Their work has classical grace and gravitas I was keen to recreate . . . The end result is an Anglicised version of ancient Rome."

In 2020 James Tottle echoed the Nathan reverse with a warlike Britannia again standing by crashing waves, trident in hand. Now though her shield bears the head of a lion and the previous shield design, the Union Flag, can be seen in the background. 2021 saw not one but two different designs by P.J. Lynch issued as proof coins alongside those bearing the Nathan reverse. The first showed a seated Britannia with a lion by her side, the second depicted a profile head with Roman style helmet. This latter design came to the attention of the press as it featured a Britannia whose facial features seemed more African than European and it was dubbed by some as the first "black Britannia". Following the success of the "double designs" the previous year, 2022 saw another two coins issued in addition to the Nathan reverse. Created by Italian designer and sculptor Sandra Deina, the first depicts a warrior queen, wearing a helmet more Greek than Roman, with trident in hand and her shield once again bearing the lion's head, the Union Flag appears again in the background. The second design, entitled "A celebration of Womanhood" shows not one but three female figures, a bear headed older woman, a be-helmeted Britannia and a young girl with a crown of laurel leaves. The Britannia range continues to expand and it seem likely that numerous dsigns inaddition to the standard one for bullion coins will feature heavily in the future.

On the following pages we have collated all the known information on the Britannia series and give the current market price you should expect to pay. However, for the later issues, many of which are still available from the Royal Mint, we have given the original issue price.

The Britannia was initially introduced as a bullion coin and changed hands at the prevailing rate, but today they are also collected for their numismatic interest and as such many of them can reach a value much higher than their intrinsic worth, so it is well worth checking before buying or selling coins of the series.

"Set only" indicates that the coin so listed was originally only available as part of a set and the prices are not given individually. BV indicates that the coin currently changes hands at the prevailing price of bullion gold or silver.

Note: whilst all British legal tender gold coins are VAT free, silver bullion coinage attracts VAT at the prevailing rate.

STANDING BRITANNIA
Obverse by **Raphael Maklouf**
Reverse by **Philip Nathan**

Date	Metal	Face value	Weight	No. struck	Value
1987	Gold Proof	£10.00	1/10oz	3,500	£225
1987	Gold Bullion	£10.00	1/10oz	Unlimited	BV
1987	Gold Proof	£25.00	1/4oz	3,500	£485
1987	Gold Bullion	£25.00	1/4oz	Unlimited	BV
1987	Gold Proof	£50.00	1/2oz	2,486	£800
1987	Gold Bullion	£50.00	1/2oz	Unlimited	BV
1987	Gold Proof	£100.00	1oz	2,485	£1650
1987	Gold Bullion	£100.00	1oz	Unlimited	BV
1987	Gold Proof Set	£25 and £10		11,100	£750
1987	Gold Proof Set	£100, £50, £25 and £10		10,000	£3750
1988	Gold Proof	£10.00	1/10oz	2,694	£225
1988	Gold Bullion	£10.00	1/10oz	Unlimited	BV
1988	Gold Proof	£25.00	1/4oz	Set only	—
1988	Gold Bullion	£25.00	1/4oz	Unlimited	BV
1988	Gold Proof	£50.00	1/2oz	Set only	—
1988	Gold Bullion	£50.00	1/2oz	Unlimited	BV
1988	Gold Proof	£100.00	1oz	Set only	—
1988	Gold Bullion	£100.00	1oz	Unlimited	BV
1988	Gold Proof Set	£25 and £10		894	£750
1988	Gold Proof Set	£100, £50, £25 and £10		3,505	£3750
1989	Gold Proof	£10.00	1/10oz	1,609	£225
1989	Gold Bullion	£10.00	1/10oz	Unlimited	BV
1989	Gold Proof	£25.00	1/4oz	Set only	—
1989	Gold Bullion	£25.00	1/4oz	Unlimited	BV
1989	Gold Proof	£50.00	1/2oz	Set only	—
1989	Gold Bullion	£50.00	1/2oz	Unlimited	BV
1989	Gold Proof	£100.00	1oz	Set only	—
1989	Gold Bullion	£100.00	1oz	Unlimited	BV
1989	Gold Proof Set	£25 and £10		451	£750
1989	Gold Proof Set	£100, £50, £25 and £10		2,268	£3750
1990	Gold Proof	£10.00	1/10oz	1,571	£225
1990	Gold Bullion	£10.00	1/10oz	Unlimited	BV
1990	Gold Proof	£25.00	1/4oz	Set only	—
1990	Gold Bullion	£25.00	1/4oz	Unlimited	BV
1990	Gold Proof	£50.00	1/2oz	Set only	—
1990	Gold Bullion	£50.00	1/2oz	Unlimited	BV
1990	Gold Proof	£100.00	1oz	Set only	—
1990	Gold Bullion	£100.00	1oz	Unlimited	BV
1990	Gold Proof Set	£100, £50, £25 and £10		527	£3750
1991	Gold Proof	£10.00	1/10oz	(954)	£225
1991	Gold Bullion	£10.00	1/10oz	Unlimited	BV

1987 Gold Proof 1 ounce

Date	Metal	Face value	Weight	No. struck	Value
1991	Gold Proof	£25.00	1/4oz .... Set only		—
1991	Gold Bullion	£25.00	1/4oz .... Unlimited		BV
1991	Gold Proof	£50.00	1/2oz .... Set only		—
1991	Gold Bullion	£50.00	1/2oz .... Unlimited		BV
1991	Gold Proof	£100.00	1oz .... Set only		—
1991	Gold Bullion	£100.00	1oz .... Unlimited		BV
1991	Gold Proof Set	£100, £50, £25 and £10		509	£3750
1992	Gold Proof	£10.00	1/10oz 1,000		£225
1992	Gold Bullion	£10.00	1/10oz .... Unlimited		BV
1992	Gold Proof	£25.00	1/4oz .... Set only		—
1992	Gold Bullion	£25.00	1/4oz .... Unlimited		BV
1992	Gold Proof	£50.00	1/2oz .... Set only		—
1992	Gold Bullion	£50.00	1/2oz .... Unlimited		BV
1992	Gold Proof	£100.00	1oz .... Set only		—
1992	Gold Bullion	£100.00	1oz .... Unlimited		BV
1992	Gold Proof Set	£100, £50, £25 and £10		500	£3800
1993	Gold Proof	£10.00	1/10oz 997		£225
1993	Gold Bullion	£10.00	1/10oz .... Unlimited		BV
1993	Gold Proof	£25.00	1/4oz .... Set only		—
1993	Gold Bullion	£25.00	1/4oz .... Unlimited		BV
1993	Gold Proof	£50.00	1/2oz .... Set only		—
1993	Gold Bullion	£50.00	1/2oz .... Unlimited		BV
1993	Gold Proof	£100.00	1oz .... Set only		—
1993	Gold Bullion	£100.00	1oz .... Unlimited		BV
1993	Gold Proof Set	£100, £50, £25 and £10		462	£3750
1994	Gold Proof	£10.00	1/10oz 994		£225
1994	Gold Bullion	£10.00	1/10oz .... Unlimited		BV
1994	Gold Proof	£25.00	1/4oz .... Set only		—
1994	Gold Bullion	£25.00	1/4oz .... Unlimited		BV
1994	Gold Proof	£50.00	1/2oz .... Set only		—
1994	Gold Bullion	£50.00	1/2oz .... Unlimited		BV
1994	Gold Proof	£100.00	1oz .... Set only		—
1994	Gold Bullion	£100.00	1oz .... Unlimited		BV
1994	Gold Proof Set	£100, £50, £25 and £10		435	£3800
1995	Gold Proof	£10.00	1/10oz 1,500		£225
1995	Gold Bullion	£10.00	1/10oz .... Unlimited		BV
1995	Gold Proof	£25.00	1/4oz .... Set only		—
1995	Gold Bullion	£25.00	1/4oz .... Unlimited		BV
1995	Gold Proof	£50.00	1/2oz .... Set only		—
1995	Gold Bullion	£50.00	1/2oz .... Unlimited		BV
1995	Gold Proof	£100.00	1oz .... Set only		—
1995	Gold Bullion	£100.00	1oz .... Unlimited		BV
1995	Gold Proof Set	£100, £50, £25 and £10		500	£3800
1996	Gold Proof	£10.00	1/10oz 2,379		£250
1996	Gold Bullion	£10.00	1/10oz .... Unlimited		BV
1996	Gold Proof	£25.00	1/4oz .... Set only		—
1996	Gold Bullion	£25.00	1/4oz .... Unlimited		BV
1996	Gold Proof	£50.00	1/2oz .... Set only		—
1996	Gold Bullion	£50.00	1/2oz .... Unlimited		BV
1996	Gold Proof	£100.00	1oz .... Set only		—
1996	Gold Bullion	£100.00	1oz .... Unlimited		BV
1996	Gold Proof Set	£100, £50, £25 and £10		483	£3800

BRITANNIA IN CHARIOT
Obverse by Raphael Maklouf
Reverse by Philip Nathan

Date	Metal	Face value	Weight	No. struck	Value
1997	Silver Proof	20 pence	1/10oz 8,686		£20
1997	Silver Proof	50 pence	1/4oz .... Set only		—

Date	Metal	Face value	Weight	No. struck	Value
1997	Silver Proof	£1.00	1/2oz.................................Set only		—
1997	Silver Proof	£2.00	1oz...4,173		£150
1997	Silver Proof Set	£2, £1, 50p and 20p..........................11,832			£225
1997	Gold Proof	£10.00	1/10oz...............................1,821		£225
1997	Gold Bullion	£10.00	1/10oz...........................Unlimited		BV
1997	Gold Proof	£25.00	1/4oz.....................................923		£485
1997	Gold Bullion	£25.00	1/4oz.............................Unlimited		BV
1997	Gold Proof	£50.00	1/2oz...............................Set only		—
1997	Gold Bullion	£50.00	1/2oz.............................Unlimited		BV
1997	Gold Proof	£100.00	1oz...164		£1650
1997	Gold Bullion	£100.00	1oz................................Unlimited		BV
1997	Gold Proof Set	£100, £50, £25 and £10 892			£3750

STANDING BRITANNIA
***Obverse* by Ian Rank-Broadley**
***Reverse* by Philip Nathan**

Date	Metal	Face value	Weight	No. struck	Value
1998	Silver Proof	20 pence	1/10oz................................2,724		£20
1998	Silver Proof	50 pence	1/4oz...............................Set only		—
1998	Silver Proof	£1.00	1/2oz...............................Set only		—
1998	Silver Proof	£2.00	1oz..................................Set only		—
1998	Silver Bullion	£2.00	1oz...................................88,909		£35
1998	Silver Proof Set	£2, £1, 50p and 20p............................2,500			£140
1998	Gold Proof	£10.00	1/10oz..................................392		£225
1998	Gold Bullion	£10.00	1/10oz...........................Unlimited		BV
1998	Gold Proof	£25.00	1/4oz.....................................560		£475
1998	Gold Bullion	£25.00	1/4oz.............................Unlimited		BV
1998	Gold Proof	£50.00	1/2oz...............................Set only		—
1998	Gold Bullion	£50.00	1/2oz.............................Unlimited		BV
1998	Gold Proof	£100.00	1oz................................Set only		—
1998	Gold Bullion	£100.00	1oz................................Unlimited		BV
1998	Gold Proof Set	£100, £50, £25 and £10 750			£3800

BRITANNIA IN CHARIOT (SILVER) / STANDING (GOLD)
***Obverse* by Ian Rank-Broadley**
***Reverse* by Philip Nathan**

Date	Metal	Face value	Weight	No. struck	Value
1999	Silver Bullion	£2.00	1oz...................................69,394		£35
1999	Gold Proof	£10.00	1/10oz...............................1,058		£225
1999	Gold Bullion	£10.00	1/10oz...........................Unlimited		BV
1999	Gold Proof	£25.00	1/4oz..................................1,000		£485
1999	Gold Bullion	£25.00	1/4oz.............................Unlimited		BV
1999	Gold Proof	£50.00	1/2oz...............................Set only		—
1999	Gold Bullion	£50.00	1/2oz.............................Unlimited		BV
1999	Gold Proof	£100.00	1oz................................Set only		—
1999	Gold Bullion	£100.00	1oz................................Unlimited		BV
1999	Gold Proof Set	£100, £50, £25 and £10 740			£3800

STANDING BRITANNIA
***Obverse* by Ian Rank-Broadley**
Reverse by Philip Nathan

Date	Metal	Face value	Weight	No. struck	Value
2000	Silver Bullion	£2.00	1oz...................................81,301		£35
2000	Gold Proof	£10.00	1/10oz...............................3,250		£225
2000	Gold Bullion	£10.00	1/10oz...........................Unlimited		BV
2000	Gold Proof	£25.00	1/4oz..................................1,250		£485
2000	Gold Bullion	£25.00	1/4oz.............................Unlimited		BV
2000	Gold Proof	£50.00	1/2oz...............................Set only		—
2000	Gold Bullion	£50.00	1/2oz.............................Unlimited		BV
2000	Gold Proof	£100.00	1oz................................Set only		—
2000	Gold Bullion	£100.00	1oz................................Unlimited		BV
2000	Gold Proof Set	£100, £50, £25 and £10 750			£3750

Date	Metal	Face value	Weight	No. struck	Value

UNA AND THE LION
Obverse by Ian Rank-Broadley
Reverse by Philip Nathan

Date	Metal	Face value	Weight	No. struck	Value
2001	Silver Proof	20 pence	1/10oz	10,000	£10
2001	Silver Proof	50 pence	1/4oz	Set only	—
2001	Silver Proof	£1.00	1/2oz	Set only	—
2001	Silver Proof	£2.00	1oz	10,000	£75
2001	Silver Bullion	£2.00	1oz	44,816	£39
2001	Silver Proof Set	"£2, £1, 50p and 20p"		Unknown	£225
2001	Gold Proof	£10.00	1/10oz	1,100	£225
2001	Gold Bullion	£10.00	1/10oz	Unlimited	BV
2001	Gold Proof	£25.00	1/4oz	500	£485
2001	Gold Bullion	£25.00	1/4oz	Unlimited	BV
2001	Gold Proof	£50.00	1/2oz	Set only	—
2001	Gold Bullion	£50.00	1/2oz	Unlimited	BV
2001	Gold Proof	£100.00	1oz	Set only	—
2001	Gold Bullion	£100.00	1oz	Unlimited	BV
2001	Gold Proof Set	£100, £50, £25 and £10		1,000	£3750

STANDING BRITANNIA
Obverse by Ian Rank-Broadley
Reverse by Philip Nathan

Date	Metal	Face value	Weight	No. struck	Value
2002	Silver Bullion	£2.00	1oz	36,543	£39
2002	Gold Proof	£10.00	1/10oz	2,500"	£225
2002	Gold Bullion	£10.00	1/10oz	Unlimited	BV
2002	Gold Proof	£25.00	1/4oz	1,750	£485
2002	Gold Bullion	£25.00	1/4oz	Unlimited	BV
2002	Gold Proof	£50.00	1/2oz	Set only	—
2002	Gold Bullion	£50.00	1/2oz	Unlimited	BV
2002	Gold Proof	£100.00	1oz	Set only	—
2002	Gold Bullion	£100.00	1oz	Unlimited	BV
2002	Gold Proof Set	£100, £50, £25 and £10		945	£3750

BRITANNIA'S HELMETED HEAD
Obverse by Ian Rank-Broadley
Reverse by Philip Nathan

Date	Metal	Face value	Weight	No. struck	Value
2003	Silver Proof	20 pence	1/10oz	1,179	£20
2003	Silver Proof	50 pence	1/4oz	Set only	—
2003	Silver Proof	£1.00	1/2oz	Set only	—
2003	Silver Proof	£2.00	1oz	2,016	£125
2003	Silver Bullion	£2.00	1oz	73,271	£35
2003	Silver Proof Set	£2, £1, 50p and 20p		3,669	£140
2003	Gold Proof	£10.00	1/10oz	1,382	£225
2003	Gold Bullion	£10.00	1/10oz	Unlimited	BV
2003	Gold Proof	£25.00	1/4oz	609	£485
2003	Gold Bullion	£25.00	1/4oz	Unlimited	BV
2003	Gold Proof	£50.00	1/2oz	Set only	—
2003	Gold Bullion	£50.00	1/2oz	Unlimited	BV
2003	Gold Proof	£100.00	1oz	Set only	—
2003	Gold Bullion	£100.00	1oz	Unlimited	BV
2003	Gold Proof Set	£50, £25 and £10		825	£1650
2003	Gold Proof Set	£100, £50, £25 and £10		1,250	£3750

STANDING BRITANNIA
Obverse by Ian Rank-Broadley
Reverse by Philip Nathan

Date	Metal	Face value	Weight	No. struck	Value
2004	Silver Proof	£2.00	1oz	2,174	£125
2004	Silver Bullion	£2.00	1oz	57,000	£35
2004	Gold Proof	£10.00	1/10oz	929	£225
2004	Gold Bullion	£10.00	1/10oz	Unlimited	BV
2004	Gold Proof	£25.00	1/4oz	750	£485
2004	Gold Bullion	£25.00	1/4oz	Unlimited	BV

Date	Metal	Face value	Weight	No. struck	Value
2004	Gold Proof	£50.00	1/2oz	Set only	—
2004	Gold Bullion	£50.00	1/2oz	Unlimited	BV
2004	Gold Proof	£100.00	1oz	Set only	—
2004	Gold Bullion	£100.00	1oz	Unlimited	BV
2004	Gold Proof Set	£50, £25 and £10		223	£1750
2004	Gold Proof Set	£100, £50, £25 and £10		973	£3750

BRTANNIA SEATED
Obverse by Ian Rank-Broadley
Reverse by Philip Nathan

Date	Metal	Face value	Weight	No. struck	Value
2005	Silver Proof	20 pence	1/10oz	913	£20
2005	Silver Proof	50 pence	1/4oz	Set only	—
2005	Silver Proof	£1.00	1/2oz	Set only	—
2005	Silver Proof	£2.00	1oz	1,539	£125
2005	Silver Bullion	£2.00	1oz	57,000	£39
2005	Silver Proof Set	£2, £1, 50p and 20p		2,360	£175
2005	Gold Proof	£10.00	1/10oz	1,225	£225
2005	Gold Bullion	£10.00	1/10oz	Unlimited	BV
2005	Gold Proof	£25.00	1/4oz	750	£500
2005	Gold Bullion	£25.00	1/4oz	Unlimited	BV
2005	Gold Proof	£50.00	1/2oz	Set only	—
2005	Gold Bullion	£50.00	1/2oz	Unlimited	BV
2005	Gold Proof	£100.00	1oz	Set only	—
2005	Gold Bullion	£100.00	1oz	Unlimited	BV
2005	Gold Proof Set	£50, £25 and £10		417	£1750
2005	Gold Proof Set	£100, £50, £25 and £10		1,439	£3750

STANDING BRITANNIA
Obverse by Ian Rank-Broadley
Reverse by Philip Nathan

Date	Metal	Face value	Weight	No. struck	Value
2006	Silver Proof	20 pence	1/10oz	Set only	—
2006	Silver Proof	50 pence	1/4oz	Set only	—
2006	Silver Proof	£1.00	1/2oz	Set only	—
2006	Silver Proof	£2.00	1oz	2,529	£125
2006	Silver Bullion	£2.00	1oz	50,300	£39
2006	Silver Proof "Silhouette" Set of five designs				
		5 x £2	1oz	3,000	£275
2006	Silver Proof Set	£2, £1, 50p and 20p		2,500	£175
2006	Gold Proof	£10.00	1/10oz	700	£250
2006	Gold Bullion	£10.00	1/10oz	Unlimited	BV
2006	Gold Proof	£25.00	1/4oz	728	£500
2006	Gold Bullion	£25.00	1/4oz	Unlimited	BV
2006	Gold Proof	£50.00	1/2oz	Set only	—
2006	Gold Bullion	£50.00	1/2oz	Unlimited	BV
2006	Gold Proof	£100.00	1oz	Set only	—
2006	Gold Bullion	£100.00	1oz	Unlimited	BV
2006	Gold Proof Set	£100, £50, £25 and £10		1,163	£3750
2006	Gold Proof Set of Five Designs				
		5 x £25	1/4oz	250	£2750

BRITANNIA SEATED LION AT FEET
Obverse by Ian Rank-Broadley
Reverse by Christopher le Brun

Date	Metal	Face value	Weight	No. struck	Value
2007	Silver Proof	20 pence	1/10oz	901	£20
2007	Silver Proof	50 pence	1/4oz	Set only	—
2007	Silver Proof	£1.00	1/2oz	Set only	—
2007	Silver Proof	£2.00	1oz	2,500	£125
2007	Silver Bullion	£2.00	1oz	94,000	£35
2007	Silver Proof Set (20th Anniversary) 6 Satin Finish Reverses				
		6 x £1	1/2oz	2,000	£200
2007	Silver Proof Set	£2, £1, 50p and 20p		2,500	£150
2007	Gold Proof	£10.00	1/10oz	893	£250

Date	Metal	Face value	Weight	No. struck	Value
2007	Gold Bullion	£10.00	1/10oz	Unlimited	BV
2007	Gold Proof	£25.00	1/4oz	1,000	£485
2007	Gold Bullion	£25.00	1/4oz	Unlimited	BV
2007	Gold Proof	£50.00	1/2oz	Set only	—
2007	Gold Bullion	£50.00	1/2oz	Unlimited	BV
2007	Gold Proof	£100.00	1oz	Set only	—
2007	Gold Bullion	£100.00	1oz	Unlimited	BV
2007	Gold Proof Set	£100, £50, £25 and £10		250	£3750
2007	Platinum Proof	£10	1/10oz	691	£190
2007	Platinum Proof	£25	1/4oz	210	£390
2007	Platinum Proof	£50	1/2oz	Set only	—
2007	Platinum Proof	£100	1oz	Set only	—
2007	Platinum Proof Set £100, £50, £25 and £10			250	£2750

STANDING BRITANNIA ON WAVES
Obverse by Ian Rank-Broadley
Reverse by John Bergdahl

Date	Metal	Face value	Weight	No. struck	Value
2008	Silver Proof*	20 pence	1/10oz	2,500	£20
2008	Silver Proof*	50 pence	1/4oz	Set only	—
2008	Silver Proof*	£1.00	1/2oz	Set only	—
2008	Silver Proof*	£2.00	1oz	2,500	£125
2008	Silver Bullion	£2.00	1oz	100,000	£35
2008	Silver Proof Set £2, £1, 50p and 20p			2,500	£130
2008	Gold Proof	£10.00	1/10oz	748	£250
2008	Gold Bullion	£10.00	1/10oz	Unlimited	BV
2008	Gold Proof	£25.00	1/4oz	1,000	£485
2008	Gold Bullion	£25.00	1/4oz	Unlimited	BV
2008	Gold Proof	£50.00	1/2oz	Set only	—
2008	Gold Bullion	£50.00	1/2oz	Unlimited	BV
2008	Gold Proof	£100.00	1oz	Set only	—
2008	Gold Bullion	£100.00	1oz	Unlimited	BV
2008	Gold Proof Set	£100, £50, £25 and £10		1,250	£3750
2008	Platinum Proof	£10	1/10oz	268	£190
2008	Platinum Proof	£25	1/4oz	100	£390
2008	Platinum Proof	£50	1/2oz	Set only	—
2008	Platinum Proof	£100	1oz	Set only	—
2008	Platinum Proof Set £100, £50, £25 and £10			150	£2750

*Satin finish

BRITANNIA IN CHARIOT
Obverse by Ian Rank-Broadley
Reverse by Philip Nathan

Date	Metal	Face value	Weight	No. struck	Value
2009	Silver Proof	20 pence	1/10oz	2,500	£18
2009	Silver Proof	50 pence	1/4oz	2,500	£25
2009	Silver Proof	£1.00	1/2oz	2,500	£35
2009	Silver Proof	£2.00	1oz	6,784	£80
2009	Silver Bullion	£2.00	1oz	100,000	£35
2009	Silver Proof Set £2, £1, 50p and 20p			2,500	£130
2009	Gold Proof	£10.00	1/10oz	1,546	£225
2009	Gold Bullion	£10.00	1/10oz	Unlimited	BV
2009	Gold Proof	£25.00	1/4oz	1,567	£485
2009	Gold Bullion	£25.00	1/4oz	Unlimited	BV
2009	Gold Proof	£50.00	1/2oz	797	£800
2009	Gold Bullion	£50.00	1/2oz	Unlimited	BV
2009	Gold Proof	£100.00	1oz	797	£1650
2009	Gold Bullion	£100.00	1oz	Unlimited	BV
2009	Gold Proof Set	£100, £50, £25 and £10		797	£3800

Date   Metal   Face value   Weight   No. struck   Value

BRITANNIA WEARING A CORINTHIAN HELMET
Obverse by Ian Rank-Broadley
Reverse by Suzie Zamit

Date	Metal	Face value	Weight	No. struck	Value
2010	Silver Proof	20 pence	1/10oz	4,486	£12
2010	Silver Proof	50 pence	1/4oz	3,497	£20
2010	Silver Proof	£1.00	1/2oz	3,497	£35
2010	Silver Proof	£2.00	1oz	6,539	£75
2010	Silver Bullion	£2.00	1oz	126,367	£30
2010	Silver Proof Set £2, £1, 50p and 20p			3,500	£130
2010	Gold Proof	£10.00	1/10oz	2,102	£225
2010	Gold Bullion	£10.00	1/10oz	3,530	BV
2010	Gold Proof	£25.00	1/4oz	1,670	£485
2010	Gold Bullion	£25.00	1/4oz	1,501	BV
2010	Gold Proof	£50.00	1/2oz	1,053	£800
2010	Gold Bullion	£50.00	1/2oz	1,301	BV
2010	Gold Proof	£100.00	1oz	867	£1650
2010	Gold Bullion	£100.00	1oz	13,860	BV
2010	Gold Proof Set First Strike £100, £50, £25 and £10			500	£4000
2010	Gold Proof Set £100, £50, £25 and £10			1,250	£3850

"PENNY" BRITANNIA SUPERIMPOSED ON A UNION FLAG
Obverse by Ian Rank-Broadley
Reverse by David Mach

Date	Metal	Face value	Weight	No. struck	Value
2011	Silver Proof	20 pence	1/10oz	2,483	£12
2011	Silver Proof	50 pence	1/4oz	2,483	£20
2011	Silver Proof	£1.00	1/2oz	2,483	£35
2011	Silver Proof	£2.00	1oz	4,973	£75
2011	Silver Bullion	£2.00	1oz	269,282	£30
2011	Silver Proof Set £2, £1, 50p, 20p			3,500	£130
2011	Gold Proof	£10.00	1/10oz	3,511	£225
2011	Gold Proof	£25.00	1/4oz	698	£500
2011	Gold Bullion	£25.00	1/4oz	Unlimited	BV
2011	Gold Proof	£50.00	1/2oz	847	£800
2011	Gold Bullion	£50.00	1/2oz	Unlimited	BV
2011	Gold Proof	£100.00	1oz	5,735	£1650
2011	Gold Bullion	£100.00	1oz	Unlimited	BV
2011	Gold Proof Set £50, £25 and £10			250	£1750
2011	Gold Proof Set £100, £50, £25 and £10			1,000	£3850

STANDING BRITANNIA
Obverse by Ian Rank-Broadley
Reverse by Philip Nathan

Date	Metal	Face value	Weight	No. struck	Value
2012	Silver Proof	20 pence	1/10oz	Set only	—
2012	Silver Proof	50 pence	1/4oz	Set only	—
2012	Silver Proof	£1.00	1/2oz	Set only	—
2012	Silver Proof	£2.00	1oz	5,550	£75
2012	Silver Bullion	£2.00	1oz	351,372	£25
2012	Silver BU	£2.00	1oz	Unknown	£35
2012	Silver Proof Set £2, £1, 50p and 20p			2,595	£140
2012	Silver Proof Set 9 Reverse Portraits				
		9 x £1.00		1,656	£500
2012	Gold Proof	£10.00	1/10oz	1,249	£225
2012	Gold Proof	£25.00	1/4oz	316	£500
2012	Gold Bullion	£25.00	1/4oz	Unlimited	BV
2012	Gold Proof	£50.00	1/2oz	Set only	—
2012	Gold Bullion	£50.00	1/2oz	Unlimited	BV
2012	Gold Proof	£100.00	1oz	Set only	—
2012	Gold Bullion	£100.00	1oz	Unlimited	BV
2012	Gold Proof Set £50, £25 and £10			99	£1750
2012	Gold Proof Set First Strike £100, £50, £25 and £10			200	£4000
2012	Gold Proof Set £100, £50, £25 and £10			352	£3750
2012	Gold Proof Set 9 Reverse Portraits				
		9 x £50		25	£8000

Date	Metal	Face value	Weight	No. struck	Value

BRITANNIA SEATED WITH OWL
Obverse by Ian Rank-Broadley
Reverse by Jody Clark

Date	Metal	Face value	Weight	No. struck	Value
2013	Silver Proof	10 pence	1/20oz	Set only	—
2013	Silver Proof	20 pence	1/10oz	Set only	—
2013	Silver Proof	50 pence	1/4oz	Set only	—
2013	Silver BU (SS *Gairsoppa*) Nathan Reverse				
		50 pence	1/4oz	584,946	£50
2013	Silver Proof	£1.00	1/2oz	Set only	—
2013	Silver Proof	£2.00	1oz	3,468	£125
2013	Silver Bullion (Nathan Reverse)				
		£2.00	1oz	Unlimited	£35
2013	Silver Bullion (Year of the Snake Privy Mark)				
		£2.00	1oz	Unlimited	£40
2013	Silver BU	£2.00	1oz	2,387	£35
2013	Silver Proof	£10.00	5oz	4,054	£450
2013	Silver Proof Set £2, £1, 50p , 20p and 10 pence			3,087	£250
2013	Gold Proof	£1.00	1/20oz	2,496	£150
2013	Gold Proof	£10.00	1/10oz	1,150	£170
2013	Gold Proof	£25.00	1/4oz	Set only	—
2013	Gold Bullion (Nathan Reverse)				
		£25.00	1/4oz	Unlimited	BV
2013	Gold Proof	£50.00	1/2oz	Set only	—
2013	Gold Bullion (Nathan Reverse)				
		£50.00	1/2oz	Unlimited	BV
2013	Gold Proof	£100.00	1oz	Set only	—
2013	Gold Bullion (Nathan Reverse)				
		£100.00	1oz	Unlimited	BV
2013	Gold Proof	£500.00	5oz	61	£8250
2013	Gold Proof Set £50, £25 and £10			136	£1750
2013	Gold Proof Set (Premium) £50, £25 and £10			90	£2000
2013	Gold Proof Set £100, £50, £25 and £10			261	£4000

STANDING BRITANNIA WITH GLOBE
Obverse by Ian Rank-Broadley
Reverse by Jody Clark

Date	Metal	Face value	Weight	No. struck	Value
2014	Silver Proof	5 pence	1/40oz	Set only	—
2014	Silver Proof	10 pence	1/20oz	Set only	—
2014	Silver Proof	20 pence	1/10oz	Set only	—
2014	Silver Proof	50 pence	1/4oz	Set only	—
2014	Silver Bullion (SS *Gairsoppa*) Nathan Reverse				
		50 pence	1/4oz	19,214	£25
2014	Silver Proof	£1.00	1/2oz	Set only	—
2014	Silver Proof	£2.00	1oz	2,981	£250
2014	Silver Proof Gilded Britannia 24k Gold				
		£2.00	1oz	5,000	£85
2014	Silver Bullion (Nathan Reverse)				
		£2.00	1oz	623,741	£25
2014	Silver Bullion (Year of the Horse Privy Mark)				
		£2.00	1oz	Unlimited	£40
2014	Silver Bullion Year of the Horse Obverse Mule				
		£2.00	1oz	Unknown	—
2014	Silver BU	£2.00	1oz	1,493	£35
2014	Silver Proof	£10.00	5oz	1,348	£400
2014	Silver Proof Set 20p, 10p and 5 pence			998	£65
2014	Silver Proof Set £2, £1, 50p , 20p and 10 pence			550	£450
2014	Silver Proof Set £2, £1, 50p , 20p, 10p and 5 pence			1,735	£450
2014	Gold Proof	50 pence	1/40oz	5,521	£70
2014	Gold Proof	£1.00	1/20oz	993	£150
2014	Gold Proof	£10.00	1/10oz	Set only	—
2014	Gold Bullion (Nathan Reverse)				
		£10.00	1/10oz	Unlimited	BV

Date	Metal	Face value	Weight	No. struck	Value
2014	Gold Proof	£25.00	1/4oz	Set only	—
2014	Gold Bullion (Nathan Reverse)				
		£25.00	1/4oz	Unlimited	BV
2014	Gold Proof	£50.00	1/2oz	Set only	—
2014	Gold Bullion (Nathan Reverse)				
		£50.00	1/2oz	Unlimited	BV
2014	Gold Proof	£100.00	1oz	Set only	—
2014	Gold Bullion (Nathan Reverse)				
		£100.00	1oz	Unlimited	BV
2014	Gold Proof	£500.00	5oz	75	£8000
2014	Gold Proof Set	£50, £25 and £10		140	£1750
2014	Gold Proof Set (Premium) £50, £25 and £10			98	£2000
2014	Gold Proof Set £100, £50, £25, £10 and £1			150	£4500
2014	Gold Proof Set (Premium)				
	£100, £50, £25, £10, £1 and 50 pence			225	£5000

BRITANNIA WITH TRIDENT
Obverse by Ian Rank-Broadley
Reverse by Antony Dufort

Date	Metal	Face value	Weight	No. struck	Value
2015	Silver Proof	5 pence	1/40oz	8,000	£12
2015	Silver Proof	10 pence	1/20oz	Set only	—
2015	Silver Proof	20 pence	1/10oz	Set only	—
2015	Silver Proof	50 pence	1/4oz	Set only	—
2015	Silver Proof	£1.00	1/2oz	Set only	—
2015	Silver Proof	£2.00	1oz	2,990	£60
2015	Silver Proof First Release				
		£2.00	1oz	1,250	£85
2015	Silver Proof Gilded Britannia 24k Gold				
		£2.00	1oz	5,000	£80
2015	Silver Bullion (Nathan Reverse)				
		£2.00	1oz	2,780,529	£25
2015	Silver Bullion (Year of the Sheep Privy Mark)				
		£2.00	1oz	1,000	£40
2015	Silver BU	£2.00	1oz	2,870	£25
2015	Silver Proof	£10.00	5oz	495	£395
2015	Silver Proof First Release				
		£10.00	5oz	500	£420
2015	Silver Proof	£50.00	31g	78,644	£60
2015	Silver Proof Set £2, £1, 50p , 20p, 10p and 5 pence			1,009	£250
2015	Silver Proof Set First Release				
	£2, £1, 50p , 20p and 10 pence			550	£250
2015	Gold Proof	50 pence	1/40oz	3,075	£50
2015	Gold Proof	£1.00	1/20oz	Set only	—
2015	Gold Proof	£10.00	1/10oz	Set only	—
2015	Gold Bullion (Nathan Reverse)				
		£10.00	1/10oz	Unlimited	BV
2015	Gold Proof	£25.00	1/4oz	Set only	—
2015	Gold Bullion (Nathan Reverse)				
		£25.00	1/4oz	Unlimited	BV
2015	Gold Proof	£50.00	1/2oz	Set only	—
2015	Gold Bullion (Nathan Reverse)				
		£50.00	1/2oz	Unlimited	BV
2015	Gold Proof	£100.00	1oz	Set only	—
2014	Gold Bullion (Nathan Reverse)				
		£100.00	1oz	Unlimited	BV
2015	Gold Proof	£500.00	5oz	50	£8000
2015	Gold Proof First Release				
		£500.00	5oz	10	£8500
2015	Gold Proof Set	£50, £25 and £10		176	£1750
2015	Gold Proof Set (Premium) £50, £25 and £10			99	£1950
2015	Gold Proof Set £100, £50, £25, £10 and £1			96	£4500
2015	Gold Proof Set £100, £50, £25, £10, £1 and 50 pence			138	£5000

Date	Metal	Face value	Weight	No. struck	Value

BRITANNIA AS WARRIOR QUEEN
Obverse by **Jody Clark**
Reverse by **Suzie Zamit**

Date	Metal	Face value	Weight	No. struck	Value
2016	Silver Proof	5 pence	1/40oz............................Set only		—
2016	Silver Proof	10 pence	1/20oz............................Set only		—
2016	Silver Proof	20 pence	1/10oz............................Set only		—
2016	Silver Proof	50 pence	1/4oz..............................Set only		—
2016	Silver Proof	£1.00	1/2oz..............................Set only		—
2016	Silver Proof	£2.00	1oz......................................4,137		£100
2016	Silver Proof First Release				
		£2.00	1oz..416		£100
2016	Silver Bullion (Nathan Reverse)				
		£2.00	1oz...............................Unlimited		£25
2016	Silver Bullion (Year of the Monkey Privy Mark)				
		£2.00	1oz......................................1,000		£35
2016	Silver BU	£2.00	1oz......................................2,901		£35
2016	Silver BU	£2.00	1oz in Capsule....................1,000		£35
2016	Silver Proof	£10.00	5oz..533		£395
2016	Silver Proof First Release				
		£10.00	5oz..25		£420
2016	Silver Proof 1oz Suzie Zamit and 1oz Nathan Reverse.....500				£75
2016	Silver Proof Set £2, £1, 50p , 20p, 10p and 5 pence......1,050				£250
2016	Silver Proof Set Ultra Cameo Slabbed				
		£2, £1, 50p , 20p and 10 pence..............250			£250
2016	Gold Proof	50 pence	1/40oz..................................1,447		£70
2016	Gold Proof	£1.00	1/20oz............................Set only		—
2016	Gold Proof	£10.00	1/10oz............................Set only		—
2016	Gold Proof	£25.00	1/4oz.......................................729		£500
2016	Gold Proof First Release				
		£25.00	1/4oz.......................................100		£550
2016	Gold Proof	£50.00	1/2oz..............................Set only		—
2016	Gold Proof	£100.00	1oz...................................Set only		—
2016	Gold Bullion (Nathan Reverse)				
		£100.00	1oz...............................Unlimited		BV
2016	Gold Proof	£500.00	5oz..54		£8000
2016	Gold Proof First Release				
		£500.00	5oz..10		£8000
2016	Gold Proof Set £50, £25 and £10 69				
2016	Gold Proof Set £100, £50, £25, £10, £1 and 50 pence....174				£5430

HELMETED OUTLINE OF BRITAIN
Obverse by **Jody Clark**
Reverse by **Louis Tamlyn**

Date	Metal	Face value	Weight	No. struck	Value
2017	Silver Proof	5 pence	1/40oz............................Set only		—
2017	Silver Proof	10 pence	1/20oz............................Set only		—
2017	Silver Proof	20 pence	1/10oz............................Set only		—
2017	Silver Proof	50 pence	1/4oz..............................Set only		—
2017	Silver Proof	£1.00	1/2oz..............................Set only		—
2017	Silver BU	£2.00	1oz......................................3,977		£24
2017	Silver Proof	£2.00	1oz......................................5,225		£80
2017	Silver Bullion (Nathan Reverse)				
		£2.00	1oz...............................Unlimited		£25
2017	Silver Bullion (30th Anniversary Trident Privy Mark)				
		£2.00	1oz...................................120,000		£25
2017	Silver Bullion (Year of the Rooster Privy Mark)				
		£2.00	1oz...............................Unlimited		£30
2017	Silver Proof	£10.00	5oz..656		£415
2017	Silver Proof	£250.00	20oz...103		£450
2017	Silver Proof Set £2, £1, 50p , 20p, 10p and 5 pence......1,347				£200
2017	Gold Proof	50 pence	1/40oz......................................871		£70
2017	Gold Proof	£1.00	1/20oz............................Set only		—
2017	Gold Proof	£10.00	1/10oz............................Set only		—

Date	Metal	Face value	Weight	No. struck	Value
2017	Gold bullion (Nathan Reverse)				
		£10.00	1/10oz...............................Set only		—
2017	Gold Proof	£25.00	1/4oz...687		£500
2017	Gold Bullion (Nathan Reverse)				
		£25.00	1/4oz...............................Set only		—
2017	Gold Proof	£50.00	1/2oz...............................Set only		—
2017	Gold Bullion (Nathan Reverse)				
		£50.00	1/2oz...............................Unlimited		BV
2017	Gold Proof	£100.00	1oz...................................Set only		—
2017	Gold Bullion (Nathan Reverse)				
		£100.00	1oz...................................Unlimited		BV
2017	Gold Bullion (30th Anniversary Trident Privy Mark)				
		£100.00	1oz......................................7,030		BV
2017	Gold Proof	£500.00	5oz...98		£8250
2017	Gold Proof (30th Anniversary Trident Privy Mark)				
		£500.00	30oz...6		—
2017	Gold Proof Set	£50, £25 and £10		143	£1750
017	Gold Proof Set	£100, £50, £25, £10 and £1		62	£4500
2017	Gold Proof Set	£100, £50, £25, £10, £1 and 50 pence		176	£5000
2017	Platinum Bullion (Nathan Reverse)				
		£10	1/10oz...............................Unlimited		BV
2017	Platinum Proof	£25.00	1/4oz...538		£525
2017	Platinum Bullion (Nathan Reverse)				
		£25.00	1/4oz...............................Unlimited		BV
2017	Platinum Bullion (Nathan Reverse)				
		£100.00	1oz...................................Unlimited		BV

BRITANNIA FACING RIGHT WEARING A CORINTHIAN HELMET
Obverse by Jody Clark
Reverse by David Lawrence

Date	Metal	Face value	Weight	No. struck	Value
2018	Silver Proof	5 pence	1/40oz...............................Set only		—
2018	Silver Proof	10 pence	1/20oz...............................Set only		—
2018	Silver Proof	20 pence	1/10oz...............................Set only		—
2018	Silver Proof	50 pence	1/4oz...............................Set only		—
2018	Silver Proof	£1.00	1/2oz...............................Set only		—
2018	Silver Proof	£2.00	1oz.......................................5,100		£85
2018	Silver Bullion (Nathan Reverse)				
		£2.00	1oz...................................Unlimited		BV
2018	Silver Bullion (Year of the Dog Privy Mark)				
		£2	1oz...................................Unlimited		£26
2018	Silver Bullion "Oriental Border" (Nathan Reverse)				
		£2.00	1oz.................................100,000		BV
2018	BU	£2.00	1oz.......................................7,000		BV
2018	Silver Proof	£10.00	5oz..650		£420
2018	Silver Proof	£500.00	1kg...150		£2050
2018	Silver Proof Set	£2, £1, 50p , 20p, 10p and 5 pence		1,350	£210
2018	Gold Proof	50 pence	1/40oz...............................Set only		—
2018	Gold Proof	£1.00	1/20oz...............................Set only		—
2018	Gold Proof	£10.00	1/10oz...............................Set only		—
2018	Gold bullion (Nathan Reverse)				
		£10.00	1/10oz...............................Unlimited		BV
2018	Gold Proof	£25.00	1/4oz....................................1,080		£595
2018	Gold Bullion (Nathan Reverse)				
		£25.00	1/4oz...............................Unlimited		BV
2018	Gold Proof	£50.00	1/2oz...............................Set only		—
2018	Gold Bullion (Nathan Reverse)				
		£50.00	1/2oz...............................Set only		—
2018	Gold Bullion (Nathan Reverse)				
		£100.00	1oz...................................Unlimited		BV
2018	Gold bullion "Oriental Border" (Nathan Reverse)				
		£100.00	1oz.......................................5,000		BV
2018	Gold Proof	£500.00	5oz...90		£9995

Date	Metal	Face value	Weight	No. struck	Value
2018	Gold Proof Set	£100, £50, £25, £10, £1 and 50 pence....		220	£4400
2018	Gold Proof Set	£50, £25 and £10		170	£1945
2018	Platinum Bullion (Nathan Reverse)				
		£100.00	1oz	5,000	BV
2018	Platinum Proof	£25.00	1/4oz	600	£525
2018	Platinum Bullion (Nathan Reverse)				
		£25.00	1/4oz	Unlimited	BV
2018	Platinum Bullion (Nathan Reverse)				
		£10	1/10oz	Unlimited	BV

STANDING BRITANNIA IN WARLIKE POSE
Obverse by Jody Clark
Reverse by David Lawrence

Date	Metal	Face value	Weight	No. struck	Value
2019	Silver Proof	5 pence	1/40oz	Set only	—
2019	Silver Proof	10 pence	1/20oz	Set only	—
2019	Silver Proof	20 pence	1/10oz	Set only	—
2019	Silver Proof	50 pence	1/4oz	Set only	—
2019	Silver Proof	£1.00	1/2oz	Set only	—
2019	Silver Proof	£2.00	1oz	5,200	£75
2019	Silver Proof Coin and Print Set				
		£2.00	1oz	200 each frame colour	£245
2019	Silver Bullion 'Oriental Border' (Nathan Reverse)				
		£2.00	1oz	Unlimited	BV
2019	Silver Bullion (Nathan Reverse)				
		£2.00	1oz	Unlimited	BV
2019	Silver Bullion (Year of the Pig Privy Mark)				
		£2.00	1oz	Unknown	£26
2019	BU (Year of the Pig Privy Mark)				
		£2.00	1oz	Unknown	
2019	Silver BU	£2.00	1oz	10,000	£55
2019	Silver BU	£10.00	5oz	250	£420
2019	Silver Proof	£500.00	1kg	85	£2050
2019	Silver Proof Set	£2, £1, 50p , 20p, 10p and 5 pence		950	£250
2019	Gold Proof	50 pence	1/40oz	Set only	—
2019	Gold Proof	£1.00	1/20oz	Set only	—
2019	Gold Proof	£10.00	1/10oz	Set only	—
2019	Gold bullion (Nathan Reverse)				
		£10.00	1/10oz	Unlimited	BV
2019	Gold Proof	£25.00	1/4oz	645	£555
2019	Gold Bullion (Nathan Reverse)				
		£25.00	1/4oz	Unlimited	BV
2019	Gold Proof	£50.00	1/2oz	Set only	—
2019	Gold Bullion (Nathan Reverse)				
		£50.00	1/2oz	Unlimited	BV
2019	Gold Bullion (Nathan Reverse)				
		£100.00	1oz	Unlimited	BV
2019	Gold bullion "Oriental Border" (Nathan Reverse)				
		£100.00	1oz	Unlimited	BV
2019	Gold Proof	£200.00	2oz	100	£4395
2019	Gold Proof	£500.00	5oz	57	£9995
2019	Gold Proof Set	£100, £50, £25, £10, £1 and 50 pence....		150	£3895
2019	Gold Proof Set	£50, £25 and £10		130	£1945
2019	Platinum Bullion (Nathan Reverse)				
		£10	1/10oz	Unlimited	BV
2019	Platinum Proof	£25.00	1/4oz	240	£525
2019	Platinum Bullion (Nathan Reverse)				
		£100.00	1oz	Unlimited	BV

Date	Metal	Face value	Weight	No. struck	Value

BRITANNIA SEATED WITH LION AND BRITANNIA IN PROFILE FOR PREMIUM EXCLUSIVE COINS
Obverse **by Jody Clark**
Reverse **by P.J. Lynch**

2021 Silver Proof 5 pence 1/40oz...........................Set only —
2021 Silver Proof 10 pence 1/20oz.........................Set only —
2021 Silver Proof 20 pence 1/10oz.........................Set only —
2021 Silver Proof 50 pence 1/4oz...........................Set only —
2021 Silver Proof £1.00 1/2oz..............................Set only —
2021 Silver Proof Britannia Seated with Lion
      £2.00 1oz................................2,900 £95
2021 Silver Bullion (Nathan Reverse)
      £2.00 1oz...............................Unlimited BV
2021 Silver Proof set Britannia Seated with Lion -
  1 x frosted reverse, 1 x standard
      2 x £2 1oz...500 £185
2021 Premium Exclusive (Britannia in Profile) BU
      £2.00 1oz................7,500 (7,510 struck) £62.50
  Silver Proof (Britannia seated with Lion)
      £2.00 1oz.......................................4860 £92.50
2021 Silver Proof Premium Exclusive (Britannia in Profile)
      £5.00 2oz.....................550 (560 struck) £195
2021 Silver Proof (Britannia seated with Lion)
      £10.00 5oz...285 £455
2021 Premium Exclusive' Britannia in Profile Silver Proof
      £500.00 1kg......................... 40 (50 Struck) £2,445
2021 Silver Proof (Britannia seated with Lion)
      £1000.00 2kg...110 £4,890
2021 Silver Proof Set (Britannia seated with Lion) ....
      £2, £1, 50p , 20p, 10p and 5 pence......1,100 £235
2021 Gold Proof 50 pence 1/40oz............................Set only —
2021 Gold Proof £1.00 1/20oz..............................Set only —
2021 Gold Proof £10.00 1/10oz............................Set only —
2021 Gold bullion (Nathan Reverse)
      £10.00 1/10oz...........................Unlimited BV
2021 Gold Proof Set (Britannia seated with Lion)
      £25.00 1/4oz................775 (1060 minted) £650
2021 Gold Bullion (Nathan Reverse)
      £25.00 1/4oz............................Unlimited BV
2021 Gold Proof £50.00 1/2oz..............................Set only —
2021 Gold Bullion (Nathan Reverse)
      £50.00 1/2oz..............................Set only BV
2021 Gold Bullion (Nathan Reverse)
      £100.00 1oz................................Unlimited BV
2021 Gold Proof (Britannia seated with Lion)
      £200.00 2oz...103 £8,190
      Sold price at LondonCoin Auctions

2021 Gold Proof Premium Exclusive (Britannia in Profile)
      £200.00 2oz.....................220 (230 struck) £4,650
2021 Gold Proof (Britannia seated with Lion)
      £500.00 5oz...83 £10,820
2021 Gold Proof Premium (Britannia in Profile)
      £1000.00 1kg..............................5 (6 struck) £70,275
2021 Gold Proof Premium Exclusive (Britannia in Profile)
  £100, £50, £25, £10, £1 and 50 pence.............150 £4,485
2021 Gold Proof Set (Briannia seated with Lion)
      £50, £25 and £10......................115 £1,985
2021 Platinum Bullion (Nathan Reverse)
      £10 1/10oz............................Unlimited BV
2021 Platinum Proof (Britannia seated with Lion)
      £25.00 1/4oz...150 £550
2021 Platinum Bullion (Nathan Reverse)
      £100.00 1oz................................Unlimited BV

Date	Metal	Face value	Weight	No. struck	Value

STANDING BRITANNIA WITH UNION FLAG BACKGROUND
Obverse by **Jody Clark**
Reverse by **James Tottle**

2020	Silver Proof	5 pence	1/40oz	Set only	—
2020	Silver Proof	10 pence	1/20oz	Set only	—
2020	Silver Proof	20 pence	1/10oz	Set only	—
2020	Silver Proof	50 pence	1/4oz	Set only	—
2020	Silver Proof	£1.00	1/2oz	Set only	—
2020	Silver Proof	£2.00	1oz	3,000	£85
2020	Silver Proof Coin and Print Set				
		£2.00	1oz	100	£245
2020	Silver Bullion (Nathan Reverse)				
		£2.00	1oz	Unlimited	BV
2020	Silver Bullion (Year of the Rat Privy Mark)				
		£2.00	1oz	Unlimited	£26
2020	Silver Proof Set: 1 x frosted reverse, 1 x standard				
		2 x £2	1oz	700	£170
2020	BU	£2.00	1oz	3,000	£55
2020	Silver Proof	£10.00	5oz	250	£420
2020	Silver Proof	£500.00	1kg	30	£2050
2020	Silver Proof Set £2, £1, 50p , 20p, 10p and 5 pence			1,000	£205
2020	Gold Proof	50 pence	1/40oz	Set only	—
2020	Gold Proof	£1.00	1/20oz	Set only	—
2020	Gold Proof	£10.00	1/10oz	Set only	—
2020	Gold bullion (Nathan Reverse)				
		£10.00	1/10oz	Unlimited	BV
2020	Gold Proof	£25.00	1/4oz	700	£500
2020	Gold Bullion (Nathan Reverse)				
		£25.00	1/4oz	Unlimited	BV
2020	Gold Proof	£50.00	1/2oz	Set only	—
2020	Gold Bullion (Nathan Reverse)				
		£50.00	1/2oz	Set only	—
2020	Gold Proof	£100.00	1oz	Coin and print set 25	£2600
2020	Gold Bullion (Nathan Reverse)				
		£100.00	1oz	Unlimited	BV
2020	Gold bullion "Oriental Border" (Nathan Reverse)				
		£100.00	1oz	Unlimited	BV
2020	Gold Proof	£200.00	2oz	150	£4395
2020	Gold Proof Set	£100, £50, £25, £10, £1 and 50 pence		150	£4165
2020	Gold Proof Set	£50, £25 and £10		130	£1840
2020	Gold Proof Coin and Print Set				
		£100	1oz	25	£2600
2020	Gold Proof	£500	5oz	50	£10,605
2020	Platinum Bullion (Nathan Reverse)				
		£10	1/10oz	Unlimited	BV
2020	Platinum Proof	£25.00	1/4oz	160	£525
2020	Platinum Bullion (Nathan Reverse)				
		£25.00	1/4oz	Unlimited	BV
2020	Platinum Bullion (Nathan Reverse)				
		£100.00	1oz	Unlimited	BV

Most of the later prices given above are the original Royal Mint issue prices as very few of the coins have come onto the market.

Date	Metal	Face value	Weight	No. struck	Value

BRITANNIA WITH LION SHIELD ON PROOF COIN REVERSE. THREE AGES OF BRITANNIA IN PROFILE FOR EXCLUSIVE EDITION
Mintage (Brackets indicate maximum struck). Values—Royal Mint issue price
Obverse by Jody Clark
Reverse by Dan Thorne (unless stated otherwise).

2022	Silver Proof	5 pence	1/40oz	Set only	—
2022	Silver Proof	10 pence	1/20oz	Set only	—
2022	Silver Proof	20 pence	1/10oz	Set only	—
2022	Silver Proof	50 pence	1/4oz	Set only	—
2022	Silver Proof	£1.00	1/2oz	Set only	—
2022	Silver Proof	£2.00	1oz	3,500 (3,610)	£95
2022	Silver Bullion (Nathan Reverse)				
		£2.00	1oz	Unlimited	BV
2022	Silver BU Exclusive Edition Sandra Deiana Three Women Reverse				
			1oz	5,000 (5,010)	£62.50
2022	Silver Proof Set 1 x frosted reverse, 1 x standard				
		2 x £2	1oz	1,110	190.00
2022	Silver Proof Exclusive Edition Sandra Deiana Three Women Reverse				
		£5.00	2oz	550 (556)	185.00
2022	Silver Proof	£10.00	5oz	350 (386)	465.00
2022	Silver Proof Exclusive Edition Sandra Deiana Three Women Reverse				
		£500.00	1kg	40 (43)	2,330.00
2022	Silver Proof	£1000.00	2kg	75 (78)	4,775.00
2022	Silver Proof Set £2, £1, 50p , 20p, 10p and 5 pence				
				1,300 (1,310)	235.00

2022	Gold Proof	50 pence	1/40oz	Set only	—
2022	Gold Proof	£1.00	1/20oz	Set only	—
2022	Gold Proof	£10.00	1/10oz	Set only	—
2022	Gold bullion (Nathan Reverse)				
		£10.00	1/10oz	Unlimited	BV
2022	Gold Proof	£25.00	1/4oz	775	650.00
2022	Gold Bullion (Nathan Reverse)				
		£25.00	1/4oz	Unlimited	BV
2022	Gold Proof	£50.00	1/2oz	Set only	
2022	Gold Bullion (Nathan Reverse)				
		£50.00	1/2oz	Unlimited	BV
2022	Gold Bullion (Nathan Reverse)				
		£100.00	1oz	Unlimited	BV
2022	Gold Proof	£200.00	2oz	100 (106)	5,010.00
2022	Gold Proof Exclusive Edition Sandra Deiana Three Women Reverse				
		£200.00	2oz	100 (106)	5,010.00
2022	Gold Proof	£500.00	5oz	100 (106)	12,015.00
2022	Gold Proof Exclusive Edition Sandra Deiana Three Women Reverse				
		£1000.00	1kg	5 (6)	69,445.00
2022	Gold Proof 6 Coin Set				
		£100, £50, £25, £10, £1 and 50 pence		150	4,840.00
2022	Gold Proof 3 Coin Set				
		£50, £25 and £10		150	2,140.00

2022	Platinum Bullion (Nathan Reverse)				
		£10	1/10oz	Unlimited	BV
2022	Platinum Proof	£25.00	1/4oz	150 (160)	550.00
2022	Platinum Bullion (Nathan Reverse)				
		£100.00	1oz	Unlimited	BV

PRECIOUS METAL BULLION AND COLLECTOR COINS (SERIES)

The Shengxiào Lunar Collection

The Shengxiào Collection of Lunar Coins by designer Wuon-Gean Ho was begun for the Year of the Horse in 2014 bringing the Royal Mint in line with most other major mints of the world. The Shengxiào series ended in 2018 but the Lunar series continues to be issued each year. We list them separately here, however, the larger denominatiions have also been listed under their respective headings.

Date	Weight Face value/	Auth. issue qty	No. Issued	Issue price
2014 YEAR OF THE HORSE				
Silver bullion.............................. 1 ounce /£2	—	—	BV
Silver Proof .... 1 ounce/£2	8,888	—	£85
Silver Proof ....5 ounces/£10	1,488	—	£450
Gold BU .... One-tenth ounce/£10	2,888	1,779	£225
Gold bullion............................ 1 ounce /£100	—	—	BV
Gold Proof............................ 1 ounce/£100	888	811	£1950
2015 YEAR OF THE SHEEP				
Silver bullion.............................. 1 ounce /£2	—	—	BV
Silver Proof .... 1 ounce/£2	9,888	4,463	£85
Silver Proof with gold plating...... 1 ounce/£2	4,888	1,358	£120
Silver Proof ....5 ounces/£10	1,088	—	£395
Gold BU .... One-tenth ounce/£10	2,888	922	£225
Gold bullion............................ 1 ounce /£100	—	—	BV
Gold Proof............................ 1 ounce/£100	888	548	£1950
Gold Proof............................5 ounces/£500	38	—	£7500
2016 YEAR OF THE MONKEY				
Silver bullion.............................. 1 ounce /£2	—	—	BV
Silver Proof .... 1 ounce/£2	8,888	—	£85
Silver Proof ....5 ounces/£10	588	—	£395
Silver Proof ....1 kilo/£500	88	—	£2000
Gold BU .... One-tenth ounce/£10	1,888	—	£175
Gold bullion............................ 1 ounce /£100	—	—	BV
Gold Proof............................ 1 ounce/£100	888	—	£1495
Gold Proof............................5 ounces/£500	38	—	£7500
Gold Proof............................1 kilo/£1,000	8	—	£42,500
2017 YEAR OF THE ROOSTER				
Silver bullion.............................. 1 ounce /£2	—	—	BV
Silver Proof .... 1 ounce/£2	3,888	3,846	£85
Silver Proof ....5 ounces/£10	388	369	£415
Silver Proof ....1 kilo/£500	88	—	£2050
Gold BU .... One-tenth ounce/£10	2,088	980	£205
Gold bullion............................ 1 ounce /£100	—	—	BV
Gold Proof............................ 1 ounce/£100	688	—	£1780
Gold Proof............................5 ounces/£500	38	35	£8250
Gold Proof............................1 kilo/£1,000	8	8	£49,995
2018 YEAR OF THE DOG				
Silver bullion.............................. 1 ounce /£2	—	—	BV
Silver Proof .... 1 ounce/£2	5,088	—	£85
Silver Proof ....5 ounces/£10	388	—	£415
Silver Proof ....1 kilo/£500	108	—	£2050
Gold BU .... One-tenth ounce/£10	1,088	—	£175
Gold bullion............................ 1 ounce /£100	—	—	BV
Gold Proof............................ 1 ounce/£100	888	—	£1795

The Lunar series, *continued*

From 2019 the Royal Mint has invited various artists to create the reverses for the Lunar serties as noted in each section below.

Date	Weight/ Face value	Auth. issue qty	No. Issued	Issue price

2019 LUNAR YEAR OF THE PIG
Obverse: Jody Clark Royal portrait
Reverse: by Harry Brockway

Silver bullion.............................. 1 ounce /£2		—	—	BV
Silver Proof .... 1 ounce/£2		3,888	—	£85
Silver Proof ....5 ounces/£10		288	—	£420
Silver Proof ....1 kilo/£500		38	—	£2025
Gold BU .... One-tenth ounce/£10		1,088	—	£210
Gold bullion........................... 1 ounce/£100		—	—	BV
Gold Proof............................. 1 ounce/£100		888	—	£1880
Gold Proof...........................5 ounces/£500		38	—	£8645
Gold Proof................................1 kilo/£1,000		8	—	—

2020 LUNAR YEAR OF THE RAT;
Obverse: Jody Clark Royal portrait
Reverse: by P. J. Lynch

Silver bullion.............................. 1 ounce /£2		—	—	BV
Silver Proof .... 1 ounce/£2		2,588	—	£85
Silver Proof ....5 ounces/£10		188	—	£420
Silver Proof ....1 kilo/£500		28	—	£2050
Gold BU .... One-tenth ounce/£10		1,088	—	£210
Gold Proof...................... Quarter ounce/£25		388	—	£530
Gold bullion........................... 1 ounce/£100		—	—	BV
Gold Proof............................. 1 ounce/£100		888	—	£2100
Gold Proof...........................5 ounces/£500		28	—	£9995
Gold Proof................................1 kilo/£1,000		8	—	£59,995

2021 LUNAR YEAR OF THE OX;
Obverse: Jody Clark
Reverse: Harry Brockway

Silver bullion .... 1 ounce /£2		—	—	BV
Silver Proof .... 1 ounce/£2		3,998	—	£85
Silver Proof ....5 ounces/£10		198	—	£420
Silver Proof ....1 kilo/£500		38	—	£2050
Gold Proof .... Quarter ounce/£25		398	—	£585
Gold Proof .... 1 ounce/£100		898	—	£2,320
Gold Proof ....5 ounces/£500		38	—	£10,605
Gold Proof ....1 kilo/£1,000		10	—	£63,865

2022 LUNAR YEAR OF THE TIGER
Obverse: Jody Clark
Reverse: David Lawrence

Gold Proof ....1 kilo/£1000		10	—	£67,500
Gold Proof ....Five ounces/£500		128	—	£11,125
Gold Proof ....One ounce/£100		898	—	£2,440
Gold Proof .... Quarter ounce/£25		398	—	£650
Silver Proof ....1 kilo/£500		38	—	£2,330
Silver Proof ....Five ounces/£10		228	—	£465
Silver Proof ....One ounce/£2		3,998	—	£95
Cu-Ni BU £5		—	—	£13

The Queen's Beasts

In 2016 a new series of coins was introduced by the Royal Mint entitled "The Queen's Beasts". These are intended as a homage to Her Majesty becoming Britain's longest reigning monarch and each coin in the series represents one of the heraldic animals sculpted by James Woodford, RA, for the Coronation ceremony held in Westminster Abbey in 1953. The 6-foot tall sculptures each symbolised the various strands of royal ancestry and were inspired by the King's Beasts of Henry VIII that still line the bridge at Hampton Court. In total 20 different designs have been struck, 10 for bullion coins and 10 for collector coins in proof. The bullion coins all have a patterned background whilst the proof coins have a polished field. We have included only the proof collector coins here as the bullion coins, struck in 2oz and 10oz silver and 1oz platinum and gold, will be priced according to the prevailing precious metal values. The coins all carry the effigy of Her Majesty the Queen by Jody Clark on the obverse with the heraldic beasts, by the same designer, appearing on the reverse.

Date	Weight Face value/	Auth. issue qty	No. Issued	Issue price
THE LION OF ENGLAND				
2017 Cu-Ni BU	£5	—	31,838	£13
2017 Silver Proof	1 ounce/£2	8,500	8,376	£85
2017 Silver Proof	5 ounces/£10	2,500	674	£415
2017 Silver Proof	1 kilo/£500	350	117	£2050
2017 Gold Proof	Quarter ounce/£25	2,500	2,492	£475
2017 Gold Proof	1 ounce/£100	1,000	591	£1780
2017 Gold Proof	5 ounces/£500	125	100	£8250
2017 Gold proof	1 kilo/£1,000	—	13	£49,995
THE UNICORN OF SCOTLAND				
2017 Cu-Ni BU	£5	—	31,978	£13
2017 Silver Proof	1 ounce/£2	6,250	5,952	£85
2017 Silver Proof	5 ounces/£10	750	458	£415
2017 Silver Proof	10 ounces/£10	850	—	£795
2017 Silver Proof	1 kilo/£500	225	—	£2050
2017 Gold Proof	Quarter ounce/£25	1,500	1,499	£475
2017 Gold Proof	1 ounce/£100	500	418	£475
2017 Gold Proof	5 ounces/£500	–	75	£475
2017 Gold Proof	1 kilo/£1,000	—	8	£475
THE RED DRAGON OF WALES				
2018 Cu-Ni BU	£5	—	—	£13
2018 Silver Proof	1 ounce/£2	6,000	—	£85
2018 Silver Proof	5 ounces/£10	700	—	£420
2018 Silver Proof	10 ounces/£10	600	—	£795
2018 Silver Proof	1 kilo/£500	150	—	£2025
2018 Gold Proof	Quarter ounce/£25	1,500	—	£475
2018 Gold Proof	1 ounce/£100	500	—	£1850
2018 Gold Proof	5 ounces/£500	85	—	£8565
2018 Gold Proof	1 kilo/£1000	—	—	£49,995
THE BLACK BULL OF CLARENCE				
2018 Cu-Ni BU	£5	—	—	£13
2018 Silver Proof	1 ounce/£2	6,000	—	£85
2018 Silver Proof	5 ounces/£10	700	—	£420
2018 Silver Proof	10 ounces/£10	600	—	£795
2018 Silver Proof	1 kilo/£500	150	—	£2025
2018 Gold Proof	Quarter ounce/£25	1,500	1,499	£475
2018 Gold Proof	1 ounce/£100	500	—	£1850
2018 Gold Proof	5 ounces/£500	85	—	£8565
2018 Gold Proof	1 kilo/£1000	—	—	£49,995

Date	Weight Face value/	Auth. issue qty	No. Issued	Issue price
THE YALE OF BEAUFORT				
2019 Cu-Ni BU	£5	—	—	£13
2019 Silver Proof	1 ounce/£2	5,500	—	£85
2019 Silver Proof	5 ounces/£10	400	—	£420
2019 Silver Proof	10 ounces/£10	240	—	£795
2019 Silver Proof	1 kilo/£500	120	—	£2025
2019 Gold Proof	1/4 ounce/£25	1,250	—	£475
2019 Gold Proof	1 ounce/£100	400	—	£1850
2019 Gold Proof	5 ounces/£500	70	—	£8645
2019 Gold Proof	1 kilo/£1000	13	—	£59,995
FALCON OF THE PLANTAGENETS				
2019 Cu-Ni BU	£5	—	—	£13
2019 Silver Proof	1 ounce/£2	5,510	—	£85
2019 — Proof	5 ounces/£10	400	—	£420
2019 — Proof	10 ounces/£10	350	—	£795
2019 — Proof	1 kilo/£500	100	—	£2050
2019 Gold Proof	1/4 ounce/£25	1250	—	£475
2019 — Proof	1 ounce/£100	400	—	£1900
2019 — Proof	5 ounces/£500	75	—	£9995
2019 — Proof	1 kilo/£1000	10	—	£59,995
WHITE LION OF MORTIMER				
2020 Cu-Ni BU	£5	—	—	£13
2020 Silver Proof	1 ounce/£2	4,250	—	£85
2020 — Proof	5 ounces/£10	250	—	£420
2020 — Proof	10 ounces/£10	200	—	£795
2020 — Proof	1 kilo/£500	90	—	£2025
2020 Gold Proof	1/4 ounce/£25	1,000	—	£500
2020 — Proof	1 ounce/£100	390	—	£1900
2020 — Proof	5 ounces/£500	55	—	£9995
2020 — Proof	1 kilo/£1000	10	—	—
WHITE HORSE OF HANOVER				
2020 Cu-Ni BU	£5	—	—	£13
2020 Silver Proof	1 ounce/£2	4,310	—	£85
2020 — Proof	5 ounces/£10	315	—	£420
2020 — Proof	10 ounces/£10	235	—	£795
2020 — Proof	1 kilo/£500	115	—	£2050
2020 Gold Proof	1/4 ounce/£25	1,000	—	£510
2020 — Proof	1 ounce/£100	435	—	£2020
2020 — Proof	5 ounces/£500	69	—	£9595
2020 — Proof	1 kilo/£1000	13	—	£57,750
WHITE GREYHOUND OF RICHMOND				
2021 Cu-Ni BU	£5	—	—	£13
2021 Silver Proof	1 ounce/£2	3,960	—	£85
2021 — Proof	5 ounces/£10	370	—	£420
2021 — Proof	10 ounces/£10	195	—	£795
2021 — Proof	1 kilo/£500	80	—	£2025
2021 Gold Proof	1/4 ounce/£25	1,010	—	£585
2021 — Proof	1 ounce/£100	425	—	£2320
2021 — Proof	5 ounces/£500	69	—	£10,605
2021 — Proof	1 kilo/£1000	10	—	£63,865
GRIFFIN OF EDWARD III				
2021 Cu-Ni BU	£5	—	—	£13
2021 Silver Proof	1 ounce/£2	4,400	—	£92.50
2021 — Proof	5 ounces/£10	290	—	£455
2021 — Proof	10 ounces/£10	140	—	£865
2021 — Proof	1 kilo/£500	70	—	£2270
2021 Gold Proof	1/4 ounce/£25	1,240	—	£605
2021 — Proof	1 ounce/£100	500	—	£2370
2021 — Proof	5 ounces/£500	115	—	£10,820
2021 — Proof	1 kilo/£1000	10	—	£65,275

Date	Weight Face value/	Auth. issue qty	No. Issued	Issue price
THE QUEEN'S BEASTS 2021—COMPLETER COIN				
2021 Cu-Ni BU £5	—	—	£13
2021 Silver Proof............................ 1 ounce/£2	7,460	—	£85
2021 Silver Proof.............................1kilo/£500	—	—	—
2021 Gold Proof .... 1 ounce/£100	—	—	—
2021 Gold Proof ....1 kilo/£1000	16	—	—

The above coins were issued in 2021/2 depicting all 10 designs from the Queen's Beasts series, called the "completer coin" it rounds up this popular collection.

The Valiant

The Valiant series of silver bullion-related coins portraying St George slaying the Dragon by artist Etienne Millner was introduced in 2018 with an attractive 10 ounce silver piece with the weight shown in the field. In 2019 the design was modified to give the weight in the legend around the circumference of the reverse. The obverse carries the effigy of Her Majesty the Queen by Jody Clark.

Date	Weight Face value/	Auth. issue qty	Issue price
2018 silver ....10 ounces	—	£191.58
2019 silver .... 1 ounce	100,000	£19.76
2019 silver ....10 ounces	—	£198.60
2020 silver .... 1 ounce	100,000	£25.19
2020 silver ....10 ounces	—	£250.76
2021 silver ....10 ounces	—	£256.00
2021 silver .... 1 ounce	100,000	£25.49

The information contained in this section is as supplied and is correct at the time of going to press (August 2022) but the quantities struck and the issue prices can be subject to change by the Royal Mint. To keep up to date on the new releases visit www.royalmint.com and www.royalmintbullion.com or check in COIN NEWS magazine every month.

The White Horse of Hanover, one of the Queen's beast issues at the annual trial of the Pyx.

The Royal Arms

Another bullion coin aimed at the investor, The Royal Arms series in gold and silver was introduced in 2019. The coins carry the Royal Arms as depicted by Eric Sewell in 1983 but reinterpreted in this design by Timothy Noad. The common obverse carries the effigy of Her Majesty the Queen by Jody Clark.

These coins are available in one ounce gold, one ounce platinum, 10 ounce silver and one ounce silver. As they are intended as bullion investment coins rather than for the collector market the prices asked for them will vary according to the prevailing metal markets.

> **In addition to their various investor coins, the Royal Mint regularly introduces other series of interest in various metals and weights. All can be found on the Mint's website which gives full details and issue prices**

Great Engravers series

This new series commemorates the work of the great designers of the past. The first issue released in November 2019 celebrates the skill of William Wyon, his original Una and the Lion design has been skilfully remastered using modern technology by Royal Mint engraver Gordon Summers. In addition to those listed below, just one example was struck as a 5 kilo coin. The obverse carries the effigy of Her Majesty the Queen by Jody Clark.

Date	Weight Face value/	Auth. issue qty	Issue price
UNA & THE LION			
2019 Silver Proof	2 ounces/£5	2980	£180
2019 Gold Proof	2 ounces/£200	205	£3995
2019 — Proof	5 ounces/£500	65	£9995
2019 — Proof	1 kilo/£1000	7	£59,995
2019 — Proof	2 kilos/£2000	4	£119,950
THE THREE GRACES			
2020 Silver Proof	2 ounces/£5	3500	£185
2020 Gold Proof	2 ounces/£200	325	£4995
2020 — Proof	5 ounces/£500	150	£11,995
2020 — Proof	1 kilo/£1000	20	£74,000
THE GOTHIC CROWN—Wyon REVERSE (issued 2022, dated 2021)			
2021 Silver Proof	2 ounce/£5	4,006	£
2021 — —	5 ounces/£10	506	£
2021 — —	10 ounces/£10	231	£
2021 — —	1 kilo/£500	128	£
2021 — —	2 kilos/£1000	53	£
2021 Gold Proof	2 ounce/£200	411	£4,775
2021 — —	5 ounces/£500	181	£11,430
2021 — —	10 ounces/£500	56	£22,855
2021 — —	1 kilo/£1000	22	£69,445
2021 — —	2 kilos/£2000	9	£151,135
2021 — —	5 kilos/£5000	2	£385,200
2021 — —	10 kilos/£10,000	1	£385,200

Date	Weight Face value/	Auth. issue qty	Issue price
THE GOTHIC CROWN—Wyon OBVERSE (issued 2022, dated 2021)			
2021 Silver Proof .... 2 ounce/£5	4,006	—
2021 — — ....5 ounces/£10	506	—
2021 — — ....10 ounces/£10	231	—
2021 — — ....1 kilo/£500	128	—
2021 — — ....2 kilo/£1000	53	—
2021 Gold Proof .... 2 ounce/£200	411	£4,775
2021 — — ....5 ounces/£500	181	£11,430
2021 — — ....10 ounces/£500	56	£22,855
2021 — — ....1 kilo/£1000	22	£69,445
2021 — — ....2 kilo/£2000	9	£151,135
2021 — — ....5 kilo/£5000	2	£385,200
2021 — — ....10 kilo/£10,000	1	£385,200

The James Bond Collection

Released to coincide with the 25th James Bond movie "No Time to Die" in 2020, the commemorative coin collection offered three coins in several editions from BU to precious metal including just one 7 kilo coin, a first for the Royal Mint. Precious metal gold and silver bars were also available. Designers of the reverse images were Matt Dent, Christian Davies and Laura Clancy. The common obverse carries the effigy of Her Majesty the Queen by Jody Clark.

Date	Weight Face value/	Auth. issue qty	Issue price
CORE RANGE—ASTON MARTIN			
2020 BU £5	—	£13
2020 Silver Proof .... 1/2 ounce/£1	15,017	£65
2020 — Proof .... 1 ounce/£2	8,517	£87.50
2020 Gold Proof .... 1/4 ounce/£25	1,067	£517
2020 — Proof .... 1 ounce/£100	360	£2,070
INSPIRED INNOVATION RANGE—SUBMARINE CAR			
2020 Silver Proof .... 2 ounce/£5	2017	£235
2020 Gold Proof .... 2 ounce/£200	260	£3,985
SPECIAL ISSUE RANGE—JAMES BOND'S JACKET AND TIE			
2020 Silver Proof .... 5 ounce/£10	700	£485
2020 Gold Proof .... 5 ounce/£500	64	£9,895
2020 — Proof ....1 kilo coin/£1,000	20	£59,750
2020 — Proof ....2 kilo coin/£2,000	10	£129,990
2020 — Proof ....7 kilo coin/£7,000	1	POA

The 50th anniversary of the Mr Men Collection

This delightful series of coins marked the 50th anniversary of the creation of these much-loved characters commencing with Mr Tickle who was created by Roger Hargreaves in 1971. The Mr Men, and later Little Miss, characters were featured in over 90 books, translated into 17 different languages. In 1988, the role of illustrating Mr Men and Little Miss characters was taken over by Adam Hargreaves, Roger's son. Adam provided the reverse designs for the Royal Mint 50th anniversary series. The common obverse carries the effigy of Her Majesty the Queen by Jody Clark.

Date	Weight Face value/	Auth. issue qty	Issue price
50TH ANNIVERSARY OF MR MEN—LITTLE MISS SUNSHINE			
2021 BU £5	—	£13
2021 — (coloured coin) £5	15,000	£22.50
2021 Silver Proof .... 1/2 ounce/£1	9,000	£65
2021 — Proof .... 1 ounce/£2	6,500	£97.50
2021 Gold Proof .... 1/4 ounce/£25	750	£595
2021 — Proof .... 1 ounce/£100	275	£2315

Date	Weight Face value/	Auth. issue qty	Issue price

50TH ANNIVERSARY OF MR MEN—MR HAPPY

2021 BU £5		—	£13
2021 — (coloured coin) £5		15,000	£22.50
2021 Silver Proof .... 1/2 ounce/£1		9,000	£65
2021 — Proof .... 1 ounce/£2		6,500	£97.50
2021 Gold Proof .... 1/4 ounce/£25		750	£650
2021 — Proof .... 1 ounce/£100		275	£2440

50TH ANNIVERSARY OF MR MEN—MR STRONG AND LITTLE MISS GIGGLES

2021 BU £5		—	£13
2021 — (coloured coin) £5		15,000	£22.50
2021 Silver Proof .... 1/2 ounce/£1		9,000	£65
2021 — Proof .... 1 ounce/£2		6,500	£97.50
2021 Gold Proof .... 1/4 ounce/£25		750	£650
2021 — Proof .... 1 ounce/£100		275	£2440

The Alice Collection

Two-coin set to mark 160 years since the publication by Lewis Carroll of *Alice's Adventures in Wonderland* and the later *Through the Looking Glass*. Issued as part of the *Treasury of Tales* and in partnership with the *Victoria & Albert Museum*, the designs depict the exquisite Sir John Tenniel's illustrations as used in the first editions of both books. Reverse design by Ffion Gwillim. The common obverse carries the effigy of Her Majesty the Queen by Jody Clark.

ALICE'S ADVENTURES IN WONDERLAND

2021 BU £5		—	£13
2021 — Coloured Coin £5		1,500	£20
2021 Silver Proof .... 1/2 ounce /£1		5,510	£65
2021 — — Coloured Coin .... 1 ounce /£2		3,510	£100
2021 Gold Proof .... 1/4 ounce/£25		510	£650
2021 — — .... 1 ounce/£100		160	£2440

THROUGH THE LOOKING GLASS

2021 BU £5		—	£13
2021 — Coloured Coin £5		1,500	£20
2021 Silver Proof .... 1/2 ounce /£1		5,510	£65
2021 — Coloured Coin .... 1 ounce /£2		3,510	£100
2021 Gold Proof .... 1/4 ounce/£25		510	£650
2021 — — .... 1 ounce/£100		160	£2440

The latest collections of coins from the Royal Mint are often available in a variety of collector-pack versions.

Myths and Legends Series

Taking their inspiration from UK myths and legends, this latest issue from the Royal Mint's bullion series explores the story of Robin Hood, the gallant hero who famously stole from the rich to give to the poor. The series reverse designs are by Jody Clark as is the obverse image of Her Majesty the Queen. Issues thus far are a 999.9 gold one ounce coin and a one ounce silver edition.

ROBIN HOOD

2021 Silver Proof .... 1 ounce/£2		—	£25
2021 Gold Proof .... 1 ounce/£100		—	£1,406

Myths and Legends Series/cont

Date	Weight Face value/	Auth. issue qty	Issue price
MAID MARIAN			
2021 Silver Proof	1 ounce/£2	—	£25
2021 Gold Proof	1 ounce/£100	—	£1,406
2022 Silver Bullion	1 ounce/£2	—	£25.73
2022 Gold Bullion	1 ounce/£100	—	£1644.51
LITTLE JOHN			
2022 Silver Bullion	1 ounce/£2	—	£25.73
2022 Gold Bullion	1 ounce/£100	—	£1644.51

The Music Legends Collection

This series is intended to celebrate famous bands and musicians. The first issue is dedicated to Queen and all four members of the band are named with edge lettering on the silver editions. The subsequent issues carry images synonymous with their subject. The common obverse carries the effigy of Her Majesty the Queen by Jody Clark.

MUSIC LEGENDS COLLECTION—QUEEN
The BU £5 coin comes in a special illustrated pack with one of four designs

2020 BU (with pack design 1) £5		—	£13
2020 BU (with pack design 2) £5		25,000	£15
2020 BU (with pack design 3) £5		25,000	£15
2020 BU (with pack design 4) £5		25,000	£15
2020 Silver Proof	half ounce/£1	20,000	£60
2020 — Proof	1 ounce/£2	10,000	£90
2020 Gold Proof	quarter ounce/£25	1,350	£510
2020 — Proof	1 ounce/£100	350	£2020

MUSIC LEGENDS COLLECTION—ELTON JOHN
The BU £5 coin comes in a special illustrated pack with one of four designs

2020 BU (with pack design 1) £5		—	£13
2020 BU (with pack design 2) £5		15,000	£15
2020 BU (with pack design 3) £5		15,000	£15
2020 BU (with pack design 4) £5		15,000	£15
2020 Silver Proof	half ounce/£1	15,000	£60
2020 — Proof	1 ounce/£2	10,000	£95
2020 — Proof	2 ounces/£5	500	£95
2020 — Proof	5 ounces/£10	425	£95
2020 Gold Proof	quarter ounce/£25	1,150	£585
2020 — Proof	1 ounce/£100	300	£2320
2020 — Proof	2 ounces/£200	50	£4555
2020 — Proof	5 ounces/£500	50	£2320
2020 — Proof	1 kilo/£100	4	£68,865

MUSIC LEGENDS COLLECTION—DAVID BOWIE
The BU £5 coin comes in a special illustrated pack with one of four designs

2020 BU (with pack design 1) £5		—	£13
2020 BU (with pack design 2) £5		15,000	£15
2020 BU (with pack design 3) £5		15,000	£15
2020 BU (with pack design 4) £5		15,000	£15
2020 Silver Proof	half ounce/£1	13,500	£65
2020 — Proof	1 ounce/£2	8,100	£97.50
2020 — Proof	2 ounces/£5	550	£195
2020 — Proof	5 ounces/£10	500	£520
2020 Gold Proof	quarter ounce/£25	1,400	£615
2020 — Proof	1 ounce/£100	400	£2425
2020 — Proof	2 ounces/£200	100	£4760
2020 — Proof	5 ounces/£500	60	£11,815
2020 — Proof	1 kilo/£100	11	£72,195

Date	Weight Face value/	Auth. issue qty	Issue price

MUSIC LEGENDS COLLECTION—THE WHO

The BU £5 coin comes in a special illustrated pack with one of four designs

Date	Weight Face value/	Auth. issue qty	Issue price
2021 BU £5		—	£13
2021 — Coloured coin £5		10,000	£22.50
2021 Silver Proof.....................................half ounce/£1		10,010	£65
2021 — Proof ....1 ounce/£2		8110	£97.50
2021 — Proof ....2 ounces/£5		550	£195
2020 — Proof ....5 ounces/£10		500	£520
2021 Gold Proof ....quarter ounce/£25		1,010	£595
2021 — Proof ....1 ounce/£100		360	£2315
2021 — Proof ....2 ounces/£200		150	£4530
2021 — Proof ....5 ounces/£500		64	£11,225
2021 — Proof ....1 kilo/£1000		12	£68,380

In addition to the above, other series, such as the "Tower of London", the "Portrait of Britain", etc. will be found under specific denominations or in the Proof and Specimen sets section.

British Monarchs

The British Monarchs Collection was launched in 2022 to celebrate some of the most iconic Kings and Queens in British history. The series commenced with the House of Tudor and the classic portrait of Henry VII as it would have appeared on the coinage of the time. The common obverse bears the effigy of Her Majesty the Queen by Jody Clark.

KING HENRY VII

Date	Weight Face value/	Auth. issue qty	Issue price
2022 Silver Proof.....................................1 ounce/£2		1,250	£92.50
2022 — — ....2 ounce/£5		700	£180
2022 — — ....5 ounces/£10		275	£455
2022 — — ....10 ounces/£10		150	£885
2022 Gold Proof ....1 ounce/£100		100	£2,370
2022 — — ....2 ounce/£200		175	£4,485
2022 — — ....5 ounces/£500		75	£10,820

KING JAMES I

Date	Weight Face value/	Auth. issue qty	Issue price
2022 Silver Proof.....................................1 ounce/£2		1,250	£95
2022 — — ....2 ounce/£5		700	£185
2022 — — ....5 ounces/£10		275	£465
2022 — — ....10 ounces/£10		150	£885
2022 Gold Proof ....1 ounce/£100		100	£2,505
2022 — — ....2 ounce/£200		150	£4,775
2022 — — ....5 ounces/£500		50	£11,430

Two-coin gold set

Date	Weight Face value/	Auth. issue qty	Issue price
2022 Gold Proof Coin 2 ounce/£200/Gold Crown (second coinage)		10	£8,000

KING GEORGE I

Date	Weight Face value/	Auth. issue qty	Issue price
2022 Silver Proof.....................................1 ounce/£2		1,360	£95
2022 — — ....2 ounce/£5		756	£185
2022 — — ....5 ounces/£10		281	£465
2022 — — ....10 ounces/£10		156	£885
2022 Gold Proof ....1 ounce/£100		610	£2,625
2022 — — ....2 ounce/£200		126	£5,010
2022 — — ....5 ounces/£500		56	£12,015

City Views London 2022

The City Views London Collection celebrates iconic urban landmarks from the world's greatest cities. Starting, of course, with our own capital city, the iconic Tower of London graces the first issue of the series. Struck in gold and silver, both the obverse and reverse of this inaugural issue has been designed by Jody Clark.

Date	Weight Face value/	Auth. issue qty	Issue price
2022 Silver Proof	1 ounce/£2	2010	£95
2022 — —	2 ounce/£5	1506	£185
2022 — —	5 ounces/£10	256	£465
2022 — —	1 kilo/£500	52	£2,330
2022 Gold Proof	1 ounce/£100	310	£2,505
2022 — —	2 ounce/£200	256	£4,775
2022 — —	5 ounces/£500	56	£11,430
2022 — —	1 kilo/£1000	56	£69,445

The Royal Tudor Beasts

Following the popularity of the Queen's Beast's series, a new collection commenced in 2022 depicting historic and mythical creatures. Based on the ten stone beasts that line the Moat Bridge at Hampton Court Palace—representing the lineage of Henry VIII and his third wife, Jane Seymour—these heraldic symbols make up the Royal Tudor Beasts Collection. The common obverse bears the effigy of Her Majesty the Queen by Jody Clark.

THE SEYMOUR PANTHER

2022 Cu-Ni BU	£5	—	£13
2022 Silver Proof	1 ounce/£2	7,010	£95
2022 — —	2 ounces/£5	2,006	£185
2022 — —	5 ounces/£10	306	£465
2022 — —	10 ounces/£10	156	£885
2022 — —	1 kilo/£500	72	£2,330
2022 — —	2 kilos/£1000	56	£4,995
2022 Gold Proof	1/4 ounce/£25	1,010	£650
2022 — —	1 ounce/£100	560	£2,440
2022 — —	2 ounces/£200	356	£4,650
2022 — —	5 ounces/£500	131	£11,125
2022 — —	10 ounces/£500	31	£22,250
2022 — —	1 kilo/£1000	14	£67,500
2022 — —	2 kilos/£2000	5	£147,250

THE LION OF ENGLAND

2022 Cu-Ni BU	£5	—	£13
2022 Silver Proof	1 ounce/£2	6,000	£95
2022 — —	2 ounces/£5	2,000	£185
2022 — —	5 ounces/£10	300	£465
2022 — —	10 ounces/£10	150	£885
2022 — —	1 kilo/£500	70	£2,330
2022 — —	2 kilos/£1000	55	£4,995
2022 Gold Proof	1/4 ounce/£25	1,000	£670
2022 — —	1 ounce/£100	400	£2,505
2022 — —	2 ounces/£200	175	£4,775
2022 — —	5 ounces/£500	70	£11,430
2022 — —	10 ounces/£500	10	£22,855
2022 — —	1 kilo/£1000	3	£69,445
2022 — —	2 kilos/£2000	2	£151,135

THE ROYAL TUDOR BEASTS continued

Date	Weight Face value/	Auth. issue qty	Issue price
THE YALE OF BEAUFORT			
2023 Cu-Ni BU £5		—	£13
2023 Silver Proof Two Coin Set............. £2		500	£210
2023 — — .... 1 ounce/£2		5,000	£105
2023 — — .... 2 ounces/£5		12,500	£185
2023 — — .... 5 ounces/£10		300	£465
2023 — — .... 10 ounces/£10		100	£885
2023— — ....1 kilo/£500		70	£2,330
2023 Gold Proof .... 1/4 ounce/£25		750	£700
2023 — — .... 1 ounce/£100		400	£2,625
2023 — — .... 2 ounces/£200		100	£5,010
2023 — — .... 5 ounces/£500		50	£12,015
2023 — — ....2 kilos/£2000		1	£158,650

Mahatma Gandi

Struck in the 75th year of India's Independence, a series of coins was issued to celebrate the life and legacy of Mahatma Gandhi. The coin depicts an image of a lotus, India's national flower, and a well-known quote from Gandhi—"My life is my message". This is the first time Gandhi has been commemorated on an official UK coin.

2021 BU £5		—	£13
2021 Silver Proof £2		2,500	£95
2021 Gold Proof £100		185	£2,440

The Platinum Jubilee of Her Majesty the Queen

Her Majesty the Queen became the first British monarch to reach a Platinum Jubilee in 2022 and to mark the occasion one of the Royal Mint's largest coin collections to date was issued—a number of commemorative coins as well as circulating pieces were struck.
John Bergdahl has created a commemorative Platinum Jubilee portrait depicting Her Majesty on horseback and two reverse designs for the occasion. He was also the artist who designed the reverse of the £5 hence his creations were on both sides of the coin.

2022 Silver Proof .... 2 ounce/£5		1,006	£185
2022 — — .... 5 ounces/£10		1,006	£465
2022 — — .... 10 ounces/£500		156	£885
2022 — — ....1 kilo/£500		147	£2,330
2022 Gold Proof .... 1/4 ounce/£25		1,110	£670
2022 — — .... 2 ounces/£200		206	£4,775
2022 — — .... 5 ounces/£500		136	£11,430
2022 — — .... 10 ounces/£500		56	£22,855
2022— — ....1 kilo/£1,000		17	£69,445
2022— — ....2 kilos/£2,000		8	£151,135
2022— — ....5 kilos/£5,000		2	£385,200

120 Years of Peter Rabbit

To mark 120 years since the first publication of Beatrix Potter's The Tale of Peter Rabbit, *the Royal Mint issued a series of coins (not for general circulaton) as well as a limited edition Peter Rabbit™ 2022 Minty® piggy bank.*

Date	Weight Face value/	Auth. issue qty	Issue price
2022 Cu-Ni BU £5	—	£13
2022 Cu-Ni BU (coloured coin) £5	8,600	£17
2022 Silver Proof.......................... 1 ounce/£2	3,500	£100
2022 Gold Proof .... 1 ounce/£100	120	£2505

The Life and Legacy of Dame Vera Lynn

The popular singer, whose career extended well beyond her songs of the war years for which she became famous, the late Dame Vera Lynn was commemorated on a £2 coin as well as a number of bullion issues. Perhaps, her most iconic and for some, most moving recording was that of "We'll Meet Again" which became a war-time anthem for those involved in World War II. The reverse design of the £2 coin depicts a portrait of Dame Vera as she appeared during the height of her fame, accompanied by her name and the dates denoting the years of her life. The coin's edge inscription reads "WE'LL MEET AGAIN".
The common obverse bears the effigy of Her Majesty the Queen by Jody Clark.

2022 BU £2	—	£10
2022 Silver Proof.. £2	3,500	£72.50
2022 — — Piedfort.................................... £2	175	£117.50
2022 — — ....5 ounces/£10	240	£465
2022 Gold Proof £2	350	£1,125
2022 — — ....5 ounces/£500	35	£11,430

The Harry Potter Collection

As we go to press the ROYAL MINT has announced a BRAND-NEW Harry Potter collection to celebrate the 25th publishing anniversary of Harry Potter and the Philosopher's Stone in the UK. Struck in both precious and base metal and in a variety of denominations, including the 50p, the new collection will comprise four designs in total. The first coins feature Harry himself with subsequent coins showing The Hogwarts Express, Albus Dumbledore and Hogwarts School of Witchcraft and Wizardry.

The announcement of these coins was made the day of Her Majesty's passing, whether they are still issued at all, are issued as planned with the late Queen's portrait on the obverse (we have to assume the first at least have already been struck) or issued with the new obverse of King Charles III remains to be seen. For more information see COIN NEWS magazine, published monthly.

With an interesting programme of issues intended to promote coin collecting, the Royal Mint produced a series of coins which were offered to the public at face value. The first issue was made in 2013 and was a £20 coin. The series was extended in 2015 to include a £100. In the same year the £50 silver coin in the Britannia series was offered as part of this programme. The issues are listed below.

HUNDRED POUNDS

Following on from the late 2013 introduction of the Twenty Pounds (see below) a "Hundred Pounds for £100" appeared, again a 0.999 Fine Silver coin, of two ounces weight, in early 2015.

DATE	Auth. issue qty	No. Issued	Issue price
2015 Big Ben, BU	50,000	49,147	£100
2015 Buckingham Palace, BU	50,000	47,851	£100
2016 Trafalgar Square	—	14,878	£100

FIFTY POUNDS

A new denomination introduced in 2015, with the slogan "Fifty Pounds for £50". A double first for Jody Clark, minted in 99.99 silver, diameter 34mm.

DATE	Auth. issue qty	No. Issued	Issue price
2015 Britannia BU	100,000	78,644	£50
2016 Shakespeare BU	—	14,948	£60

TWENTY POUNDS

Another new denomination was added in late 2013. Marketed by the Royal Mint under the slogan "Twenty Pounds for £20", it is a 27mm diameter 0.999 Fine silver coin.

DATE	Auth. issue qty	No. Issued	Issue price
2013 Pistrucci St George & Dragon BU	250,000		£24
2014 Centenary of the outbreak of the WWI	—	141,751	£24
2015 Sir Winston Churchill	—	132,142	£20
2015 The Longest Reigning Monarch, New Portrait	—	149,408	£20
2016 The 90th Birthday of Her Majesty the Queen	—	116,354	£20
2016 The Welsh Dragon	—	—	£25
2016 Christmas Nativity	—	29,929	£30
2017 Platinum Wedding Anniversary	70,000	24,223	£25

ABBREVIATIONS COMMONLY USED TO DENOTE METALLIC COMPOSITION			
Cu	Copper	Brass/Cu-Ni	Brass outer, cupro-nickel inner
Cu/Steel	Copper plated steel	Ni-Brass	Nickel-brass
Ag/Cu	Silver plated copper	Ag	Silver
Ae	Bronze	Au/Ag	Gold plated silver
Cu-Ni	Cupro-nickel	Au	Gold
Ni-Ag	Nickel silver (note—does not contain silver)	Pl	Platinum

PROOF AND SPECIMEN SETS

The following listings are an attempt to include all officially marketed products from the Royal Mint of two coins or more, but excluding those which included non-UK coins. It is appreciated that not all have been advertised as new to the public, but it is assumed that at some time they have been, or will be, available. In a few cases, therefore, the prices may be conjectural but are, nevertheless, attempts at listing realistic values, in some instances based on an original retail price. In the case of Elizabeth II sets, if no metal is stated in the listing, the coins in the sets are of the same metal as the circulation coin equivalent. In addition to the above we have excluded historical gold coin sets, such as sets of sovereigns from different mints, where the dates of the coins vary from one set to another.

DATE   FDC

GEORGE IV
1826 £5–farthing (11 coins) ....From £50,000

WILLIAM IV
1831 Coronation £2–farthing (14 coins) ....From £40,000

VICTORIA
1839 "Una and the Lion" £5–farthing (15 coins).. — *
1853 Sovereign–quarter farthing, including "Gothic"crown (16 coins) .... From £85,000
1887 Golden Jubilee £5–3d (11 coins) .... From £35,000
1887 Golden Jubilee Crown–3d (7 coins)... From £6500
1893 £5–3d (10 coins) .... From £35,000
1893 Crown–3d (6 coins).. From £5500

EDWARD VII
1902 Coronation £5–Maundy penny, matt proofs (13 coins) .... From £8500
1902 Coronation Sovereign–Maundy penny, matt proofs (11 coins) .... From £4500

GEORGE V
1911 Coronation £5–Maundy penny (12 coins).. From £8000
1911 Sovereign–Maundy penny (10 coins) .... From £3500
1911 Coronation Halfcrown–Maundy penny (8 coins) .... From £2000
1927 New types Crown–3d (6 coins).. From £1000

GEORGE VI
1937 Coronation £5–half sovereign (4 coins) £8500
1937 Coronation Crown–farthing including Maundy money (15 coins) £550
1950 Mid-century Halfcrown–farthing (9 coins) £200
1951 Festival of Britain, Crown–farthing (10 coins) £250

ELIZABETH II
1953 Proof Coronation Crown–farthing (10 coins) £125
1953 Currency (plastic) set halfcrown–farthing (9 coins)..£15
1968 Specimen decimal set 10p, 5p and 1971-dated bronze in blue wallet (5 coins)............£5
1970 Proof Last £sd coins (issued from 1972) Halfcrown–halfpenny (8 coins)....................£20
1971 Proof (issued 1973) 50p–half penny (6 coins)..£20
1972 Proof (issued 1976) 50p–half penny (7 coins including Silver Wedding crown) £25
1973 Proof (issued 1976) 50p–half penny (6 coins)..£16
1974 Proof (issued 1976) 50p–half penny (6 coins)..£20

* In recent months prices for individual Una and the Lion coins have reached astronomical proportions. For example, in August 2021 one was sold at Heritage Auctions in the USA for over $1 million, therefore it is impossible to list an accurate price.

DATE   FDC

1975 Proof (issued 1976) 50p–half penny (6 coins)..£20
1976 Proof 50p–half penny (6 coins)..£18
1977 Proof 50p–half penny (7 coins including Silver Jubilee crown) £22
1978 Proof 50p–half penny (6 coins)..£16
1979 Proof 50p–half penny (6 coins)..£18
1980 Proof gold sovereign series (4 coins)...£3500
1980 — 50p–half penny (6 coins)...£16
1981 Proof £5, sovereign, Royal Wedding Silver crown, 50p–half penny (9 coins) £2500
1981 — 50p–half penny (6 coins)...£18
1982 Proof gold sovereign series (4 coins)...£2500
1982 — 50p–half penny (7 coins)...£20
1982 Uncirculated 50p–half penny (7 coins) £15
1983 Proof gold double-sovereign to half penny (3 coins)..£1350
1983 — £1–half penny (8 coins) (includes H. J. Heinz sets) £25
1983 Uncirculated £1–half penny (8 coins) (includes Benson & Hedges and Martini sets) £30
1983 — — (8 coins) (only Benson & Hedges and Martini sets) with "2 NEW PENCE" legend £1350
1983 — 50p–half penny (7 coins) (H. J. Heinz sets)..£16
1983 — — (7 coins) (H. J. Heinz set) with "2 NEW PENCE" legend £1250
1984 Proof gold five pounds, sovereign and half-sovereigns (3 coins)..£2500
1984 — £1 (Scottish rev.)–half penny (8 coins) £20
1984 BU £1 (Scottish rev.)–half penny (8 coins) £16
1985 New portrait proof gold sovereign series (4 coins)..£4000
1985 Proof £1–1p in de luxe case (7 coins) £25
1985 — in standard case £20
1985 BU £1–1p (7 coins) in folder £15
1986 Proof gold Commonwealth Games £2, sovereign and half sovereign (3 coins)............................£1500
1986 — Commonwealth Games £2–1p, de luxe case (8 coins) £30
1986 — — in standard case (8 coins) £25
1986 BU £2–1p in folder (8 coins) £20
1987 Proof gold double- to half sovereign (3 coins) £1500
1987 — £1–1p in de luxe case (7 coins)...£35
1987 — £1–1p in standard case (7 coins) £25
1987 BU £1–1p in folder (7 coins)..£20
1988 Proof gold double- to half sovereign (3 coins) £1500
1988 — £1–1p in de luxe case (7 coins)...£35
1988 — £1–1p in standard case (7 coins) £30
1988 BU £1–1p in folder (7 coins) (includes Bradford & Bingley sets)..£18
1989 Proof gold 500th anniversary of the sovereign series set (4 coins) £4000
1989 — — — double- to half sovereign (3 coins) £2250
1989 — Silver Bill of Rights £2, Claim of Right £2 (2 coins)...£65
1989 — — Piedfort as above (2 coins)..£125
1989 BU £2 in folder (2 coins)..£25
1989 Proof £2 (both)–1p in de luxe case (9 coins) £35
1989 — in standard case (9 coins) £30
1989 BU £1–1p in folder (7 coins) £25
1990 Proof gold sovereign series set (4 coins)..£2750
1990— double- to half sovereign (3 coins) £1250
1990 — silver 5p, 2 sizes (2 coins) £28
1990 — £1–1p in de luxe case (8 coins)...£35
1990 — £1–1p standard case (8 coins)..£30
1990 BU £1–1p in folder (8 coins)..£20
1991 Proof gold sovereign series set (4 coins)..£3500
1991 — — double- to half sovereign (3 coins) £1500
1991 — £1–1p in de luxe case (7 coins)...£35
1991 — £1–1p in standard case (7 coins) £28
1991 BU £1–1p in folder (7 coins)..£18
1992 Proof gold Britannia set (4 coins) £2500
1992 — sovereign series set (4 coins) £3000
1992 — — double- to half sovereign (3 coins) £1500
1992 — £1–1p including two each 50p and 10p in de luxe case (9 coins) £75
1992 — £1–1p as above in standard case (9 coins) £65
1992 BU £1–1p as above in folder (9 coins) £60
1992 — with Enhanced Effigy on obverse of 20p £60

291

DATE	FDC
1992 Proof silver 10p, two sizes (2 coins)	£25
1993 Proof gold sovereign series set (4 coins plus silver Pistrucci medal)	£3500
1993 — — double- to half sovereign (3 coins)	£1500
1993 — Coronation anniversary £5–1p in de luxe case (8 coins)	£38
1993 — — in standard case (8 coins)	£35
1993 BU £1–1p including 1992 EU 50p (8 coins)	£65
1994 Proof gold sovereign series set (4 coins)	£3500
1994 — — £2 to half sovereign (3 coins)	£1500
1994 — Bank of England Tercentenary £2–1p in de luxe case (8 coins)	£38
1994 — — in standard case (8 coins)	£35
1994 BU £2–1p in folder (9 coins)	£18
1994 Proof gold 1992 and 1994 50p (2 coins)	£450
1994 — "Family silver" set £2–50p (3 coins)	£65
1995 Proof gold sovereign series (4 coins)	£3000
1995 — — £2 to half sovereign (3 coins)	£1500
1995 — 50th Anniversary of WWII £2–1p in de luxe case (8 coins)	£40
1995 — — as above in standard case (8 coins)	£35
1995 BU as above in folder (8 coins)	£16
1995 Proof "Family Silver" set £2 (two) and £1 (3 coins)	£90
1996 Proof gold sovereign series set (4 coins)	£3000
1996 — — double- to half sovereign (3 coins)	£1500
1996 — Royal 70th Birthday £5–1p in de luxe case (9 coins)	£50
1996 — — as above in standard case (9 coins)	£45
1996 BU Football £2–1p in folder (8 coins)	£20
1996 Proof gold Britannia £10 and half-sovereign (2 coins)	£750
1996 — — sovereign and silver £1 (2 coins)	£250
1996 — — "Family silver" set £5–£1 (3 coins)	£100
1996 — silver 25th Anniversary of Decimal currency £1–1p (7 coins)	£150
1996 Circulation and BU 25th Anniversary of Decimalisation 2s 6d–halfpenny (misc.) and £1–1p in folder (14 coins)	£25
1997 Proof gold sovereign series set (4 coins)	£3000
1997 — — — £2 to half sovereign (3 coins)	£1500
1997 — Golden Wedding £5–1p in red leather case	£45
1997 — — as above in standard case (10 coins)	£35
1997 BU £2 to 1p in folder (9 coins)	£25
1997 Proof silver 50p set, two sizes (2 coins)	£45
1997/1998 Proof silver £2 set, both dates (2 coins)	£70
1998 Proof gold sovereign series set (4 coins)	£3500
1998 — — double- to half sovereign (3 coins)	£1500
1998 Prince of Wales £5–1p (10 coins) in red leather case	£45
1998 — as above in standard case (10 coins)	£38
1998 BU £2–1p in folder (9 coins)	£16
1998 Proof silver European/NHS 50p set (2 coins)	£60
1998 BU Britannia/EU 50p set (2 coins)	£8
1999 Proof gold Sovereign series set (4 coins)	£3500
1999 — — £2 to half sovereign (3 coins)	£1500
1999 Princess Diana £5–1p in red leather case (9 coins)	£65
1999 — as above in standard case (9 coins)	£45
1999 BU £2–1p (8 coins) in folder	£20
1999 Proof "Family Silver" set. Both £5, £2 and £1 (4 coins)	£150
1999/2000 Reverse frosted proof set, two x £1 (2 coins)	£75
2000 Proof gold Sovereign series set (4 coins)	£3500
2000 — — — double- to half sovereign (3 coins)	£1500
2000 Millennium £5–1p in de luxe case (10 coins)	£50
2000 — — as above in standard case (10 coins)	£45
2000 — Silver set Millennium £5 to 1p plus Maundy (13 coins)	£225
2000 BU £2–1p set in folder (9 coins)	£20
2000 Millennium "Time Capsule" BU £5 to 1p (9 coins)	£30
2001 Proof gold Sovereign series set (4 coins)	£3500
2001 — — £2–half sovereign (3 coins)	£1500
2001 — Victoria £5–1p in Executive case (10 coins)	£100
2001 — — as above in red leather case (10 coins)	£75
2001 — — as above in "Gift" case (10 coins)	£48
2001 — — as above in standard case (10 coins)	£40

DATE	FDC
2001 BU £2–1p in folder (9 coins)	£20
2002 Proof gold Sovereign series set, all Shield rev. (4 coins)	£3500
2002 — — double- to half sovereign (3 coins)	£1500
2002 — Golden Jubilee set £5–1p plus Maundy (13 coins)	£4500
2002 — Golden Jubilee £5–1p in Executive case (9 coins)	£75
2002 — — as above in red leather de luxe case (9 coins)	£50
2002 — — as above in "Gift" case (9 coins)	£42
2002 — — as above in standard case (9 coins)	£40
2002 BU £2–1p (8 coins) in folder	£16
2002 Proof Gold Commonwealth Games £2 set (4 coins)	£2500
2002 — Silver Piedfort Commonwealth Games £2 set (4 coins)	£250
2002 — — Commonwealth Games £2 set (4 coins)	£125
2002 — Commonwealth Games £2 set (4 coins)	£30
2002 BU Commonwealth Games £2 set (4 coins) in folder	£25
2003 Proof gold Sovereign series set (4 coins)	£3500
2003 — — series £2–half sovereign (3 coins)	£1500
2003 — — type set (one of each £2 reverse) (4 coins)	£85
2003 — £5 to 1p, two of each £2 and 50p in Executive case (11 coins)	£80
2003 — — as above in red leather case (11 coins)	£55
2003 — — as above in standard case (11 coins)	£48
2003 BU £2 (two)–1p in folder (10 coins)	£22
2003 Proof silver Piedfort set. DNA £2, £1 and Suffragette 50p (3 coins)	£150
2003 Proof "Family Silver" set £5, Britannia and DNA £2, £1 and Suffragette 50p (5 coins)	£175
2003 Circ & BU "God Save the Queen" Coronation anniversary set 5s/0d to farthing (1953) and £5 to 1p (2003) in folder (19 coins)	£55
2003 Circulation or bullion "Royal Sovereign" collection, example of each Elizabeth II date (21 coins)	£4000
2004 Proof Gold Sovereign series set (4 coins)	£3500
2004 — — Series £2–half sovereign (3 coins)	£1500
2004 (Issue date) Royal Portrait gold sovereign set, all proof except the first: Gillick, Machin, Maklouf and Rank-Broadley sovereigns, and the 2nd, 3rd and 4th of above half-sovereigns, various dates (7 coins)	£3500
2004 Proof "Family Silver" set £5, Britannia and Trevithick £2, £1 and Bannister 50p (5 coins)	£200
2004 — Silver Piedfort set, Trevithick £2, £1 and Bannister 50p (3 coins)	£200
2004 — £2 to 1p, two each of £2 and 50p in Executive case (10 coins)	£125
2004 — — as above in red leather case (10 coins)	£45
2004 — — as above in standard case (10 coins)	£40
2004 BU £2 to 1p in folder (10 coins)	£22
2004 — "New Coinage" set, Trevithick £2, £1 and Bannister 50p (3 coins)	£10
2004 BU "Season's Greetings" £2 to 1p and Royal Mint Christmas medal in folder (8 coins)	£18
2005 Proof Gold Sovereign series set (4 coins)	£3500
2005 — — series, double to half sovereign (3 coins)	£1500
2005 — Gold Trafalgar and Nelson £5 crowns (2 coins)	£4000
2005 — Silver, as above (2 coins)	£85
2005 — — Piedfort, as above (2 coins)	£150
2005 — Silver Piedfort set, Gunpowder Plot and World War II £2, £1 and Johnson 50p (4 coins)	£200
2005 — £5 to 1p, two of each of £5, £2 and 50p in Executive case (12 coins)	£80
2005 — — as above in red leather case (12 coins)	£60
2005 — — as above in standard case (12 coins)	£45
2005 BU Trafalgar and Nelson £5 crowns in pack (2 coins)	£35
2005 — £2 (two) to 1p in folder (10 coins)	£25
2005 — "New Coinage" set, Gunpowder Plot £2, £1 and Johnson 50p (3 coins)	£10
2005 — "Merry Xmas" £2 to 1p and Royal Mint Christmas medal in folder (8 coins)	£20
2006 Proof Gold Sovereign Series set (4 coins)	£3500
2006 — — series, double to half sovereign (3 coins)	£1500
2006 — Silver Brunel £2 coin set (2 coins)	£75
2006 — — Piedfort Brunel £2 coin set (2 coins)	£125
2006 — Gold Brunel £2 coin set (2 coins)	£950
2006 — Silver VC 50p coin set (2 coins)	£75
2006 — Silver Piedfort VC 50p coin set (2 coins)	£115
2006 — Gold VC 50p coin set (2 coins)	£1750
2006 — Silver proof set, £5 to 1p plus Maundy coins (13 coins)	£325
2006 — — Piedfort collection £5, with trumpets enhanced with 23 carat gold, both Brunel £2, £1, both VC 50p (6 coins)	£450

DATE	FDC
2006 — £5 to 1p, three of each £2 and 50p in Executive case (13 coins)	£80
2006 — as above in red leather case (13 coins)	£55
2006 — as above in standard case (13 coins)	£45
2006 BU £2 (two), £1, 50p (two) and to 1p in folder (10 coins)	£18
2006 Proof Brunel £2 in folder (2 coins)	£15
2006 — VC 50p in folder (2 coins)	£15
2006 — Gold Half-Sovereign set dated 2005 Noad and 2006 Pistrucci St George and the Dragon (2 coins)	£350
2007 — — Sovereign Series set (4 coins)	£3500
2007 — — — series, double to half sovereign (3 coins)	£1500
2007 — — Sovereign and half-sovereign (2 coins)	£475
2007 — "Family Silver" set, Britannia, £5 crown, Union and Slavery £2, Gateshead £1 and Scouting 50p (6 coins)	£250
2007 Proof Silver Piedfort Collection, as "Family Silver" above but excluding a Britannia (5 coins)	£300
2007 — Silver £1 Bridge series coins, dated 2004 to 2007 (4 coins)	£135
2007 — Silver Proof Piedfort £1 Bridge Series, dated 2004 to 2007 (4 coins)	£275
2007 — Gold £1 Bridge series coins, dated as above (4 coins)	£2500
2007 — £5 to 1p, three £2 and two 50p in Executive case (12 coins)	£85
2007 — as above, Deluxe in red leather case (12 coins)	£65
2007 — as above, in standard case (12 coins)	£50
2007 BU £2 (two) to 1p in (9 coins)	£18
2007 50th Anniversary Sovereign set, 1957 circulation standard and 2007 Proof (2 coins)	£750
2008 Proof Gold Sovereign series set (4 coins)	£3500
2008 — — — double to half-sovereign (3 coins)	£1500
2008 — — Sovereign and half-sovereign (2 coins)	£750
2008 — "Family silver" set, 2x £5, Britannia £2, Olympiad £2 and Royal Arms £1 (5 coins)	£250
2008 — Silver Piedfort Collection, 2x £5, Olympiad £2 and Shield of Royal Arms £1 (4 coins)	£325
2008 — 2 x £5, 2 x £2, £1 to 1p in Executive case (11 coins)	£85
2008 — as above, Deluxe in black leather case (11 coins)	£55
2008 — as above, in standard back case (11 coins)	£60
2008 BU 2 x £2, Royal Arms £1 to 1p (9 coins)	£20
2008 — "Emblems of Britain" ("old" Revs) Royal Arms £1 to 1p (7 coins)	£15
2008 — "Royal Shield of Arms" ("new" Revs) Shield of Royal Arms £1 to 1p (7 coins)	£15
2008 — Above two sets housed in one sleeve	£28
2008 Proof Base Metal "Royal Shield of Arms" set, £1 to 1p (7 coins)	£40
2008 — Silver "Emblems of Britain" set, £1 to 1p (7 coins)	£160
2008 — — "Royal Shield of Arms" set, £1 to 1p (7 coins)	£160
2008 — — Above two sets in one black case	£325
2008 — Gold "Emblems of Britain" set, £1 to 1p (7 coins)	£3550
2008 — — "Royal Shield of Arms" set, £1 to 1p (7 coins)	£3550
2008 — — Above two sets in one oak-veneer case	£7000
2008 — Platinum "Emblems of Britain" set, £1 to 1p (7 coins)	£8500
2008 — — "Royal Shield of Arms" set, £1 to 1p (7 coins)	£8500
2008 — — Above two sets in one walnut veneer case	£15,750
2008 — Silver Piedfort "Royal Shield of Arms" set, £1 to 1p (7 coins)	£325
2008 — Gold set of 14 £1 coins, one of each Rev used since 1983, all dated 2008 (25th anniversary) (14 coins)	£9500
2008 — Silver with gold Rev highlighting as above (14 coins)	£500
2008 — 2 x £2, Royal Arms £1 to 1p (9 coins) Christmas Coin Sets, two different outer sleeves, Father Christmas or Three Wise men	£20
2009 Proof Gold Sovereign series set (5 coins)	£3500
2009 — — double to half-sovereign (3 coins)	£1500
2009 — — sovereign and half-sovereign (2 coins)	£550
2009 — "Family Silver" set, Henry VIII £5, Britannia £2, Darwin and Burns £2, £1 and Kew 50p (6 coins)	£250
2009 — Silver Piedfort collection, Henry VIII £5, Darwin and Burns £2 and Kew Gardens 50p (4 coins)	£375
2009 — Silver Set, £5 to 1p (12 coins)	£275
2009 — Base metal Executive set, £5 to 1p (12 coins)	£80
2009 — — — Deluxe set, £5 to 1p (12 coins)	£55
2009 — — — Standard set, £5 to 1p (12 coins)	£45
2009 BU Base metal set, £2 to 1p (11 coins)	£22
2009 — — —, £1 to 1p "Royal Shield of Arms" set (7 coins)	£12
2009 — — —, £2 to 1p (8 coins)	£15

DATE   FDC

2009 Proof set of 50p coins as detailed in FIFTY PENCE section, CuNi (16 coins) £350
2009 — Silver (16 coins) £650
2009 — Gold (16 coins) £8250
2009 — Gold Piedfort (16 coins) £22,000
2009 "Mind" set of £5 coins, silver (6 coins) £350
2010 Proof Gold Olympic Series "Faster", £100 and £25 (2), (3 coins) £2500
2010 — — Sovereign series set (5 coins) £2750
2010 — — double to half (3 coins) £1250
2010 — — sovereign to quarter (3 coins) £575
2010 — "Silver Celebration" set, Restoration £5, Nightingale £2, London and Belfast £1
     and Girlguiding 50p (5 coins) £185
2010 Silver Piedfort set, coins as in "Silver Celebration" set (5 coins) £350
2010 — Silver Collection, £5 to 1p (13 coins) £300
2010 — Base Metal Executive Set, £5 to 1p (13 coins) £80
2010 — — Deluxe set £50
2010 — — Standard set £40
2010 BU — Capital Cities £1 (2 coins) £15
2010 — — Set, £2 to 1p (12 coins) £35
2010 — — Definitive pack, £2 to 1p (8 coins) £20
2010 Proof "Body" Collection of £5 coins, silver (6 coins) £350
2010 Proof "Spirit" Collection of £5 coins, silver (6 coins) £300
2011 Proof Gold Sovereign set (5 coins) £3500
2011 — — double to half (3 coins) £1500
2011 — — sovereign to quarter (3 coins) £750
2011 — Olympic gold "Higher" set (3 coins) £2750
2011 — — "Faster" (2010) and "Higher" set (6 coins) in 9-coin case £6000
2011 — Silver Collection, £5 to 1p (14 coins) £400
2011 — — Celebration set, Duke of Edinburgh £5, Mary Rose and King James bible
     Cardiff and Edinburgh £1 and WWF 50p (6 coins) £250
2011 — — — Piedfort, as above (6 coins) £395
2011 Executive Proof Base metal set (14 coins) £85
2011 De-luxe Proof Base metal set (14 coins) £50
2011 Standard Proof Base metal set (14 coins) £40
2011 BU set including £2, £1 and 50p commemoratives (13 coins) £26
2011 BU set of Definitives (8 coins) £25
2012 Proof Gold Sovereign set (5 coins) £4000
2012 — — Double to Half (3 coins) £1650
2012 — — Sovereign to Quarter (3 coins) £825
2012 BU Sovereign set Double to Half (3 coins) £1550
2012 Proof Olympic gold Stronger set (3 coins) £3500
2012 — — — 2x £25 (2 coins) £1200
2010, 2011, 2012 Proof Olympic gold complete set (9 coins) £10,500
2009, 2010, 2011, 2012 Complete Countdown sets:
     Gold Proof (4 coins) £11,500
     Silver Proof Piedport (4 coins) £850
     Silver Proof (4 coins) £325
     CuNi BU (4 coins) £45
2012 Proof Gold set, Diamond Jubilee £5, Dickens & Technology £2, £1 to 1p (10 coins) £8500
2012 — Silver set, as above with Selective Gold plating on £1 to 1p coins (10 coins) £490
2012 — set (Premium) (10 coins) £100
2012 — set (Collector) (10 coins) £55
2012 BU set, include Diamond Jubilee £5 (10 coins) £40
2012 — set, Technology £2 to 1p (8 coins) £21
2012 Proof Gold, Diamond Jubilee £5 and Double Sovereign (2 coins) £3200
2012 — Olympic and Paralympic (2 coins) £5500
2012 — Gold Piedfort 50p set, one each of the coins of Olympic sports in which Team GB gained gold
     medals (11 coins) £25,000
2013 Proof Gold Sovereign set (5 coins) £4000
2013 — — Double to Half (3 coins) £1650
2013 — — One to Quarter (3 coins) £825
2013 — Gold £5 Portraits set (4 coins) £9500
2013 — Silver Portraits set (4 coins) (1,465) £400

DATE	FDC
2013 — Silver Piedfort Portraits set (4 coins) (697)...	£800
2013 — Gold set, £5 Coronation anniversary to 1p (15 coins)	£12,500
2013 — Gold set of both London Underground £2 (2 coins)	£2000
2013 — Silver Piedfort set, as above (2 coins)...	£200
2013 — Silver set, as above (2 coins)	£100
2013 BU set, as above (2 coins)...	£20
2013 — Gold set, 30th anniversary of the One Pound coin, reverses from 1983 (Sewell), 1988 (Gorringe) and 2013 (Dent). (3 coins)...	£3600
2013 — Silver, as above (3 coins)	£150
2013 BU Sovereign set, Double to Half (3 coins), struck June 2, 2013	£1550
2013 Proof Silver annual set, £5 Coronation anniv to 1p (15 coins)	£600
2013 — — Piedfort commemorative set (7 coins)	£650
2013 — "Premium" set (15 coins plus a "Latent Image" item)...	£150
2013 — "Collector" set (15 coins)	£110
2013 — Commemorative set (7 coins)	£65
2013 BU annual set (15 coins)..	£50
2013 — Definitive Set (8 coins)	£25
2014 Proof Gold Britannia (Clark) set £100 to 50p (6 coins)..	£2600
2014 — — — £50 to £10 (3 coins)	£1175
2014 — — — £25 to £1 (3 coins)	£595
2014 — Silver Britannia (Clark) set £2 to 5p (6 coins)	£200
2014 — — — 20p to 5p (3 coins)	£45
2014 — Sovereign set (5 coins)..	£3300
2014 — — Double to half (3 coins)	£1300
2014 — — One to quarter (3 coins)...	£625
2014 — Gold Commemorative set, £5 Queen Anne, 2 x £2, 2 x £1, 50p (6 coins)......................	£5500
2014 — Silver Piedfort set, as above (6 coins)...	£570
2014 — — set as above (6 coins)	£295
2014 — — all major coins of 2014 (14 coins)...	£560
2014 — Premium set (14 coins and a premium medal)	£155
2014 — Collector set (14 coins)	£110
2014 — Commemorative set (6 coins)	£65
2014 BU Annual set (14 coins)	£50
2014 — Definitive set (8 coins)	£25
2014 — Floral £1 set, Scotland and Northern Ireland (2 coins)	£18
2014 Proof Silver Outbreak of First World War set of £5 (6 coins)	£450
2014 — Gold set as above (6 coins)	—
2014 — Silver Portrait of Britain £5 Silver collection (4 coins)	£36
2015 Proof Gold Sovereign set, Rank-Broadley portrait (5 coins)	£2700
2015 — — Double to half, Rank-Broadley portrait (3 coins)	£1300
2015 — — One to quarter, Rank-Broadley portrait (3 coins)	£625
2015 — Gold Commemorative set, 2 x £5, 2 x £2, 2 x £1, 50p, Rank-Broadley portrait (5 coins)	£5500
2015 — Silver Piedfort set, as above (5 coins)...	£570
2015 — — set as above (5 coins)	£295
2015 — Base metal set as above (5 coins)	£65
2015 — Platinum definitive set £2 to 1p, Rank-Broadley portrait plus £2 to 1p Clark portrait (16 coins)	£12,500
2015 — Gold ditto..	£7600
2015 — Silver ditto..	£480
2015 — Base metal ditto	£120
2015 BU definitive set as per Platinum set above (16 coins)	£50

The above four entries are also available as 8-coin sets with either the Rank-Broadley ("Final Edition") or the Clark ("First Edition") portrait. These are issued at half the prices quoted above.

2015 Proof Silver set of definitive and commemorative coins, Rank-Broadley portrait (13 coins)	£560
2015 — Premium set as above (13 coins and a Premium medal)...	£155
2015 Collector set as above (13 coins and medal)	£110
2015 Proof Double to half sovereign, Clark portrait (3 coins)	£1200
2015 — Silver commemorative set, Anniversary of First World War (6 coins)	£450
2015 Portrait of Britain Silver Proof Collection (4x£5 with colour)	£310
2016 Proof Gold Sovereign set, Butler Portrait (5 coins)	£2700
2016 — — Double to half, Butler Portrait (3 coins)	£1200
2016— — One to quarter, Butler Portrait (3 coins)...	£625
2016 — Gold Commemorative set, £5, 5x £2, £1, 50p (8 coins)	£6100

DATE   FDC

2016 — Silver Piedfort set, as above (8 coins)..£595
2016 — — set as above (8 coins) £395
2016 — Base metal set as above (8 coins)..£95
2016 — silver set, commemoratives and definitives (16 coins) £595
2016 — Base metal set as above, Premium plus Medal (16 coins) £195
2016 — — Collector set (16 coins)...£145
2016 Portrait of Britain Silver Proof Collection (4x£5 with colour) £310
2016 BU Annual set including commemoratives (16 coins)..............................£55
2016 — Definitive set (8 coins)..£30
2016 Proof Silver set of £5 coins, Anniversary of First World War (6 coins) £450
2016 Beatrix Potter 150th Anniversary 50p coin set (5 coins) £75
2017 BU Annual "Premium" set (13 coins & premium medal) £195
2017 BU Annual set (13 coins as above)..£55
2017 — Definitive set (8 coins)...£30
2017 Proof Annual "Collector" set (13 coins & medal) £145
2017 — Commemorative set (5 coins), 2x£5, 2x£2, 50p £95
2017 — Silver Piedfort Commemorative set (coins as above)..........................£595
2017 — Silver Commemorative set (coins as above).....................................£350
2017 — Silver set (13 coins £5–1p)...£625
2017 — Silver Portrait of Britain Collection (4x£5 with colour) £310
2017 — Silver Outbreak of First World War set of £5 (6 coins) £450
2018 BU Annual set (13 coins)..£55
2018 — Definitive set (8 coins)..£30
2018 Proof Annual set (13 coins) £155
2018 — "Premium" set (13 coins & premium medal)....................................£210
2018 — Portrait of Britain Silver Proof Collection (4x£5 with colour)................£310
2018 — Centenary of World War I Silver Proof set of £5 (6 coins) £465
2018 — — Gold (6 coins) £11,100
2018 — — Silver Piedfort set (5 coins)...£555
2018 Silver set (5 commemorative and 8 circulating coins)............................£610
2018 Commemorative coin set (5 coins)...£95
2019 BU Annual set (13 coins)...£55
2019 — Annual definitive set (8 coins)..£30
2019 Proof Annual coin set with Medal (13 coins £5–1p)...............................£210
2019 — Silver set (13 coins £5–1p)..£610
2019 — Gold Proof commemorative set (5 coins £5–50p)..............................£6300
2019 — Silver Proof Piedfort commemorative set (5 coins) £550
2019 — Sovereign Proof set (5 coins)..£4200
2019 — "Premium" Sovereign Proof set (3 coins).......................................£1695
2019 — Sovereign Proof set (3 coins)..£890
2019 — Paddington Bear Silver Proof set (2 coins)......................................£65
2019 BU Paddington Bear BU set (2 coins)...£10
2019 Proof set Celebrating 50 Years of the 50 pence (3 types):
    i. *British Military and Culture Set* (10 coins): New 50 Pence, Girl Guides, Kew Gardens, Roger Bannister,
      Scouting, Battle of Hastings, Battle of Britain, D-Day, Victoria Cross 150th Anniversary,
      Victoria Cross Heroic Acts, BU £76.50
    ii. *British Military Set* (5 coins): Battle of Hastings, Battle of Britain, D-Day, Victoria Cross 150th Anniversary,
      Victoria Cross Heroic Acts, BU £45
    iii. *British Culture Set* (5 coins): New 50 Pence, Girl Guides, Kew Gardens, Roger Bannister, Scouting, BU.....£45
2019 — — Proof (3,500)..£90
2019 — — Silver Proof (1,969)...£225
2019 — — Gold Proof (75)..£3825
2020 Monumental Coin Designs (5 coins) including Team GB 50p, 75th Anniversary of VE Day £2, 400th Anniversary
    of the Mayflower £2, Centenary of Agatha Christie £2, 200th Anniversary since the reign of George III £5 .... —
2020 BU Annual coin set, 1p–£2 plus the 5 above (13 coins) £55
2020 — Definitive coin set, 1p–£2 (8 current circulating coinage designs only)....£30
2020 Proof Annual coin set (13 coins) (7000)..£155
2020 — Premium set (13 coins) (2500) £210
2020 — Silver set (13 coins) (500) £610
2020 — Silver Piedfort set (5 coins, 50p–£5) (300)....................................£550
2020 — Gold Proof Sovereign series (5 coins) (75)....................................£6150

DATE   FDC

2021 BU Annual coin set £2–1p (8 coins) £30
2021 — including coins from the 5-piece coin set below (13 coins)... £55
2021 Proof Annual coin set (13 coins) (7000).. £155
2021 — Premium Proof set (13 coins) (2500).. £210
2021 — Silver Proof set (13 coins) (550) £640
2021 — Gold Proof Sovereign series set (5 coins, £5–quarter sovereign).. £4785
2021 — — (4 coins, £2–quarter sovereign) £2050
2021 — — (3 coins, Sovereign–quarter sovereign) £1015
2021 — — Special commemorative Sovereign set comprising George V 1926, EII 1957 and a "Struck on the Day" 2021 (3 coins) (100)... £1995
2021 5 piece coin set comprising: 50th Anniversary of Decimal Day 2021 UK 50p, Celebrating the life and work of John Logie Baird 2021 UK 50p, Celebrating the life and work of H. G. Wells 2021UK £2, 250th Anniversary of the birth of Sir Walter Scott 2021 UK £2. The 95th Birthday of Her Majesty the Queen 2021 UK £5. Silver Proof Piedfort (5 coins) (300).. £587.50
2021 — — Gold Proof (95) £7100
2021 10 piece coin set comprising: The Lion of England, The Unicorn of Scotland, The Red Dragon of Wales, The Black Bull of Clarence, The Falcon of Plantagenets, The Yale of Beaufort, The White Lion of Mortimer, The White Horse of Hanover, The Greyhound of Richmond, The Griffin of Edward III. Silver Proof 1/4 ounce/50p (1250)... £360
2021 — — Silver Proof 2 ounce/£5 (300)... £1835
2021 — — Gold Proof 1/4 ounce/£25 (250)... £5840
2022 BU Definitive Annual coin set (8 coins) (Unlimited) £30
2022 13 piece coin set comprising: Platinum Jubilee of Her Majesty the Queen 2022 UK 50p, Birmingham 2022 Commonwealth Games UK 50p, Life and Legacy of Dame Vera Lyynn 2022 UK £2, Life and Legacy of Alexander Graham Bell 2022 UK £2, Platinum Jubilee of Her Majesty the Queen 2022 UK £5 and the following denominations: £2, £1, 50p, 20p, 10p, 5p, 2p, 1p. BU (13 coins. Unlimited)....................................£60
2022 — Proof set (7000).. £155
2022 — Premium Proof set (2500) £210
2022 — Silver Proof set (550).. £647.50
2022 HRH Duke of Cambridge 40th Birthday. 2 piece Gold Coin set comprising 1982 Uncirculated Sovereign & 2022 Quarter ounce/£25 Gold Proof coin (100)... £1300
2022 5 piece coin set comprising: Platinum Jubilee of Her Majesty the Queen 2022 UK 50p, Birmingham 2022 Commonwealth Games UK 50p, Life and Legacy of Dame Vera Lynn 2022 UK £2, Life and Legacy of Alexander Graham Bell 2022 UK £2, Platinum Jubilee of Her Majesty the Queen 2022 UK £5. Silver Proof Piedfort (5 coins) (370) £597.50
2022 — Gold Proof set (100).. £7100
2022 — Platinum Proof set (30).. £9895
2022 Dame Vera Lynn two-coin set comprising 1917 Sovereign & 2022 1/4 ounce Gold Proof coin (400)......... £1300
2022 — — comprising 1917 Half Crown & 2022 £2 Silver Proof coin (373) £150
2022 Platinum Jubilee Gold Sovereign Proof set (5 coins, £5–1/4 Sovereign) (700) £4795
2022 Gold Sovereign Proof set (4 coins, Double Sovereign–1/4 Sovereign) (500) £2055
2022 Gold Sovereign Proof set (3 coins, Sovereign–1/4 Sovereign) (1000) £955

In addition to the above the Royal Mint produce the BU sets detailed above in Wedding and in Baby gift packs each year. Also various patterns and sets have been made available from time to time. These include the following:

1999 (dated 1994) Bi-metal £2, plus three unprocessed or part-processed elements............................ —
2003 Set of patterns of £1 coins with "Bridges" designs, in gold, hall-marked on edges (4 coins)........................... —
2003 — Silver £1 as above (4 coins)... £150
2004 — Gold £1 featuring heraldic animal heads, hall-marked on edge (4 coins) £1000
2004 — Silver £1 featuring heraldic animal heads, hall-marked on edge (4 coins) £150
The Centenary of the Burial of the Unknown Warrior Historic coin set comprising: Remembrance Day 2020 UK Silver Proof £5 Coin, George VI Half Penny, George V Farthing, Sixpence, Shilling, Florin, Half Crown, Penny, Three-pence (100)... £280

SCOTLAND

The coins illustrated are pennies representative of the reign, unless otherwise stated.

	F	VF

DAVID I (1124–53)
Berwick, Carlisle, Edinburgh and Roxburgh Mints

	F	VF
Penny in the name of David	£3000	£10500
Cut Halfpenny		Extremely rare
Penny in name of Stephen	£1000	£4000

David I

HENRY (1136–52)
Bamborough, Carlisle and Corbridge Mints for the Earl of Huntingdon and Northumberland

	F	VF
Penny	£1500	£6250
Cut Halfpenny		Extremely rare

MALCOLM IV (1153–65)
Berwick and Roxburgh Mints

Penny (5 different types)		Extremely rare

Henry

WILLIAM THE LION (1165–1214)
Berwick, Edinburgh, Dun (Dunbar?), Perth and Roxburgh Mints

		F	VF
Penny - cross pattee early issue	from	£2500	£7000
Penny – pellet & crescent	from	£225	£600
Penny – short cross & stars – mint & moneyer	from	£160	£450
Penny – short cross & stars HVE WALTER & var	from	£125	£325

ALEXANDER II (1214–49)
Berwick and Roxburgh Mints

		F	VF
Penny – in the name of William the Lion	from	£400	£1200
Penny – in own name	from	£650	£1900

William the Lion

ALEXANDER III (1249–86)
FIRST COINAGE (1250–80)
Pennies struck at the Mints at

		F	VF
Aberdeen	from	£160	£425
Ayr	from	£220	£725
Berwick	from	£85	£225
Dun (Dumfries / Dunfermline? / Dundee?)	from	£185	£525
Edinburgh	from	£155	£400
Forfar	from	£320	£950
Fres (Dumfries)	from	£295	£850
Glasgow	from	£295	£850
Inverness	from	£290	£775
Kinghorn	from	£325	£995
Lanark	from	£270	£825
Montrose	from	£585	£1500
Perth	from	£115	£325
Roxburgh	from	£125	£375
St Andrews	from	£300	£875
Stirling	from	£225	£695

Alexander II

Alexander III First Coinage

SECOND COINAGE (1280–86)

	F	VF
Penny	£85	£250
Halfpenny	£100	£325
Farthing	£275	£825

Alexander III Second Coinage

F   VF

JOHN BALIOL (1292–1306)

FIRST COINAGE *(Rough Surface issue)*

		F	VF
Penny	from	£165	£475
Halfpenny	from	£450	Ex. rare
Penny – St. Andrews	from	£200	£575
Halfpenny – St. Andrews	from	£850	Ex. rare

SECOND COINAGE *(Smooth Surface issue)*

		F	VF
Penny	from	£200	£525
Halfpenny	from	£175	£550
Farthing		Extremely rare	
Penny – St. Andrews	from	£350	£950
Halfpenny – St. Andrews		Extremely rare	

John Baliol

ROBERT BRUCE (1306–29)

Berwick Mint

		F	VF
Penny	from	£700	£1950
Halfpenny	from	£575	£1500
Farthing	from	£850	£2250

Robert Bruce

DAVID II (1329–71)

Aberdeen and Edinburgh Mints

		F	VF
Noble		Extremely Rare	
Groat (Edinburgh)	from	£150	£350
Groat (Aberdeen)	from	£750	£2250
Halfgroat (Edinburgh)	from	£125	£325
Halfgroat (Aberdeen)	from	£600	£1700
Penny 1st Coinage 2nd Issue	from	£75	£225
Penny 2nd Coinage (Edinburgh)	from	£125	£325
Penny 2nd Coinage (Aberdeen)	from	£495	£1350
Halfpenny	from	£250	£725
Farthing	from	£350	£950

David II

ROBERT II (1371–90)

Dundee, Edinburgh and Perth Mints

		F	VF
Groat	from	£125	£325
Halfgroat	from	£150	£495
Penny	from	£95	£250
Halfpenny	from	£125	£350

Robert II

ROBERT III (1390–1406)

Aberdeen, Dumbarton, Edinburgh, Perth Mints

		F	VF
Lion or crown	from	£1750	£5750
Demy lion or halfcrown	from	£1500	£5250
Groat	from	£150	£375
Halfgroat	from	£175	£425
Penny	from	£250	£725
Halfpenny	from	£275	£850

JAMES I (1406–37)

Aberdeen, Edinburgh, Inverness, Linlithgow, Perth, Stirling Mints

		F	VF
Demy	from	£1500	£4250
Half demy	from	£1250	£3950
Groat Edinburgh	from	£225	£625
Groat Other Mints	from	£425	£1250
Penny	from	£250	£650
Halfpenny		Extremely rare	

Robert III Lion

	F	VF

JAMES II (1437–60)

Aberdeen, Edinburgh, Linlithgow, Perth, Roxburgh, Stirling Mints

	F	VF
Demy .... from	£1250	£3750
Lion... from	£1500	£4950
Half lion..	Extremely rare	
Early groats (fleur-de-lis) Edinburgh .... from	£225	£650
Early groats (fleur-de-lis) Other Mints..................	Extremely rare	
Later groats (crown) Edinburgh	£375	£1100
Later groats (crown) Other Mints...................... from	£675	£2250
Later Halfgroats (crown) Edinburgh...................	£750	£2125
Later Halfgroats (crown) Other Mints	Extremely rare	
Penny (billon) .... from	£250	£650

JAMES III (1460–88)

Aberdeen, Berwick and Edinburgh Mints

	F	VF
Rider...	£2250	£8000
Half rider	£2000	£6500
Quarter rider..	£3000	£9000
Unicorn...	£3000	£9000
Groat (facing bust) Edinburgh .... from	£325	£900
Groat (facing bust) Berwick .... from	£750	£2250
Groat (thistle & mullet) Edinburgh.....................	£325	£995
Groat (threequarter bust) Edinburgh................... from	£625	£1750
Groat (threequarter bust) Aberdeen .... from	£825	£2500
Halfgroat... from	£550	£1750
Penny (silver) .... from	£325	£950
Plack (billon) .... from	£175	£450
Half plack.. from	£195	£525
Penny (billon) .... from	£150	£425
Farthing (copper)	£200	£650
Penny – ecclesiastical issue............................. from	£90	£225
Farthing – ecclesiastical issue.......................... from	£125	£350

James III Groat, Berwick Mint

JAMES IV (1488–1513)

Edinburgh Mint

	F	VF
Unicorn...	£1650	£4950
Half unicorn	£1650	£4950
Lion or crown...	Extremely rare	
Half lion..	Extremely rare	
Groat.. from	£950	£2950
Halfgroat... from	£1250	£4950
Penny (silver) .... from	£150	£400
Plack.. from	£40	£100
Half plack	Extremely rare	
Penny (billon) .... from	£40	£120

James IV Unicorn

JAMES V (1513–42)

Edinburgh Mint

	F	VF
Unicorn	£2050	£7500
Half Unicorn	Extremely rare	
Crown...	£1350	£4750
Ducat or Bonnet piece .... from	£2000	£8500
Two-thirds ducat..	£2500	£6500
One-third ducat	£3500	£9500
Groat.. from	£400	£1350
One-third groat .... from	£325	£975
Plack.. from	£50	£125
Bawbee .... from	£75	£185
Half bawbee .... from	£140	£325
Quarter bawbee..	Extremely rare	

James V Ducat or Bonnet Piece

F   VF

MARY (1542–67)

Edinburgh and Stirling Mints

FIRST PERIOD (1542–58)

	F	VF
Crown	£1750	£6500
Twenty shillings	Extremely rare	
Lion (Forty-four shillings)	£2000	£8500
Half lion (Twenty-two shillings)	£1750	£6500
Ryals (Three pounds)	£5000	£17500
Half ryal	£4500	£12500
Portrait testoon	£5500	£15000
Non-portrait testoon .... from	£500	£1250
Half testoon .... from	£350	£995
Bawbee .... from	£125	£375
Half bawbee .... from	£150	£425
Bawbee - Stirling	£195	£525
Penny (facing bust) .... from	£350	£995
Penny (no bust) .... from	£225	£650
Lion .... from	£50	£145
Plack .... from	£85	£225

SECOND PERIOD (Francis and Mary, 1558–60)

	F	VF
Ducat (Sixty shillings)	Extremely rare	
Non-portrait testoon .... from	£375	£1000
Half testoon .... from	£375	£1000
12 penny groat .... from	£95	£325
Lion .... from	£55	£135

Mary Lion or Forty-Four Shillings

THIRD PERIOD (Widowhood, 1560–65)

	F	VF
Portrait testoon	£4500	£11500
Half testoon.	£3000	£8500

FOURTH PERIOD (Henry and Mary, 1565–67)

	F	VF
Portrait ryal.	£45000	£125000
Non-portrait ryal .... from	£875	£2250
Two-third ryal .... from	£725	£1850
One-third ryal .... from	£925	£2750

FIFTH PERIOD (Second widowhood, 1567)

	F	VF
Non-portrait ryal .... from	£850	£1950
Two thirds ryal .... from	£550	£1450
One-third ryal .... from	£725	£1700

JAMES VI (1567–1603)

(Before accession to the English throne)

FIRST COINAGE (1567–71)

	F	VF
Ryal .... from	£450	£1250
Two-thirds ryal .... from	£350	£1100
One-third ryal .... from	£400	£1200

SECOND COINAGE (1571–80)

	F	VF
Twenty pounds	£25,000	£75,000
Noble (or half merk) .... from	£125	£300
Half noble (or quarter merk) .... from	£125	£300
Two merks or Thistle dollar .... from	£2250	£6750
Merk .... from	£3000	£8500

THIRD COINAGE (1580–81)

	F	VF
Ducat	£5000	£14500
Sixteen shillings	£2500	£7250

James VI Fourth coinage
Ten Shillings

	F	VF
Eight shillings	£1950	£5750
Four shillings	£4000	£9500
Two shillings	Extremely rare	

FOURTH COINAGE (1582–88)

	F	VF
Lion noble	£5500	£15000
Two-third lion noble	£4750	£13500
One-third lion noble	Extremely rare	
Forty shillings	£5750	£18500
Thirty shillings	£800	£2500
Twenty shillings	£425	£1500
Ten shillings	£425	£1500

FIFTH COINAGE (1588)

	F	VF
Thistle noble	£2150	£7500

James VI Seventh Coinage Rider

SIXTH COINAGE (1591–93)

	F	VF
"Hat" piece	£4000	£10000
"Balance" half merk .... from	£350	£1150
"Balance" quarter merk	£800	£2200

SEVENTH COINAGE (1594–1601)

	F	VF
Rider	£1250	£3500
Half rider	£1200	£3500
Ten shillings .... from	£160	£500
Five shillings .... from	£125	£400
Thirty pence .... from	£225	£625
Twelve pence .... from	£130	£375

EIGHTH COINAGE (1601–04)

	F	VF
Sword and sceptre piece .... from	£850	£2350
Half sword and sceptre piece .... from	£675	£2100
Thistle-merk .... from	£110	£350
Half thistle-merk .... from	£65	£175
Quarter thistle-merk .... from	£55	£135
Eighth thistle-merk .... from	£50	£110

*James VI Seventh Coinage
10 Shillings*

BILLON AND COPPER ISSUES

	F	VF
Eightpenny groat .... from	£45	£125
Fourpenny groat .... from	£350	£1000
Twopenny plack .... from	£130	£375
Hardhead .... from	£30	£85
Twopence .... from	£80	£230
Penny plack .... from	£160	£750
Penny .... from	£500	£1250

JAMES VI (1603–25)
(After accession to the English throne)

	F	VF
Unit .... from	£950	£2500
Double crown .... from	£1100	£3250
British crown .... from	£550	£1550
Halfcrown .... from	£750	£2150
Thistle crown .... from	£650	£2050
Sixty shillings .... from	£450	£1550
Thirty shillings .... from	£225	£625
Twelve shillings .... from	£175	£575
Six shillings .... from	£600	£3750
Two shillings .... from	£75	£225
One shilling .... from	£125	£350
Copper twopence .... from	£25	£70
Copper penny .... from	£85	£250

*James VI after accession thirty
shillings*

	F	VF

CHARLES I (1625–49)

FIRST COINAGE (1625-36)

	F	VF
Unit	£1250	£3500
Double crown	£1000	£3150
British crown	Extremely rare	
Sixty shillings	£800	£2750
Thirty shillings	£175	£575
Twelve shillings	£175	£575
Six shillings .... from	£650	£2000
Two shillings	£45	£110
One shilling	£150	£495

SECOND COINAGE (1636)

	F	VF
Half merk	£120	£300
Forty penny piece	£75	£210
Twenty penny piece	£70	£200

Charles I Third Coinage Sixty Shillings

THIRD COINAGE (1637–42)

	F	VF
Unit .... from	£1750	£6750
Half unit .... from	£1225	£3750
British crown .... from	£675	£2000
British half crown .... from	£575	£1750
Sixty shillings	£875	£3250
Thirty shillings .... from	£150	£475
Twelve shillings .... from	£150	£550
Six shillings .... from	£125	£325
Half merk .... from	£120	£395
Forty pence .... from	£75	£195
Twenty pence .... from	£35	£95

FOURTH COINAGE (1642)

	F	VF
Three shillings thistle	£60	£150
Two shillings large II	£40	£110
Two shillings small II	£60	£155
Two shillings no value	£80	£225

Charles I Fourth Coinage Two Shillings

COPPER ISSUES

(1629 Issue)

	F	VF
Twopence (triple thistle	£25	£70
Penny	£175	£500

(1632-39 Issue)

	F	VF
Twopence (Stirling turner .... from	£25	£70

(1642-50 ISSUE)

	F	VF
Twopence (CR crowned	£20	£55

CHARLES II (1660–85)

FIRST COINAGE

Four merks

	F	VF
1664 Thistle above bust	£1250	£4000
1664 Thistle below bust	£2500	£7250
1665	Extremely rare	
1670 .... varieties from	£1550	£6950
1673	£1550	£6950
1674 F below bust .... varieties from	£1250	£4000
1675	£950	£2750

Two merks

	F	VF
1664 Thistle above bust	£1000	£2500

Charles II two merks

	F	VF
1664 Thistle below bust	£2500	£7250
1670	£1200	£3000
1673	£750	£1950
1673 F below bust	£1350	£3250
1674	£1200	£3000
1674 F below bust	£1200	£3000
1675	£750	£1950

Merk

	F	VF
1664 .... varieties from	£250	£715
1665	£275	£780
1666	£325	£950
1668	£325	Ex. rare
1669 .... varieties from	£100	£275
1670	£145	£375
1671	£110	£300
1672 .... varieties from	£100	£275
1673 .... varieties from	£110	£300
1674	£250	£715
1674 F below bust	£225	£650
1675 F below bust	£200	£550
1675	£210	£585

Charles II Dollar

Half merk

	F	VF
1664	£275	£725
1665 .... varieties from	£325	£600
1666 .... varieties from	£300	£750
1667	£325	£600
1668	£150	£400
1669 .... varieties from	£105	£325
1670 .... varieties from	£150	£400
1671 .... varieties from	£105	£285
1672	£150	£400
1673	£175	£475
1675 F below bust	£175	£575
1675	£195	£550

SECOND COINAGE
Dollar

	F	VF
1676	£750	£2000
1679	£650	£1650
1680	£750	£1650
1681	£550	£1325
1682	£475	£1250

Charles II Sixteenth Dollar

Half Dollar

	F	VF
1675	£650	£1500
1676	£750	£1950
1681	£400	£1100

Quarter Dollar

	F	VF
1675	£195	£550
1676 .... varieties from	£100	£295
1677 .... varieties from	£145	£400
1678	£165	£450
1679	£185	£500
1680	£135	£325
1681	£105	£275
1682 .... varieties from	£145	£400

Eighth Dollar

	F	VF
1676 .... varieties from	£85	£210

Charles II Bawbee

	F	VF
1677	£125	£300
1678/7	£195	£495
1679	£300	Ext. rare
1680 .... varieties from	£150	£345
1682 .... varieties from	£225	£495

Sixteenth Dollar

1677	£85	£210
1678/7 .... varieties from	£120	£320
1679/7	£135	£360
1680 .... varieties from	£135	£360
1681	£75	£175

Copper Issues

Twopence CR crowned .... varieties from	£25	£70
Bawbees 1677-79 .... varieties from	£65	£195
Turners 1677-79 .... varieties from	£45	£125

JAMES VII (1685–89)

Sixty shillings

1688 proof only .... varieties from	—	£3250

Forty shillings

1687 .... varieties from	£400	£950
1688 .... varieties from	£400	£950

Ten shillings

1687	£165	£525
1688 .... varieties from	£250	£700

James VII ten shillings

WILLIAM & MARY (1689–94)

Sixty shillings

1691	£525	£1950
1692	£850	£2350

Forty shillings

1689 .... varieties from	£295	£850
1690 .... varieties from	£185	£525
1691 .... varieties from	£195	£550
1692 .... varieties from	£225	£600
1693 .... varieties from	£195	£550
1694 .... varieties from	£225	£775

Twenty shillings

1693	£500	£1650
1694	Extremely rare	

William & Mary ten shillings

Ten shillings

1689	Extremely rare	
1690 .... varieties from	£295	£750
1691 .... varieties from	£195	£600
1692 .... varieties from	£195	£600
1694 .... varieties from	£250	£700

Five shillings

1691	£200	£575
1694 .... varieties from	£120	£350

Copper Issues

Bawbees 1691–94 .... varieties from	£100	£275
Bodle (Turners) 1691–94 .... varieties from	£55	£180

	F	VF

WILLIAM II (1694–1702)

		F	VF
Pistole		£3000	£7500
Half pistole		£3750	£8500

Forty shillings

		F	VF
1695	varieties from	£225	£650
1696		£250	£625
1697		£300	£650
1698		£250	£595
1699		£375	£750
1700		Extremely rare	

Twenty shillings

		F	VF
1695		£200	£625
1696		£200	£625
1697	varieties from	£250	£700
1698	varieties from	£175	£650
1699		£225	£625

William II ten shillings

Ten shillings

		F	VF
1695		£150	£375
1696		£150	£375
1697	varieties from	£150	£375
1698	varieties from	£150	£375
1699		£295	£750

Five shillings

		F	VF
1695		£70	£195
1696		£65	£180
1697	varieties from	£75	£225
1699		£95	£275
1700		£85	£230
1701		£125	£350
1702		£125	£350

Anne five shillings

Copper Issues

		F	VF
Bawbee 1695–97	varieties from	£85	£325
Bodle (Turners) 1695–97	varieties from	£50	£150

ANNE (1702–14)

Pre -Union 1702–7 (For POST-UNION 1707–1 See listing in the English section)

Ten shillings

		F	VF
1705		£175	£450
1706	varieties from	£225	£650

Five shillings

		F	VF
1705	varieties from	£85	£225
1706		£85	£225

JAMES VIII (The Old Pretender) (1688–1766)

A number of Guineas and Crowns in various metals were struck in 1828 using original dies prepared by Norbert Roettiers, all bearing the date 1716. These coins are extremely rare and are keenly sought after.

Guinea

1716 Gold Old Bust Right Type 1	Generally EF+	£12000
1716 Silver Old Bust Right Type 1	Generally EF+	£1500
1716 Silver Young Bust Left Type	Generally EF+	£1750

Crown

1716	Generally EF+	£2500

> *Our grateful thanks go to David Stuart of ABC Coins & Tokens for updating this Scottish section of the Yearbook*

ISLE OF MAN

HIBERNO-MANX PENNY

Recent research has established that a Mint did exist in the Isle of Man and evidence suggests that silver pennies were minted on the Island from c.1025. Resulting from finds in various locations on the Island, it had been suggested that Hiberno-Manx pennies were coined at a mint located in the northern area, perhaps Maughold. However, the mint was more likely to have been in the fortress on St. Patrick's Isle at Peel in the west of the Island. They have been found in hoards from Park Llewellyn (Maughold), West Nappin (Jurby), Kirk Andreas and at Kirk Michael. The dies for these Hiberno-Manx silver pennies may have originally come from a moneyer called Færemin in Dublin.

Hiberno-Manx silver penny, c.1025

JOHN MURREY'S PENNIES OF 1668

The first Manx tokens to become 'official' legal tender in the Isle of Man are attributed to John Murrey's Pennies of 1668. British coins circulated alongside these tokens, together with much extraneous coinage. At this time there was a severe shortage of pennies and halfpennies. An Act of Tynwald dated 24th June 1679 proclaimed that "...no copper or brass money called Butchers' halfpence, Patrick's halfpence and copper farthings, or any of that nature, shall pass in the Island from the first day of January next." The Act also stated that only the King's (Charles II) farthings and halfpence, and the brass money called Ino Murrey's pence was to pass as currency. Consequently, the Act had the effect of making John Murrey's brass tokens legal tender pennies. The Isle of Man thus had its own distinctive legal currency for the first time. John Murrey was a merchant of Douglas and lived at Ronaldsway near Castletown. Two distinct types of his penny have been recorded and both are rare.

The two known types of John Murrey's penny of 1668

Murrey's coins remained in circulation as legal tender until the 1710 Coinage Act of Tynwald. This Act authorised the new coinage of James Stanley, Earl of Derby, and declared all coins previously circulating to be illegal. When this Act was promulgated, it is believed that a descendant of John Murrey redeemed nearly all the "murreys" then in circulation and destroyed them.

The new Stanley coinage was cast at Castle Rushen in Castletown and dated 1709. The penny and halfpenny were proclaimed legal currency on 24th June 1710.

DATE	F	VF	EF	UNC
PENNY (Copper except where stated)				
"Derby" coinage				
1709 Cast	£55	£185	£350	—
1709 Silver cast Proof	—	—	—	£2000
1709 Brass	£50	£175	£350	—
1733 "Quocunque"	£40	£75	£275	£450
1733 "Ouocunoue"	£45	£85	£300	£750
1733 Bath metal "Quocunque"	£30	£75	£300	—
1733 Silver Proof	—	—	—	£850
1733 Bronze Proof	—	—	—	£500
1733 Proof	—	—	—	£675

Cast penny.

DATE	F	VF	EF	UNC
1733 Cap frosted..	£35	£75	£300	£500
1733 Brass, cap frosted	£40	£75	£325	£650
1733 Silver Proof cap frosted....................	—	—	—	£650
1733 Bronze annulets instead of pellets	£50	£100	£400	£500
"Atholl" coinage				
1758..	£30	£50	£250	£450
1758 — Proof	—	—	—	£650
1758 — Silver Proof	—	—	—	£1000
Regal coinage				
1786 Engrailed edge	£35	£65	£275	£450
1786 Engrailed edge Proof	—	—	—	£600
1786 Plain edge Proof	—	—	—	£1000
1786 Pellet below bust..............................	£35	£65	£275	£550
1798..	£35	£65	£250	£500
1798 Proof..	—	—	—	£450
1798 Bronze Proof.....................................	—	—	—	£450
1798 Copper-gilt Proof..............................	—	—	—	£2000
1798 Silver Proof	—	—	—	£2500
1813	£40	£75	£300	£500
1813 Proof..	—	—	—	£650
1813 Bronze Proof.....................................	—	—	—	£650
1813 Copper-gilt Proof..............................	—	—	—	£2500
1839	£35	£75	£200	£450
1839 Proof..	—	—	—	£500

"Derby" coinage.

HALF PENCE (Copper except where stated)

	F	VF	EF	UNC
"Derby" coinage				
1709 Cast	£50	£125	£250	—
1709 Brass	£55	£185	£500	—
1723 Silver	£725	£1250	£3500	—
1723 Copper	£300	£600	£1750	£2500
1733 Copper	£35	£55	£225	£450
1733 Bronze	£35	£55	£225	£450
1733 Silver Proof plain cap	—	—	—	£700
1733 Silver Proof frosted cap	—	—	—	—
1733 Bronze Proof.....................................	—	—	—	£500
1733 Bath metal plain cap.........................	£40	£50	£215	—
1733 Bath metal frosted cap	£40	£50	£215	—
"Atholl" coinage				
1758	£40	£50	£215	£450
1758 — Proof	—	—	—	£800
Regal coinage				
1786 Engrailed edge	£30	£45	£120	£350
1786 Proof engrailed edge	—	—	—	£450
1786 Plain edge..	£40	£65	£250	£350
1786 Proof plain edge	—	—	—	£650
1786 Bronze Proof.....................................	—	—	—	£450
1798..	£35	£45	£150	£350
1798 Proof..	—	—	—	£450
1798 Bronze Proof.....................................	—	—	—	£400
1798 Copper-gilt Proof..............................	—	—	—	£1500
1798 Silver Proof	—	—	—	£1500
1813	£30	£45	£150	£300
1813 Proof..	—	—	—	£375
1813 Bronze Proof.....................................	—	—	—	£350
1813 Copper-gilt Proof..............................	—	—	—	£1250
1839	£30	£45	£150	£300
1839 Bronze Proof.....................................	—	—	—	£450

Regal coinage.

FARTHING
Regal coinage

	F	VF	EF	UNC
1839 Copper	£30	£45	£150	£300
1839 Bronze Proof	—	—	—	£450
1839 Copper-gilt Proof	—	—	—	£2500

"Atholl" coinage.

MANX DECIMAL COINS FROM 1971

This section lists the circulating coins issued by the Isle of Man Government Treasury. The Royal Mint produced the initial issue in 1971 which satisfied the needs of the Island until 1975. In 1972, 73 and 74 the Pobjoy Mint sent to the Government 1,000 samples of each denomination of the current series in anticipation of securing future contracts for the minting of Manx coins. Pobjoy won the contract in 1975 and minted all Isle of Man coins up to and including 2016. One exception was the 1972 Royal Silver Wedding crown which was minted by the Royal Canadian Mint in Ottawa. In 1975 the Manx Government released the Pobjoy samples into circulation with the 1975 coins. In 2016 the Tower Mint in London won the contract for minting Manx coins from 2017.

From 1979 Pobjoy introduced die marks on their coins in the form of small Celtic letters in the form AA, AB, AC, etc. Alternative letter(s) were used for diamond finish and precious metal coins. 'PM' mint marks also appear on most Pobjoy minted coins. The positions of die marks and mint marks can randomly appear on both obverse and reverse. There are many variations on practically all denominations and are outside the scope of this yearbook.

Where known, minting figures are shown in the lists but from about 1986 Pobjoy did not release minting quantities. On the Christmas 50p coins where the 'Minting Limit' is quoted the actual quantities produced were far less, usually up to 5,000 coins for circulation in the Isle of Man.

In some years when no coins were required for circulation, the only source for certain denominations of that year was from uncirculated sets. Unsold sets were often broken up by the Treasury and the coins put into circulation. Coins bearing those dates are, therefore, scarce.

Sculptors of Queen's Profile used on Manx Coins

1971-1984	Arnold Machin
1985-1997	Raphael Maklouf (full bust on Crowns)
1998-2016	Ian Rank-Broadley (full bust on Crowns)
2017-	Jody Clark (full bust version)

Privy and Provenance Marks

Privy marks can be found on a number of Manx circulating coins. A stylised Triskeles was used on coins dated 1979 to commemorate the Millennium of Tynwald - The Manx Parliament. Some coins dated 1982 bore a baby crib to commemorate the birth of Prince William. In 1985 the Manx Year of Sport logo was incorporated into the designs of circulating coins.

Provenance marks may be found on some £1 coins dated 1980 and 1981 minted at the Daily Mail Ideal Home Exhibition in London (D.M.I.H.E.) and minted at the Daily Mail Ideal Home Exhibition in Birmingham (D.M.I.H.E./N.). Also Belfast Ideal Home Exhibition (I.I.H.E.) on the 1981 £1 and £5 coins minted at this location. In 1980 a number of £1 coins bore the T.T. (Tourist Trophy motorcycle races) provenance mark.

A few two pounds (£2) and five pounds (£5) coins dated 1991 bore the privy mark 'RAOB'. Both are scarce

Precious Metals Coins

Many coins have been produced in various precious metals such as silver, gold, platinum and palladium.

Coins not intended for Circulation

Fractional coins, odd denominations and unusual shapes have all featured and a few examples are listed at the end of this section, however, details of these coins are outside the scope of this yearbook.

DATE	Mintage	UNC

HALF PENNY
Metal: Bronze
Size: 17mm diameter

		Mintage	UNC
1971	Cushag (Ragwort)	495,000	£2
1972		1,000	£25
1973		1,000	£25
1974		1,000	£25
1975		705,610	£1
1976	Herring on Map of Island	335,554	£1
1977		887,803	£1
1978		120,225	£2
1979		251,152	£2
1980	Stylised Norse Herring	117,665	£2
1981		169,772	£2
1981	Herring on Map - World Food Day	10,000	£3
1982	Stylised Norse Herring	17,385	£2
1983		24,576	£2
1984	Fuchsia	39,009	£2
1985		25,000	£3

Half pennies are no longer legal tender in the Isle of Man

Cushag

Herring on Map of Island

Stylised Norse Herring

Fuchsia

PENNY
Metal: Bronze up to 1995 then Bronze Plated Steel
Size: 20mm diameter

		Mintage	UNC
1971	Ring Chain Pattern	100,000	£2
1972		1,000	£25
1973		1,000	£25
1974		1,000	£25
1975		826,032	£1
1976	Loughtan Sheep on Map of Island	823,572	£1
1977		479,751	£1
1978		850,415	£1
1979		1,096,285	£1
1980	Tailless Manx Cat	593,401	£1
1981		224,126	£2
1982		324,440	£2
1983		447,820	£1
1984	Cormorant on Shield	406,858	£1
1985		25,000	£2
1986			£2
1987			£2
1988	Metalwork Lathe & Cog		£1
1989			£1
1990			£1
1991			£1
1992			£1
1993			£1
1994			£1
1995			£1
1996	Rugby Ball & Goal Posts		£1
1997			£1
1998			£1
1999			£1
2000	St. Michael's Chapel, Langness		£1
2001			£1
2002			£1
2003			£1
2004	Santon War Memorial		£1
2005			£1
2006			£1
2007			£1

Ring Chain Pattern

Loughtan Sheep on map

Tailless Manx Cat

Cormororant on Shield

Metalwork Lathe & Cog

Rugby Ball & Goal Posts

St. Michael's Chapel

Santon War Memorial

DATE	Mintage	UNC
2008		£1
2009		£1
2010		£1
2011		£1
2012		£1
2013		£1
2014		£1
2015		£1
2016		£1

Pennies are no longer minted for circulation in the Isle of Man.

Cast of Falcons

TWO PENCE

Metal: Bronze up to 1995 then Bronze Plated Steel
Size: 26mm diameter

DATE		Mintage	UNC
1971	Cast of Falcons	100,000	£3
1972		1,000	£30
1973		1,000	£30
1974		1,000	£30
1975		683,549	£1
1976	Manx Shearwater	875,146	£1
1977		458,089	£1
1978		620,695	£1
1979		602,593	£1
1980	Chough & Hiberno-Norse Bronze	569,993	£1
1981		172,170	£2
1982		236,376	£1
1983		371,735	£1
1984	Peregrine Falcon on Shield	178,296	£1
1985		25,000	£2
1986			£2
1987			£2
1988	Ancient Manx Crafts		£1
1989			£1
1990			£1
1991			£1
1992			£1
1993			£1
1994			£1
1995			£1
1996	Racing Pedal Cyclists		£1
1997			£1
1998			£1
1999			£1
2000	Manx Fishermens Evening Hymn		£1
2001			£1
2002			£1
2003			£1
2004	Albert Tower, Ramsey		£1
2005			£1
2006			£1
2007			£1
2008			£1
2009			£1
2010			£1
2011			£1
2012			£1
2013			£1
2014			£1
2015			£1
2016			£1

Two Pence coins are no longer minted for circulation in the Isle of Man.

*Peregrine Falcon
on Shield*

Ancient Manx Crafts

*Manx Fishermens
Evening Hymn*

Albert Tower, Ramsey

DATE Mintage UNC

FIVE PENCE

Metal: Cupro Nickel to 2016 then Nickel Plated Steel
Size: 23,5mm diameter up to 1989 then 18mm diameter from 1990

Date	Description	Mintage	UNC
1971	Tower of Refuge	100,000	£3
1972		1,000	£30
1973		1,000	£30
1974		1,000	£30
1975		1,017,103	£1
1976	Laxey Wheel on Map of Island	677,404	£1
1977		201,306	£2
1978		677,031	£1
1979		271,526	£2
1980	Loughtan Ram on Norse Brooch	403,296	£1
1981		67,289	£3
1982		405,381	£1
1983		137,365	£2
1984	Cushag & a la Bouche Shield	313,994	£1
1985		25,000	£3
1986			£2
1987			£2
1988	Windsurfer		£3
1989			£3
1990	Windsurfer (small diameter)		£1
1991			£1
1992			£1
1993			£1
1994	Golf Ball & Crossed Clubs		£3
1995			£3
1996	Golfer in Action		£2
1997			£2
1998			£2
1999			£2
2000	Gaut's Cross		£1
2001			£1
2002			£1
2003			£1
2004	Tower of Refuge, Douglas		£1
2005			£1
2006			£1
2007			£1
2008			£1
2009			£1
2010			£1
2011			£1
2012			£10
2013			£1
2014			£1
2015			£1
2016			£1
2017	Manx Shearwater in Flight	460,000	£1
2018		20,000	£2
2019		2,000	£5
2020		2,000	£5
2021			£5

Tower of Refuge

Laxey Wheel

Loughtan Ram

Golf Ball & Clubs

Gaut's Cross

Tower of Refuge

DATE	Mintage	UNC

TEN PENCE

Metal: Cupro Nickel to 2016 then Nickel Plated Steel
Size: 28mm diameter up to 1992 then 24,5mm diameter from 1992

Triskeles

Peregrine Falcon

Portcullis on Map

Triskeles

Chicken Rock Lighthouse

DATE		Mintage	UNC
1971	Triskeles (Three Legs oF Mann)	100,000	£3
1972		1,000	£30
1973		1,000	£30
1974		1,000	£30
1975		1,454,265	£1
1976	Triskeles on Map of Island	1,412,309	£1
1977		483,550	£1
1978		103,383	£2
1979		276,554	£2
1980	Peregrine Falcon	90,657	£3
1981		760,086	£1
1982		378,912	£2
1983		98,797	£3
1984	Loughtan Ram on Shield	289,789	£2
1985		25,000	£3
1986			£2
1987			£2
1988	Portcullis on Map of World		£3
1989			£3
1990			£3
1991			£20
1992			£15
1992	Triskeles (small diameter)		£1
1993			£10
1994			£10
1995			£10
1996	Sailing Boat		£5
1997			£5
1998			£3
1999			£5
2000	St. German's Cathedral, Peel		£2
2001			£2
2002			£2
2003			£2
2004	Chicken Rock Lighthouse		£2
2005			£2
2006			£2
2007			£2
2008			£2
2009			£2
2010			£2
2011			£2
2012			£15
2013			£2
2014			£2
2015			£2
2016			£2
2017	Manx Tailless Cat	220,000	£1
2018		20,000	£2
2019		720,000	£1
2020		500,000	£1
2021			£1

A comprehensive listing of all the coins and tokens produced for the Isle of Man, together with a detailed history and all recorded variations including die marks, can be found in the book *Coins of the Isle of Man* by Mike J. Southall. ISBN 9 780995 738720 third edition.

COINS
of the
ISLE OF MAN

by Mike J. Southall, MBE

This book contains a comprehensive history of coins used in the Isle of Man and a definitive study of Manx decimal coins that have been in circulation since 1971. Adding further interest, the die marks, mint marks, provenance marks, etc. found on the 1979–2016 Manx decimal coins are also included. A section listing the non-circulating, precious metal and bullion coins follows that of the circulating coins.

After John Murrey's first legal penny token of 1668, the first official Manx coins, halfpennies and pennies, were issued by the Lord of Mann, James Stanley 10th Earl of Derby. They were made legal tender by an Act of Tynwald on 24th June 1710. Manx coins, and a variety of tokens, were circulating on the Island until 1839. Thereafter British coins became the only legal currency until decimalisation in 1971.

This updated third edition book makes compelling reading and is a most useful and comprehensive reference work for anyone with the slightest interest in the coins of the Isle of Man.

ISBN 9 780995 738720 from Lily Publications Limited, PO Box 33, Ramsey, Isle of Man. IM99 4LP £29.95 plus postage.

DATE		Mintage	UNC

TWENTY PENCE
Metal: Cupro Nickel
Wider border with incuse lettering from 1993

Viking Arms

DATE		Mintage	UNC
1982	Viking Arms & Armour	824,892	£2
1983		115,610	£2
1984	Three Herrings on Shield	141,393	£2
1985		25,000	£3
1986			£3
1987			£3
1988	Combine Harvester		£3
1989			£2
1990			£2
1991			£2
1992			£2
1993			£3
1994			£2
1995			£3
1996	Rally Racing Car		£2
1997			£2
1998			£2
1999			£2
2000	Manx Bible at Rushen Abbey		£2
2001			£3
2002			£2
2003			£3
2004	Castle Rushen 1597 Clock		£2
2005			£2
2006			£2
2007			£2
2008			£2
2009			£2
2010			£2
2011			£2
2012			£15
2013			£2
2014			£2
2015			£2
2016			£2
2017	Sailing Viking Longship	281,250	£1
2018		262,500	£1
2019		937,500	£2
2020		625,000	£2
2021			£1

Three Herrings

Combine Harvester

Castle Rushen 1597 Clock

TOURIST TROPHY (TT) FIFTY PENCE
Metal: Cupro Nickel
Size: 30mm diameter up to 1997 then 27,3mm diameter from 1997

DATE		Mintage	UNC
1981	Joey Dunlop	30,000	£20
1982	Mick Grant	30,000	£20
1983	Ron Haslam	30,000	£20
1984	Mick Boddice	30,000	£20
1999	Leslie Graham	4,500	£50
2004	Tourist Trophy (TT)	3,000	£50
2007	Dave Molyneux and Sidecar	3,500	£30
2007	Tourist Trophy (TT)	3,500	£75
2009	John McGuinness	3,500	£40
2010	Suzuki Team Rider		£30
2011	Yamaha Motorcycle		£20
2012	Mark Cavendish Cyclist		£40
2012	Dave Knight Enduro Motorcyclist		£40
2014	John McGuinness Twenty TT Wins		£25
2015	TT Legends, TT Winners, Duke etc.		£15
2016	TT Legends, TT Winners, Dunlop etc.		£15

Joey Dunlop, TT Champion

Geoff Duke, etc. TT Legends

Regular circulating coins issued in 1996 to 1999 inclusive depict TT motorcyclist Phil McCallen. They were not part of the 50p series commemorating TT riders and events.

DATE		Mintage	UNC

FIFTY PENCE
Metal: Cupro Nickel
Size: 30mm diameter up to 1997 then 27,3mm diameter from 1997

Date	Description	Mintage	UNC
1971	Viking Longship	100,000	£3
1972		1,000	£30
1973		1,000	£30
1974		1,000	£30
1975		121,817	£1
1976	Viking Longship on Map	116,242	£1
1977		131,784	£1
1978		76,203	£2
1979		164,316	£1
1979	Odin's Raven Longship	100,000	£3
1979	Odin's Raven, Royal Visit (edge)	50,000	£4
1980	Odin's Raven, New York (edge)	20,000	£6
1980	Stylised Viking Longship	203,138	£1
1981		332,940	£1
1982		118,166	£2
1983		162,524	£2
1984	Viking Longship on Shield	282,567	£2
1985		25,000	£3
1986			£3
1987			£3
1988	Triskelion on Computer Screen		£5
1989			£10
1990			£15
1991			£30
1992			£30
1993			£30
1994			£40
1994	Tynwald Legislative Centenary	2,500	£20
1995	Triskelion on Computer Screen		£50
1996	TT Motorcycle Racing, Phil McCallen	6,000	£200
1997			£250
1997	As above but small 27,3mm diameter		£2
1998			£5
1999			£20
2000	Calf of Man Crucifixion Stone		£2
2001			£2
2002			£2
2003			£2
2004	Milner's Tower, Bradda Head		£2
2005			£2
2006			£2
2007			£2
2008			£2
2009			£2
2010			£2
2011			£2
2012			£25
2012	Queen's Diamond Jubilee		£10
2013	Milner's Tower, Bradda Head		£2
2014			£2
2015			£2
2016			£2
2017	Manx Loughton Sheep	325,000	£1
2018		200,000	£2
2019		937,500	£1
2020		375,000	£1

Viking Longship

*Viking Longship
on Shield*

*TT Motorcycle Racing
Phil McCallen*

*Calf of Man
Crucifixion Stone*

*Miner's Tower
Bradda Head*

DATE	Mintage	UNC

CHRISTMAS FIFTY PENCE
Metal: Cupro Nickel
Size: 30mm diameter up to 1997 then 27,3mm diameter from 1997

Date	Description	Mintage	UNC
1980	Steam Packet's Mona's Isle	30,000	£20
1981	Manx Nikki Fishing Boat	30,000	£10
1982	Carol Singers at Castletown	30,000	£25
1983	Model T Ford Car	30,000	£25
1984	Steam Engine No.1 Sutherland	50,000	£25
1985	De Haviland Rapide Aircraft	30,000	£25
1986	Douglas Corporation Horse Tram	30,000	£25
1987	Douglas Vosper Thorneycroft Bus	30,000	£25
1988	Motorcycle & Sidecar at Cregneash	30,000	£40
1989	Laxey Tram Station	50,000	£20
1990	Steam Packet's Lady of Mann	30,000	£30
1991	Nativity Scene	30,000	£30
1992	Manks Mercury Newspaper	30,000	£110
1993	St. Georges Stained Glass Window	30,000	£70
1994	Hunting the Wren	30,000	£125
1995	Snowball scene on S.M.R.	30,000	£115
1996	Choir Boys at Lonan Old Church	30,000	£80
1997	Thomas Edward Brown, Manx Poet	30,000	£55
1998	Victorian Manx Family Scene	30,000	£45
1999	Decorating Christmas Tree	30,000	£80
2000	Manx Bible at Rushen Abbey	30,000	£80
2001	Victorian Fluted Pillar Box	30,000	£50
2002	Charles Dickens Christmas Carol	30,000	£50
2003	The Snowman and James	10,000	£260
2004	The Great Laxey Wheel	30,000	£40
2005	12 Days of Christmas, Pear Tree	30,000	£120
2006	12 Days of Christmas, Turtle Doves	30,000	£100
2007	12 Days of Christmas, French Hens	30,000	£60
2008	12 Days of Christmas, Calling Birds	30,000	£50
2008	The Snowman and James	30,000	£310
2009	12 Days of Christmas, Gold Rings	30,000	£50
2010	12 Days of Christmas, Geese	30,000	£50
2011	Santa with Sack and Parcel	30,000	£50
2012	Christmas Angel	30,000	£35
2013	Christmas Stocking	30,000	£35
2014	Snowman and Snowdog	30,000	£35
2015	No issue	—	—
2016	Christmas Pudding	30,000	£15

Numbers of Christmas 50p coins circulated in the Isle of Man are usually around 5,000 and sometimes much less. The Christmas theme after 2016 was continued by the Tower Mint with £5 and £2 coins.

ONE POUND
Metal: Virenium to 1995. Nickel-Brass from 1996
Size: 22mm diameter x 1,5mm thick to 1982. 3mm thick from 1983 -

Date	Description	Mintage	UNC
1978	Triskeles on Map of Isle of Man	323,071	£3
1979		67,687	£5
1979	As above, X-oars Prov. Mark	1,000	£50
1980		78,288	£8
1980	As above, D.M.I.H.E. Prov. Mark	100,000	£15
1980	As above, D.M.I.H.E./N Prov. Mk.		£20
1980	As above, T.T. Prov. Mark		£10
1981		12,590	£8
1981	As above, I.I.H.E. Prov. Mark		£75
1982			£50
1982	As above, Baby Crib Prov. Mark		£25

1980 Mona's Isle Paddle Steamer

1984 Steam Engine No.1 Sutherland

1997 T. E. Brown Manx Poet

2003 The Snowman and James

Triskeles on Map

DATE		Mintage	UNC
1983	Town Arms—Peel	19,619	£5
1984	Town Arms—Castletown	25,000	£15
1985	Town Arms—Ramsey	25,000	£15
1986	Town Arms—Douglas		£20
1987	Viking on Horseback		£10
1988	Cellnet Telephone		£3
1989			£4
1990			£4
1991			£4
1992			£4
1993			£4
1994			£4
1995			£4
1996	Douglas Corporation Centenary		£8
1996	Cricket Stumps, Bat and Ball		£5
1997			£5
1998			£5
1999			£5
2000	Triskeles with Millennium Bells		£4
2001			£4
2002			£4
2003			£4
2004	Tynwald Hill and St.Johns Church		£3
2005			£3
2006			£3
2007			£3
2008			£3
2009			£3
2010			£3
2011			£3
2012			£3
2013			£3
2014			£3
2015			£3
2016			£3
2017	Manx Shearwater in Flight	460,000	£2
2018		20,000	£3
2019		2,000	£5
2020		2,000	£5
2021			£5

Town Arms Ramsey

Cellnet Telephone

Triskeles with Milennium Bells

Tynwald Hill and St. John's Church

The Isle of Man has retained the round pound but the UK dodecagonal coin is often seen alongside in circulation.

TWO POUNDS
Metal:Virenium up to 1997. Bi-metal Nickel-Brass / Cupro-Nickel 1997
Size: 28,4mm diameter

1986	Tower of Refuge (Metal: Virenium)	£15
1987		£15
1988	Manx Airlines BAe 146-100 Jet	£15
1989	Manx Airship Dirigible	£400
1990	Manx Airlines BAe 146-100 Jet	£15
1991		£15
1992		£20
1993		£20
1993	Nigel Mansell Formula 1	£30
1994	Nigel Mansell PPG Indi Car	£25
1995	Royal British Legion VE / VJ Day	£25
1996	E-Type Jaguar Racing (Virenium)	£25
1997		£25
1997	E-Type Jaguar Racing (Bi-Metal)	£5
1998		£5
1999		£10
2000	Thorwald's Cross, Andreas Church	£15

Manx Airlines BAe 145-100 Jet

DATE		Mintage	UNC
2001			£15
2002			£15
2003			£15
2004	Round Tower Peel Castle		£10
2005			£10
2006			£10
2007			£10
2008			£10
2009			£10
2010			£10
2011			£10
2011	Commonwealth Games, Tosha the Cat		£120
2012	Round Tower Peel Castle		£30
2013			£10
2014			£10
2015			£10
2016			£20
2017	Tower of Refuge	300,000	£4
2018		20,000	£8
2019		176,000	£5
2020		156,000	£5
2021			£5

E-Type Jaguar Racing Virenium version

E-Type Jaguar Racing Bi-metal version

FIVE POUNDS

Metal: Virenium up to 2016. Alpaca (nickel silver) from 2017
Size: 36mm diameter up to 2016. 32mm diameter from 2017

Year		Mintage	UNC
1981	Triskeles on Map of Isle of Man	22,414	£10
1982		1,075	£30
1983			1,473
			£25
1984			—
1984	Knight on Horseback	2,068	£25
1985		25,000	£20
1986			£25
1987			£25
1988	Peel Inshore Fishing Boat		£25
1989			£25
1990			£25
1991			£25
1992			£25
1993			£25
1993	Nigel Mansell, Formula 1		£35
1994	Nigel Mansell, PPG Indi Car		£30
1995	50 Years, End of World War II		£30
1996	Footballers Euro96		£30
1997	Footballers		£25
1997	Royal Golden Wedding Anniv.		£30
1998	Prince Charles 50th Birthday		£30
1998	Footballers		£25
1999			£25
1999	175th Anniversary of RLNI		£30
2000	St. Patrick's Hymn		£25
2001			£30
2002			£30
2003			£30
2004	The Great Laxey Wheel		£30
2005			£30
2006			£50
2007			£30
2008			£30
2009			£50
2010			£50

Knight on Horseback

Peel Inshore Fishing Boat

St. Patrick's Hymn

DATE		Mintage	UNC
2011	....		£50
2012	....		£70
2013	....		£50
2014	....		£50
2015	....		£30
2016	....		£40
2017	Manx Triskele Symbol................................	20,000	£15
2018	20,000		£25
2019	1,000		£35
2020	1,000		£35
2021	....		£35

The Great Laxey Wheel

ISLE OF MAN CROWNS

Isle of Man crowns minted from 1970 to 2016 have a face value of twenty five pence (25p) or five shillings (5/- 1970 pre-decimal issue). Manx Crowns were revalued at five pounds (£5) by the Isle of Man Government from 2017.

Crowns listed in this section are standard size coins 38.61mm diameter made of cupro-nickel (CuNi) and have a nominal value of 25p. Howsever, the supply and demand for these coins is very erratic according to the retail source, therefore it has been decided not to price them.

Many of these Crowns were also struck from precious metals such as Silver (Ag), Gold (Au), Platinum (Pt) and Palladium (Pd). There are also many odd-shaped Crowns and part Crowns issued in CuNi and various precious metals. Multiple Crown values also exist. These coins to detail individually are outside the scope of this Year Book but a selection is illustrated after this list.

A comprehensive listing of all the coins and tokens produced for the Isle of Man, together with a detailed history and all recorded variations including die marks, can be found in the book *Coins of the Isle of Man* by Mike J. Southall. ISBN 9 780995 738720 third edition.

DATE

1970 Manx Cat
1972 Royal Silver Wedding
1974 Centenary of Churchill's birth
1975 Manx Cat
1976 Bi-Centenary of American Independence
1976 Centenary of the Horse Drawn Tram
1977 Silver Jubilee
1977 Silver Jubilee Appeal
1978 25th Anniversary of the Coronation
1979 300th Anniversary of Manx Coinage
1979 Millennium of Tynwald (5 coins)
1980 22nd Olympics (3 coins)
1980 80th Birthday of Queen Mother
1980 Derby Bicentennial
1980 Winter Olympics—Lake Placid
1981 Duke of Edinburgh Award Scheme (4 coins)
1981 Prince of Wales' Wedding (2 coins)
1981 Year of Disabled (4 coins)
1982 12th World Cup—Spain (4 coins)
1982 Maritime Heritage (4 coins)
1983 Manned Flight (4 coins)
1984 23rd Olympics (4 coins)
1984 Commonwealth Parliamentary Conference (4 coins)
1984 Quincentenary of College of Arms (4 coins)
1985 Queen Mother (6 coins)
1986 13th World Cup—Mexico (6 coins)
1986 Prince Andrew Wedding (2 coins)
1987 200th Anniversary of the United States Constitution
1987 America's Cup Races (5 coins)
1988 Australia Bicentennial (6 coins)

DATE

1988 Bicentenary of Steam Navigation (6 coins)
1988 Manx Cat
1989 Queen Elizabeth II & Prince Philip Royal Visit
1989 Bicentenary of the Mutiny on the Bounty (4 coins)
1989 Bicentenary of Washington's Inauguration (4 coins)
1989 Persian Cat
1989 Royal Visit
1989 13th World Cup Mexico (2 coins)
1990 150th Anniversary of the Penny Black
1990 25th Anniversary of Churchill's Death (2 coins)
1990 Alley Cat
1990 Queen Mother's 90th Birthday
1990 World Cup—Italy (4 coins)
1991 1992 America's Cup
1991 Centenary of the American Numismatic Association
1991 Norwegian Forest Cat
1991 10th Anniversary of Prince of Wales' Wedding (2 coins)
1992 1992 America's Cup
1992 Discovery of America (4 coins)
1992 Siamese Cat
1993 Maine Coon Cat
1993 Preserve Planet Earth—Dinosaurs (2 coins)
1994 Japanese Bobtail Cat
1994 Normandy Landings (8 coins)
1994 Preserve Planet Earth—Endangered Animals (3 coins)
1994 Preserve Planet Earth—Mammoth
1994 World Football Cup (6 coins)
1994 Year of the Dog
1994 D-Day Normandy Landings (8 coins)
1994 Man in Flight—Series i (8 coins)
1995 Aircraft of World War II (19 coins)
1995 America's Cup
1995 Famous World Inventions—Series i (12 coins)
1995 Man in Flight—Series ii (8 coins)
1995 Preserve Planet Earth—Egret and Otter
1995 Queen Mother's 95th Birthday
1995 Turkish Cat
1995 Year of the Pig
1996 70th Birthday of HM the Queen
1996 Burmese Cat
1996 European Football Championships (8 coins)
1996 Explorers (2 coins)
1996 Famous World Inventions—Series ii (6 coins)
1996 Football Championships Winner
1996 King Arthur & the Knights of the Round Table (5 coins)
1996 Olympic Games (6 coins)
1996 Preserve Planet Earth—Killer Whale and Razorbill (2 coins)
1996 Robert Burns (4 coins)
1996 The Flower Fairies—Series i (4 coins)
1996 Year of the Rat
1997 10th Anniversary of the "Cats on Coins" series (silver only)
1997 Royal Golden Wedding
1997 90th Anniversary of the TT Races (4 coins)
1997 Explorers—Eriksson and Nansen (2 coins)
1997 Long-haired Smoke Cat
1997 Royal Golden Wedding (2 coins)
1997 The Flower Fairies—Series ii (4 coins)
1997 Year of the Ox
1998 The Millennium (4 coins)
1998 125th Anniversary of Steam Railway (8 coins)
1998 18th Winter Olympics, Nagano (4 coins)
1998 Birman Cat
1998 Explorers—Vasco da Gama and Marco Polo (2 coins)
1998 FIFA World Cup (4 coins)
1998 International Year of the Oceans (4 coins)
1998 The Flower Fairies—Series iii (4 coins)
1998 The Millennium (16 coins issued over 3 years)
1998 Year of the Tiger
1999 The Millennium (4 coins)

DATE

1999 27th Olympics in Sydney (5 coins)
1999 Rugby World Cup (6 coins)
1999 The Millennium (4 coins)
1999 Titanium Millennium crown
1999 Wedding of HRH Prince Edward and Sophie Rhys-Jones
1999 Year of the Rabbit
2000 The Millennium (4 coins)
2000 Millennium Intertwined MM (Issued to every Manx school child)
2000 18th Birthday of HRH Prince William
2000 60th Anniversary of the Battle of Britain
2000 BT Global Challenge
2000 Explorers, Francisco Piarro and Wilem Brents (2 coins)
2000 Life and times of the Queen Mother (4 coins)
2000 Millennium—own a piece of time
2000 Queen Mother's 100th Birthday
2000 Scottish Fold cat
2000 Year of the Dragon
2001 75th Birthday of HM the Queen
2001 Explorers, Martin Frobisher and Roald Amundsen (2 coins)
2001 Harry Potter (6 coins)
2001 Joey Dunlop
2001 Life and times of the Queen Mother (2 coins)
2001 The Somali cat
2001 Year of the Snake
2002 A Tribute to Diana Princess of Wales—5 years on
2002 Introduction of the Euro
2002 The Bengal Cat
2002 The Queen's Golden Jubilee—i (1 coin)
2002 The Queen's Golden Jubilee—ii (4 coins)
2002 The XIX Winter Olympiad, Salt Lake City (2 coins)
2002 World Cup 2002 in Japan/Korea (4 coins)
2002 Year of the Horse
2003 Golden Coronation Jubilee
2003 XII Olympic Games 2004 (4 coins)
2003 Anniversary of the "Star of India"
2003 Lord of the Rings (5 coins)
2003 Prince William's 21st Birthday
2003 The Balinese Cat
2003 Year of the Goat
2004 Year of the Monkey
2004 100 Years of Powered Flight (2 coins)
2004 Olympics (4 coins)
2004 Ten New EU Entries
2004 Harry Potter—Prisoner of Azkaban
2004 Queen Mary 2—World's Largest Passenger Liner
2004 D-Day Re-enactment—Parachute Jump
2004 Football, Euro 2004 (2 coins)
2004 Lord of the Rings—Return of the King
2004 Tonkinese Cats
2004 Battle of Trafalgar
2004 60th Anniversary of D-Day (6 coins)
2005 60th Anniversary of Peace (coins as 2004 D-Day) (6 coins)
2005 60th Anniversary of Victory in Europe
2005 Bicentenary of the Battle of Trafalgar (6 coins)
2005 175th Anniversary of Isle of Man Steam Packet (2 coins)
2005 400th Anniversary of the Gunpowder Plot (2 coins)
2005 Bicentenary of Hans Christian Andersen
2005 Harry Potter and the Goblet of Fire (4 coins)
2005 Italy and the Isle of Man TT races (2 coins)
2005 Manx Hero Lt. John Quilliam (2 coins)
2005 The Himalayan Cat with kittens
2005 Bicentenary of the Battle of Trafalgar (6 coins)
2006 150th Anniversary of the Victoria Cross (2 coins)
2006 30th Anniversary of the first Translantic Flight
2006 80th Birthday of Her Majesty the Queen (4 coins)
2006 The Battles that Changed the World—Part II (6 coins)
2006 Transatlantic Flight (2 coins)
2006 Exotic Short Hair Cat
2006 World Cup FIFA 2006

DATE

2006 Queen's Beasts
2006 Fairy Tales (2 coins)
2006 Aircraft of World War II—Spitfire
2006 The Battles that Changed the World—Part I (6 coins)
2007 The Tales of Peter Rabbit
2007 Fairy Tales (3 coins)
2007 The Centenary of the Scouting
2007 The Centenary of the TT races (5 coins)
2007 The Graceful Swan
2007 The Ragdoll Cat
2007 The Royal Diamond Wedding Anniversary (4 coins)
2008 50th Anniversary of Paddington Bear
2008 Burmilla Cat
2008 Prince Charles 60th Birthday
2008 The Adorable Snowman
2008 The Return of Tutankhamun (2 coins)
2008 UEFA European Football Championships
2008 Year of Planet Earth
2008 Olympics China (6 coins)
2009 40th Anniversary of the 1st Concorde Test Flight
2009 Fifa World Cup South Africa 2010
2009 The Chinchilla Cat
2009 Winter Olympics (2 coins)
2009 500th Anniversary of Henry VIII (2 coins)
2009 BeeGees—Freedom of Douglas
2009 Fall of the Berlin Wall
2009 40th Anniversary of the First Man on the Moon
2009 Olympics 2012 (6 coins)
2010 Olympics 2012 (6 coins)
2010 Vancouver Olympics 2010 (2 coins)
2010 Buckingham Palace
2010 Abyssinian Cat and her Kitten
2011 A Lifetime of Service—Queen Elizabeth II and Prince Philip
2011 Buckingham Palace
2011 Royal Wedding of HRH Prince William and Catherine Middleton
2011 The Turkish Angora Cat
2011 TT Mountain Course 100 years
2011 Year of the Rabbit
2012 Life of Queen Elizabeth II (2 coins)
2012 Centenary of RMS *Titanic* (2 coins)
2012 European Football Championships (4 coins)
2012 Juno Moneta Coin
2012 Manx Cat Coin
2012 Olympics (6 coins).
2012 River Thames Diamond Jubilee Pageant
2013 Anniversary of Queen Victoria and Queen Elizabeth II Coronations
2013 Kermode Bear
2013 60th Anniversary of Coronation
2013 Siberian Cat
2013 St. Patrick Commemorative
2013 Winter Olympic (4 coins)
2014 Centenary of WWI (2 coins). Coloured Silver Proof.
2014 200th Anniversary of Matthew Flinders
2014 70th Anniversary of D-Day (3 coins)
2014 Snowman and Snow Dog Crown (£5)
2014 Snowshoe Cat
201 Snow Dog
2014 Winter Olympic Games (4 Coin Collection)
2015 175th Anniversary of the Penny Black Stamp (issued in a pack)
2015 200th Anniversary of the Battle of Waterloo—Napoleon
2015 200th Anniversary of the Battle of Waterloo—Wellington
2015 75th Anniversary of the Battle of Britain (search lights in yellow)
2015 Her Majesty the Queen Elizabeth II Longest reigning Monarch
2015 Paddington Bear
2015 Selkirk Rex Cat
2015 Sir Winston Churchill
2016 90th Birthday Queen Elizabeth II
2016 Tobacco Brown Cat

Tower Mint has produced commemorative
crowns from 2017 with a nominal value of £5.

CROWNS FROM THE TOWER MINT

Crowns listed in this section are standard size coins 38.61mm diameter made of cupro-nickel (CuNi) and have a nominal value of £5.Some of these Crowns were also struck from precious metals such as Silver (Ag) and/or Gold (Au) and a few issues were minted piedfort.

2017 Duke of Edinburgh 70 Years of Service
2017 Platinum Wedding Anniversary
2017 Viking Scenes (*CuNi Antique silver plate finish*) (5 coins)
2017 Centenary of the House of Windsor (*CuNi gold plated*)
2017 Sapphire Wedding of Her Majesty and Prince Philip
2018 60th Anniversary of Queen Elizabeth II Coronation
2019 Centenary of the First Man on the Moon
2019 200th Anniversary of the Birth of Queen Victoria (3 coins)
2022 Isle of Man TT Races

Other Crowns Minted only in Precious Metals:
2018 World War I Armistice Centenary (poppies in red and black) *Ag*
2018 Birth of Prince Louis Arthur Charles. *Ag*
2020 Manx Wildlife Series Part I. *Ag, Au*

Coins with High Denominations have also been minted:
2017 £10 King Canute (*Ag with antique finish*)
2018 £10 WWI Armistice Centenary (poppies in red and black) *Ag*
2019 £10 50th Anniversary of the Moon Landing *Ag*
2018 £50 World War I Armistice Centenary (poppies in red) *Ag*
2019 £100 Age of the Vikings (*Ag with antique finish*)

*60th Anniversary of
Queen Elizabeth II Coronation*

*Viking Scenes (CuNi Antique
silver plate finish) (5 coins)*

*Centenary of the First Man
on the Moon*

TT Races

*Centenary of the House of
Windsor (CuNi gold plated)*

ODD SIZE AND IRREGULAR SHAPED CROWNS

Many odd shaped Crowns have been produced by the Pobjoy Mint and a representative selection is illustrated here. A variety of metals, from cupro-nickel, silver, gold, platinum and palladium have been used in the minting of these coins. Parts and multiples of a Crown struck in precious metals also exist. Denominations that exist for some Crown issues are 1/64 Crown, 1/32 Crown, 1/25 Crown, 1/20 Crown, 1/10 Crown, 1/5 Crown, 1/4 Crown, 1/2 Crown, 2 Crowns, 5 Crowns, 10 Crowns, 13 Crowns, 32 Crowns, 64 Crowns, 100 Crowns and 130 Crowns. Coins illustrated here are not to scale.

NOTABLE MANX FIRSTS

*Golden Jubilee of Queen Elizabeth II 2002
3kg .9999 fine silver*

*2010 750th Anniv. of
Mongol ruler Kublai Khan*

*1978 World's
First £1 Coin*

*2012 Queen's Diamond
Jubilee. ½ Crown silver*

2009 Terracotta Army - 1/5 Crown

*1990 First Black Coin
Penny Black
Anniversary*

1 crown

*2008 Tutankhamun's Death Mask
½ Crown. Fine 999.9 gold.*

*Commemorating the 2008 - 09
Tutankhamun Exhibition in London*

*1999 First White Gold
Coins 1/25, 1/10, 1/5
and 1/2 Platina*

*Tower Mint
Crown (£5)*

2019 Manannan - First King of Mann. 99.9% Silver Crown.

*2002 First Spinning Coin
Currency Converter*

COINS OF OTHER DENOMINATIONS

SOVEREIGNS, PARTS & MULTIPLES

Isle of Man sovereigns, multiples and parts were minted in gold in certain years between the years 1965 and 1993. Sovereigns were of standard imperial size, contained between 91.6% and 99.9% gold and depicted a Viking in armour on horseback.

The 1965 gold coins (Five, One and Half Sovereign) to mark the bicentenary of the Act of Revestment are 98% (23.5ct). They were also minted in 91.7% (22ct) gold.

Sovereigns in 99.99 gold were again minted from 2019 by the Tower Mint in London.

The "ace value"of a sovereign is one pound sterling (£1) but its intrinsic or bullion value is much greater owing to the value of its metal content.

ANGELS, PARTS & MULTIPLES

In addition to the Sovereign, bullion coinage has been issued in several different denominations, viz. Angels and Nobles. Bullion coins are legal tender and their face value is equal to the current market or bullion value of the metal content in the coins.

The Angel was launched in the Isle of Man for legal tender status purposes on 13th March 1985. However, a token issue of the 1oz gold Angels dated 1984 were struck by the Pobjoy Mint and sent to the United States for 'test marketing' ahead of the official release by the Isle of Man Treasury.

Pobjoy Mint produced Angels until 2016 when Tower Mint continued the series in 2017.

The reverse of the Angel coin depicts the Archangel Michael slaying the Dragon. The series of Christmas 1/20 Angels have been struck in fine gold and others in 22ct. gold and many also exist as proof coins.

NOBLES, PARTS & MULTIPLES

The first Manx 1 Noble coin was issued in 1983 followed by the 1/10 Noble in 1984. The latter was known then as a 'Noblette'. Pobjoy Mint produced Nobles periodically until 2016 when the Tower Mint continued the series in 2017.

The reverse of the Noble coin depicts the Viking Ship 'Thusly' in full sail. Nobles have been struck in fine gold and others in gold and platinum. Proof coins exist for some issues.

A full listing of crowns, with their multiples and parts and a full listing of Angel and Noble coins, with their multiples and parts, can be found in the book *Coins of the Isle of Man* by Mike J. Southall. ISBN 9 780995 738720 third edition.

TOWER MINT CIRCULATING COIN DESIGNS

No Isle of Man **One Penny** or **Two Pence** coins have been produced by the Tower Mint. All 1p and 2p coins from 1971 to 2016 inclusive remain legal tender on the island and circulate with their UK equivalents.

Jody Clark's portrait of Her Majesty the Queen was adopted for use on coins of the Commonwealth countries, including the Isle of Man, and this effigy was first used by the Tower Mint from 2017 for Manx coins. These coins from the Tower MInt are included in the general list of Manx Decimal Coins from 1971.

The **five pence** (5p) design depicts the Manx Shearwater, a medium-sized sea bird of the family *Procellaridae*. It is an amber-listed species of particular conservation concern in the Isle of Man. It is found around the cliffs on the east coast and on the Calf of Man.

The **ten pence** (10p) design depicts the famous Manx tailless cat with its most distinguishing characteristics of its elongated hind legs and rounded head. Manx cats are best known as being entirely tailless and are affectionately called a "rumpy", but some have a small stub of a tail and they are known as a "stumpy".

The **twenty pence** (20p) design depicts a typical sailing Viking longship. The Isle of Man has a significant Viking heritage, particularly with the Viking longship *Odin's Raven*, a replica of which is in the House of Mannan at Peel.

The **fifty pence** (50p) design shows the famous breed of Manx Loaghtan sheep native to the Isle of Man. The sheep, which has dark brown wool, is depicted full-face with its characteristic four horns.

The **one pound** (£1) design depicts a Pergrine Falcon and a Raven. The Isle of Man was granted a coat-of-arms by Queen Elizabeth II in 1966 in which the two birds are shown. They are both symbolically associated with the island.

The **two pounds** (£2) design depicts the Tower of Refuge, an important landmark built on Conister Rock in Douglas Bay. It was built in 1832 by Sir William Hilary, founder of the Royal National Lifeboat Institution, who lived at Fort Anne overlooking Douglas Bay.

The **five pounds** (£5) design depicts the famous Triskelion or Triskele, symbol of the Isle of Man. It is based on the Manx coat-of-arms, dating back to the 13th century. The three legs are known in Manx as "ny tree cassyn".

The Tower Mint produces commemorative coins for general circulation at appropriate intervals. In addition, coins are also minted in various precious metals. Bullion coins in precious metals have also been minted.

COMMEMORATIVE CIRCULATING COINS
FROM THE TOWER MINT

Quantities shown as "No. Minted" are for coins circulated in the Isle of Man, where known.

DATE	No. Minted	UNC

FIFTY PENCE

2017 150th Anniversary of House of Keys	33,000	£3
2018 Platinum Wedding Queen & Prince Philip (8 coins) .... each design	2,500	£30
2018 Sapphire Coronation of Her Majesty QEII (5 coins) .... each design	2,500	£25
2018 Centenary of World War I Armistice, Plain.....................	25,000	£3
2018 Centenary of World War I Armistice, Coloured..............	15,000	£10
Coloured coins were given to all school pupils.		
2019 ICC Cricket World Cup (5 coins).............. each design	12,000	£20
2019 Peter Pan, Part I (6 coins)........................... each design	25,000	£20
2020 75th Anniversary of VE Day—Individual letters spelling "VICTORY" on 7 coin designs.	25,000	£25
2020 Rupert Bear (5 coins)................................. each design	25,000	£30
2020 Peter Pan, Part 2 (6 coins)........................ each design	25,000	£30
2021 Alice in Wonderland (5 Coins) .... each design	10,000	£30
2021 HM Queen 95th Birthday (6 coins) .... each design	10,000	£30
2021 Alice through the Looking Glass (5 coins)		£30
2021 Prince Philip in Memoriam		£10
2021 Prince Philip in Memoriam (6 coins)		£120
2022 HM Queen's Platinum Jubilee (5 coins).....................................		£30

TWO POUNDS

2018 Prince Harry & Meghan Markle Wedding	2,500	£5
2018 Mike Hailwood, TT 40 Years	15,000	£5
2018 Mike Hailwood, TT 60 Years	15,000	£5
2018 Christmas, Hunt the Wren	10,000	£6
2019 D-Day, King George VI	2,500	£8
2019 D-Day, Winston Spencer Churchill	2,500	£8
2019 D-Day, Field Marshall Montgomery	2,500	£8
2019 Steve Hislop's 120mph TT Lap......................................	15,000	£5
2019 Steve Hislop's 11 TT Wins...	12,500	£5
2019 Father Christmas	12,500	£6
2020 Operation Dynamo. 80th Anniversary (2 coins) .... each design	3,000	£15
2020 Dickens Christmas (3 coins) .... each design	3,500	£15
2020 Mayflower 400th Anniversary .... each design	3,500	£10
2021 Pioneering Women's Suffrage (4 coins)................................	—	£30
2021 Remembrance Day (2 coins)	—	£15
2021 Christmas "Nollick Ghennal"	—	£10
2022 Isle of Man TT Races (2 coins)	—	£20

FIVE POUNDS

2017 110 Years of the Tourist Trophy	20,000	£20
2017 Christmas - Dove of Peace..	10,000	£25

GUERNSEY

DATE	F	VF	EF	UNC

TEN SHILLINGS

1966	—	£5	£10	£15
1966 Proof	—	—	—	£35

THREEPENCE

1956	£1	£4	£8	£10
1956 Proof	—	—	—	£15
1959	£1	£4	£8	£15
1966 Proof	—	—	—	£15

EIGHT DOUBLES

1834	£10	£15	£65	£250
1858 5 berries	£6	£10	£50	£150
1858 4 berries	£6	£10	£55	£175
1864 1 stalk	£6	£10	£40	£75
1864 3 stalks	£6	£10	£45	£85
1868	£6	£10	£30	£75
1874	£4	£6	£20	£55
1885H	£4	£6	£20	£50
1889H	£3	£4	£20	£45
1893H small date	£3	£4	£20	£45
1893H large date	£3	£4	£20	£50
1902H	£3	£4	£20	£45
1903H	£3	£4	£20	£45
1910	£3	£4	£20	£45
1911H	£3	£4	£20	£50
1914H	£1	£3	£10	£35
1918H	£1	£3	£8	£25
1920H	£1	£3	£8	£25
1934H	£1	£3	£10	£35
1934H Proof	—	—	—	£275
1938H	£1	£3	£10	£25
1945H	£1	£2	£8	£15
1947H	£1	£2	£8	£15
1949H	—	£2	£10	£18
1956	—	£1	£7	£15
1956	—	£1	£5	£15
1959	—	£1	£5	£15
1966 Proof	—	—	—	£35

FOUR DOUBLES

1830	£4	£10	£55	£165
1830 Mule with obv. St Helena 1/2d	—	£850	—	—
1858	£6	£15	£55	£150
1864 Single stalk	£2	£6	£20	£65
1864 3 stalks	£2	£6	£25	£75
1868	£3	£7	£22	£75
1874	£2	£6	£22	£75
1885H	£2	£6	£20	£45
1889H	£2	£3	£15	£35
1893H	£2	£3	£15	£35
1902H	£2	£3	£10	£30
1903H	£2	£3	£13	£30
1906H	£2	£3	£10	£25
1908H	£2	£3	£10	£25
1910H	£2	£3	£10	£25
1911H	£2	£3	£8	£25
1914H	£2	£3	£15	£50
1918H	£2	£3	£12	£35
1920H	£2	£3	£10	£35
1945H	£2	£3	£10	£35
1949H	£2	£3	£12	£35
1956	£1	£2	£8	£15
1966 Proof	—	—	—	£25

DATE	F	VF	EF	UNC
TWO DOUBLES				
1858..	£6	£10	£50	£265
1868 Single stick	£6	£12	£55	£265
1868 3 stalks	£7	£15	£85	£275
1874...	£4	£12	£75	£175
1885H...	£3	£6	£20	£35
1889H...	£3	£5	£20	£35
1899H...	£3	£5	£25	£50
1902H...	£3	£5	£20	£35
1903H...	£3	£5	£20	£35
1906H...	£3	£5	£20	£35
1908H...	£3	£5	£20	£35
1911H...	£3	£5	£25	£45
1914H...	£3	£5	£25	£45
1917H...	£7	£25	£95	£275
1918H...	£3	£5	£15	£35
1920H...	£3	£5	£15	£35
1929H...	£2	£5	£12	£30

	F	VF	EF	UNC
ONE DOUBLE				
1830...	£3	£5	£25	£55
1868...	£4	£12	£55	£175
1868/30	£5	£7	£35	£100
1885H...	£2	£5	£15	£35
1889H...	£1	£3	£8	£25
1893H...	£1	£3	£8	£25
1899H...	£1	£3	£8	£25
1902...	£1	£3	£8	£25
1903H...	£1	£3	£8	£25
1911H...	£1	£4	£10	£35
1911 (new shield)	£1	£3	£8	£25
1914H	£1	£4	£10	£25
1929H...	£1	£3	£6	£25
1933H...	£1	£3	£6	£25
1938H...	£1	£3	£6	£25

DECIMAL COINAGE

Ordinary circulating coinage from 1986 onwards is usually available in uncirculated condition at a small premium above face value thus it is not listed here. The coins listed are cupro-nickel unless otherwise stated. The coins listed are cupro-nickel unless otherwise stated.

	UNC
ONE HUNDRED POUNDS	
1994 50th Anniversary of Normandy Landings. Gold proof....................	£1650
1995 Anniversary of the Liberation. Gold proof	£1650
FIFTY POUNDS	
1994 50th Anniversary of Normandy Landings. Gold proof....................	£1250
1995 Anniversary of the Liberation. Gold proof	£1250
1998 Queen Elizabeth and Queen Mother Gold proof............................	£1250
1999 Queen Elizabeth and Queen Mother Gold	£1250
2004 Anniversary of D-Day. Gold	£1250
2013 70th Anniversary of the Dambuster Raid. Silver proof 10oz	£350
2015 Magna Carta 800th anniversary. Silver proof 10oz	£350
2016 Her Majesty the Queen's 90th Birthday. Gold Proof	£13,000
TWENTY-FIVE POUNDS (x22mm gold)	
1994 50th Anniversary of Normandy Landings. Gold	£400
1994 — Gold proof...	£450
1995 Anniversary of the Liberation. Gold proof	£450
1995 Queen Mothers 95th Birthday. Gold...	£400
1996 European Football Championships. Gold proof..............................	£450
1997 Royal Golden Wedding. Gold proof	£450
1998 Royal Air Force. Gold proof..	£450
2000 Queen Mother 100th Birthday. Gold proof....................................	£450
2001 Queen Victoria centennial Gold proof	£450
2001 Queen Victoria Gold proof..	£450

> In recent years a number of companies have been involved in marketing the coins of the Channel Islands. As a consequence many special limited edition commemorative coins have been issued in a wide variety of sizes, metals and finishes. These are very numerous with some issues being produced in very small numbers and many are omitted from our listings. These issues are generally outside of the scope of this catalogue.

DATE	UNC
2001 HM the Queen's 75th Birthday. Gold proof	£450
2002 Princess Diana memorial. Gold proof	£ 450
2002 Duke of Wellington. Gold proof	£450
2002 Golden Jubilee. Gold proof	£450
2002 Queen Mother. Gold proof	£450
2003 Golden Jubilee. Gold proof	£450
2003 Golden Hind. Gold proof	£450
2004 Anniversary of D-Day. Gold proof	£450
2004 Age of Steam—Truro. Gold proof	£450
2004 Age of Steam—Mallard. Gold proof	£450
2004 HMS Invincible. Gold proof	£450
2005 HMS Ark Royal. Gold proof	£450
2006 FIFA World Cup. Gold proof	£450

TEN POUNDS

1994 50th Anniversary of Normandy Landings. Gold proof	£350
1995 Anniversary of the Liberation. Gold proof	£350
1997 Royal Golden wedding. 5oz Silver proof	£250
2000 Century of Monarchy. 5oz Silver proof	£250
2000 Guernsey Gold proof "Nugget"	£350
2001 19th Century Monarchy. Silver proof	£150
2002 18th Century Monarchy. Silver proof	£150
2003 1700 Years of Monarchy. Silver proof	£150
2004 16th Century Monarchy. Silver proof	£150
2004 Anniversary of D-Day. Silver proof	£150
2004 150th anniversary of the Crimean War. 5oz Gold proof	£8000
2005 Return of the Islanders. Silver proof	£50
2005 — 5oz Gold proof	£8000
2005 Anniversary of Trafalgar. 5oz Gold proof	£8000
2005 End of World War II. Silver proof	£25
2005 — 5oz Gold proof	£8000
2005 — 5oz Platinum proof	£8250
2009 Anniversary of Moon Landing. Silver proof	£75
2009 — 5oz Gold proof	£8000
2012 Diamond Jubilee. 5oz Silver proof	£250
2013 Coronation Jubilee. 5oz Silver proof	£250
2015 Reflections of the Reign 5oz gold proof	£8000
2017 Sapphire Jubilee. 5oz Silver proof	£450
2017 The House of Windsor. 5oz Silver proof	£450
2018 RAF Centenary 5oz Silver proof	£450
2019 200th Anniversary of Queen Victoria birth. 5oz Silver Proof, Gold detail	£550
2022 Alexander Graham Bell Silver Proof 5oz	£545

FIVE POUNDS

1995 Queen Mother's 95th birthday	£25
1995 — Silver proof	£55
1995 — Small size Gold	£350
1996 HM the Queen's 70th birthday	£20
1996 — Silver proof	£55
1996 European Football Championships	£15
1996 — Silver proof	£25
1997 Royal Golden Wedding	£15
1997 — Silver proof	£25
1997 — Small size Gold. BU	£350
1997 Castles of the British Isles—Castle Cornet, Guernsey	£15
1997 — Silver proof	£25
1997 Castles of the British Isles—Caernarfon Castle. Silver proof	£30
1997 Castles of the British Isles—Leeds Castle. Silver proof	£30
1998 Royal Air Force.	£15
1998 Royal Air Force. Silver proof	£30
1999 Millennium. Brass	£15
1999 — Silver proof	£25
1999 Wedding of HRH Prince Edward and Sophie Rhys-Jones	£15
1999 — Silver proof	£25
1999 Queen Mother	£25
1999 — Silver proof	£80
1999 Winston Churchill	£15

DATE	UNC
1999 — 1oz Gold	£1800
2000 Queen Mother's 100th Birthday	£10
2000 — Silver proof	£85
2000 — Small size Gold proof	£375
2000 Centuries of the British Monarchy	£45
2000 — Silver proof	£85
2000 — Small size Gold proof	£375
2001 The Reign of Queen Victoria	£20
2001 — proof	£60
2001 — Silver proof	£60
2001 — Gold proof	£400
2001 HM the Queen's 75th Birthday	£15
2001 — Silver proof	£25
2001 — Small size Gold proof	£3750
2001 19th Century Monarchy	£20
2001 — Silver proof	£25
2001 — Small size Gold proof	£375
2002 Golden Jubilee (two types)	£15
2002 — Silver proof	£25
2002 Princess Diana Memorial	£15
2002 — proof	£35
2002 — Gold proof	£1500
2002 Century of Monarchy	£15
2002 — Silver proof	£35
2002 — Small size Gold proof	£350
2002 Queen Mother Memoriam	£15
2002 — proof	£20
2002 — Silver proof	£35
2002 — Small size Gold proof	£350
2002 — Large size Gold proof	£1500
2003 Duke of Wellington	£15
2003 — Silver proof	£25
2003 — Small size Gold proof	£350
2003 — Large size Gold proof	£1500
2003 Prince William	£20
2003 — Silver proof	£35
2003 — Gold proof	£1500
2003 Golden Hind	£20
2003 17th Century Monarchy	£20
2003 History of the Royal Navy, Nelson	£20
2003 — Nelson with coloured flag proof	£25
2004 — Invincible. Silver proof	£30
2004 16th Century monarchs	£15
2004 History of the Railways, Mallard	£12
2004 — City of Truro	£15
2004 — The Boat Train	£12
2004 — The Train Spotter	£15
2004 History of the Royal Navy, Henry VIII	£15
2004 — Invincible	£15
2004 Anniversary of D-Day	£12
2004 — Silver proof	£25
2004 — Gold proof	£1500
2004 Anniversary of the Crimean War. Plain	£12
2004 — with colour	£15
2004 — Silver proof	£25
2004 — Gold proof with colour	£1500
2005 200th Anniversary of the Battle of Trafalgar	£20
2005 60th Anniversary of the Liberation of the Channel Islands	£20
2005 End of World War II. Silver proof	£25
2005 — Gold proof	£1500
2005 Anniversary of Liberation. Gold proof	£1500
2006 Royal 80th Birthday. Silver proof	£25
2006 FIFA World Cup. Silver proof	£25
2006 Great Britons—Sir Winston Churchill Silver. Issued as part of set.	£60
2006 80th Birthday of Her Majesty the Queen	£20
2007 History of the Royal Navy—Henry VIII, The Golden Hind (2 coins). ea.	£65
2007 Royal Diamond Wedding	£20

Note: Many of these issues have also been produced in different metals and finishes to those listed here.

DATE	UNC
2008 90th Anniversary of the RAF (10 designs in silver proof)........... ea.	£35
2009 British Warships (6 designs in silver proof) .... ea.	£35
2009 Anniversary of Apollo Moon landings. Cu-ni	£5
2009 — Silver proof	£35
2010 Charles II Unite. Gold proof	£1750
2010 Florence Nightingale. Gold proof	£1750
2010 Battle of Britain 70th anniversary. Silver and coloured	£55
2011 350th Anniversary of the Crown Jewels. Silver proof.....................	£95
2011 90th Anniversary of the British Legion (Gold-plated copper)...........	£45
2011 — Silver proof...	£95
2011 40th Anniversary of decimalisation proof......................................	£20
2011 Anniversary of the sinking of the *Titanic*	£20
2011 — Silver proof...	£55
2011 30th Birthday of Duke of Cambridge...	£20
2011 — Silver proof...	£55
2011 Wedding of Prince William and Kate Middleton..............................	£25
2011 — Silver proof...	£55
2011 400th Anniversary of the King James Bible	£25
2012 Diamond Jubilee £5...	£25
2012 — Gold proof...	£1750
2012 Tribute to the British Army. Gold proof..	£2000
2013 70th Anniversary of the Dambuster Raid.	£20
2013 — Silver proof...	£65
2013 — Gold proof...	£2000
2013 Coronation Jubilee	£25
2013 — Silver proof...	£55
2013 — Gold proof...	£2000
2013 200th Guinea Anniversary	£25
2013 — Silver proof	£55
2013 — Gold proof...	£2000
2014 Centenary of the First World War. Silver proof	£85
2014 — 5oz Silver proof...	£450
2014 — Gold proof...	£2500
2015 VE Day 70th Anniversary	£15
2015 Magna Carta 800th anniversary	£15
2016 90th Birthday of HM the Queen BU	£15
2016 — Silver Proof	£75
2016 Battle of the Somme..	£12
2016 Battle of Hastings Anniversary	£15
2017 Sapphire Jubilee. Silver plated..	£10
2017 Prince Philip Years of Service (only available in 3-coin set)	£20
2017 70th Royal Wedding Anniversary Silver proof	£75
2018 Centenary of WWI	£15
2018 — Silver proof	£75
2018 Prince Harry Royal Wedding Silver proof	£75
2018 65th Coronation Jubilee Silver proof..	£75
2018 Prince of Wales 70th Birthday. Cu-Ni with gold ink	£25
2018 — Silver proof...	£85
2018 — 5oz Silver Proof...	£500
2019 The King's Speech Outbreak of WWII 80th anniversary Silver proof	£85
2019 — Silver Proof 5oz...	£495
2019 75th Anniversary of D-Day. Cu-Ni with gold ink..............................	£25
2019 — Coloured BU	£15
2019 Remembrance Poppy..	£5
2020 Battle of Britain 80th Anniversary. BU	£12
2020 — Gold Plated Proof	£40
2020 — 3 coin sets. Silver Proof...	£270
2020 VE Day	£12
2020 75th Anniversary of the Liberation of the CI...................................	£12
2020 —date stamped pair...	£40
2020 Florence Nightingale Bicentenary	£25
2020 — Silver Proof	£85
2020 — 5oz Silver Proof...	£495
2020 — Gold Proof...	£2750
2021 Queen Elizabeth II 95th Birthday BU..	£15
2021 — Silver Proof	£75
2021 50 years of Decimalisation	£15

DATE	UNC

2021 — Silver Proof with selected gold plating £75
2022 40th Birthday of the Duke of Cambridge proof £25
2022 — Gold proof... £3400
2022 — Silver proof.. £95
2022 — Silver proof Gold detail £545
2022 70th Anniversary Accession of Queen Elizabeth II proof £29
2022 Alexander Graham Bell Silver proof Date stamped....................... £125

TWO POUNDS

1985 40th anniversary of Liberation... £10
1985 — Proof £30
1985 — Silver proof... £55
1986 Commonwealth Games, in plastic case..................................... £12
1986 — in special folder.. £12
1986 — .500 Silver.. £45
1986 — .925 Silver proof... £55
1987 900th Anniv. of death of William the Conqueror, in folder.......... £15
1987 — Silver proof... £55
1987 — Gold proof... £1500
1988 William II, in presentation folder £15
1988 — Silver proof... £55
1989 Henry I, in presentation folder £15
1989 — Silver proof... £55
1989 Royal Visit... £15
1989 — Silver proof... £55
1990 Queen Mother's 90th birthday... £15
1990 — Silver proof... £55
1991 Henry II, in presentation folder £15
1991 — Silver proof... £55
1993 40th Anniversary of the Coronation.. £15
1993 — Silver proof... £60
1994 Anniversary of the Normandy Landings £15
1994 — Silver proof... £55
1995 50th Anniversary of Liberation £154
1995 — Silver proof... £55
1995 — Silver Piedfort proof... £100
1997 Conserving Nature i.. £12
1997 — Silver proof... £55
1997 Bimetallic Latent image.. £8
1997 — proof £10
1998 Conserving Nature ii... £10
1998 Bimetallic Latent image.. £6
2003 — £6
2006 — £8
2011 Prince Philip's 90th Birthday (conjoined portraits) £6
2011 — Silver proof... £50
2011 40th Anniversary of Decimalisation.. £12
2012 Diamond Jubilee proof £20
2012 "8 Doubles" modern variant .... —
2022 1,900 years of Hadrian's Wall set: Emperor Hadrian, General Julius
Agricola Severus Septimius, Roman soldiers and Pict Warriors. BU £62.50
2022 — Coloured Silver proof set £425

ONE POUND

1981 .... £10
1981 Gold proof £350
1981 Gold piedfort £650
1983 New specification, new reverse... £10
1985 New design (in folder)... £10
1995 Queen Mother's 95th Birthday. Silver proof £50
1996 Queen's 70th Birthday. Silver proof... £55
1997 Royal Golden Wedding. Silver BU.. £20
1997 — Silver proof... £55
1997 Castles of the British Isles—Tower of London. Silver proof only ... £35
1998 Royal Air Force. Silver proof.. £45
1999 Wedding of Prince Edward. Silver proof £55

DATE	UNC
1999 Queen Mother. Silver proof..	£55
1999 Winston Churchill. Silver proof	£55
2000 Millennium. Silver proof (Gold plated)	£65
2000 Queen Mother's 100th Birthday. Silver proof	£45
2001	£2
2001 HM the Queen's 75th Birthday. Silver proof	£45
2002 William of Normandy. Silver	£20
2003	£2
2006..	£2
2015 Magna Carta 800th anniversary. Gold proof	£500
2018 HRH Prince Charles 70th Birthday. Gold proof	£500
2018 RAF Centenary	£15
2018 — Gold proof..	£500
2022 1900 years of Hadrian's Wall Gold proof.....................................	£845

FIFTY PENCE (initially 7-sided, some issues round)

1969 Ducal cap reverse...	£4
1970..	£6
1971 proof	£9
1981..	£4
1982..	£4
1985 New flower design...	£4
2000 60th Anniversary of the Battle of Britain.	£4
2000 — Silver proof..	£55
2000 — Silver piedfort..	£55
2000 — Gold proof	£375
2003..	£2
2003 Coronation Jubilee (four types)	£2
2003 — Proof	£4
2006..	£2
2008..	£2
2012 The Diamond Jubilee (coloured portrait)	£10
2012 — Cu-Ni Fine Gold-Plated	£5

2013 60th Anniversary of Coronation (two different designs: Queen in State Coach and Queen in White Dress), Gold clad steel .... ea.	£5
2013 The RAF 617 Squadron Gold-plated copper	£15
2013 The RAF No. 1 Squadron Gold-plated copper.............................	£15
2013 The Red Arrows. Gold-plated copper..	£15
2013 Battle of Britain Memorial Flight. Gold-plated copper	£15
2013 50th Anniversary of the Flying Scotsman's retirement in 1963......	£25
2014 New Queen Elizabeth II	£45
2015 Queen Elizabeth II — Reflections of a Reign, Cu-Ni	£5
2016 90th Birthday of Queen Elizabeth II (two round crown-size coloured coins) .... ea.	£5
2016 Churchill Tank. Gold-plated copper	£10
2016 Centenary of the WWI Tank. Gold-plated copper	£10
2017 The Spitfire. Silver-plated copper...	£12
2017 Sapphire Jubilee, Cu-Ni	£10
2017 Prince George's Birthday. Gold-plated	£75
2017 70th Anniversary Royal Wedding. Gold-plated Copper	£40
2018 RAF Centenary. Gold-plated	£45
2019 Concorde 50th Anniversary	£10
2019 — — set (3 designs: Runway, Take Off, Flight) .... ea.	£25
2019 — (paired with a Jersey 50p)	£12
2019 — Silver Proof	£125
2019 50th Anniversary of the 50p (paired with Jersey). BU x 2	£20
2019 — — Silver Proof...	£125
2019 — Moon Landings. Coloured Titanium 3-coin set	£150
2019 — — Orange Titanium	£50
2019 — — Green Titanium	£50
2019 — — Blue Titanium	£50
2019 Pantomime 5 coin set. BU..	£30
2019 — Silver, coloured Proof set...	£325
2020 75th Anniversary of the Liberation of the CI. 2 coins. BU	£12
2020 — Date stamped BU x 2 coins..	£40

DATE	UNC
2020 — Cu-Ni Proof x 2 coins	£60
2020 Offical RAF Battle of Britain Spitfire. Copper with 24ct gold plating	£40
2020 Christmas Carol 5-coin set	£30
2020 — Silver Proof coloured 5-coin set	£250
2021 Mr Benn 5-coin set	—
2021 — Silver Proof coloured 5-coin set	—
2022 Around the World in 80 Days 50p set: London, Yokohama, Singapore, Allahabad, San Francisco BU	£36
2022 — Coloured BU	£62.50
2022 — Coloured Silver proof	£349
2022 — Gold Proof	£4800

TEN PENCE

2022 Great British Wildlife. Birds: Barn Owl, Golden Eagle, Kestrel, Buzzard, Hen Harrier and Red Kite, Coloured BU	£20
2022 — Uncirculated	£17.50
2022 — Woodland Mammals: Dormouse, Lesser Horseshoe Bat, New Forest Pony, Pine Marten, Scottish wildcat, Wood Mouse. Coloured BU	£20

Note: in addition to the coins listed here, there are many others produced for Guernsey, often in tandem with the other Channel Islands. Regretfully information on many of these issues is difficult or impossible to obtain, thus they are omitted from this guide. Ordinary circulating coinage from 1986 onwards is usually available in uncirculated condition at a small premium above face value thus it is not listed here.

JERSEY

DATE	F	VF	EF	UNC

FIVE SHILLINGS

	F	VF	EF	UNC
1966	—	£3	£7	£15
1966 Proof	—	£3	£9	£25

ONE QUARTER OF A SHILLING

	F	VF	EF	UNC
1957	—	£2	£5	£10
1960 Proof	—	—	£5	£15
1964	—	—	£4	£10
1966	—	—	£4	£10

ONE TWELFTH OF A SHILLING

	F	VF	EF	UNC
1877H	£2	£3	£20	£65
1877H Proof in nickel	—	—	—	£1275
1877 Proof only	—	—	—	£500
1877 Proof in nickel	—	—	—	£1275
1881	£3	£3	£15	£60
1888	£2	£3	£15	£50
1894	£2	£3	£20	£50
1909	£2	£3	£15	£50
1911	£2	£3	£10	£30
1913	£2	£3	£10	£30
1923 Spade shield	£2	£3	£12	£45
1923 Square shield	£2	£3	£10	£30
1926	£2	£3	£12	£45
1931	£2	£3	£8	£15
1933	£2	£3	£8	£15
1935	£2	£3	£8	£15
1937	£2	£3	£8	£15
1946	£2	£3	£8	£15
1947	—	£3	£8	£15
"1945" GVI	—	—	£2	£10
"1945" QE2	—	—	£2	£8
1957	—	—	£2	£7
1960 1660–1960 300th anniversary	—	—	£3	£10
1960 Mule	—	—	—	£200
1964	—	£2	£3	£10
1966 "1066–1966"	—	—	£1	£8

ONE THIRTEENTH OF A SHILLING

	F	VF	EF	UNC
1841	£4	£8	£40	£200
1844	£4	£9	£40	£200
1851	£5	£12	£60	£250
1858	£4	£9	£45	£200
1861	£5	£13	£60	£175
1865 Proof only	—	—	—	£750
1866 with LCW	£2	£5	£95	£150
1866 without LCW Proof only	—	—	—	£450
1870	£4	£8	£40	£125
1871	£4	£8	£42	£125

ONE TWENTY-FOURTH OF A SHILLING

	F	VF	EF	UNC
1877H	£3	£4	£15	£60
1877 Proof only	—	—	—	£300
1888	£3	£4	£15	£45
1894	£3	£4	£15	£45
1909	£3	£4	£15	£45
1911	£2	£3	£10	£45

DATE	F	VF	EF	UNC
1913	£2	£3	£10	£45
1923 Spade shield	£2	£3	£10	£35
1923 Square shield	£2	£3	£8	£35
1926	£2	£3	£10	£25
1931	£2	£3	£10	£25
1933	£2	£3	£10	£25
1935	£2	£3	£10	£25
1937	£1	£2	£6	£20
1946	£1	£2	£6	£20
1947	£1	£2	£6	£20

ONE TWENTY-SIXTH OF A SHILLING

	F	VF	EF	UNC
1841	£4	£7	£30	£100
1844	£4	£7	£25	£100
1851	£3	£6	£25	£100
1858	£4	£11	£50	£200
1861	£3	£6	£25	£65
1866	£3	£6	£30	£85
1870	£3	£6	£20	£55
1871	£3	£6	£20	£55

ONE FORTY-EIGHTH OF A SHILLING

	F	VF	EF	UNC
1877H	£6	£12	£60	£150
1877 Proof only	—	—	—	£450

ONE FIFTY-SECOND OF A SHILLING

	F	VF	EF	UNC
1841	£9	£25	£60	£200
1861 Proof only	—	—	—	£650

DECIMAL COINAGE

Ordinary circulating coinage from 1986 onwards is usually available in uncirculated condition at a small premium above face value thus it is not listed here.

ONE HUNDRED POUNDS

1990 50th Anniversary of the Battle of Britain. Gold Proof.	£2000
1995 50th Anniversary of Liberation. Gold proof	£2000
2020 75th Anniversary VE Day. 1kg of silver gold-plated proof	£2500

FIFTY POUNDS

1972 Silver Wedding. Gold proof	£1000
1990 50th Anniversary of the Battle of Britain. Gold proof	£1000
1995 50th Anniversary of Liberation. Gold proof	£1000
2003 Golden Jubilee. Silver Proof (100mm)	£650
2013 RMS Titanic Centenary. 10oz Silver proof	£600

TWENTY-FIVE POUNDS

1972 25th Royal Wedding anniversary. Gold	£450
1972 — Gold proof	£500
1990 50th Anniversary of Battle of Britain. Gold proof	£450
1995 50th Anniversary of Liberation. Gold proof	£450
2002 Princess Diana memorial. Gold proof	£450
2002 Queen Mother. Gold proof	£450
2002 Golden Jubilee. Gold proof	£450
2002 Duke of Wellington. Gold proof	£450
2003 Golden Jubilee. Gold proof	£450
2003 History of the Royal Navy. Naval Commanders	£450
2003 — Francis Drake	£450
2003 — Sovereign of the Seas	£450
2004 60th Anniversary of D-Day. Gold proof	£450
2004 Charge of the Light Brigade. Gold proof	£450
2004 HMS Victory. Gold proof	£450
2004 John Fisher 1841–1920 Gold proof	£450
2004 The Coronation Scot. Gold proof	£450
2004 The Flying Scotsman. Gold proof	£450

Since the introduction of decimal coinage a number of companies have been involved in marketing the coins of the Channel Islands. As a consequence many special limited edition commemorative coins have been issued in a wide variety of sizes, metals and finishes. These are very numerous with some issues being produced in very small numbers and many are omitted from our listings. These issues are generally outside of the scope of this catalogue.

DATE	UNC
2004 Golden Arrow. Gold proof	£350
2004 Rocket and Evening Star. Gold proof	£350
2005 Andrew Cunningham. Gold proof	£350
2005 HMS Conqueror. Gold Proof	£350
2005 200th Anniversary of Nelson. Gold proof	£350
2009 500th Anniversary of Accession. Gold proof	£350

TWENTY POUNDS

1972 Royal Wedding. The Ormer. Gold	£350
1972 — Gold proof	£450

TEN POUNDS (65mm unless stated o/wise)

1972 25th Royal Wedding anniversary. Small gold	£275
1972 — Gold proof	£350
1990 50th Anniversary of the Battle of Britain. Gold proof	£350
1995 50th Anniversary of Liberation. Gold proof	£350
2003 Coronation Anniversary. Gold/silver proof	£375
2004 150th anniversary of the Crimean War. Gold proof	£6000
2005 Trafalgar. Gold proof	£5000
2005 End of World War II. Silver proof	£25
2007 Diamond Wedding. Platinum proof	£280
2008 History of RAF. Silver proof	£25
2011 Royal Wedding of HRH Prince William & Catherine Middleton, silver (65mm)£395
2012 Poppy. 5oz Silver Proof	£375
2013 Flying Scotsman. 5oz Silver proof	£375
2014 First World War Centenary 5oz Silver proof	£450
2017 Masterpiece Poppy. 5oz Silver proof	£400
2017 Battle of Britain Memorial Flight. 5oz Silver proof	£400
2018 Prince George's 5th Birthday 5oz Silver proof	£400
2018 Coronation Anniversary. 5oz Silver proof	£400
2018 Prince George's 5th birthday 5oz Silver proof	£425
2019 Remembrance Poppy. Gold proof 5oz (20 struck)	£12,000
2019 Remembrance Poppy. 5oz Silver proof	£550
2019 50th Anniversary of Concord 5oz Silver Proof	£495
2020 Battle of Britain 80th Anniversary 5oz Silver Proof	£495

(Enlarged)

FIVE POUNDS (38mm unless stated o/wise)

1972 Gold proof (2.62g)	£125
1990 50th Anniversary of the Battle of Britain. Silver Proof (5 ounces)	£250
1997 Royal Golden Wedding	£10
1997 — Silver proof	£25
2000 Millennium. Silver proof	£35
2002 Princess Diana memorial	£12
2002 — Silver proof	£30
2002 — Gold proof (38mm)(38mm)	£1250
2002 Royal Golden Jubilee	£25
2003 Golden Jubilee	£20
2003 — Silver proof	£55
2003 — Gold proof	£1250
2003 Prince William 21st Birthday	£15
2003 — Silver Proof	£55
2003 —Gold proof	£1250
2003 Naval Commanders	£15
2003 — Silver proof	£55
2003 — Gold proof	£1250
2003 Francis Drake	£15
2003 — Silver proof	£55
2003 — Gold proof	£1250
2003 Sovereign of the Seas	£15
2003 — Silver proof	£55
2003 — Gold proof	£1250
2004 60th Anniversary of 'D' Day	£15
2004 — Silver proof	£55
2004 — Gold proof	£1250

(Enlarged)

341

DATE	UNC
2004 Charge of the Light Brigade	£15
2004 — Silver proof	£50
2004 — Gold proof	£1250
2004 HMS Victory	£15
2004 — Silver proof	£55
2004 — Gold proof	£1250
2004 John Fisher 1841–1920	£15
2004 — Silver proof	£55
2004 —Gold proof	£1250
2004 The Coronation Scot	£15
2004 — Silver proof	£55
2004 — Gold proof	£1250
2004 The Flying Scotsman	£15
2004 — Silver proof	£55
2004 — Silver/Gold proof	£500
2004 — Gold proof	£1250
2004 Golden Arrow	£15
2004 — Silver proof	£55
2004 — Gold proof	£1250
2005 Driver and Fireman	£15
2005 — Silver proof	£45
2005 — Gold proof	£1250
2005 Box Tunnel and King Loco	£15
2005 — Silver Proof	£45
2005 — Gold Proof	£1250
2005 Rocket and Evening Star	£15
2005 — Silver proof	£45
2005 — Silver/Gold proof	£500
2005 — Gold proof	£1250
2005 200th Anniversary of the Battle of Trafalgar	£30
2005 Andrew Cunningham	£20
2005 — Silver proof	£65
2005 — Gold proof	£1250
2005 HMS Conqueror	£15
2005 — Silver proof	£20
2005 — Gold proof	£1250
2005 Battle of Trafalgar	£15
2005 — Silver proof	£45
2005 — Gold proof (9mm)	£500
2005 — Gold proof (38.6mm)	£1750
2005 Returning Evacuees	£15
2005 — Silver proof	£45
2005 — Gold proof	£1250
2005 Searchlights and Big Ben	£15
2005 — Silver proof	£45
2005 — Gold proof	£1250
2006 60th Anniversary of the Liberation of the Channel Islands	£30
2006 80th Birthday of Her Majesty the Queen (3-coin set)	—
2006 Sir Winston Churchill	£15
2006 — Silver proof	£45
2006 — Gold proof	£1250
2006 Charles Darwin	£15
2006 — Silver proof	£45
2006 — Gold proof	£1250
2006 Bobby Moore	£20
2006 — Silver Proof	£55
2006 — Gold Proof	£1250
2006 Florence Nightingale	£20
2006 — Silver proof	£55
2006 — Gold proof	£1250
2006 Queen Mother	£20
2006 — Silver proof	£55
2006 — Gold proof	£1250
2006 Henry VIII	£15
2006 — Silver proof	£55
2006 — Gold proof	£1250

DATE	UNC
2006 Princess Diana	£20
2006 — Silver Proof	£60
2006 — Gold Proof	£1250
2006 Sir Christopher Wren	£15
2006 — Silver proof	£55
2006 — Gold proof	£1250
2006 HM the Queen's 80th Birthday—Streamers	£15
2006 — Silver proof	£60
2006 — Gold proof	£1250
2006 HM the Queen's 80th Birthday—Trooping colour	£25
2006 — Proof	£60
2006 — Silver proof	£1250
2006 — Silver/Gold proof	£750
2006 — Gold proof	£1250
2006 HM the Queen's 80th Birthday—Wembley Stadium	£20
2006 — Silver proof	£55
2006 — Gold proof	£1250
2006 Guy Gibson	£15
2006 — Silver proof	£55
2006 — Gold proof	£1250
2006 Eric James Nicholson	£15
2006 — Silver proof	£55
2006 — Gold proof	£1250
2006 Hook, Chard and Bromhead	£15
2006 — Silver proof	£55
2006 — Gold proof	£1250
2006 1st Lancs Fusiliers	£15
2006 — Silver proof	£55
2006 — Gold proof	£1250
2006 Noel Chavasse	£15
2006 — Silver proof	£55
2006 — Gold proof	£1250
2006 David Mackay	£15
2006 — Silver proof	£55
2006 — Gold proof	£1250
2006 Coronation Scot. Silver proof	£60
2006 Flying Scotsman. Silver proof	£60
2006 Fireman and Driver. Silver proof	£60
2006 Box Tunnel. Silver proof	£60
2007 Diamond Wedding balcony scene waving	£15
2007 — Silver proof	£60
2007 Diamond Wedding cake	£15
2007 — Silver proof	£60
2007 Diamond Wedding balcony scene waving	£15
2007 —Silver proof	£60
2007 Diamond Wedding HM the Queen and Prince Philip	£20
2007 — Silver proof	£60
2007 Diamond Wedding arrival at Abbey	£20
2007 — Silver proof	£55
2007 — Gold proof	£1250
2008 George & Dragon	£20
2008 Dambusters, Wallis, Chadwick, Gibson	£15
2008 — Silver/Copper proof	£30
2008 — Silver proof	£55
2008 Frank Whittle	£15
2008 — Silver proof	£55
2008 — Gold proof	£1250
2008 R. J. Mitchell	£15
2008 — Silver proof	£55
2008 — Gold proof	£1250
2008 Maj. Gen. Sir Hugh Trenchard	£15
2008 — Silver proof	£55
2008 — Gold proof	£1250
2008 Bomber Command	£15
2008 — Silver proof	£55
2008 — Gold proof	£1250

DATE	UNC
2008 Coastal Command	£20
2008 — Silver proof	£60
2008 — Gold proof	£1250
2008 Fighter Command	£20
2008 — Silver proof	£60
2008 — Gold proof	£1250
2008 Battle of Britain	£20
2008 — Silver proof	£75
2008 — Gold proof	£1250
2008 RBL Poppy	£20
2008 — Silver proof	£60
2008 — Gold proof	£1250
2008 Flying Legends	£15
2008 — Silver proof	£55
2008 — Gold proof	£1250
2009 George & Dragon. Silver proof	£50
2009 Great Battles Series (8 coins). Silver proof. each.	£25
2009 Capt. Cook and *Endeavour.* Silver proof	£55
2009 500th Anniversary of Accession of Henry VIII. Silver proof	£55
2010 Battle of Britain heroes (3 coins available). Silver proof. each.	£50
2011 Landmark birthdays of HM the Queen & Prince Philip	£15
2011 90th Anniversary of the British Legion (poppy-shaped)	£40
2011 — Silver proof	£95
2011 — 5oz silver	£500
2011 — Gold proof	£2500
2011 30th Birthday of the Duke of Cambridge. Silver proof	£50
2011 Wedding of Prince William and Kate Middleton. Silver proof	£50
2011 — Gold proof	£2000
2011 Spirit of the Nation (4 coins). Silver proof, each	£50
2012 HM the Queen's Diamond Jubilee. Gold proof	£2000
2012 Poppy. Silver Proof	£65
2012 — Gold Proof	£2000
2012 RMS *Titanic* Centenary. Cu-Ni Gold plated	£15
2012 — Silver Proof	£65
2013 Coronation Jubilee. Silver proof	£65
2013 — Gold Proof	£2000
2013 The Flying Scotsman. Silver proof	£65
2013 350th Guinea Anniversary. Silver proof	£55
2013 — Gold Proof	£2000
2013 Poppy Coin. Silver proof	£95
2014 70th Anniversary of D-Day. Silver proof	£85
2014 — Gold Proof	£2500
2014 Remembrance Day (two designs), Cu-Ni	£10
2014 — Silver	£50
2014 — Gold proof	£2000
2014 The Red Arrows 50th Display Season. Silver proof	£95
2014 William Shakespeare—450th Birthday. Silver proof	£80
2015 Remembrance day "Lest we forget", Cu-Ni	£10
2015 50th Anniversary of Winston Churchill's death, Cu-Ni	£10
2015 The Longest Reign, Cu-Ni	£10
2015 200th Anniversary of the Battle of Waterloo, Cu-Ni	£10
2015 Red Arrows, Cu-Ni	£10
2016 90th Birthday of Queen Elizabeth II	£10
2016 Remembrance Day, Cu-Ni	£10
2017 Royal 70th Wedding Anniversary. Cu-Ni	£10
2017 Prince Philip 70 Years of Service. Cu-Ni	£12
2017 — Silver proof	£75
2017 Remembrance Day. Cu-Ni	£12
2017 — Cu-Ni Gold plated	£25
2017 — Silver proof	£85
2018 Prince George's 5th Birthday. Silver proof	£75
2018 Coronation 65th Anniversary. Cu-Ni	£10
2018 — Silver proof	£75
2018 Remembrance Day. Cu-Ni	£12
2018 — Cu-Ni Gold plated	£20
2018 — Silver proof	£75
2018 — Gold proof	£2000

DATE	UNC
2018 Dove of Peace. Cu-Ni..	£12
2018 RAF 100. Cu-Ni	£15
2018 — Silver proof...	£85
2019 Remembrance Poppy Gold Proof	£3250
2019 — Silver Proof	£90
2019 —Cu-Ni..	£5
2019 Concorde's first supersonic flight comm. Silver Proof......................	£85
2019 50th Anniversary of Moon Landing. Silver with Black Proof finish....	£125
2020 Captain Cook's Voyage of Discovery. Silver Proof...........................	£90
2020 Battle of Britain 80th Anniversary. Silver Proof. 3-coin set	£270
2021 Queen Elizabeth II 95th Birthday BU..	—
2021 — Silver Proof	—
2021 50 years of Decimalisation	—
2021 — Silver Proof with selected gold plating	—

TWO POUNDS FIFTY PENCE

1972 Royal Silver Wedding	£25
1972 — Silver proof..	£35

TWO POUNDS

(note all modern Proof coins have frosted relief)

1972 Royal Silver Wedding. Silver..	£25
1972 — Silver proof...	£35
1981 Royal Wedding, nickel silver (crown size)..	£5
1981— in presentation pack	£8
1981 — Silver proof...	£20
1981 — Gold proof..	£550
1985 40th Anniversary of Liberation (crown size)..............................	£5
1985 — in presentation pack	£12
1985 — Silver proof...	£20
1985 — Gold proof..	£1250
1986 Commonwealth Games...	£6
1986 — in presentation case...	£8
1986 — .500 silver..	£12
1986 — .925 silver proof...	£20
1987 World Wildlife Fund 25th Anniversary	£80
1987 — Silver proof...	£25
1989 Royal Visit	£15
1989 — Silver proof...	£25
1990 Queen Mother's 90th Birthday	£15
1990 — Silver proof...	£25
1990 — Gold proof..	£750
1990 50th Anniversary of the Battle of Britain, silver proof......................	£30
1993 40th Anniversary of the Coronation.......................................	£15
1993 — Silver proof...	£20
1993— Gold proof...	£750
1995 50th Anniversary of Liberation..	£15
1995 — Silver Proof	£25
1995 — — Piedfort..	£75
1996 HM the Queen's 70th Birthday	£15
1996 — Silver proof...	£25
1997 Bi-metal	£5
1997 — Silver proof...	£50
1997 — new portrait..	£5
1998 —	£5
2003 —	£5
2005 —	£5
2006 —	£5
2007 —	£5
2011 Prince Philip's 90th Birthday	£12
2012 HM the Queen's Diamond Jubilee. Gold proof	£1500
2019 Red Arrows..	£10
2020 Battle of Britain 80th Anniversary 3-coin set.	£45

DATE	UNC
2020 150th Anniversary of Sandringham House..	£12
2020 150th Anniversary of death of Charles Dickens 5-coin set	£50
2020 — Silver Proof with coloured highlights	£250
2021 150th Anniversary of the RFU 5 coin set..	—
2021 —Silver Proof 5-coin set	—
2021 Her Majesty the Queen's 95th Birthday 12-coin set	—
2022 Lighthouses Set—England, Ireland, Scotland, Wales, and the Channel Islands	£62.50

ONE POUND

1972 Royal Silver Wedding	£15
1972 — Silver proof...	£20
1981..	£15
1981 Silver proof	£15
1981 Gold proof	£550
1983 New designs and specifications on presentation card (St Helier).....	£5
1983 — Silver proof...	£20
1983 — Gold proof...	£650
1984 Presentation wallet (St Saviour)..	£20
1984 — Silver proof...	£45
1984 — Gold proof...	£650
1984 Presentation wallet (St Brelade)	£20
1984 — Silver proof...	£45
1984 — Gold proof...	£650
1985 Presentation wallet (St Clement)	£25
1985 — Silver proof...	£45
1985 — Gold proof...	£600
1985 Presentation wallet (St Lawrence)	£25
1985 — Silver proof...	£40
1985 — Gold proof...	£650
1986 Presentation wallet (St Peter)	£15
1986 — Silver proof...	£35
1986 — Gold proof...	£650
1986 Presentation wallet (Grouville)	£20
1986 — Silver proof...	£40
1986 — Gold proof...	£650
1987 Presentation wallet (St Martin)..	£20
1987 — Silver proof...	£40
1987 — Gold proof...	£650
1987 Presentation wallet (St Ouen)	£18
1987 — Silver proof...	£40
1987 — Gold proof...	£650
1988 Presentation wallet (Trinity)...	£20
1988 — Silver proof...	£40
1988 — Gold proof...	£650
1988 Presentation wallet (St John)...	£15
1988 — Silver proof...	£40
1988 — Gold proof...	£650
1989 Presentation wallet (St Mary)...	£15
1989 — Silver proof...	£40
1989 — Gold proof...	£650

1991 Ship Building in Jersey Series

1991 "Tickler". Nickel-brass	£5
1991 — Silver proof...	£25
1991 — Gold proof Piedfort	£750
1991 "Percy Douglas". Nickel-brass	£5
1991 — Silver proof...	£25
1991 — Gold proof Piedfort	£750
1992 "The Hebe". Nickel-brass..	£5
1992 — Silver proof...	£25
1992 — Gold proof Piedfort	£750
1992 "Coat of Arms". Nickel-brass...	£5
1992 — Silver proof...	£25

DATE	UNC
1992 — Gold proof Piedfort	£750
1993 "The Gemini". Nickel-brass	£5
1993 — Silver proof	£25
1993 — Gold proof Piedfort	£750
1993 "The Century". Nickel-brass...	£5
1993 — Silver proof	£25
1993 — Gold proof Piedfort	£750
1994 "Resolute". Nickel-brass	£5
1994 — Silver proof	£25
1994 — Gold proof Piedfort	£750

Coat of Arms design

1997..	£5
1998..	£5
2003..	£5
2005..	£5
2006..	£5
2007 Diana Commemoration. Gold proof	£650
2012 Diamond Jubilee. Gold proof	£650
2013 Coronation Jubilee. Gold proof	£750
2018 WWI Armistice. Gold proof...	£700
2022 Trooping the Colour Silver proof	£60

FIFTY PENCE (initially 7-sided, some issues round)

1969	£10
1972 Royal Silver Wedding	£12
1972 — Silver proof...	£35
1980..	£2
1980 Proof	£8
1981..	£2
1981 Proof	£8
1983 Grosnez Castle...	£12
1983 — Silver proof...	£35
1984	£2
1985 40th Anniversary of Liberation...	£3
1986	£3
1986	£3
1987	£3
1988	£3
1989	£3
1990	£3
1992	£3
1994	£3
1997	£5
1997 Smaller size	£4
1998	£3
2003	£3
2003 Coronation Anniversary (4 types) .... ea.	£5
2003 — 4 types. Silver proof... ea.	£15
2005	£4
2006..	£4
2009	£5
2011 Diamond Jubilee (full colour reverse, gold-plated)............................	£15
2013 Coronation Jubilee	£25
2014 Lord Kitchener. Gold plated steel...	£15
2015 Battle of Britain. Gold plated steel	£25
2016 Battle of Hastings, Halley's Comet. Silver..............................	£25
2016 Bayeux Tapestry. Silver	£25
2016 Battle of the Somme. Gold plated steel	£25
2018 RAF Centenary. Gold plated brass...	£22
2019 50th Anniversary of the 50p. Silver proof	£45
2019 — BU...	£15
2020 75th Anniversary of VE Day. Gold plated steel proof	£40
2020 75th Anniversary of the Liberation of Channel Islands (2 BU coins) . ea.£12	

DATE	UNC
2020 — date stamped (2 BU coins)	ea.£40
2020 — Proof (2 coins)	ea.£25
2021 Centenary of the Royal British Legion...............................	£10
2021 —Silver with coloured poppy	£50
2022 Virtues of a Queen 50p set. Charity, Truth, Justice, Victory and Courage. BU	£35
2022 — Double diameter Date Struck Silver proof	£375

TWENTY-FIVE PENCE
1977 Royal Jubilee..	£3
1977 — Silver proof...	£20

TWENTY PENCE
1982 Corbiere Lighthouse (cased)	£8
1982 — Silver proof piedfort	£35
1983 — Obv. with date, rev. no date on rocks	£5
1983 — — Silver proof...	£15
1984 to date	£1 ea.

SOVEREIGN—Gold sovereign size
1999 The Millennium. King William on Throne. Gold	£400
1999 — Gold proof..	£475

TEN PENCE
1968 Arms	£1
1975 Arms	£1
1979 (dated 1975 on thick flan)...	£5
1980 —	£1
1980 — Proof	£5
1981 -	£1
1981 — Proof	£5
1983 L'Hermitage	£1
1983 — Silver proof...	£12
1984 to date -	£1 ea.
2022 Garden Flowers - Rose, Sunflower, Gerbera, Jersey Lilly, Pansy and Sweetpea. BU	£17.50

Other denominations are generally available at face value or a small premium above. However, one penny denomination coins are struck in precious metals each year to commemorate special occasions.

Note: in addition to the coins listed here, there are many others produced for Jersey, often in tandem with the other Channel Islands. Regretfully information on many of these issues is difficult or impossible to obtain, thus they are omitted from this guide. Ordinary circulating coinage from 1986 onwards is usually available in uncirculated condition at a small premium above face value thus it is not listed here.

ALDERNEY

DATE   UNC

ONE THOUSAND POUNDS
2003 Concorde. Gold proof..   —
2004 D-Day Anniversary. Gold proof...   —
2005 Prince Harry's 21st Birthday. Gold proof..............................   —
2011 Wedding of Prince William and Catherine Middleton. Gold proof.....   —

ONE HUNDRED POUNDS
1994 50th Anniversary of D-Day Landings. Gold proof ....   —
2003 Prince Wiliam. Gold proof (100mm) ....   —
2005 Trafalgar Anniversary. Gold proof (100mm) ....   —
2022 Queen Elizabeth II Platinum Jubilee Gold Proof £2000

FIFTY POUNDS
1994 50th Anniversary of D–Day Landing. Gold proof............................. £500
2002 Royal Golden Jubilee. Silver proof (100mm) £850
2003 Anniversary of Coronation (4 types). Silver proof (100mm).......... ea. £750
2003 Prince William. Silver proof (100mm)... £750
2004 Anniversary of D-Day. Silver proof (100mm) £750
2005 200th Anniversary of the Battle of Trafalgar. Silver proof (100mm)... £750

TWENTY FIVE POUNDS
1993 40th Anniversary of Coronation. Gold proof.................................... £350
1994 50th Anniversary of D-Day Landings. Gold proof £350
1997 Royal Golden Wedding. Gold proof £350
1997 — Silver proof... £40
1999 Winston Churchill. Gold proof £350
2000 Queen Mother. Gold proof.. £375
2000 60th Anniversary of the Battle of Britain. Gold proof £400
2001 Royal Birthday. Gold proof £350
2002 Golden Jubilee. Gold proof £350
2002 Princess Diana. Gold proof £350
2002 Duke of Wellington. Gold proof £350
2003 Prince William. Gold proof... £300
2003 HMS Mary Rose. Gold proof.. £350
2004 D-Day Anniversary. Gold proof.. £400
2004 The Rocket. Gold proof... £350
2004 Merchant Navy Class Locomotive. Gold proof £350
2005 Battle of Saints Passage. Gold proof £350
2006 World Cup 2006 (4 Coins). Gold ea.. £400
2020 Three Graces Silver Proof £2000

TEN POUNDS
1994 50th Anniversary of D–Day Landing. Gold proof............................. £250
2003 Concorde. Silver proof (65mm) £300
2005 60th Anniversary of the Liberation of the Channel Islands (65mm)... £250
2007 80th Birthday of Her Majesty the Queen (65mm)............................ £180
2008 Concorde. Silver proof £180
2008 90th Anniversary of the end of WWI. Silver Proof £180
2009 50th Anniversary of the Mini—Silver with colour............................. £180
2012 Prince William's 30th Birthday .... —
2022 Queen Elizabeth II Platinum Jubilee Matte Silver Proof £800

FIVE POUNDS
1995 Queen Mother £15
1995 — Silver proof... £50
1995 — Silver piedfort... £155
1995 — Gold proof.. £1250
1996 HM the Queen's 70th Birthday £20

349

DATE	UNC
1996 — Silver proof..	£60
1996 — Silver piedfort..	£150
1996 — Gold proof...	£1250
1999 Eclipse of the Sun	£25
1999 — Silver proof with colour centre	£55
1999 Winston Churchill. Gold proof	£1750
2000 60th Anniversary of the Battle of Britain............................	£25
2000 — Silver proof..	£55
2000 Queen Mother. 100th Birthday. Silver proof	£50
2000 Millennium. Silver proof...	£35
2001 HM Queen's 75th Birthday.	£15
2001 — Silver proof..	£45
2002 Golden Jubilee. Silver proof	£50
2002 50 Years of Reign.	£15
2002 —Silver proof...	£50
2002 Diana memorial	£15
2002 — Silver proof..	£45
2002 — Gold proof...	£1250
2002 Duke of Wellington	£20
2002 — Silver proof..	£50
2002 — Gold proof...	£1250
2003 Prince William..	£20
2003 — Silver proof..	£50
2003 — Gold proof...	£1250
2003 Mary Rose	£20
2003 — Silver proof..	£120
2003 Alfred the Great. Silver proof	£150
2003 —Gold proof..	£1250
2003 Last Flight of Concorde..	£25
2003 — Silver proof..	£150
2003 — Gold proof...	£1250
2004 Anniversary of D-Day	£20
2004 — Silver proof..	£75
2004 — Gold proof...	£1250
2004 Florence Nightingale..	320
2004 — Silver proof..	£45
2004 150th Anniversary of the Crimean War...............................	£20
2004 — Silver proof..	£45
2004 — Gold proof...	£1250
2004 The Rocket	£20
2004 — Silver proof..	£45
2004 — Gold proof...	£1250
2004 Royal Scot	£20
2004 — Silver proof..	£45
2004 Merchant Navy Class Locomotive	£20
2004 — Silver proof..	£45
2005 End of WWII. Silver proof	£45
2005 — Gold proof...	£1250
2005 200th Anniversary of the Battle of Trafalgar	£16
2005 — Silver proof..	£50
2005 History of the Royal Navy. John Woodward. Silver proof	£30
2005 Anniversary of Liberation. Gold proof	£1250
2005 Anniversary of the Battle of Saints Passage	£15
2005 — Silver proof..	£45
2005 HMS Revenge 1591	£15
2005 — Silver proof..	£45
2005 Prince Harry's 21st Birthday. Gold proof............................	£1250
2006 80th Birthday of Her Majesty the Queen (3-coin set) ea	£20
2006 Gold plated portraits of Her Majesty the Queen	—
2006 80th Birthday of Her Majesty the Queen (3-coin set) ea	£16
2007 History of the Royal Navy—*Mary Rose* (2 coins) ea	£16
2007 150th Anniversary of the Victoria Cross (18 coin set). Silver proof ...	£250
2007 Monarchs of England (12 coin set). Gold plated...............	£150

DATE	UNC
2008 90th Anniversary of the end of WWI (3 coins). Gold proof	£2750
2008 Classic British Motorcars (18 coin set). Silver proof.	£250
2008 Concorde. Gold proof..	£1250
2009 50th Anniversary of the Mini (4 coins). Silver proof ea.	£50
2011 Royal Engagement gold proof..	£1250
2011 — Gold plated silver proof	£150
2011 — Silver proof	£55
2011 — Cupro Nickel	£15
2011 John Lennon Silver proof	£55
2011 Battle of Britain 70th Anniversary silver proof	£55
2012 RMS *Titanic*	£15
2012 Remembrance Day (Re-issued 2013)...	£25
2014 70th Anniversary of D-Day	£15
2014 — Silver proof..	£25
2014 — Gold proof..	£1250
2014 Destiny to Dynasty. Silver proof	£25
2014 300th Anniversary of the Coronation of King George I.....................	£20
2014 — Silver proof..	£25
2014 — Gold proof..	£1500
2014 Centenary of the birth of poet Dylan Thomas	£15
2014 — Silver proof..	£45
2014 — Gold proof..	£1500
2014 Remembrance Day "Remember the Fallen"	—
2015 Churchill Quotations (4-coin set)	£40
2015 — Silver proof (4-coin set)...	£250
2015 70th Anniversary of VE Day..	£15
2015 — Silver proof..	£45
2015 — Silver proof piedfort	£75
2015 150th Anniversary of the Salvation Army	£10
2015 — Silver proof..	£45
2015 Remembrance Day..	£10
2015 — Silver	£45
2015 — — piedfort	£85
2016 The FIFA World Cup	£15
2016 — Silver proof..	£45
2016 — Gold proof..	£1250
2016 Remembrance Day..	£15
2016 — Silver Proof	£35
2016 — — piedfort	£85
2017 Remembrance Day	£17
2017 — Silver Proof	£90
2017 — Silver Piedfort	£170
2019 The Puffin	£12
2019 — Silver proof..	£35
2019 Una and the Lion	£12
2019 — Silver proof..	£35
2019 — Gold proof	£2000
2019 Anniversary of the Moon Landing	£25
2019 — Silver proof..	£35
2019 — Gold proof..	£2000
2019 Concorde...	£25
2019 — Silver proof..	£35
2019 —Gold proof...	£2000
2020 Remembrance day	£15
2020 — Silver proof..	£35
2020 —Gold proof...	£2000
2020 Sir Winston Churchill"s speech	£15
2020 — Silver proof..	£35
2020 Three Graces Silver Proof	£525
2022 RNLI BU Coloured..	£25
2022 Queen Elizabeth II Platinum Jubilee BU	£17
2022 — Silver Proof	£420

DATE	UNC

TWO POUNDS

1989 Royal Visit	£12
1989 — Silver proof	£25
1989 — Silver piedfort	£45
1989 — Gold proof	£1200
1990 Queen Mother's 90th Birthday	£12
1990 — Silver proof	£25
1990 — Silver piedfort	£45
1990 — Gold proof	£1200
1992 40th Anniversary of Accession	£15
1992 — Silver proof	£35
1992 — Silver piedfort	£50
1992 — Gold proof	£1200
1993 40th Anniversary of Coronation	£15
1993 — Silver proof	£35
1993 — Silver piedfort	£50
1994 50th Anniversary of D-Day Landings	£15
1994 — Silver proof	£35
1994 — Silver piedfort	£50
1995 50th Anniversary of Return of Islanders	£15
1995 — Silver proof	£35
1995 — Silver piedfort	£50
1995 — Gold proof	£1250
1997 WWF Puffin	£18
1997 — Silver proof	£35
1997 Royal Golden Wedding	£20
1997 — Silver proof	£50
1999 Eclipse of the Sun. Silver	£20
1999 — Silver proof	£50
1999 — Gold proof	£1250
2000 Millennium. Silver proof	£50

ONE POUND

1993 40th Anniversary of Coronation Silver proof	£50
1995 50th Anniversary of VE Day Silver proof	£45
1995 — Gold proof	£500
2005 Nelson	£100
2008 Concorde. Gold proof	£375
2009 50th Anniversary of the Mini. Gold proof	£475
2020 Dunkirk	£10
2020 — Silver proof	£30

DOUBLE SOVEREIGN

2022 Platinum Jubilee Struck on the Day in Platinum	£570

SOVEREIGN

2020 Three Graces Gold Ultra Cameo	£72
2022 Platinum Jubilee Struck on the Day Platinum	£285

HALF SOVEREIGN

2020 Three Graces Gold Ultra Cameo	£485

QUARTER SOVEREIGN

2020 Three Graces Gold Ultra Cameo	£216
2020 — Gold proof	£650

In recent years a number of companies have been involved in marketing the coins of the Channel Islands. As a consequence many special limited edition commemorative coins have been issued in a wide variety of sizes, metals and finishes. These are very numerous with some issues being produced in very small numbers and many are omitted from our listings. These issues are generally outside of the scope of this catalogue.

IRELAND

As in the English hammered section (q.v.) the prices given here are for the most common coins in the series. For a more specialised listing the reader is referred to Coincraft's *Standard Catalogue of Scotland, Ireland, Channel Islands & Isle of Man*, or other specialised publications. Collectors should be aware that with most of the coins of the Irish series there are many varieties struck at different mints. The coins listed are all silver unless mentioned otherwise. Another important factor to consider when collecting early Irish coins is that few examples exist in high grades.

	F	VF

HIBERNO-NORSE ISSUES (995–1155)
Penny, imitating English silver pennies,
many various types £300 £650

Hiberno-Norse phase II example.

JOHN, Lord of Ireland (1185–99)
	F	VF
Halfpenny, profile		Extremely rare
Halfpenny, facing	£200	£550
Farthing	£500	£1850

JOHN de COURCY, Lord of Ulster (1177–1205)
	F	VF
Halfpenny		Extremely rare
Farthing	£750	£3750

John Lord of Ireland penny.

JOHN as King of England and Lord of Ireland (c. 1199–1216)
	F	VF
Penny	£75	£500
Halfpenny	£175	£5000
Farthing	£650	£2500

HENRY III (1216–72)
Penny £150 £575

EDWARD I (1272–1307)
	F	VF
Penny	£75	£250
Halfpenny	£75	£175
Farthing	£150	£450

No Irish coins were struck for Edward II (1307–27).

Henry III penny.

EDWARD III (1327–77)
Halfpenny .... Extremely rare

No Irish coins were struck for Richard II (1377–99), Henry IV (1399–1413) or Henry V (1413–22).

HENRY VI (1422–61)
Penny .... Extremely rare

Edward I penny.

	F	VF

EDWARD IV (1461–83)

	F	VF
"Anonymous crown" groat	£700	£14500
— penny	£1200	—
"Titled crown" groat	£1600	—
— halfgroat..		Extremely rare
— penny		Extremely rare
Cross on rose/Sun groat	£1850	—
Bust/Rose on sun double groat	£2250	£7500
— groat...	£2250	—
— halfgroat..		Extremely rare
— penny		Extremely rare
Bust/Cross & pellets groat—First issue	£150	£585
— halfgroat..	£650	£1700
— penny	£100	£375
— halfpenny		Extremely rare
— Second (light) issue..........................	£150	£550
— halfgroat..	£650	£1700
— penny	£100	
£250— halfpenny		Extremely rare
Bust/Rose on cross groat......................	£570	£1500
— penny	£80	£250
Billon/Copper issues		
Small crown/Cross farthing (1460–61) ..	£1700	—
— half farthing ("Patrick").....................	£1100	—
Large crown/Cross farthing (1462)........		Extremely rare
Patricius/Salvator farthing (1463–65)	£350	£2000
— half farthing.....................................		Extremely rare
Shield/Rose on sun farthing	£250	£1000

Edward IV groat.
"Anonymous crown" issue.

Edward IV penny struck in
Dublin.

RICHARD III (1483–85)

	F	VF
Bust/Rose on cross groat......................	£1100	£4000
— halfgroat..		Unique
— penny		Unique
Bust/Cross and pellets penny	£100	£3500
Shield/Three-crowns groat....................	£650	£3000

HENRY VII (1485–1509)

Early issues (1483–90)

	F	VF
Shield/Three crowns groat	£170	£550
— halfgroat..	£250	£565
— penny	£650	£2600
— halfpenny		Extremely rare

Later issues (1488–90)

	F	VF
Shield/Three crowns groat	£150	£475
— halfgroat..	£200	£650
— penny	£500	£1400
Facing bust groat (1496–1505)..............	£200	£500
— halfgroat..	£1100	—
— penny	£1000	—

Richard III bust/rose on
cross groat.

LAMBERT SIMNEL
(as EDWARD VI, Pretender, 1487)

	F	VF
Shield/Three crowns groat	£1300	£5000

Henry VII groat.

	F	VF

HENRY VIII (1509–47)

	F	VF
"Harp" groat	£150	£4000
— halfgroat	£500	£2750

The "Harp" coins have crowned initials either side of the reverse harp, e.g. HR (Henricus Rex), HA (Henry and Anne Boleyn), HI (Henry and Jane Seymour), HK (Henry and Katherine Howard).

Posthumous (Portrait) issues

	F	VF	
Sixpence	£185	£575	
Threepence	£160	£575	
Threehalfpence	£500	£1800	*Henry VIII Posthumous portrait*
Threefarthings	£650	£2500	*issues threepence.*

EDWARD VI (1547–53)

	F	VF
Shilling (base silver) 1552 (MDLII)	£1100	£3750
Brass contemporary copy	£110	£400

MARY (1553–54)

	F	VF
Shilling 1553 (MDLIII)	£1000	£3500
Shilling 1554 (MDLIIII)		Extremely rare
Groat		Extremely rare
Halfgroat		Extremely rare
Penny		Extremely rare

PHILIP & MARY (1554–58)

	F	VF
Shilling	£350	£1500
Groat	£150	£475
Penny		Extremely rare

ELIZABETH I (1558–1603)

Base silver portrait coinage

	F	VF	
Shilling	£500	£1750	*Philip & Mary shilling*
Groat	£250	£800	

Fine silver, portrait coinage (1561)

	F	VF
Shilling	£300	£1200
Groat	£350	£1200

Third (base silver) shield coinage

	F	VF
Shilling	£250	£800
Sixpence	£200	£575

Copper

	F	VF
Threepence	£275	£750
Penny	£75	£275
Halfpenny	£150	£350

JAMES I (1603–25)

	F	VF
Shilling	£125	£500
Sixpence	£125	£475

Coins struck under Royal Licence from 1613

	F	VF	
"Harrington" farthing (small size)	£75	£295	
"Harrington" farthing (large size)	£75	£250	
"Lennox" farthing	£75	£275	*Elizabeth I "fine" shilling of 1561.*

CHARLES I (1625–49)

During the reign of Charles I and the Great Rebellion many coins were struck under unusual circumstances, making the series a difficult but fascinating area for study. Many of the "coins" were simply made from odd-shaped pieces of plate struck with the weight or value.

Coins struck under Royal Licence from 1625

	F	VF
"Richmond" farthing	£65	£250
"Maltravers" farthing	£50	£250
"Rose" farthing	£50	£275

Siege money of the Irish Rebellion, 1642–49

"Inchiquin" Money (1642)

	F	VF
Crown	£2500	£6500
Halfcrown	£2000	£5750
Shilling		Extremely rare
Ninepence		Extremely rare
Sixpence		Extremely rare
Groat		Extremely rare

"Dublin" Money (1643)

	F	VF
Crown	£1000	£3750
Halfcrown	£600	£2750

"Ormonde" Money (1643–44)

	F	VF
Crown	£575	£1600
Halfcrown	£375	£1275
Shilling	£150	£475
Sixpence	£150	£475
Groat	£120	£425
Threepence	£120	£350
Twopence	£500	£1700

Charles I "Ormonde" crown.

"Ormonde" gold coinage (1646)

Double pistole. 2 known (both in museums)	Extremely rare
Pistole. 10 known (only 1 in private ownership	Extremely rare

"Ormonde" Money (1649)

	F	VF
Crown		Extremely rare
Halfcrown	£1300	£4000

Dublin Money 1649

	F	VF
Crown	£3000	£8000
Halfcrown	£2200	£5500

Issues of the Confederated Catholics

Kilkenny issues (1642–43)

	F	VF
Halfpenny	£350	£1000
Farthing	£450	£1200

Rebel Money (1643–44)

	F	VF
Crown	£2600	£5750
Halfcrown	£2000	£5850

"Blacksmith's" Money (16??)

A rare Charles I "Rebel" halfcrown.

	F	VF
Imitation of English Tower halfcrown.....	£750	£3500

Local Town issues of "Cities of Refuge"

Bandon
Farthing (copper) .... — Extremely rare

Cork
Shilling .... — Extremely rare
Sixpence.. £775 — £1500
Halfpenny (copper) .... — Extremely rare
Farthing (copper) .... £635 — —

Kinsale
Farthing (copper) .... £425 — —

Youghal
Farthing (copper) £500 £2500

Halfpenny of Charles I.

CHARLES II (1660–85)

	Fair	F	VF	EF
"Armstrong" coinage				
Farthing (1660–61)...............................	£75	£250	—	—
"St Patrick's" coinage				
Halfpenny	£235	£475	—	—
Farthing	£85	£200	£600	£1850
Legg's Regal coinage				
Halfpennies				
1680 large lettering...............................	£35	£100	£325	—
1681 large lettering...............................	—	£200	£695	—
1681 small lettering			Extremely rare	
1682 small lettering	—	£200	£675	—
1683 small lettering	£35	£45	£465	—
1684 small lettering	£50	£125	£675	—

JAMES II (1685–88)

REGAL COINAGE

Halfpennies

1685...	£35	£85	£320	£750
1686...	£35	£65	£200	£625
1687...			Extremely rare	
1688...	£45	£125	£300	£1400

"St Patrick" farthing of Charles II.

	Fair	F	VF	EF

EMERGENCY COINAGE

GUN MONEY
Most of these coins were struck in gun metal but a few rare specimens are also known struck in gold and in silver

Crowns

	Fair	F	VF	EF
1690 (many varieties).....................from	£45	£65	£650	—

Large halfcrowns
Dated July 1689–May 1690

....from	£35	£65	£250	—

Small halfcrowns
Dated April–October1690

....from	£35	£65	£250	—

Large shillings
Dated from July 1689–April 1690

....from	£35	£75	£125	£925

Small shillings
Dated from April–September 1690

....from	£30	£35	£125	£800

Sixpences
Dated from June 1689–October 1690

....from	£35	£60	£300	—

"Gun Money" crown.

PEWTER MONEY (1689–90)

	Fair	F	VF	EF
Crown..	£700	£1200	£3500	—
Groat..			Extremely rare	
Penny large bust....................................	£230	£675	—	—
— small bust	£165	£485	£1500	—
Halfpenny large bust	£130	£345	£900	—
— small bust	£110	£245	£700	—

LIMERICK MONEY (1690–91)

	Fair	F	VF	EF
Halfpenny, reversed N in HIBERNIA......	£35	£75	£275	—
Farthing, reversed N in HIBERNIA.........	£35	£75	£275	—
— normal N	£45	£135	£335	—

WILLIAM & MARY (1689–94)

Halfpennies

	Fair	F	VF	EF
1692..	£15	£50	£100	£725
1693..	£15	£50	£85	£725
1694..	£25	£75	£135	£895

William & Mary half-penny of 1693.

WILLIAM III (1694–1702)

	Fair	F	VF	EF
1696 Halfpenny draped bust.................	£35	£85	£275	—
1696 — crude undraped bust	£45	£275	£900	—

DATE	F	VF	EF	UNC

No Irish coins were struck during the reign of Queen Anne (1706–11).

GEORGE I (1714–27)

Farthings

	F	VF	EF	UNC
1722 D.G. REX Harp to left (Pattern)	£650	£1600	£2500	—
1723 D.G. REX Harp to right	£120	£225	£525	—
1723 DEI GRATIA REX Harp to right	£35	£65	£275	£650
1723 — Silver Proof	—	—	—	£2500
1724 DEI GRATIA REX Harp to right	£60	£150	£365	£875

Halfpennies

	F	VF	EF	UNC
1722 Holding Harp left	£55	£130	£395	£1200
1722 Holding Harp right	£45	£120	£350	£800
1723/2 Harp right	£50	£150	£350	£800
1723 Harp right	£30	£65	£200	£565
1723 Silver Proof	—	—	—	£3700
1723 Obv. Rs altered from Bs	£35	£100	£295	—
1723 No stop after date	£25	£80	£295	£565
1724 Rev. legend divided	£40	£100	£300	—
1724 Rev. legend continuous	£40	£110	£395	—

GEORGE II (1727–60)

Farthings

	F	VF	EF	UNC
1737	£35	£60	£185	£500
1737 Proof	—	—	—	£525
1737 Silver Proof	—	—	—	£1300
1738	£35	£65	£165	£495
1744	£35	£65	£165	£495
1760	£30	£50	£100	£385

Halfpenny of George II

Halfpennies

	F	VF	EF	UNC
1736	£25	£60	£225	£675
1736 Proof	—	—	—	£695
1736 Silver Proof	—	—	—	£1400
1737	£25	£50	£225	—
1738	£30	£60	£225	—
1741	£30	£60	£225	—
1742	£30	£60	£225	—
1743	£30	£60	£200	—
1744/3	£30	£60	£200	—
1744	£30	£60	£375	—
1746	£30	£60	£250	—
1747	£30	£60	£225	—
1748	£30	£60	£225	—
1749	£30	£60	£225	—
1750	£35	£60	£225	—
1751	£30	£60	£225	—
1752	£30	£60	£225	—
1753	£30	£60	£250	—
1755	£30	£110	£350	—
*1760	£30	£75	£250	—

GEORGE III (1760–1820)

All copper unless otherwise stated

Pennies

	F	VF	EF	UNC
1805	£20	£40	£185	£500
1805 Proof	—	—	—	£625
1805 in Bronze Proof	—	—	—	£600
1805 in Copper Gilt Proof	—	—	—	£600
1805 in Silver Proof (restrike)	—	—	—	£3500

George III proof penny 1805

DATE	F	VF	EF	UNC

Halfpennies

	F	VF	EF	UNC
1766	£30	£55	£165	—
1769	£30	£55	£165	—
1769 Longer bust	£40	£75	£250	£765
1774 Pattern only Proof	—	—	—	£3500
1775	£30	£55	£200	£475
1775 Proof	—	—	—	£675
1776	£55	£140	£400	—
1781	£45	£60	£175	£465
1782	£45	£60	£175	£465
1805	£18	£45	£120	£465
1805 Copper Proof	—	—	—	£465
1805 in Bronze	—	—	—	£320
1805 in Gilt Copper	—	—	—	£475
1805 in Silver (restrike)	—	—	—	£2000

Farthings

	F	VF	EF	UNC
1806	£20	£35	£100	£200
1806 Copper Proof	—	—	—	£375
1806 Bronzed Copper Proof	—	—	—	£275
1806 Copper Gilt Proof	—	—	—	£350
1806 Silver Proof (restrike)	—	—	—	£1600

One of the scarcer dates, a 1776 George III halfpenny.

GEORGE IV (1820–30)

Pennies

	F	VF	EF	UNC
1822	£20	£40	£195	£525
1822 Proof	—	—	—	£625
1823	£12	£25	£150	£475
1823 Proof	—	—	—	£625

Halfpennies

	F	VF	EF	UNC
1822	£20	£40	£125	£400
1822 Proof	—	—	—	£650
1823	£20	£40	£125	£400
1823 Proof	—	—	—	£695

NB Prooflike Uncirculated Pennies and Halfpennies of 1822/23 are often mis-described as Proofs. The true Proofs are rare. Some are on heavier, thicker flans.

Farthings

	F	VF	EF	UNC
1822 (Pattern) Proof	—	—	—	£1875

TOKEN ISSUES BY THE BANK OF IRELAND

Five Pence in Silver

	F	VF	EF	UNC
1805	£30	£45	£75	£375
1806	£30	£65	£150	£410
1806/5	£60	£145	£450	£1475

Ten Pence in Silver

	F	VF	EF	UNC
1805	£20	£35	£95	£275
1806	£20	£65	£150	£295
1813	£20	£35	£95	£335
1813 Proof	—	—	—	£475

Thirty Pence in Silver

	F	VF	EF	UNC
1808	£45	£100	£250	£675

Six Shillings

	F	VF	EF	UNC
1804 in Silver	£100	£250	£465	£1875
1804 Proof	—	—	—	£1800
1804 in Copper (restrike)	—	—	—	£800
1804 Copper Gilt	—	—	—	£1850
1804 in Gilt Silver	—	—	—	£3100

1804 six shillings.

In this series fully struck specimens, with sharp hair curls, etc., are worth appreciably more than the prices quoted.

IRISH FREE STATE/EIRE

DATE	F	VF	EF	UNC
TEN SHILLINGS				
1966 Easter Rising	—	£12	£18	£45
1966 Cased Proof	—	—	—	£45
1966 Special double case	—	—	—	£100
HALF CROWNS				
Silver				
1928	£7	£12	£45	£100
1928 Proof	—	—	—	£125
1930	£12	£35	£175	£575
1931	£12	£35	£175	£545
1933	£12	£25	£175	£575
1934	£20	£12	£55	£275
1937	£60	£200	£650	£2000
Modified obverse: Eire				
1938				Unique
1939	£7	£17	£30	£85
1939 Proof	—	—	—	£650
1940	£8	£18	£35	£95
1941	£7	£17	£35	£95
1942	£7	£20	£35	£110
1943	£85	£300	£995	£3450
Cupro-nickel				
1951	£2	£3	£20	£75
1951 Proof	—	—	—	£525
1954	£2	£3	£15	£95
1954 Proof	—	—	—	£525
1955	£2	£3	£15	£45
1955	—	—	—	£600
1959	£2	£3	£12	£50
1961	£2	£3	£25	£60
1961 Obv as 1928, rev. as 1951	£30	£75	£325	£900
1962	£2	£3	£6	£35
1963	£2	£3	£6	£35
1964	£2	£3	£6	£35
1966	£2	£3	£6	£35
1967	£2	£3	£6	£45
FLORINS				
Silver				
1928	£5	£8	£25	£75
1928 Proof	—	—	—	£85
1930	£5	£20	£150	£495
1930 Proof				Unique
1931	£5	£20	£175	£475
1933	£5	£18	£140	£500
1934	£15	£125	£275	£850
1934 Proof	—	—	—	£3250
1935	£5	£18	£65	£200
1937	£6	£25	£140	£425
Modified obverse: Eire				
1939	£3	£6	£35	£85
1939 Proof	—	—	—	£685
1940	£5	£6	£30	£85
1941	£5	£6	£35	£85
1941 Proof	—	—	—	£875
1942	£7	£15	£30	£100
1943	£3000	£6000	£10000	£22750

Beware of fake 1943 florins.

DATE	F	VF	EF	UNC
Cupro-nickel				
1951...	60p	£2	£15	£50
1951 Proof.....................................	—	—	—	£525
1954...	60p	£2	£10	£50
1954 Proof.....................................	—	—	—	£400
1955...	—	£2	£6	£50
1955 Proof.....................................	—	—	—	£600
1959...	40p	£2	£6	£45
1961...	60p	£3	£15	£55
1962...	40p	£2	£6	£30
1963...	30p	£2	£6	£30
1964...	30p	£2	£6	£30
1965...	30p	£2	£6	£30
1966...	30p	£2	£6	£30
1968...	30p	£2	£6	£30

SHILLINGS
Silver

	F	VF	EF	UNC
1928...	£5	£10	£25	£60
1928 Proof.....................................	—	—	—	£75
1930...	£6	£25	£100	£465
1930 Proof.....................................	—	—	—	£875
1931...	£3	£17	£95	£485
1933...	£3	£17	£95	£470
1935...	£3	£13	£50	£160
1937...	£10	£75	£250	£1500
1939...	£3	£6	£25	£80
1939 Proof.....................................	—	—	—	£775
1940...	£3	£6	£17	£60
1941...	£3	£5	£17	£165
1942...	£3	£5	£12	£55

Cupro-nickel

	F	VF	EF	UNC
1951...	£1	£2	£6	£25
1951 Proof.....................................	—	—	—	£450
1954...	£1	£2	£6	£25
1954 Proof.....................................	—	—	—	£550
1955...	£1	£2	£6	£25
1959...	£1	£2	£6	£35
1962...	50p	£2	£5	£22
1963...	50p	£2	£5	£15
1964...	50p	£2	£5	£15
1966...	50p	£2	£5	£15
1968...	50p	£2	£5	£15

SIXPENCES
Nickel

	F	VF	EF	UNC
1928...	£1	£6	£25	£65
1928 Proof.....................................	—	—	—	£65
1934...	£1	£3	£18	£100
1935...	£1	£3	£25	£150
Modified obverse: Eire				
1939...	£1	£2	£10	£65
1939 Proof.....................................	—	—	—	£675
1940...	£1	£2	£6	£65
Cupro-nickel				
1942...	£1	£2	£9	£65
1945	£3	£12	£35	£100
1946...	£5	£10	£100	£450
1947...	£2	£2	£25	£95
1948...	£1	£3	£15	£75
1949...	£1	£2	£10	£50
1950...	£2	£3	£25	£125
1952...	£1	£2	£5	£30

DATE	F	VF	EF	UNC
1953	£1	£2	£5	£35
1953 Proof	—	—	—	£135
1955	£1	£2	£4	£30
1956	£1	£2	£3	£30
1956 Proof	—	—	—	£195
1958	£4	£6	£12	£75
1958 Proof	—	—	—	£400
1959	50p	60p	£3	£25
1960	50p	60p	£2	£25
1961	—	£2	£3	£25
1962	£2	£6	£35	£80
1963	£2	£3	£6	£20
1964	£2	£3	£6	£15
1966	£2	£3	£6	£15
1967	£2	£3	£6	£12
1968	£2	£3	£6	£12
1969	£5	£8	£10	£30

THREEPENCES

Nickel

	F	VF	EF	UNC
1928	£2	£3	£10	£45
1928 Proof	—	—	—	£45
1933	£3	£13	£75	£400
1934	£1	£3	£15	£85

Modified obverse: Eire

	F	VF	EF	UNC
1935	£2	£4	£30	£235
1939	£3	£7	£60	£400
1939 Proof	—	—	—	£1300
1940	£2	£3	£13	£75

Cupro-nickel

	F	VF	EF	UNC
1942	—	£2	£6	£65
1942 Proof	—	—	—	£550
1943	£2	£3	£15	£80
1946	£2	£5	£10	£55
1946 Proof	—	—	—	£550
1948	£2	£3	£25	£85
1949	—	£2	£6	£45
1950	—	£2	£6	£35
1950 Proof	—	—	—	£600
1953	—	£2	£4	£20
1956	—	£2	£3	£15
1961	—	60p	£2	£5
1962	—	60p	£2	£12
1963	—	60p	£2	£12
1964	—	60p	£2	£5
1965	—	60p	£2	£5
1966	—	60p	£2	£5
1967	—	60p	£2	£5
1968	—	—	£2	£5

PENNIES

	F	VF	EF	UNC
1928	£2	£3	£12	£55
1928 Proof	—	—	—	£65
1931	£2	£4	£35	£125
1931 Proof	—	—	—	£1200
1933	£2	£5	£50	£275
1935	£1	£2	£25	£85
1937	£1	£2	£35	£135
1937 Proof	—	—	—	£1200

Modified obverse: Eire

	F	VF	EF	UNC
1938			Only two known	
1940	£10	£50	£175	£800
1941	£1	£2	£10	£35
1942	—	£2	£5	£25

DATE	F	VF	EF	UNC
1943	—	£2	£6	£50
1946	—	£2	£4	£20
1948	—	£2	£4	£20
1949	—	£2	£4	£20
1949 Proof	—	—	—	£500
1950	—	£2	£6	£40
1952	—	£2	£4	£15
1962	—	£2	£4	£15
1962 Proof	—	—	—	£225
1963	—	—	£2	£20
1963 Proof	—	—	—	£200
1964	—	—	£2	£10
1964 Proof	—	—	—	£550
1965	—	—	£1	£5
1966	—	—	£1	£5
1967	—	—	£1	£5
1968	—	—	£1	£5
1968 Proof	—	—	—	£300

HALFPENNIES

DATE	F	VF	EF	UNC
1928	£2	£3	£15	£45
1928 Proof	—	—	—	£45
1933	£6	£20	£100	£520
1935	£5	£10	£50	£235
1937	£5	£10	£25	£75

Modified obverse: Eire

DATE	F	VF	EF	UNC
1939	£5	£10	£50	£200
1939 Proof	—	—	—	£900
1940	£2	£4	£50	£350
1940 Proof	—	—	—	Ex. rare
1941	£1	£2	£6	£25
1942	£1	£2	£6	£25
1943	£1	£2	£8	£35
1946	£2	£5	£20	£100
1949	£1	£2	£6	£25
1953	—	£2	£3	£12
1953 Proof	—	—	—	£500
1964	—	—	£1	£5
1965	—	—	£1	£6
1966	—	—	£1	£4
1967	—	—	£1	£4

FARTHINGS

DATE	F	VF	EF	UNC
1928	£3	£4	£15	£32
1928 Proof	—	—	—	£45
1930	£3	£4	£10	£32
1931	£4	£6	£15	£35
1931 Proof	—	—	—	£955
1932	£4	£6	£18	£45
1933	£3	£4	£12	£32
1935	£4	£6	£18	£35
1936	£4	£6	£18	£35
1937	£4	£6	£18	£35

Modified obverse: Eire

DATE	F	VF	EF	UNC
1939	£3	£4	£10	£20
1939 Proof	—	—	—	£695
1940	£4	£5	£10	£25
1941	£3	£4	£6	£12
1943	£3	£4	£6	£12
1944	£3	£4	£6	£12
1946	£3	£4	£6	£12
1949	£4	£6	£8	£25
1949 Proof	—	—	—	£475
1953	£3	£4	£5	£12
1953 Proof	—	—	—	£400
1959	£3	£4	£5	£12
1966	£3	£4	£5	£12

For the 1928–50 copper issues it is worth noting that UNC means UNC with some lustre. BU examples with full lustre are extremely elusive and are worth much more than the quoted prices.

IRISH DECIMAL COINAGE

DATE	MINTAGE	BU
HALF PENCE		
1971	100,500,000	£5
1975	10,500,000	£6
1976	5,500,000	£6
1978	20,300,000	£5
1980	20,600,000	£4
1982	9,700,000	£4
1985	2,800,000	Rare
1986. Only issued in the 1986 set	19,750,000	£145

ONE PENNY

1971	100,500,000	£5
1974	10,000,000	£15
1975	10,000,000	£18
1976	38,200,000	£5
1978	25,700,000	£8
1979	21,800,000	£12
1980	86,700,000	£3
1982	54,200,000	£5
1985	19,200,000	£8
1986	36,600,000	£5
1988	56,800,000	£5
1990	65,100,000	£5
1992	25,600,000	£6
1993	10,000,000	£8
1994	45,800,000	£5
1995	70,800,000	£3
1996	190,100,000	£1
1998	40,700,000	£1
2000	Unknown	£1

TWO PENCE

1971	75,500,000	£5
1975	20,000,000	£12
1976	5400,000	£15
1978	12,000,000	£12
1979	32,400,000	£8
1980	59,800,000	£6
1982	30,400,000	£5
1985	14,500,000	£6
1986	23,900,000	£6
1988	35,900,000	£5
1990	34,300,000	£5
1992	10,200,000	£12

DATE	MINTAGE	BU
1995	55,500,000	£5
1996	69,300,000	£2
1998	33,700,000	£2
2000	Unknown	£2

FIVE PENCE

1969 Toned	5,000,000	£10
1970	10,000,000	£5
1971	8,000,000	£8
1974	7,000,000	£10
1975	10,000,000	£10
1976	20,600,000	£5
1978	28,500,000	£5
1980	22,200,000	£5
1982	24,400,000	£4
1985	4,200,000	£8
1986	15,300,000	£5
1990	7,500,000	£8
Size reduced to 18.4mm		
1992	74,500,000	£5
1993	89,100,000	£5
1994	31,100,000	£5
1995	12,000,000	£5
1996	14,700,000	£2
1998	158,500,000	£2
2000	Unknown	£1

TEN PENCE

1969	27,000,000	£12
1971	4,000,000	£15
1973	2,500,000	£16
1974	7,500,000	£12
1975	15,000,000	£12
1976	9,400,000	£12
1978	30,900,000	£10
1980	44,600,000	£8
1982	7,400,000	£10
1985	4,100,000	£12
1986. Only issued in the 1986 set	11,280	£300
Size reduced to 22mm		
1992	2 known	—
1993	80,100,000	£5
1994	58,500,000	£5

DATE	MINTAGE	BU
1995	16,100,000	£5
1996	18,400,000	£3
1997	10,000,000	£4
1998	10,000,000	£4
1999	24,500,000	£3
2000	Unknown	£3

TWENTY PENCE

DATE	MINTAGE	BU
1985. Only 600 minted and 556 melted down, only 3 known	Extremely rare	
1986	50,400,000	£8
1988	20,700,000	£6
1992	14,800,000	£5
1994	11,100,000	£5
1995	18,200,000	£5
1996	29,300,000	£5
1998	25,000,000	£3
1999	11,000,000	£3
2000	Unknown	£2

FIFTY PENCE

DATE	MINTAGE	BU
1970	9,000,000	£10
1971	650,000	£7
1974	1,000,000	£55
1975	2,000,000	£55
1976	3,000,000	£45
1977	4,800,000	£55
1978	4,500,000	£45
1979	4,000,000	£45
1981	6,000,000	£25
1982	2,000,000	£25
1983	7,000,000	£25
1986 Only issued in the 1986 set	10,000	£325
1988	7,000,000	£5
1988 Dublin Millennium	5,000,000	£5
1988 — Proof	50,000	£35
1996	6,000,000	£7
1997	6,000,000	£7
1998	13,800,000	£5
1999	7,000,000	£4
2000	Unknown	£4

ONE POUND

DATE	MINTAGE	BU
1990	42,300,000	£5
1990 Proof	50,000	£25
1994	14,900,000	£5
1995	9,200,000	£5
1995 UN silver proof in case of issue	2,850	£200
1996	9,200,000	£5
1998	22,960,000	£4
1999	10,000,000	£5
2000	4,000,000	£5

	MINTAGE	BU
2000 Millennium	5,000,000	£8
2000 – Silver Proof Piedfort	90,000	£45

OFFICIAL COIN SETS ISSUED BY THE CENTRAL BANK

1971 Specimen set in green wallet. 6 coins	£35
1975 6 coin set	£65
1978 6 coin set	£65
1978 6 coin set. Black cover, scarce	£75
1982 6 coin set. Black cover	£75
1986 Specimen set in card folder 1/2p to 50p, 7 coins. Very scarce. Most sets have glue problems	£650
1996 7 coin set	£70
1998 7 coin set	£50
2000 Millennium set. Last decimal set	£145
2000 — With 1999 instead of the 2000 £1 coin	£295

Dublin Millennium 50p

OFFICIAL AND SEMI-OFFICIAL COMMEMORATIVE MEDALS

It is probably a strong love of history, rather than the strict disciplines of coin collecting that make collectors turn to commemorative medals. The link between the two is intertwined, and it is to be hoped that collectors will be encouraged to venture into the wider world of medallions, encouraged by this brief guide, originally supplied by Daniel Fearon (author of the *Catalogue of British Commemorative Medals)* and kindly updated again this year by Charles Riley.

DATE	VF	EF
JAMES I		
1603 Coronation (possibly by C. Anthony), 29mm, Silver	£1500	£2500
QUEEN ANNE		
1603 Coronation, 29mm, AR	£1000	£1750
CHARLES I		
1626 Coronation (by N. Briot), 30mm, Silver	£1200	£1800
1633 Scottish Coronation (by N. Briot), 28mm, Silver	£650	£1250
1649 Memorial (by J. Roettier). Struck after the Restoration, 50mm, Bronze	£90	£175
CROMWELL		
1653 Lord Protector (by T. Simon), 38mm, Silver	£700	£1700
— Cast examples	£350	£600
CHARLES II		
1651 Scottish Coronation, in exile (from design by Sir J. Balfour), 32mm, Silver	£3000	£4000
CHARLES II		
1661 Coronation (by T. Simon), 29mm		
— Gold	£3500	£7000
— Silver	£400	£600
1685 Death (by N. Roettier), 39mm, Bronze	£150	£325

James I Coronation, 1603

Charles II Coronation, 1661

DATE	VF	EF

JAMES II
1685 Coronation (by J. Roettier), 34mm
— Gold £3500 £7000
— Silver £600 £800

MARY
1685 Coronation (by J. Roettier), 34mm
— Gold £3500 £7000
— Silver £400 £650

WILLIAM & MARY
1689 Coronation (by J. Roettier), 32mm
— Gold £3200 £5500
— Silver £350 £550
1689 Coronation, "Perseus" (by G. Bower),
38mm, Gold £3200 £5500

MARY
1694 Death (by N. Roettier), 39mm, Bronze........ £95 £245

WILLIAM III
1697 "The State of Britain" (by J. Croker), 69mm,
Silver £850 £1500

ANNE
1702 Accession, "Entirely English" (by J. Croker), 34mm
— Gold £3200 £5500
— Silver £150 £225
1702 Coronation (by J. Croker), 36mm
— Gold £3500 £7000
— Silver £300 £400
1707 Union with Scotland (by J. Croker, rev. by S. Bull), 34mm
— Gold £3200 £5500
— Silver £200 £300
1713 Peace of Utrecht (by J. Croker—issued in gold to Members
of Parliament), 34mm
— Gold £1500 £2750
— Silver £150 £250

Queen Anne, 1702–1713.

GEORGE I
1714 Coronation (by J. Croker), 34mm
— Gold £3200 £4500
— Silver £250 £350
1727 Death (by J. Dassier), 31mm, Silver £150 £275

GEORGE II
1727 Coronation (by J. Croker), 34mm
— Gold £3200 £4500
— Silver £250 £350

QUEEN CAROLINE
1727 Coronation (by J. Croker), 34mm
— Gold £3200 £5500
— Silver £250 £375
1732 The Royal Family (by J. Croker), 70mm
— Silver £1500 £3000
— Bronze.. £400 £700

George I Coronation, 1714.

DATE	VF	EF

GEORGE III
1761 Coronation (by L. Natter), 34mm
- Gold £2750 £4250
- Silver £500 £600
- Bronze.. £150 £250

QUEEN CHARLOTTE
1761 Coronation (by L. Natter), 34mm
- Gold £1850 £3500
- Silver £375 £600
- Bronze.. £150 £295
1810 Golden Jubilee, "Frogmore", 48mm, Silver £130 £275
- Bronze.. £95 £175

GEORGE IV
1821 Coronation (by B. Pistrucci), 35mm
- Gold £1600 £2500
- Silver £350 £450
- Bronze.. £95 £150

WILLIAM IV
1831 Coronation (by W. Wyon; rev.shows
   Queen Adelaide), 33mm
- Gold £1250 £2500
- Silver £175 £325
- Bronze.. £95 £150

QUEEN VICTORIA
1838 Coronation (by B. Pistrucci), 37mm
- Gold £1500 £2500
- Silver £300 £400
- Bronze.. £60 £120

George III, Coronation, 1761

Queen Victoria Coronation, 1838

Queen Victoria Diamond Jubilee 1897

DATE	VF	EF
1887 Golden Jubilee (by J. E. Boehm, rev. by Lord Leighton)		
— Gold, 58mm	£6500	£8500
— Silver, 78mm	£250	£500
— Bronze, 78mm	£95	£180
1897 Diamond Jubilee (by G. de Saulles),		
— Gold, 56mm	£6500	£8500
— Silver, 56mm	£95	£125
— Bronze, 56mm	£35	£60
— Gold, 25mm	£1250	£1500
— Silver, 25mm	£20	£35

EDWARD VII

1902 Coronation (August 9) (by G. W. de Saulles)

	VF	EF
— Gold, 56mm	£6500	£8500
— Silver, 56mm	£95	£150
— Bronze, 56mm	£30	£55
— Gold, 31mm	£1250	£1500
— Silver, 31mm	£20	£30

Some rare examples of the official medal show the date as June 26, the original date set for the Coronation which was postponed because the King developed appendicitis.

George V Silver Jubilee, 1935

GEORGE V

1911 Coronation (by B. Mackennal)

	VF	EF
— Gold, 51mm	£6500	£8500
— Silver, 51mm	£95	£250
— Bronze, 51mm	£30	£65
— Gold, 31mm	£1250	£1500
— Silver, 31mm	£20	£35

1935 Silver Jubilee (by P. Metcalfe)

	VF	EF
— Gold, 58mm	£6500	£8500
— Silver, 58mm	£100	£150
— Gold, 32mm	£1250	£1500
— Silver, 32mm	£20	£30

PRINCE EDWARD

1911 Investiture as Prince of Wales (by W. Goscombe John)

	VF	EF
— Gold, 31mm	£2500	£5000
— Silver, 31mm	£50	£85

Edward, Prince of Wales, 1911

EDWARD VIII

1936 Abdication (by L. E. Pinches), 35mm

	VF	EF
— Gold	£1750	£2500
— Silver	£45	£65
— Bronze	£20	£35

GEORGE VI

1937 Coronation (by P. Metcalfe)

	VF	EF
— Gold, 58mm	£6500	£8500
— Silver, 58mm	£65	£95
— Gold, 32mm	£1250	£1500
— Silver, 32mm	£25	£35
— Bronze, 32mm	£12	£15

Edward VIII, Abdication, 1936.

DATE	VF	EF

ELIZABETH II
1953 Coronation (by Spink & Son)—illustrated

— Gold, 57mm	£5500	£6500
— Silver, 57mm	£65	£125
— Bronze, 57mm	£35	£65
— Gold, 32mm	£750	£950
— Silver, 32mm	£25	£35
— Bronze, 32mm	£12	£15

1977 Silver Jubilee (by A. Machin)

— Silver, 57mm	—	£70
— Silver, 44mm	—	£40

*The gold medals are priced for 18ct—they can also be found as 22ct and 9ct, and prices should be adjusted accordingly.

PRINCE CHARLES
1969 Investiture as Prince of Wales (by M. Rizello)

— Silver, 57mm	—	£75
— Bronze gilt, 57mm..	—	£40
— Silver, 45mm	—	£50
— Gold, 32mm	—	£1250
— Silver, 32mm	—	£35
— Bronze, 32mm	—	£10

QUEEN ELIZABETH THE QUEEN MOTHER
1980 80th Birthday (by L. Durbin)

— Silver, 57mm	—	£65
— Silver, 38mm	—	£38
— Bronze, 38mm	—	£25

N.B.—Official Medals usually command a premium when still in their original case of issue.

Prince Charles, Prince of Wales 1969.

The Royal Mint Museum contains a charming group of medallic portraits of seven of the children of Queen Victoria and Prince Albert. They appear to have been made in 1850 and therefore do not include the two children who were born after that date. The skilfully-executed portraits are the work of Leonard Wyon, a member of the extremely talented family of engravers whose name is so well known to numismatists. The son of William Wyon, he was actually born in the Royal Mint in 1826. These particular portraits were not commissioned by the Mint and little is known about the circumstances in which they were prepared, but for some reason the dies have survived in the Royal Mint Museum, along with single-sided bronze impressions roughly the size of a half-crown.

Images and information courtesy of Dr Kevin Clancy, The Royal Mint.

Directory
section

O N the following pages will be found the most useful names and addresses needed by the coin collector.

At the time of going to press with this edition of the YEARBOOK the information is correct, as far as we have been able to ascertain. However, people move and establishments change, so it is always advisable to make contact with the person or organisation listed before travelling any distance, to ensure that the journey is not wasted.

Should any of the information in this section not be correct we would very much appreciate being advised in good time for the preparation of the next edition of the COIN YEARBOOK.

BRITISH NUMISMATIC TRADE ASSOCIATION

BNTA

DEALER MEMBERS BY COUNTY

LONDON AREA
*Apollo Galleries Ltd -
www. apollogalleries.com
*ArtAncient Ltd - www.artancient.com
*ATS Bullion Ltd - www.atsbullion.com
*AH Baldwin & Sons Ltd -
www.baldwin.co.uk
Jon Blyth - www.jonblyth.com
Bonhams 1793 Ltd - www.bonhams.com
*Classical Numismatic Group LLC -
www.cngcoins.com
*Philip Cohen Numismatics -
www.coinheritage.co.uk
André de Clermont - www.declermont.com
Christopher Eimer -
www.christophereimer.co.uk
*Heritage Auctions UK - www.ha.com
*Knightsbridge Coins -
info@knightsbridgecoins.com
C.J. Martin (Coins) Ltd -
www.antiquities.co.uk
*Morton & Eden Ltd -
www.mortonandeden.com
Noonans - www.noonans.co.uk
*Numismatica Ars Classica -
www.arsclassicacoins.com
Physical Gold Ltd -
www.physicalgold.co.uk
Simmons Gallery -
www.simmonsgallery.co.uk
*Sovereign Rarities Ltd - www.sovr.co.uk
*Spink & Son Ltd - www.spink.com
St James's Auctions - www.stjauctions.com
*The Coin Cabinet Ltd -
www.thecoincabinet.co.uk
The London Coin Company Ltd -
www.thelondoncoincompany.com

BERKSHIRE
*Douglas Saville Numismatic Books -
www.douglassaville.com

BUCKINGHAMSHIRE
Charles Riley - www.charlesriley.co.uk

CAMBRIDGESHIRE
Den Of Antiquity International Ltd -
www.denofantiquity.co.uk
*Cambridgeshire Coins -
www.cambridgeshirecoins.com

CHESHIRE
Colin Cooke - www.colincooke.com

CORNWALL
Richard W. Jeffery - richard@trebehor.co.uk

DEVON
Glenn S. Ogden - www.glennogdencoins.com

DORSET
*Dorset Coin Co Ltd -
www.dorsetcoincompany.co.uk
Timothy Medhurst Coins & Antiquities -
www.timothymedhurst.co.uk

ESSEX
DRG Coins and Antiquities -
www.drgcoinsandantiquities.com
*Time Line - www.timelineauctions.com

GLOUCESTERSHIRE
Silbury Coins Ltd - www.silburycoins.com

HAMPSHIRE
Asprey Coins - www.aspreycoins.co.uk
M J Hughes - www.mjhughescoins.com-
Victory Coins - vcpompey@yahoo.co.uk
Wessex Coins - www.wessexcoins.co.uk
West Essex Coin Investment - 01425-656459

HEREFORDSHIRE
Whitmore Coins, Tokens and Medallions -
www.whitmorectm.com

HERTFORDSHIRE
KB Coins - www.kbcoins.com

KENT
*London Coins Ltd - www.londoncoins.co.uk
*Peter Morris - www.petermorris.co.uk
*T&T Auctions Ltd - www.tandtauctions.com

LEICESTERSHIRE
Hall's Hammered Coins -
www.hallshammeredcoins.com

MERSEYSIDE
*Merseyside Collectors Centre -
www.mccentre.co.uk

MONMOUTHSHIRE
Anthony M. Halse -
www.coinsandtokens.com

NORFOLK
*BucksCoins – www. buckscoins.com
Roderick Richardson -
www.roderickrichardson.com
Chris Rudd - www.celticcoins.com

NOTTINGHAMSHIRE
History in Coins - www.historyincoins.com

OXFORDSHIRE
Richard Gladdle - Gladdle@plumpudding.org

SHROPSHIRE
M. Veissid - m.veissid@btinternet.com

SOMERSET
Hammered British Coins -
mail@hammeredbritishcoins.com

STAFFORDSHIRE
*English Coin Company -
www.englishcoincompany.com

SUFFOLK
* Lockdale Coins Ltd - www.lockdales.com
Simon Monks - www.simonmonks.co.uk

SURREY
Mark Rasmussen Numismatist - www.rascoins.com

SUSSEX
John Newman Coins -
www.johnnewmancoins.com

TYNE AND WEAR
*Corbitts Ltd - www.corbitts.com

WARWICKSHIRE
Brittonum Ltd - www.brittonum.com
* Peter Viola - 07770897707
* Warwick & Warwick Ltd -
www.warwickandwarwick.com

WEST MIDLANDS
*Atkinsons Coins and Bullion -
www.atkinsonsbullion.com
*Birmingham Coins -
cannockcollectibles@hotmail.com
David Craddock -
davidcraddock373@btinternet.com
Paul Davis Birmingham Ltd -
pjdavis79@btinternet.com

WILTSHIRE
*Gold-Traders (UK) Ltd -
www.britanniacoincompany.com

YORKSHIRE
AMR Coins - www.amrcoins.com
Keith Chapman - www.anglosaxoncoins.com
Paul Clayton -
paulnormanclayton@googlemail.com
Paul Davies Ltd - paul@pauldaviesltd.co.uk
*Paul Dawson York Ltd -
pauldawsonyork@hotmail.co.uk

SCOTLAND
Paul Menzies Ltd - www.paulmenziesltd.com
*Scotmint Ltd - www.scotmint.com

WALES
Anthony M Halse - www.coinsandtokens.com
Lloyd Bennett - www.coinsofbritain.com
Colin Rumney - pru@rumneyp.fsnet.co.uk

*Retail premises

WWW.BNTA.NET

Museums
and libaries

Listed below are the Museums and Libraries in the UK which have coins or items of numismatic interest on display or available to the general public.

A

• Kings Museum, University of Aberdeen, Old Aberdeen Town House, **Aberdeen**, AB9 1AS. Tel: 01224 274 330.

• Curtis Museum (1855), High Street, **Alton**, Hants, GU34 1BA. Tel: 0142082802. *General collection of British coins.*

• Ashburton Museum, The Bullring, **Ashburton**, Devon, TQ13 7DT. *Ancient British and Roman antiquities including local coin finds.*

• Ashwell Village Museum (1930), Swan Street, **Ashwell**, Baldock, Herts, SG7 5NY. Tel: 01462 742 956 *Roman coins from local finds, local trade tokens, Anglo-Gallic coins and jetons.*

• Buckinghamshire County Museum (1862), Church Street, **Aylesbury**, Bucks, HP20 2QP. Tel: 01296 331 441. *Roman and medieval English coins found locally, 17th/18th century Buckinghamshire tokens, commemorative medals.*

B

• Banbury Museum, Castle Quay Shopping Center, Spiceball Park Road, **Banbury**, Oxon, OX16 2PQ. Tel: 01295 236165. *Wrexlin Hoard of Roman coins.*

• Museum of Barnstaple and North Devon (1931). **The Square, Barnstaple, EX23 8LN.** Tel: 01271 346 747. *General coin and medal collection, including local finds. Medals of the Royal Devonshire Yeomanry.*

• Roman Baths Museum, Abbey Church Yard, Stall St, **Bath**, Avon, BA1 1LZ. Tel: 01225 477 785. *Comprehensive collection of Roman coins from local finds.*

• Bagshaw Museum and Art Gallery (1911), Wilton Park, **Batley**, West Yorkshire, WF17 0AS. Tel: 01924 324 765. *Roman, Scottish, Irish, English hammered, British and foreign coins, local traders' tokens, political medalets, campaign medals and decorations.*

• The Higgins Art Gallery and Museum (1961), Castle Lane, **Bedford**, MK40 3XD. Tel: 01234 718 618. *Collections of the Bedford Library and Scientific Institute, the Beds Archaeological Society and Bedford Modern School (Pritchard Memorial) Museum.*

• Ulster Museum (1928), Botanic Gardens, **Belfast**, BT9 5AB. Tel: 028 9044 0000 *Irish, English and British coins and commemorative medals.*

• Berwick Museum and Art Gallery (1867), The Clock Block, Berwick Barracks, Parade, **Berwick**, TD15 1DQG. Tel: 01289 309538. *Roman, Scottish and medievial coins.*

• Treasure House and Art Gallery (1910), Champney Road, **Beverley**, Humberside, HU17 8HE. Tel: 01482 393939. *Beverley trade tokens, Roman, English, British and foreign coins.*

• Bignor Roman Villa (1811), **Bignor**, nr Pulborough, West Sussex, RH20 1PH. Tel: 01798 869 259. *Roman coins found locally.*

• City Museum and Art Gallery (1861), Chamberlain Square, **Birmingham**, B3 3DH. Tel: 0121 348 8000. *Coins, medals and tokens - special emphasis on the products of the Soho, Heaton, Birmingham and Watt mints.*

• Blackburn Museum, Museum Street, **Blackburn**, Lancs, BB1 7AJ. Tel: 01254 667 130. *Incorporates the Hart (5,000 Greek, Roman and early English) and Hornby (500 English coins) collections, as well as the museum's own collection of British and Commonwealth coins.*

• Bognor Regis Museum, 25 – 27 West Street, **Bognor Regis**, West Sussex, PO21 1XA. Tel: 01243 865 636 *Roman, English and British coins and trade tokens.*

• Bolton Museum and Art Gallery,(1893), Le Mans Crescent, **Bolton**, Lancashire, BL1 1SE. **Tel: 01204 332211**

• Roman Town and Museum (1949) Front Street, Aldborough, **Boroughbridge**, N. Yorks, YO51 9ES. Tel: 01423 322 768. *Roman coins.*

• The Museum (1929),Boston Guildhall, South Street, **Boston**, Lincs, PE21 6HT. Tel: 01205 365 954. *Small collection of English coins.*

• Natural Science Society Museum (1903), 39 Christchurch Road, **Bournemouth**, Dorset, BH1 3NS. Tel: 01202 553 525. *Greek, Roman and English hammered coins (including the Hengistbury Hoard), local trade tokens.*

• Bolling Hall Museum (1915), Bowling Hall Road, **Bradford**, West Yorkshire, BD4 7LP. Tel: 01274 431 826. *Some 2,000 coins and tokens, mostly 18th–20th centuries.*

• Bridport Museum (1932), 25 South Street, **Bridport**, Dorset DT6 3RJ. Tel: 01308 458 703. *Roman coins, mainly from excavations at Claudian Fort.*

• Bristol Museum and Art Gallery (1820), Queen's Road, **Bristol**, BS8 1RL. Tel: 0117 922 3571. *Ancient British, Roman (mainly from local hoards), English hammered coins, especially from the Bristol mint, and several hundred local trade tokens.*

• Buxton Museum and Art Gallery (1891), Terrace Road, **Buxton**, Derbyshire, SK17 6DA. Tel: 01629 533 540. *English and British coins, tokens and commemorative medals. Numismatic library.*

C

• Segontium Fort Museum (1928), Beddgelert Road, **Caernarfon**, Gwynedd, LL55 2LN. Tel: 0300 025 6000. *Roman coins and artifacts excavated from the fort.*

• Fitzwilliam Museum (1816), Trumpington Street, **Cambridge**, CB2 1RB. Tel: 01223 332 900. *Ancient, English, medieval European, oriental coins, medals, plaques, seals and cameos.*

• National Museum & Galleries of Wales, Cathays Park, **Cardiff**, CF10 3NP. Tel: 0300 111 2 333. *Greek, Celtic, Roman and British coins and tokens with the emphasis on Welsh interest. Also military, civilian and comm. medals.*

• Guildhall Museum (1979), 31-33 Fisher Street, **Carlisle**, Cumbria, CA3 8JE. Tel: 01228 618 718. *General collection of coins and medals.*

• Tullie House (1877), Castle Street, **Carlisle**, Cumbria, CA3 8TP. Tel: 01228 618 718. *Roman, medieval and later coins from local finds, including medieval counterfeiter's coin-moulds.*

• Gough's Caves Museum (1934), The Cliffs, **Cheddar**, Somerset, BS27 3QF. Tel: 01934 742 343. *Roman coins.*

• Chelmsford Museum (1835), Oaklands Park, Moulsham Street, **Chelmsford**, Essex, CM2 9AQ. Tel: 01245 605 700. *Ancient British, Roman, medieval and later coins mainly from local finds, local medals.*

• Chepstow Museum, Bridge Street, Chepstow, (1949), **Chepstow**, Gwent, NP15 5EZ. Tel: 01291 625 981. *Local coins and trade tokens.*

• Grosvenor Museum (1886), 27 Grosvenor Street, **Chester**, CH1 2DD. **Tel:** 01244 972 197. *Roman coins from the fortress site, Anglo-Saxon, English medieval and post-medieval coins of the Chester and Rhuddlan mints, trade tokens, English and British milled coins.*

• Chesterfield Museum (1879). *Roman coins from local finds, Derbyshire trade tokens, medals, seals and railway passes. Numismatic library and publications.* **Temporarily Closed. Reopens Winter 2024.**

• Red House Museum (1919), Quay Road, **Christchurch**, Dorset. Tel: 01202 482 860. *Coins of archaeological significance from Hampshire and Dorset, notably the South Hants Hoard, ancient British, Armorican, Gallo-Belgic, Celtic and Roman coins, local trade tokens and medals.*

• Corinium Museum (1856), Park Street, **Cirencester**, Glos.Tel:01285 655 611. *Roman coins.*

• Colchester and Essex Museum (1860), The Castle, **Colchester**, Essex. Tel: 01206 282 931. *Ancient British and Roman coins from local finds, medieval coins (especially the Colchester Hoard), later English coins and Essex trade tokens, commemorative medals.*

D

• Public Library, Museum and Art Gallery (1921), Crown Street, **Darlington**, Co Durham DL1 1ND. Tel: 01325 462 034. *Coins, medals and tokens.*

• Borough Museum (1908), 18 - 20 Market Street, **Dartford**, Kent, DA1 1EU. Tel: 01322 224 739. *Roman, medieval and later English hammered coins, trade tokens and commemorative medals.*

• Dartmouth Museum (1953), The Butterwalk, **Dartmouth**, Devon TQ6 9PZ. Tel: 01803 832 923. *Coins and medals of a historical and maritime nature.*

• Museum and Art Gallery (1878), The Strand, **Derby**, DE1 1BS. Tel:01332 641 901. *Roman coins, English silver and copper regal coins, Derbyshire tradesmen's tokens, British campaign medals and decorations of the Derbyshire Yeomanry and the 9/12 Royal Lancers.*

• Danum Gallery, Library and Museum, (1909), Waterdale, Doncaster DN1 3BZ Tel: 01302 737555. *General collection of English and foreign silver and bronze coins. Representative collection of Roman imperial silver and bronze coins, including a number from local hoards. English trade tokens, principally of local issues, medals.*

• Dorset County Museum (1846), High West Street, **Dorchester**, Dorset, DT1 1XA. Tel: 01305 262 735. *British, Roman, medieval and later coins of local interest.*

• Dumfries Museum (1835), The Observatory, Rotchell Road, **Dumfries** Tel: 01387 253 374. *Greek, Roman, Anglo-Saxon, medieval English and Scottish coins, especially from local hoards. Numismatic library.*

• The McManus Dundee's Art Galleries and Museums (1873). Albert Square, **Dundee**, DD1 1DA. Tel:01382 307 200. *Coins and medals of local interest.*

• The Cathedral Treasury (995 AD), The College, **Durham**, DH1 3EH. Tel: 0191 338 7178. *Greek and Roman coins bequeathed by Canon Sir George Wheeler (1724), Renaissance to modern medals, medieval English coins, especially those struck at the Durham ecclesiastical mint.*

• Durham Heritage Centre, St Mary le Bow, North Bailey, **Durham**, DH1 3ET. Tel: 0191 384 5589. *Roman, medieval and later coins, mainly from local finds.*

E

• National Museum of Scotland (1781), Chambers Street, **Edinburgh**, EH1 1JF. Tel: 0300 123 6789. *Roman, Anglo-Saxon, Englsh and Scottish coins, trade tokens, commemorative medals and communion tokens. Numismatic library. Publications.*

• Royal Albert Memorial Museum (1868), Queen Street, **Exeter**, EX4 3RX. Tel: 01392 265 858. *Roman and medieval. Coins of the Exeter Mint.*

G

• Hunterian Museum (1807), Gilbert Scott Building, University Of Glasgow, University Avenue, **Glasgow**, G12 8QQ. Tel: 0141 330 4221. *Greek, Roman, Byzantine, Scottish, English and Irish coins, Papal and other European medals, Indian and Oriental coins, trade and communion tokens.*

• Kelvingrove Art Gallery and Museum (1888), Argyle Street, **Glasgow.** Tel: 0141 276 9599. *General collection of coins, trade tokens, communion tokens, commemorative and military medals.*

• Riverside Museum (1974), 100 Pointhouse Place **Glasgow**, G3 8RS. Tel: 0141 287 2720. *Transport tokens and passes, commemorative medals, badges and insignia of railway companies and shipping lines.*

• City Museum and Art Gallery (1859), Brunswick Road, **Gloucester.** Tel: 01452 396 131. *Ancient British, Roman, Anglo-Saxon (from local finds), early medieval (from local mints), Gloucestershire trade tokens.*

• Guernsey Museum and Art Gallery, St Peter Port, **Guernsey.** Tel: 01481 726 518. *Armorican, Roman, medieval and later coins, including the coins, medals, tokens and paper money of Guernsey.*

• Guildford Museum (1898), Castle Hill, **Guildford**, Surrey, GU1 3SX. Tel: 01483 444 751. *Roman and medieval coins and later medals.*

H

• Gray Museum and Art Gallery, Church Square, Clarence Road, **Hartlepool**, Cleveland. Tel: 01429 523 438. *General collection, including coins from local finds.*

• Public Museum and Art Gallery (1890), John's Place, Bohemia Road , **Hastings**, East Sussex. Tel: 01424 451 052 *General collection of English coins, collection of Anglo-Saxon coins from Sussex mints.*

• City Museum (1874), Broad Street, **Hereford** HR4 9AU. Tel: 01432 260692

• Hertford Museum (1902), 18 Bull Plain, **Hertford.** Tel: 01992 582 686. *British, Roman, medieval and later English coins and medals.*

• Honiton and Allhallows Public Museum (1946), High Street, **Honiton**, Devon. Tel:01404 44966. *Small general collection, including coins from local finds.*

• Museum and Art Gallery (1891), 19 New Church Road, **Hove**. Tel:0300 029 0200. *English coins, Sussex trade tokens and hop tallies, campaign medals, orders and decorations, comm. medals.*

• Tolson Memorial Museum (1920), Ravensknowle Park, **Huddersfield**, West Yorkshire. Tel: 01484 223 240. *Representative collection of British coins and tokens, Roman and medieval coins, mainly from local finds.*

• Hull and East Riding Museum (1928), 36 High Street, **Hull.** Tel: 01482 300 300. *Celtic, Roman and medieval coins and artifacts from local finds. Some later coins including tradesmen's tokens.*

I

• The Manx Museum, Douglas, **Isle of Man.** Tel: 01624 648 000. *Roman, Celtic, Hiberno-Norse, Viking, medieval English and Scottish coins, mainly from local finds, Manx traders' tokens from the 17th to 19th centuries, Manx coins from 1709 to the present day.*

J

• Jersey Museum, Weighbridge, St Helier, **Jersey** Tel: 01534 633 300. *Armorican, Gallo-Belgic, Roman, medieval English and French coins, coins, paper money and tokens of Jersey.*

K

• Cliffe Castle Museum, Spring Gardens Lane, **Keighley** West Yorkshire. Tel: 01535 618 231. *Roman coins found locally.*

• Dick Institute Museum and Art Gallery (1893), Elmbank Avenue, **Kilmarnock**, Ayrshire. Tel: 01563 554 300. *General collection of coins and medals, and the Hunter-Selkirk collection of communion tokens.*

L

• City Museum (1923), Old Town Hall, Market Square, **Lancaster.** Tel: 01524 64637. *Roman, Anglo-Saxon, medieval English coins, provincial trade tokens, medals of the King's Own Royal Lancashire Regiment.*

• City Museum (1820), Millenium Square, **Leeds**, West Yorkshire. Tel: 0113 378 5001. *Greek, Roman, Anglo-Saxon, English medieval, Scottish, Irish, British, Commonwealth and foreign coins. Several Roman and Saxon hoards. The Backhouse collection of Yorkshire banknotes, the Thornton collection of Yorkshire tokens, British and foreign commemorative medals.*

• New Walk Museum (1849), 53 New Walk, **Leicester.** Tel: 0116 225 4900. *Roman, medieval and later coins, mainly from local finds, tokens, commemorative medals, campaign medals and decorations.*

• Pennington Hall Museum and Art Gallery, **Leigh**, Lancashire. *Roman and British coins and medals.*

• Litchfield Museum (1859), Market Square **Lichfield**, Staffs WS13 6LG. Email: info@lichfieldheritage. org.uk. *Roman, medieval and later English coins, Staffordshire trade tokens and commemorative medals.*

• World Museum(1851), William Brown Street, **Liverpool**, L3 8EN. Tel: 0151 478 4393. *General collection of Roman, medievaland later British coins, tokens.*

• Bank of England Museum, Bartholomew Lane, **London.** Tel: 020 3461 5545. *Exhibits relating to gold bullion, coins, tokens and medals, the design and manufacture of banknotes, and a comprehensive collection of bank notes dating from the 17th century to the present day.*

• British Museum(1752), HSBC Coin Gallery, Great Russell Street, **London**, WC1. Tel: 020 7323 8000. *Almost a million coins, medals, tokens and badges of all period from Lydia, 7th century BC to the present time. Extensive library of books and periodicals.*

• British Numismatic Society (1903), Warburg Institute, Woburn Square, **London**, WC1. *Library containing over 5,000 volumes, including sale catalogues, periodicals and pamphlets. Open to members only.*

• Gunnersbury Park Museum (1927), Acton, **London**, W3. Tel: 0203 9610280

• Horniman Museum and Library (1890), 100 London Road, Forest Hill, **London**, SE23 3PQ Tel: 020 8699 1872. *General collection, primitive currency, some tokens.*

• Imperial War Museum, Lambeth Road, **London**, SE1 6HZ. Tel: 020 7416 5000. *Emergency coinage of two world wars, occupation and invasion money, extensive collection of German Notgeld, commemorative, propaganda and military medals, badges and insignia.*

• Sir John Soane's Museum (1833), 13 Lincoln's Inn Fields, **London**, WC2. Tel: 020 7405 2107. *Napoleonic medals and medallic series of the late 18th and early 19th centuries.*

• National Maritime Museum, Romney Road, Greenwich, **London**, SE10. Tel: 020 8858 4422. *Commemorative medals with a nautical or maritime theme, naval medals and decorations.*

• Victoria and Albert Museum (1852), Cromwell Road, South Kensington, **London**, SW7 2RL. Tel: 020 7942 2000. *Byzantine gold and medieval Hispano-Mauresque coins (Department of Metalwork), large collection of Renaissance and later medals (Department of Architecture and Sculpture). Numismatic books.*

• Ludlow Museum (1833). The Assembly Rooms. Castle Square, **Ludlow.** Tel: 01584 878 697. *Roman and medieval coins from local finds.*

• Luton Museum and Art Gallery (1927), Wardown House, Old Bedford Road, **Luton**, Beds. Tel: 01582 546722. *Coins, tokens and medals.*

M

• Museum and Art Gallery (1858), St Faiths Street, **Maidstone**, Kent. Tel: 01622 602838. *Ancient British, Roman, Anglo-Saxon and medieval coins found in Kent, modern British coins, Kent trade tokens, banknotes, hop tallies and tokens, primitive currency, collections of Kent Numismatic Society.*

• The Manchester Museum (1868). The University, **Manchester**. Tel: 0161 275 2648. *Very fine collections of Greek and Roman coins, comprehensive collections of English, European and Oriental coins, over 30,000 in all.***Temporarily closed. Reopens February 2023.**

• Margate Museum (1923), Market Place, Margate Old Town, **Margate**, Kent. Tel: 01843 231 213. *Small collection of coins, including Roman from local finds.*

• Montrose Museum and Art Gallery (1836). Panmure Place, **Montrose**, Angus, DD10 8HF. Tel: 01674 907447. *Scottish and British coins.*

N

• Newark-on-Trent Museum (1912), 14 Appletongate, **Newark**, Notts. Tel 01636 655765 *Siege pieces, trade tokens and coins from local finds and hoards.*

• West Berkshire Museum, The Wharf, **Newbury**, Berkshire. Tel: 01635 519562. *Ancient British, Roman and medieval coins and artifacts, later coins and tokens.*

• Great North Museum, Hancock Barras Bridge, **Newcastle-upon-Tyne.** Tel: 0191 208 6765. *Ancient coins.*

O

• Heberden Coin Room, Ashmolean Museum (1683), **Oxford**. Tel: 01865 278058. *Extensive collections of all periods, notably Greek, Roman, English and Oriental coins, Renaissance portrait and later medals, tokens and paper money. Large library. Numerous publications.*

P

• Peterborough Museum (1881), Priestgate, **Peterborough**, Cambs. Tel: 01733 864 663. *Roman (mainly from local hoards and finds), Anglo-Saxon, medieval English and modern European coins, English and British commemorative medals and tokens.*

• The Box (1897), The Box, Tavistock Pl, Plymouth PL4 8AX.

• Waterfront Museum, 4 High Street, **Poole**, BH15 1BW. Tel: 01202 262 600. *General collection of British and foreign coins, medals and tokens (view by appointment).*

• Portsmouth Museum (1972), Museum Road, Old **Portsmouth**, PO1 2LJ. Tel: 023 9283 4779. *Roman, medieval and later coins mainly from local finds and archaeological excavation, British coins, trade tokens of Hampshire, commemorative medals.*

• Harris Museum and Art Gallery (1893) Market Square, **Preston**, PR1 2PP. Tel: 01772 258 248. *English and British coins, tokens and medals.* **Temporarily closed.**

R

• The Museum of Reading (1883), Blagrave Street, **Reading**, RG1 1QH. Tel: 0118 937 3400. *British, Roman and medieval English coins, many from local finds, tradesmen's tokens and commemorative medals.*

• Rochdale Pioneers Museum (1905), 31 Toad Lane, **Rochdale**, OL12 0NU. Tel: 01706 524 920. *Roman and medieval coins from local finds, Rochdale trade tokens, miscellaneous British and foreign coins and medals.*

• Clifton Park Museum (1893), Clifton Park, **Rotherham**, S65 2AA. Tel: 01709 336 633. *Collection includes Roman coins from Templeborough Forts, medieval English coins from local hoards and a general collection of British coins.*

S

• Saffron Walden Museum (1832) (1939), Museum Street, **Saffron** Walden, CB10 1JL. Tel: 01799 510 333. *Ancient British, Roman, medieval and later coins, mainly from local finds and archaeological excavation, trade tokens and commemorative medals.*

• Verulamium Museum, St Michael's, **St Albans**, Herts . Tel: 01727 751 810. *Coins and artifacts excavated from the Roman town.*

• Salisbury and South Wiltshire Museum (1861), The Kings House 65 The Close, **Salisbury**, Wilts. Tel: 01722 332 151. *Collection of coins minted or found locally, including finds of Iron Age, Roman, Saxon and medieval coins, as well as 18th and 19th century tradesmen's tokens.*

• Richborough Castle Museum (1930) **Sandwich**, Kent. Tel: 0304 612013. *Roman coins of 1st–5th centuries from excavations of the Richborough site.* **Temporarily closed. Reopens 2023.**

• Rotunda Museum (1829), Vernon Road, **Scarborough**, YO11 2PS. Tel: 01723 353 665. *Collection of over 4,000 Roman coins, 1,500 English and 600 coins from local finds, siege pieces and trade.*

• Gold Hill Museum (1946), Gold Hill, **Shaftesbury**, Dorset, SP7 8JW. Tel: 01747 852 157. *Hoard of Saxon coins.*

• Weston Park Museum (1875), Western Bank, **Sheffield**. Tel: 0114 278 2600. *Over 5,000 coins of all periods, but mainly English and modern British. European coins, imperial Roman (including three hoards of about 500 coins each), Yorkshire trade tokens, British historical medals, campaign medals. Library.*

• Shrewsbury Museum and Art Gallery, The Music Hall, Market Street, **Shrewsbury**. Tel: 01743 258 885 *Coins minted at Shrewsbury 925-1180, Civil War coinage of 1642, Shropshire tradesmen's tokens, English coins and medals.*

• Atkinson Art Gallery (1878), Lord Street, **Southport,** Lancs. Tel: 01704 53333 *Roman coins.*

• Southwold Museum (1933), 9-11 Victoria Street, **Southwold**, IP18 6HZ. Tel: 07708 781317. *General collection of coins, specialised Suffolk trade tokens.*

• Stockport Museum (1860), 30-31 Market Place, **Stockport**, Cheshire SK1 1ES. Tel: 0161 474 4444 *Miscellaneous collection of coins, tokens and medals.*

• Museum in the Park (1899), Stratford Park, Stratford Road, **Stroud**, Glos GL5 4AF. Tel: 01453 7633 394. *Ancient British, Roman, Saxon, Norman, later medieval English, British coins and Gloucestershire trade tokens.*

• Sunderland Museum and Winter Gardens (1846), Burdon Road, **Sunderland,** Tyne & Wear SR1 1PP. Tel: 0191 553 2323. *Roman imperial, medieval and later English, including examples of the pennies minted at Durham, modern British and foreign coins, 17th-19th century tradesmen's tokens and local medallions.*

• Swansea Museum (1835), Victoria Road, **Swansea**, W. Glamorgan, SA1 1SN. Tel: 01792 653 763. *Coins and medals of local interest.*

T

• Tamworth Castle and Museum (1899), The Holloway, **Tamworth**, Staffs. Tel: 01827 709 626. *Anglo-Saxon coins, medieval English including coins of the Tamworth mint, later English and British coins, tokens, commemorative medallions and medals.*

• The Museum of Somerset, Taunton Castle, Castle Green, **Taunton**, Somerset TA1 4AA. Tel: 01823 255 088. *Celtic, Roman, Anglo-Saxon, early Medieval, tokens, medallions and banknotes. Strong emphasis on locally-found items.*

• Thurrock Museum and Heritage Service (1956), Second Floor, Thameside Complex, Orsett Road, Grays, Essex, RM17 5DX. Tel: 01375 413 965. *Roman coins.*

• Royal Cornwall Museum (1818), River Street, **Truro**, Cornwall TR1 2SJ. Tel: 01872 272 205. *Coins, tokens and medals pertaining principally to the county of Cornwall.*

W

• Wakefield Museum (1919), Burton Street, **Wakefield,** West Yorkshire WF1 2EB. Tel: 01924 305 376. *Roman and medieval English silver and copper coins.*

• Epping Forest District Museum, 39/41 Sun Street, **Waltham Abbey**, Essex, EN9 1EL. Tel: 01992 716882 *Ancient British, Roman and medieval coins, Essex tradesmen's tokens of local interest.*

• Warrington Museum and Art Gallery (1848). Bold Street, **Warrington**, Cheshire, WA1 1DR. Tel: 01925 442399. *Coins, medals and tokens.*

• Worcester City Museum (1833), Foregate Street, **Worcester**. Tel: 01905 25371. *Roman, medieval and later coins and tokens. Coins of the Worcester mint.*

• Wells Museum (18903), 8 Cathedral Green, **Wells,** Somerset. Tel: 01749 673 477. *Ancient and modern British and world coins, local trade tokens and medals.*

• Museum of Wigan Life (1878), 41 Library Street, **Wigan**, Lancashire. WN1 1NU Tel: 01942 828 128. *British, Commonwealth and foreign coins from about 1660 to the present. Roman coins from local sites, commemorative medals.*

• City Museum (1851), The Square, **Winchester**, Hants. SO23 9ES. Tel: 01962 863064. *Roman and medieval coins chiefly from local hoards and finds. Hampshire tradesmen's tokens and commemorative medals. Small reference library.*

• Wisbech and Fenland Museum (1835), Museum Square, **Wisbech**, Cambridgeshire, PE13 1ES. Tel: 01945 583 817, *British Roman, medieval and later coins, medals and tokens.*

Y

• York Castle Museum (1938), Eye of York, **York**, YO1 9RY. Tel: 01904 687 687. *English and British coins, campaign medals, orders and decorations, commemorative medals.*

• Jorvik Viking Centre (1984), Coppergate, **York, YO1 9WT**. Tel: 01904 615 505. *Coins and artefacts pertaining to the Viking occupation of York.*

• The Yorkshire Museum (1823), Museum Gardens, **York** YO1 7FR. Tel: 01904 687 687. *Roman imperial, medieval English and later coins, about 12,000 in all.*

Club
directory

Details given here are the names of Numismatic Clubs and Societies, their date of foundation, and their usual venues, days and times of meetings. Meetings are monthly unless otherwise stated. Finally, the telephone number of the club secretary is given; the names and addresses of club secretaries are withheld for security reasons, but full details may be obtained by writing to the Secretary of the British Association of Numismatic Societies, Bill Pugsley, bill@pugsley.co or visiting the website at www.coinclubs.org.uk.

Ayeshire Coin Club 1st Thurs, Oct to April, 19.30. Call for Venue, Tel: 07527 240 016

Banknote Society of Scotland (1994) Meetings are held four times a year in Edinburgh. Email, bnss2006@ntlworld.com

Bath & Bristol Numismatic Society (1950). The Globe Inn, Newton St Loe, Bath BA2 9BB 2nd Thu, 19.30. Email: adrian@bathandbristol-ns.org.uk.

Bedfordshire Numismatic Society (1966). 2nd Mon, call for venue details: 07541 461021

Birmingham Numismatic Society (1964). Friend's Meeting House, Bull Street. Email for dates: bhamns@hotmail.co.uk.

Matthew Boulton Lunar Society (1994). The Old School House, Chapel Lane, Birmingham, B47 6JX Tel: 01564 821 582.

British Banking History Society. 22 Delamere Road, Gatley, Cheadle, SK8 4PH.

British Numismatic Society (1903). Call for venue and dates; 02070161802.

Cambridgeshire Numismatic Society (1946). Friends' Meeting House, 12 Jesus Lane Cambridge, CB5 8BA. Call for dates. Tel: 01223 332 918.

Chester & North Wales Coin & Banknote Society (1996). Nags Head, Bunbury, Cheshire, CW6 9PB 4th Sat, 20.00. Tel: 01829 260 897.

Crewe & District Coin and Medal Society. Memorial Hall, Church Lane, Wistaston, Crewe, CW2 8ER. 2nd Tue, (exc Jan & July), 19.30 Tel: 07828 602 611.

Derbyshire Numismatic Society The Friends Meeting House, St Helen's Street, Derby. Tel: 01283 211623.

Devon & Exeter Numismatic Society, Courtenay Room, The St James Centre, Stadium Way, Exeter. 3rd Wed. Tel: 01395 568830.

Essex Numismatic Society (1966). Christchurch URC, 164 New London Road. 4th Fri (exc Dec), 20.00. Tel: 01279 814 216.

Glasgow & West of Scotland Numismatic Society (1947). Ibrox Parish Church Halls, Clifford Street, Glasgow, G51 1QH. 2nd Thu, Oct-April, 19.30. Tel: 07949 194036, Email: glasgowcoinclub@aol.com.

Harrow Coin Club (1968). The Scout Building, off Walton Road, Wealdstone, Harrow, HA1 4UX. 2nd Mon, 19.30. Tel: 0208 8952 8765.

Havering Numismatic Society (1967). Fairkytes Arts Centre, Billet Lane, Hornchurch, Essex, RM11 1AX 1st Tue, 19.30. Tel: 0208 5545 486. Email: mail@havering-ns.org.uk

Huddersfield Numismatic Society (1947). Lindley Liberal Club, 36 Occupation Road, Huddersfield, HD3 3EQ. 1st Mon (Sept to June) unless Bank Holiday then following Monday. Tel: 01484 866 814.

International Bank Note Society (London Branch) (1961). Spink, 69 Southampton Row, Bloomsbury, London, WC1B 4ET. Last Thu (exc Sept & Dec), 18.30. Tel: 0208 6413 224

International Bank Note Society (East Mids) , Highfields Community Fire Station, Hassocks Lane, Beeston, Nottingham, NG9 2 GQ. Last Saturday of every odd month. Tel: 0115 928 9720.

Ireland, Numismatic Society of (Northern Branch). Cooke/Instonians RFC, Shaws Bridge Sports Asson, 123 Milltown Road, Belfast. Call for dates; 07843 450597 www.numsocirelandnb.com.

Ireland, Numismatic Society of, Ely House, 8 Ely Place, Dublin 2. For dates and venues visit; 07843 450597, www.numismaticsocietyofireland.com.

Ipswich Coin Club, Archdeacons House, 11 Northgate Street, Ipswich, IP1 3BX. 2nd Tues. Tel; 0789 443 7847, www.ipnumsoc.org.uk.

Lancashire & Cheshire Numismatic Society (1933). Call for venue details. 3rd Sat, 14.00. Tel: 01204 849 469

London Numismatic Club (1947). Call for Venue details and dates; 0208 3030510 Email: g.buddle@btopenworld.com.

Loughborough Coin & Search Society (1964). Rosebery Medical Center, Rosebery Street, Loughborough, Leics, LE11 5DX 1st Thu, 19.30.

Norwich Coin & Medal Society, The White Horse Inn, Trowse, Norwich, NR14 8ST. 3rd Mon. Tel: 07894437847.

Numismatic Society of Nottinghamshire (1948). Highfield Fire Station, Hassocks Lane, Beeston, Nottingahm, NG9 2GQ. 2nd Mon (Sep-Apr). Tel: 0115 928 0347.

Orders & Medals Research Society (1942). Spink, 69 Southampton Row, Bloomsbury, London, WC1B 4ET. Last Monday of the month (except a Bank Holiday) of the odd numbered months plus April and October. 18.00.

Ormskirk & West Lancashire Numismatic Society (1970). The Eagle & Child, Maltkiln Lane, Bispham Green L40 1SN. 1st Thu, 20.15. Tel: 01704 232 494

Peterborough & District Numismatic Society (1967). Belsize Community Centre, Celta Road Peterborough, Cambs. 4th Tue (exc June, July & Aug), 19.30. Tel: 01733 567 763.

Plymouth Numismatic Society. 3rd Tue. Call for venue details. Tel: 07399 276295.

Reading Coin Club (1964). Abbey Baptist Church, Abbey Square, Reading, RG1 3BE 1st Mon, 19.00. Tel: 01344 774 155.

Royal Numismatic Society (1836). Warburg Institute, Woburn Square, London, WC1H 0AB. (some meetings held at Spink, 69 Southampton Row, Bloomsbury Road, London WC1B 4ET). 3rd Tues 18.00. Email: info@numismatics.org.uk. Tel: 0207 323 8541.

Southampton and District Numismatic Society (1953). Email for venue details: sue717@btinternet.com.

South Manchester Numismatic Society. Nursery Inn, 258 Green Lane, Heaton Norris, Stockport, SK4 2NA. 1st and 3rd Tue (Mar–Oct), 1st Tue (Nov–Feb). Tel: 07818 422696.

South Wales & Monmouthshire Numismatic Society (1958). 1st Mon (except Bank Holidays when 2nd Mon), 19.30. For venue call Tel: 02920 561 564.

Tyneside Numismatic Society (1954). The Plough Inn, 369 Old Durham Road, Gateshead, NE9 5LA. 2nd Weds, 19.30. Tel: is 07306 896 532

Wiltshire Numismatic Society (1965). The Raven Inn, Poulshot, Nr. Devizes, Wiltshire. 3rd Weds, (March–Dec), 20.00. Tel: 01225 703143. Email: verityjeffery2@gmail.com.

Worthing & District Numismatic Society (1967). The Ardington Hotel, Worthing, BN11 3DZ. 2nd Thu, 20.00. www.worthingnumismatics.co.uk.

Yorkshire Numismatic Society (1909). Email for venues and dates. Email: yorkshirenumismaticsociety@gmail.com.

Important Notice to Club Secretaries:

If your details as listed are incorrect please let us know in time for the next edition of the **COIN YEARBOOK.**

Amendments can be sent via post to: 8 Oaktree Place, ManatonClose, Exeter, EX2 8WA or via email to: jayne@tokenpublishing.com

IMPORTANT ORGANISATIONS

ADA
The Antiquities
Dealers Association

Secretary: Madeleine Perridge, c/o Kallos Gallery, 6 Chesterfield Gardens, London W1J 5BQ

IBNS
International
Bank Note Society

UK Membership Secretary: Kelvin Revere uk-secretary@theibns.org

ANA
The American
Numismatic Association

818 North Cascade Avenue, Colorado Springs, CO 80903, USA

RNS
Royal Numismatic Society

Dept of Coins & Medals, British Museum, London WC1B 3DG.

BNTA
The British Numismatic
Trade Association

Secretary: Christel Swan 3 Unwin Mansions, Queens Club Gardens, London, W14 9TH

BAMS
British Art Medal Society

Philip Attwood, Dept of Coins & Medals, British Museum, London WC1B 3DG.

IAPN
International Association of
Professional Numismatists

Secretary: Jean-Luc Van der Schueren, 14 Rue de la Bourse, B–1000, Brussels.

BNS
British Numismatic Society

Secretary: Peter Preston-Morley. Email: secretary@britnumsoc.org

Society activities are featured every month in the "Diary Section" of COIN NEWS magazine—available from all good newsagents or on subscription.
Telephone 01404 46972 for more details or log onto
www.tokenpublishing.com

There was a welcome return to fair attendance up and down the country as life began to get back to normal once Covid restrictions had eased. Fairs provide such a great opportunity to meet with collectors and learn more about coins as new Deputy Editor for COIN NEWS, Louise Bray (right), found out when she attended the highly successful Harrogate Coin fair held in April 2022 at the Old Swan Hotel, Harrogate.

Directory
of auctioneers

Listed here are the major auction houses which handle coins, medals, banknotes and other items of numismatic interest. Many of them hold regular public auctions, whilst others handle numismatic material infrequently. A number of coin companies also hold regular Postal Auctions—these are marked with a **℗**

Auction World Company Ltd
1-15-5 Hamamatsucho,Minato-ku,
Tokyo, 105-0013 Japan. www.auction-world.co

Baldwin's Auctions (BNTA)
399 Strand, London, WC2R 0LX.
Tel: 020 7930 6879,
Email: auctions@baldwin.co.uk,
www.baldwin.co.uk.

Biddle & Webb
Icknield Square, Birmingham, B16 0PP.
Tel: 0121 455 8042, www.biddleandwebb.com

Blyth & Co
Arkenstall Center, Haddenham, Cambs, CB6
3XD. Tel: 01353 930 094, www.blyths.com

BSA Auctions
Units 1/2, Cantilupe Court, Cantilupe Road, Ross on
Wye, Herefordshire, HR9 7AN . Tel: 01989 769 529,
www.the-saleroom.com

cgb.fr
36, Rue Vivienne, 75002, Paris, France.
Email: contact@cgb.fr, www.cgb.fr.

Chilcotts Auctioneers
The Dolphin Saleroom, High St, Honiton, Devon
EX14 1HT. Tel: 01404 47783,
email: info@chilcottsauctioneers.co.uk

Christies
8 King Street, St James's, London SW1Y 6QT.
Tel: 020 7839 9060.

Classical Numismatic Group Inc (Seaby Coins)
20 Bloomsbury Street, London, WC1B 3QA.
Tel: 020 7495 1888 ,fax 020 7499 5916,
Email: cng@cngcoins.com
www.historicalcoins.com. **℗**

The Coinery
Tel 01132 407900, www.auctions.thecoinery.co.uk.

The Coin Cabinet
First Floor, St James's Street, London SW1A 1LE
Tel 020 3808 5855, www.thecoincabinet.co.uk.

Corbitts
5 Moseley Sreet, Newcastle upon Tyne NE1 1YE.
Tel: 0191 232 7268, fax 0191 261 4130.
www.corbitts.com

Croydon Coin Auctions
4 Sussex Street, Rhyl LL18 1SG. Tel: 01492 440763,
www.croydoncoinauctions.com.

Davissons Ltd.
PO Box 323, Cold Spring, MN 56320 USA.
Tel: 001 320 685 3835, info@davcoin.com,
www.davcoin.com.

Duke's
Brewery Square, Dorchester, Dorset DT1 1GA.
Tel: 01305 265 080,
enquiries@dukesauctions.com,
www.dukes-auctions.com

David Duggleby Auctioneer
The Vine Street Salerooms, Scarborough,
North Yorkshire YO11 1XN. Tel: 01723 507111

English Coin Auctions
3 Elders Street, Scarborough, YO11 1DZ
Tel: 01723 364 760, wwwenglishcoinauctionscom

Jean Elsen & ses Fils s.a.
Avenue de Tervueren 65, B–1040, Brussels.
Tel: 0032 2 734 6356, Email: numismatique@e
lsen.euwww.elsen.eu.

Fellows & Sons
Augusta House, 19 Augusta Street, Hockley,
Birmingham, B18 6JA. Tel: 0121 212 2131,
www.fellows.co.uk.

B. Frank & Son
3 South Avenue, Ryton, Tyne & Wear NE40 3LD.
Tel: 0191 413 8749, Email: bfrankandson@aol.com,
www.bfrankandson.com.

Gadoury
57, rue Grimaldi, 98000 MONACO.
Tel: 0 377 93 25 12 96, Email: contact@gadoury.com,
www.gadoury.com.

Goldberg Coins & Collectibles
11400 W. Olympic Blvd, Suite 800, Los Angeles,
Hills CA 90064. Tel: 001 310.551 2646, info@
goldbergcoins.com, www.goldbergcoins.com.

Gorny & Mosch GmbH
Giessener Münzhandlung, Maximiliansplatz 20,
80333 Munich. Phone: +49-89/24 22 643-0,
info@gmcoinart.de

Heritage World Coin Auctions (BNTA)
UK address: 6 Shepherd Street, Mayfair,
London, W1J 7JE.
Tel: 001 214 528 3500, Bid@HA.com,
www.ha.com.

International Coin Exchange
Charter House, 5 Pembroke Row, Dublin 2.
Tel: 00353 8684 93355, www.ice-auction.com.
Kleeford Coin Auctions
Tel: 07484 272837, www.kleefordcoins.co.uk
email: kleeford@btinternet.com ℗
Fritz Rudolf Künker
Nobbenburger, Strasse 4A, 49076, Osnabrüeck,
Germany. Tel: 0049 5419 62020, fax: 0049 541 96 20
222, email: service@kuenker.de, www.kuenker.de
Lawrence Fine Art Auctioneers
The Linen Yard, South Street, Crewkerne, Somerset
TA18 8AB. Tel: 01460 73041, email: enquiries@
lawrences.co.uk, www.lawrences.co.uk.
Lockdale Coins (BNTA)
52 Barrack Square, Martlesham Heath, Ipswich,
Suffolk, IP5 3RF. Tel: 01473 627 110, sales@
lockdales.com, www.lockdales.com.
London Coins
Tel: 01474 871464, email: info@londoncoins.
co.uk, www.londoncoins.co.uk.
Mavin International
20 Kramat Lane, #01-04/05 United House,
Singapore 228773. Tel: +65 6238 7177,
MDC Monaco sarl
Allées Lumières Park Palace, 27 Avenue de la Costa,
98000 Monaco. Tel: +377 93 25 00 42, info@mdc.mc,
www.mdc.mc.
Mitchells
47 Station Road, Cockermouth, Cumbria, CA13 9PZ.
www.mitchellsantiques.co.uk
Morton & Eden Ltd (BNTA)
Nash House, St Georges Street, London W1S
2FQ. Tel: 020 7493 5344, info@mortonandeden.com,
www.mortonandeden.com.
Mowbray Collectables
Private Bag 63000, Wellington 6140, New Zealand
Tel: +64 6 364 8270, email: auctions@mowbrays.nz,
www.mowbraycollectables.com
Myntauktioner i Sverige AB
Banergatan 17, 115 22 Stockholm.
Nesbits Auctioneer & Valuers
7 Clarendon Road, Soouthsea, Hants, PO5 2ED.
Tel: 02392 295568, email: auctions@nesbits.co.uk
Noble Numismatics
169 Macquire Street, Sydney, NSW 2000
Australia. Tel: 0061 2922 34578,
Email: info@noble.com.au, www.noble.com.au.
Noonans (IAPN, BNTA)
16 Bolton Street, Mayfair, London, W1J 8BQ
Tel: 020 7016 1700, www.noonans.co.uk.
Numismatica Ars Classica NAC AG
Suite 1, Claridge House, 32 Davies Street,
London W1K 4ND. Tel: 020 7839 7270,
email: info@arsclassicacoins.com.
Numis-Or
4, Rue des Barques 1207, Geneva Switzerland
email: info@numisor.ch, www.numisor.ch.
Pacific Rim Online Auction
P O Box 847, North Sydney, NSW 2060, Australia. Tel
0061 29588 7111,
www.pacificrimonlineauctions.com
Online coin auction.
Penrith, Farmers' & Kidds PLC
Skirsgill Saleroom, Penrith, Cumbria, CA11 0DN.
Tel: 01768 890 781, email: info@pfkauctions.
co.uk,www.pfkauctions.co.uk

Roma Numismatics Ltd
20 Fitzroy Square, London, W1T 6EJ.
Tel: 020 7121 6518. www.romanumismatics.com
Chris Rudd Ltd (IAPN, BNTA)
PO Box 1500, Norwich, NR10 5WS
Tel: 01263 735 007, email: liz@celticcoins.com,
www.celticcoins.com
Simmons Gallery (BNTA)
PO Box 104, Leytonstone, London. Tel: 020 8989
8097. simmonsgallery.co.uk ℗
Smiths of Newent
The Old Chapel, Culver Street, Newent, GL18 1DB.
Tel: 01531 821 776, email: enquiries@smithsauction-
room.co.uk, www.smithsnewentauctions.co.uk.
Sovereign Rarities Ltd (BNTA)
17–19 Maddox Street, London W1S 2QH Tel: 0203
019 1185, www.sovr.co,uk.
Spink & Son Ltd (BNTA)
69 Southampton Row, Bloomsbury, London
WC1B 4ET. Tel: 020 7563 4000, fax 020 7563
4066, email: concierge@spink.com,
www.spink.com.
Stacks, Bowers and Ponterio
1231 East Dyer Road, Suite 100, Santa Ana,
California, 92705, USA. Tel: 001 800 458 4646,
email: info@StacksBowers.com,
www.stacksbowers.com
St James's Auctions (BNTA)
10 Charles II Street, London, SW1Y 4AA.
Tel: 020 7930 7888, fax 0207 930 8214,
Email: info@sjauctions.com,
www.sjauctions.com.
Tennants Auctioneers
The Auction Centre, Leyburn, North Yorkshire,
DL8 5SG. Tel: 01969 623 780, email: enquiry@
tennants-ltd.co.uk, www.tennants.co.uk.
The-saleroom.com
The Harlequin Building, 65 Southwark Street,
London, SE1 0HR. Tel: 0203 725 555, email: sup
port@auctiontechnologygroup.com,
www.the-saleroom.com.
Thomson Roddick Auctioneers
The Auction Centre, Marconi Road, Carlisle,
CA2 7NA. Tel: 01228 528 939, email: carlisle@
thomsonroddick.com. www.thomsonroddick.com.
Timeline Auctions (BNTA)
The Court House, 363 Main Road, Harwich,
Essex CO12 4DN Tel: 01277 815 121, email:
enquiries@timelineauctions.com
www.timelineauctions.com.
Trevanion and Dean
The Joyce Building, Station Road, Whitchurch, SY13
1RD. Tel: 01948 800 202, email: info@trevanionand
dean.co.uk
Warwick & Warwick (BNTA)
Chalon House, Scarbank, Millers Road, Warwick
CV34 5DB. Tel: 01926 499 031 fax 01926 491 906,
email: richard.beale@warwickandwarwick.com,
www.warwickandwarwick.com.
Peter Wilson Fine Art Auctioneers LLP
Victoria Gallery, Market Street, Nantwich,
Cheshire, CW5 5DG. Tel: 01270 623878,
www.peterwilson.co.uk.
Woolley & Wallis
51-61 Castle Street, Salisbury, Wiltshire SP1 3SU.
Tel: 01722 424500, email: nc@woolleyandwallis.co.uk,
www.woolleyandwallis.co.uk

Directory
of fairs

Listed below are the names of the fair organisers, their venue details where known along with contact telephone numbers. Please call the organisers direct for information on dates etc.

Aberdeen
Doubletree by Hilton Hotel Aberdeen TreeTops, Springfield Road, Aderdeen, AB15 7AQ. Alba Fairs Tel: 07767 020343.

ANA World's Fair of Money (2021)
Donald E. Stephens Convention Center; Rosemont (Chicago), IL, United States. Organised by the American Numismatic Association and held in a different venue each year. www.money.org.

Berlin. World Money Fair
Estrel Convention Center, Sonnenalle, 12057 Berlin, Germany. Tel: +41(0)61 3825504.

Berlin
Messegelände am Funkturm, Hall 11/2, Messedamm 22, 14055 Berlin. Numismata International Tel: +49 (0) 89 268 359.

Birmingham
National Motor Cycle Museum, Bickenhill, Birmingham. Midland Stamp & Coin Fair Tel: 01694 731 781, www.coinfairs.co.uk.

Britannia Medal Fair
Carisbrooke Hall, The Victory Services Club, 63/79 Seymour Street, London, W2 2HF. Noonans Tel: 020 7016 1700.

Cardiff
City Hall, Cathays Park, Cardiff, CF10 3ND. M. J. Promotions. Tel: 01792 415293.

Cheltenham
The Regency Hotel, Gloucester Road, GL51 0SS. St Andrews United Reform Church, Montpellier, GL50 1SP. Mark Grimsley Tel: 0117 962 3203.

Crewe
Memorial Hall, Church Lane, Wistaston, Crewe. CW2 8ER. Crewe & District Coin & Medal Society. Tel: 01270 661181.

Dublin Coin Fair
Serpentine Hall, RDS, Ballsbridge, Dublin 4. Mike Kelly Tel: 00353 86 8714 880.

East Grinstead
Chequer Mead Arts Center, De La Warr Road, East Grinstead, RH19 3BS. John Perryman Tel: 01903 244875.

Exeter
The America Hall, De La Rue Way, Pinhoe, EX4 8PX. Michael Hale Collectors Fairs Tel: 01749 677669.

Frankfurt 2019
Ludwig-Erhard-Anlage1, 60327 Frankfurt, Hesse. Numismata International Tel: +49 (0) 89 268 359.

Harrogate
Old Swan Hotel, Swan Road, HG1 2SR. Bloomsbury Fairs Tel: 01242 898 107.

Inverness
Kingsmills Hotel, Culcabock Road, Inverness, IV2 3LP. Alba Fairs Tel: 07767 020343.

London
Holiday Inn, Coram Street, Bloomsbury, WC1 1HT. London Coin Fair, Lu Vessid Tel: 01694 731 781.

London COINEX
*Biltmore Hotel, 44 Grosve*nor Square, Mayfair, W1K 2HP. BNTA. Email: secretary@bnta.net.

London IBNS
Ambassador Bloomsbury Hotel, 12 Upper Woburn Place, Euston, London. WC1H 0HX. IBNS Web: www.theibns.org.

Maastricht
Maastricht Exhibiton and Convention Center, Forum 100, 6229 GV Maastricht, The Netherlands. mif events Tel: +32 (0) 89 46 09 33.

Munich 2023
To Be Confirmed

New York International Numismatic Convention
Grand Hyatt Hotel, 109 East 42nd Street, New York 10022, USA. www.nyinc.info/

Plymouth
The Guildhall, Armada Way, PL1 2ER Peter Jones Tel: 01489 582673.

Weston-super-Mare
Victoria Methodist Church Hall, Station Road, BS23 1XU. Michael Hale Tel: 01749 677 669

Worthing
Chatsworth Hotel, The Steyne, Worthing, BN11 3DU. Organised by the Worthing & District Numismatic Society. Tel: 01903 239867

York
The Grandstand, York Race Course, YO23 1EX *York Coin Fair, Tel: 01793 513 431 (Chris Rainey), 020 8946 4489 (Kate Puleston).*

Yorkshire
Cedar Court Hotel, Lindley Moor Road, Ainley Top, Huddesfield, HD3 3RH. Neil Smith Tel: 01522 522 722.

> **Information correct at the time of going to press. Please check with event organisers before finalising your travel plans.**

THE LONDON COIN FAIR

HOLIDAY INN
London, Bloomsbury,
Coram Street,
WC1N 1HT

2022 dates: 5th November

2023 dates: 4th February,
3rd June, 2nd September
& 4th November

70+ dealers in GB
& foreign coins
Ancient coins and antiquities
Medals, tokens and notes

THE MIDLAND COIN FAIR

NATIONAL MOTORCYCLE MUSEUM
Bickenhill, Birmingham,
B92 0EJ

(Opposite the NEC on the M42/A45 junction)

2022 dates: 9th October,
13th November & 11th December

2023 dates: 8th January,
12th February,12th March,
9th April, 14th May, 11th June,
9th July, 13th August, 10th September,
8th October, 12th November
& 10th December

Please check our website for up to date information.

For more information please contact:
Lu Veissid, Hobsley House, Frodesley, Shrewsbury SY5 7HD
Tel: 01694 731781   Email: l.veissid@btinternet.com

www.coinfairs.co.uk

Like us on facebook **f** @ coin and medal fairs

Dealers
directory

The dealers listed below have comprehensive stocks of coins and medals, unless otherwise stated. Specialities, where known, are noted. Many of those listed are postal dealers only, so to avoid disappointment always make contact by telephone or mail in the first instance, particularly before travelling any distance.

Abbreviations:
ADA— — Antiquities Dealers Association
ANA — American Numismatic Association
BADA — British Antique Dealers Association
BNTA — British Numismatic Trade Association
IAPN — International Association of Professional Numismatists
IBNS — International Bank Note Society
P — — Postal only
L — — Publishes regular lists

ABC Coins & Tokens
PO Box 52, Alnwick, Northumberland, NE66 1YE. Tel: 01665 603 851, www.abccoinsandtokens.com. *British (particularly Scottish) and world coins, tokens.*

Absolutely Banknotes (Chris Burch)
Tel: 07870 504849, www,absolutelybanknotes.co.uk *English and Scottish notes. Treasury to modern.*

A. Ackroyd (IBNS)
62 Albert Road, Parkstone, Poole, Dorset BH12 2DB. Tel/fax: 01202 739 039, www.AAnotes.com. **P L** *Banknotes and Cheques*

Allgold Coins
P.O Box 260, Wallington, SM5 4H. Tel: 0844 544 7952, email: sales@allgoldcoins.co.uk, wwwallgoldcoins.co.uk. *Quality Sovereigns.*

A. J. W. Coins
Tel: 08456 807 087, email: andrewwide@ajw-coins. co.uk, www.ajw-coins.com. **P** *Sovereigns and CGS-UK specialist.*

AMR COINS (BNTA)
PO Box 352, Leeds, LS19 9GG. Tel: 07527 569 308, www.amrcoins.com. *Quality English Coins specialising in rare hammered and milled coins of exceptional quality.*

Ancient & Gothic
Tel: 01202 431 721 **P L** *Ancients and Biblical coins. Hammered & Antiquities.*

Asprey Coins (BNTA)
Langstone Park, Langstone Road, Havant, PO9 1SA.
Email: info@aspreycoins.co.uk, Tel: 01243 915155. www.aspreycoins.co.uk. British Coins and Banknotes

ARL Collectables
P O Box 380, Reigate, Surrey, RH2 2BU. Tel: 01737 242 975, www.litherlandcollectables.com. Coins, Banknotes, Medallions and Paper Emphemera.

Athens Numismatic Gallery
Akadimias 39, Athens 10672, Greece. Tel: 0030 210 364 8386, www.athensnumismaticgallery.com. *Rare & Common Sovereigns. British & World Coins.*

Atlas Numismatics
Tel: 001 718643 4383, email, info@atlasnumismatics. com, www.atlasnumismatics.com *Ancient, W***ABC Coins & Tokens**
P*and US Coinage*

ATS Bullion (BNTA)
2, Savoy Court, Strand. London, WC2R 0EZ. Tel: 020 7240 4040, email: sales@atsbullion.com, www.atsbullion.com. *Bullion and Modern Coins.*

A. H. Baldwin & Sons Ltd (ANA, BADA, BNTA, IAPN)
399 The Strand, London WC2R 0LX. Tel: 020 7930 6879, fax 020 7930 9450, email: coins@baldwin.co.uk *Coins, Tokens, Numismatic Books.*

B & G Coins
PO Box 1219, Spalding, PE11 9FY. Email: info@ bandgcoins.co.uk. *Coins, Banknotes and Medals*

Baird & Co
20 - 21 Gemini Business Park, Hornet Way, London, E6 7FF. Tel: 020 7474 1000, www.goldline.co.uk. *Bullion Merchants*

T. Barna
64 High Street, Lyndhurst, SO43 7BJ. Email: tbarna_ and sonuk@hotmail.com. Ancient Greek and Roman Coins.

Bath Stamp and Coin Shop
12 -13 Pulteney Bridge, Bath, Avon BA2 4AY. Tel: 01225 431 918, *Vintage Coins and Banknotes.*

Michael Beaumont
PO Box 8, Carlton, Notts NG4 4QZ. Tel: 0115 9878361.**P** *Gold & Silver bullion, English and Foreign Coins.*

R. P. & P. J. Beckett
Maes y Derw, Capel Dewi, Llandyssul, Dyfed SA44 4PJ. Tel: 01559 395 276, email: beckett@xin.co.uk. **P** *Coin Sets and Banknotes.*

Lloyd Bennett (BNTA)
PO Box 2, Monmouth, Gwent NP25 3YR. Tel: 07714 284 939, email: Lloydbennett@Coinofbritain. biz, www.coinsofbritain.com *English Hammered and Milled Coins.*

Berkshire Coin Centre
35 Castle Street, Reading, RG1 7SB. Tel: 0118 957 5593. *British and World Coins. Militaria.*

Stephen J. Betts
49-63 Spencer Street, Hockley, Birmingham B18
6DE. Tel: 0121 233 2413 **P L**,
*Medieval and Modern Coins, Counters, Jetons,
Tokens and Countermarks.*

Jon Blyth (BNTA)
Office 63, 2 Lansdowne Row, Mayfair, London
W1J 6HL. Tel:07919 307 645, jonblyth@hotmail.com,
www.jonblyth.com. *Specialists in quality British Coins*

Barry Boswell and Kate Bouvier
24 Townsend Lane, Upper Boddington, Daventry,
Northants, NN11 6DR. Tel: 01327 261 877, email:
kate@thebanknotestore.com. *British and World
Banknotes.*

James & Chester Brett
jc.brett@btinternet.com **P L** *British and World
Coins.*

Stephen Betts
4 Victoria Street, Narborough, Leicester, LE19 2DP.
P L *World Coins, Tokens, Countermarks, Jettsons,
Medallions etc.*

J. Bridgeman Coins
129a Blackburn Road, Accrington, Lancs
Tel: 01254 384757. *British & World Coins.*

Brittonum (BNTA)
PO Box 3, 41 Oxford Street, Leamington Spa, CV32
4RA Tel: 07768 645 686, email: info@brittonum.com
www.brittonum.com. *British Coins and Medals.*

BRM Coins
3 Minshull Street, Knutsford,Cheshire, WA16 6HG.
Tel: 01565 651 480. *British Coins.*

Bucks Coins (BNTA)
St Mary's House, Duke Street, Norwich NR3 1QA
Callers by appointment only. Tel: 01603 927 020.
English Milled Coins, Celtic and Roman.

Iain Burn
2 Compton Gardens, 53 Park Road, Camberley,
Surrey GU15 2SP. Tel: 01276 23304.
Bank of England & Treasury Notes.

Cambridgeshire Coins (BNTA)
12 Signet Court, Swanns Road Cambridge,
CB5 8LA. Tel: 01223 503 073, email, info
cambridgeshirecoins.com,
wwwcambridgeshirecoins.com.
Coins, Banknotes and Accessories.

Castle Galleries
81 Castle Street, Salisbury, Wiltshire SP1 3SP.
Tel: 01722 333 734. *British Coins and collectables.*

Cathedral Coins
23 Kirkgate, Rippon, North Yorkshire, HG4 1PB.
Tel: 01765 701 400

Cathedral Court Medals
First Floor Office, 30A Market Place, West Ripon,
North Yorks HG4 1BN. Tel: 01765 601 400. *Coin and
Medal Sales. Medal Mounting and Framing.*

Cathedral Stamps & Coins
Unit B14, KCR Industrial Estate, Ravensdale Park,
Kimmage, Co. Dublin, Ireland. Tel: +353 1 490 6392
*Coins, medals, banknotes & accessories.Stockist of
Token Publishing titles in Ireland.*

Central Bank of Ireland
PO Box 559, Dublin 1. Tel: +353 (0) 1248 3605,
Ireland. *Issuer of new Coin and Banknote issues of
Ireland. Commemorative Coins and Coin Sets*

Lance Chaplin
17 Wanstead Lane, Ilford, Essex IG1 3SB.
Tel: 020 8554 7154. www.shaftesburycoins.com.
P L *Ancient, Hammered Coins and Antiquities.*

Chard
32-36 Harrowside, Blackpool, FY4 1RJ. Tel: 01253
343081, www.chards.co.uk, *British and World Coins.*

Charing Cross Collectors' Market
Charing Cross, 1, Villiers Street/Northumberland Ave,
London.Tel: 07540 144433,
www.charingcrossmarket.com, *Market in Central
London with dealers offering coins, stamps,
postcards, medals & ephemera.*

Jeremy Cheek Coins Ltd
Tel: 01923 450385/07773 872686, email:
jeremycoins@aol.com. *Advice, valuation and
representation at auctions.*

Simon Chester Coins
196, High Road, London, Farnham, N22 8HH
Tel: 07774 886688, email: simosimonchestercoins.
com. *British Milled Coins*

Nigel A. Clark
28 Ulundi Road, Blackheath, London SE3 7UG.
Tel: 020 8858 4020, email: nigel.a.clark@btinternet.
com. **P L** *17th & 19th century Tokens. Farthings.*

Classical Numismatic Group (IAPN) (BNTA)
20 Bloomsbury Street, London, WC1B 3QA.
Tel: 020 7495 1888, email cng@cngcoins.com,
www.cngcoins.com. **P** *Ancient and world coins.
Publishers of the Classical Numismatic Review.
Regular High Quality Auctions of Ancient Coins.*

Paul Clayton (BNTA)
PO Box 21, Wetherby, West Yorkshire LS22 5JY.
Tel: 01937 582 693. *Modern Gold Coins.*

André de Clermont (BNTA)
10 Charles II Street, London, SW1Y 4AA. Tel: 020
7584 7200. *World Coins, especially Islamic.*

Philip Cohen Numismatics (ANA, BNTA)
20 Cecil Court, Charing Cross Road, London,
WC2N 4HE. Tel: 020 7379 0615, www.coinheritage.
co.uk

Coin & Collectors Centre
PO Box 22, Pontefract, West Yorkshire WF8
1YT. Tel: 01977 704 112, email sales@coincentre.
co.uk, www.coincentre.co.uk. **P** *British Coins.*

Coinage of England
P.O. Box 118, 8 Shepherd Market, Mayfair, London,
W1J 7JY. Tel: 07557 819 104
Email: info@coinageofengland.co.uk. *Fine and Rare
English Coins.*

Coincraft (ANA, IBNS)
45 Great Russell Street, London, WC1B 3JL.
Tel: 020 7636 1188 or 020 7637 8785, fax 020
7323 2860, email: info@coincraft.com. **L**
(newspaper format). *Coins and Banknotes.*

The Coinery
Tel 01132 407900, www.thecoinery.co.uk.

Coinote
74 Elwick Road, Hartlepool TS26 9AP. Tel: 01429 890
894. www.coinnote.co.uk. *Coins, Medals, Banknotes
and Accessories.*

Coins on a Budget
*wwwcoinsonabudget.com. Incorporating budget
stamps. World Coins and Banknotes.*

Coinswap.co.uk
Swap, Sell or Trade Coins.

Coins of Canterbury
PO Box 47, Faversham, Kent,, ME13 7HX. Tel: 01795
531 980. **P** *English Coins.*

Coins of the Realm
*PO Box 12131, Harlow, Essex, CM20 9LY.
www.coinsoftherealm.com. Dealers in Precious and
Historical Coinage*

Colonial Collectables
*P.O.Box 35625, Browns Bay, Auckland 0753, New
Zealand. Email: richard@colonialcollectables.com
British & World Coins.*

Collectors' World (Mark Ray)
190 Wollaton Road, Wollaton, Nottingham NG8 1HJ.
www.collectorsworld-nottingham.com.
Tel: 01159 280 347. *Coins, Banknotes, Accessories.*

Constania CB
15 Church Road, Northwood, Middlesex, HA6 1AR.
P *Roman and Medieval Hammered Coins.*

Colin Cooke (BNTA)
P.O. Box 602, Altrincham, WA14 5UN. Tel: 0161
927 9524, fax 0161 927 9540, email coins@colin
cooke.com, www.colincooke.com. **L** *British Coins.*

Colonial Coins & Medals
218 Adelaide Street, Brisbane, QLD 4001.
Email: coinshop@bigpond.net.au.
Auctions of World Coins.

Coopers Coins
*PO Box 12703, Brentwood, Essex, CM14 9RB.
Tel: 01277 560348, email: jack@cooperscoins.com.
wwwcooperscoins.com. British Coins.*

Corbitts (BNTA)
5 Mosley Street, Newcastle Upon Tyne NE1 1YE.
Tel: 0191 232 7268, fax: 0191 261 4130. *Dealers and
Auctioneers of all Coins and Medals.*

David Craddock (BNTA)
PO Box 3785, Camp Hill, Birmingham, B11 2NF.
Tel: 0121 733 2259 **L** *Crown to Farthings. Copper
and Bronze Specialist. Some foreign.*

Roy Cudworth
8 Park Avenue, Clayton West, Huddersfield HD8
9PT. *British and World Coins.*

Curtis Coin Care
www.curtiscoincare.com. *Numismatic accessories
and storage solutions.*

Paul Dawson (BNTA)
47 The Shambles, York, YO1 7XL. Tel: 01904 654
769, email: pauldawsonyork@hotmail.com, www.
pauldawsonyork.co.uk. *Ancient and British coins,
medals.*

Mark Davidson
PO Box 197, South Croydon, Surrey, CR3 0ZD.
Tel: 020 8651 3890. *Ancient, Hammered & milled
Coinage.*

Paul Davies Ltd (ANA, BNTA, IAPN)
PO Box 17, Ilkley, West Yorkshire LS29 8TZ.
Tel: 01943 603 116, fax 01943 816 326, paul@
pauldaviesltd.co.uk. **P** *World Coins. British Gold
and silver bullion.*

Paul Davis (BNTA)
PO Box 418, Birmingham, B17 0RZ.
Tel: 0121 427 7179. *British and World Coins.*

R. Davis
Tel: 01332 862 755 days / 740828 evenings, email:
robdaviscc@gmail.com. *Maker of Traditional Coin
Cabinets.*

Ian Davison
PO Box 256, Durham DH1 2GW. Tel 0191 3750 808.
L *English Hammered and Milled Coins 1066–1910.*

Davissons
*PO Box 323, Cold Spring, MN, 56320, USA.
Tel: (001)320 685 3835, Email: infodavcoin.com,
www.davcoin.com. North American Specialists.
British Coins, Tokens and Medals.*

Dei Gratia
PO Box 3568, Buckingham MK18 4ZS Tel: 01280
848 000. **P** **L** *Pre–Roman to Modern Coins.
Antiquities, Banknotes.*

Den of Antiquity (BNTA)
PO Box 1114, Cambridge, CB25 9WJ. Tel: 01223
863 002, www.denofantiquity.co.uk.)
Ancient and Medieval Coins.

Clive Dennett
66 St Benedicts Street, Norwich, Norfolk, NR2 4AR.
Tel: 01603 624 315, **L** *Specialising in paper money.*

C. J. Denton (ANA, FRNS)
PO Box 25, Orpington, Kent BR6 8PU. Tel: 01689
873 690. **P** *Irish Coins.*

Michael Dickinson (ANA)
Ramsay House, 825 High Road Finchley, London
N12 8UB. Tel: 0181 441 7175. **P**
British and World Coins.

Douglas Saville (BNTA)
Tel: 0118 918 7628, www.douglassaville.com. *Out
of Print, Second-Hand and Rare Coin and Medal
Books.*

Eagle Coins
Winterhaven, Mourneabbey, Mallow, Co. Cork,
Ireland. Tel: 010 35322 29385. **P** **L** *Irish Coins.*

East of England Coins
Leprosy Mission Orton Goldhay, Peterborough,
Cambridgeshire, PE2 5GZ. Tel: 01733235277
Coins, Tokens and Banknotes

John Eccles
*www.eccleswellington.co.nz. New Zealand and
Pacific Islands Coins and Banknotes*

Educational Coin Company
Box 892, Highland, New York 12528, USA. Tel:001
845 691 6100. *World Banknotes.*

Christopher Eimer (ANA, BNTA, IAPN)
PO Box 352 London NW11 7RF. Tel: 020 8458 9933,
email: art@christophereimer.co.uk **P**
Commemorative Medals.

Malcolm Ellis Coins
Petworth Road, Witley, Surrey, GU8 5LX. Tel: 01428
685 566, www.malcolmelliscoins.co.uk). *Collectors
and Dealers of British and Foreign Coins*

Elm Hill Collectables
41-43 Elm Hill, Norwich, Norfolk NR3 1HG. Tel:
01603 627 413. *Coins & Banknotes .*

Europa Numismatics (ANA)
PO Box 119, High Wycombe, Bucks HP11 1QL.
Tel: 01494 437 307 **P** *European Coins.*

Evesham Stamp & Coin Centre
Magpie Antiques, Manchester House,1 High Street,
Evesham, Worcs WR11 4DA. Tel: 01386 41631.
British Coins.

Robin Finnegan Stamp Shop
83 Skinnergate, Darlington, Co Durham DL3 7LX.
Tel: 01325 489 820/357 674. *World coins.*

B. Frank & Son
3 South Avenue, Ryton, Tyne & Wear NE40 3LD.
Tel: 0191 413 8749, Email: bfrankandson@aol.
com, www.bfrankandson.com. *Coins, notes, tokens.*

Galata Coins Ltd (ANA)
The Old White Lion, Market Street, Llanfylin,
Powys SY22 5BX. Tel: 01691 648 765. **P** *British and
World Coins.*

A. & S. Gillis
59 Roy Kilner Way, Wombwell, Barnsley,
South Yorkshire S73 8DY. Tel: 01226 750 371,
www.gilliscoins.com. *Ancient Coins and Antiquities.*

Richard Gladdle—Northamptonshire (BNTA)
Suite 80, 29/30 Horse Fair, Banbury, Oxfordshire,
OX16 0BW. Tel: 01327 858 511, email: gladdle@
plumpudding.org. *Tokens.* **P** **L**

GM Coins
Tel: 01242 627 344, email: info@gmcoinsco.
uk, www.gmcoins.co.uk. *Hammered and Milled
Coins.*

Adrian Gorka Bond
Tel: 07500 772 080, email: sales@ 1stsovereign.
co.uk, www.1stsovereign.co.uk. *World gold coins*

Goulborn
4 Sussex Street, Rhyl LL18 1SG. Tel: 01745
338 112. *English Coins and Medallions.Organiser of Chester Coin Auctions.*
Ian Gradon
PO Box 359, Durham DH7 6WZ. Tel 0191 3719 700, email: rarebanknote@gmail.com, www.worldnotes. co.uk. 🅛 *World Banknotes.*
Eric Green—Agent in UK for Ronald J. Gillio Inc
1013 State Street, Santa Barbara, California, USA 93101. Tel: 020 8907 0015, Mobile 0468 454948. *Gold Coins, Medals and Paper Money of the World.*
Philip Green (GB Classic Coins)
Suite 207, 792 Wilmslow Road, Didsbury, Manchester M20 6UG. Tel: 0161 440 0685. *Gold Coins.*
Gurnhills of Leicester
8 Nothampton Street, Leicester, LE1 1PA.Tel: 07434 010 925. *British and World Coins and Banknotes.*
Halls Hammered Coins (BNTA)
From early Saxon to late Stuart.
Tel: 07830 019 584 www.hallshammeredcoins.com
Anthony Halse (BNTA)
PO Box 1856, Newport, Gwent NP18 2WA. Tel: 01633 413 238.🅟🅛*English/Foreign coins, tokens.*
A. D. Hamilton & Co (ANA)
7 St Vincent Place, Glasgow, G1 2DW. Tel: 0141 221 5423, email: jefffineman@hotmail.com, www. adhamilton.co.uk.*British and World Coins.*
Hammered British Coins (BNTA)
PO Box 2330, Salisbury, SP2 2LN. Tel: 07825 226 435, www.hammeredbritishcoins.com. *British Coins.*
Peter Hancock
40–41 West Street, Chichester, West Sussex, PO19 1RP. Tel: 01243 786 173. *World Coins, Medals and Banknotes.*
Hattons of London
PO Box 3719, Newcastle, ST55 9HH. Tel: 0333 234 3103. Email: enquiries@hattonsoflondon.co.uk 🅛 *Rare and Exclusive Coins.*
Tom Hart Coins
Based in Devon. Tel: 07745 985 510. Email: wooosworlduk@aol.com. Coins, Medals and Antiques.
Munthandel G. Henzen
PO Box 42, NL – 3958ZT, Amerogngen, Netherlands. Tel: 0031 343 430564 fax 0031 343 430542, email: info@henzen.org, www.henzen.org. 🅛*Ancients, Dutch and Foreign Coins.*
History In Coins (BNTA)
Tel: 07944 374600, email:historyincoins@gmail.com, www.historyincoins.com. *Hammered to milled, English, Irish and Scottish coins.*
Craig Holmes
6 Marlborough Drive, Bangor, Co Down BT19 1HB. 🅟🅛*Low cost Banknotes of the World.*
R. G. Holmes
11 Cross Park, Ilfracombe, Devon EX34 8BJ. Tel: 01271 864 474. 🅟🅛 *Coins, World Crowns and Banknotes.*
HTSM Coins
26 Dosk Avenue, Glasgow G13 4LQ. Tel: 0141 562 9530, www.thomasgreaves1.com🅟🅛 *British and foreign coins and Banknotes.*
M. J. Hughes Coins (BNTA)
27 Market Street, Alton, Hampshire, GU34 1HA. Tel: 01420 768 161, email: info@mjhughes.co.uk *World Coins and Bullion.*
T. A. Hull
15 Tangmere Crescent, Hornchurch, Essex RM12 5PL.🅟🅛 *British Coins, Farthings, Tokens.*

J. Hume
107 Halsbury Road East, Northolt, Middlesex UB5 4PY. Tel: 020 8864 1731.🅟🅛 *Chinese Coins.*
D. A. Hunter
Email: coins@dahunter.co.uk, www.dahunter.co.uk/ coins. 🅟🅛 *UK and World Coins.*
D. D. & A. Ingle
380 Carlton Hill, Nottingham, NG4 1JA. Tel: 0115 987 3325. *World Coins.*
R. Ingram Coins
2 Avonbourne Way, Chandlers Ford, Eastleigh, SO53 1TF. Tel: 023 8027 5079, email: info@ ringramcoins.com, www.ringramcoins.com.🅟🅛 *Dealers in UK Coins.*
F. J. Jeffery & Son Ltd
Haines Croft, Corsham Road, Whitley, Melksham, Wilts, SN12 8QF. Tel: 01225 703 143.🅟 🅛, *British, Commonwealth and Foreign Coins.*
Richard W. Jeffery (BNTA)
Tel: 01736 871 263. 🅟 *British,World Coins, notes.*
JN Coins
PO Box 1030, Ipswich, OP1 9XL. Tel: 07916 145 038, info@jncoins.co.uk, www.jncoins.co.uk). *British Coins from Celtic to Modern.*
KB Coins (BNTA)
PO BOX 499, Stevenage, Herts, SG1 9JT. Tel: 01438 312 661, fax 01438 311 990. www.kbcoins.com 🅛 *English coins and medals. Specialists in gold sovereigns, rare dates and varieties.*
Kleeford Coins
Tel: 07484 272 837, kleeford@btinternet.com www.kleefordcoins.co.uk, . 🅟 *Monthly Auctions of Coins, Banknotes, Tokens & Medals.*
K&M Coins
PO Box 3662, Wolverhampton WV10 6ZW. Tel: 0771 238 1880, email: M_Bagguley@hotmail. com. *English Milled Coins.*
Knightsbridge Coins (ANA, BNTA, IAPN, PNG)
43 Duke Street, St James's, London, SW1Y 6DD. Tel: 020 7930 8215/7597, info@knightsbridgecoins. com. *Quality Coins of the World..*
Liberty Coins and Bullion
17g Vyse Street, Birmingham, B18 6LE. Tel: 0121 554 4432, www.libertycoinsbullion.co.uk. *Coins and Precious Metals.*
Lindner Publications Ltd (Prinz)
Unit 20A, Longrock Industrial Estate, Longrock, Cornwall TR20 8HX. Tel: 01736 751 910, email: prinzpublications@gmail.com.
🅛 *Coin Albums, accessories.Stockist of the Lindner range of coin storage solutions.*
Jan Lis
Beaver Coin Room, 57 Philbeach Gardens, London SW5 9ED. Tel: 020 7373 4553 fax 020 7373 4555. By appointment only. *European Coins.*
Keith Lloyd
1 Dashwood Close, Pinewood, Ipswich, Suffolk IP8 3SR. Tel: 01473 403 506.🅟🅛 *Ancient Coins.*
Lockdale Coins (BNTA)
52 Barrack Square, Martlesham Heath, Ipswich, Suffolk, IP5 3RF. Tel: 01473 627 110, www.lockdales. com.🅛 *World Coins, Medals and Banknotes.*
Stephen Lockett (BNTA)
4–6 Upper Street, New Ash Green, Kent, DA3 8JJ. Tel: 01474 871464. *British and World Coins.*
The London Coin Company (BNTA)
PO Box 495, Stanmore, Greater London, HA7 9HS Tel: 0800 085 2933, 020 8343 2231, www.thelondoncoincomany.com. *Modern Gold and Silver Coins.*

The London Mint Office
Tel: 0330 024 1001, londonmintoffice.org
Gold, Silver and Commemorative Coins.

Mike Longfield Detectors
83 Station Road, Balsall Common, Warks CV7 7FN.
Tel: 01676 533 274. *Metal Detectors.*

MA Shops
www.mashops.com. On-line coin mall. *Coins, Medals, Banknotes and Accessories.*

Manston Coins of Bath
8 Bartletts St. Antique Centre, Bath. Tel: 01225 487 888. *Coins, Tokens and Medals.*

C. J. Martin Coins (BNTA)
The Gallery, Trent Park Equestrian Centre, Bramley Road, London, N14 4UW. 🅿🅛 Bi– monthly catalogue. www.ancientart.co.uk.
Greek, Roman & English Hammered Coins.

Maverick Numismatics — Matt Bonaccorsi
07403 111843, www.mattbonaccorsi.com.
Coin and Currency Design.

M. G. Coins & Antiquities
12 Mansfield, High Wych, Herts CM21 0JT. Tel 01279 721 719. 🅛*Ancient and Hammered Coins, Antiquities.*

M & H Coins
PO Box 10985, Brentwood, CM14 9JB. Tel: 07504 804 019, www.mhcoins.co.uk. 🅛 *British Hammered and Milled Coins.*

Michael Coins
PO Box 3100 Reading RG1 9ZL. *World Coins and Banknotes.*

Middlesex Coins
www.middlesexcoins.co.uk. Tel: 07753618613,
Email: marksaxby25@hotmail.com.
Quality rare coins specialists since 1999

Timothy Millett
PO Box 20851, London SE22 0YN. Tel: 0208 693 1111, www.historicmedals.com. 🅛 *Historical Medals.*

Nigel Mills
PO Box 53126, London, E18 1YR. Email: nigelmills@onetel.com,
www.nigelmills.net *Coins and Antiquities.*

Monetary Research Institute
PO Box 3174, Houston, TX 77253-3174, Tel: 001 713 827 1796, email: info@mriguide.com. *Bankers Guide to Foreign Currency*

Moore Antiquities
Unit 12, Ford Lane Industrial Estate, Ford, nr. Arundel, West Sussex BN18 0AA. Tel: 01243 824 232, email moore.antiquities@virgin.net.
Coins and Artefacts up to the 18th Century.

Mike Morey
19 Elmtrees, Long Crendon, Bucks HP18 9DG.🅿 🅛
British Coins, Halfcrowns to Farthings.

Peter Morris (BNTA, IBNS)
1 Station Concourse, Bromley North Station, Bromley, BR1 1NN or PO Box 223, Bromley, BR1 4EQ. Tel: 020 8313 3410,
email: info@petermorris.co.uk,
www.petermorris.co.uk
British and World Coins, Proof Sets and Numismatic Books, Medals and Banknotes.

Colin Narbeth & Son Ltd (ANA, IBNS)
20 Cecil Court, Leicester Square, London,WC2N. 4HE .Tel: 020 7379 6975, www.colin–narbeth.com *World Banknotes.*

Newcastle Coin Dealers
7 Nile Street, North Shields, NE29 0BD. Tel: 07939 999 286, email: newcastlecoin@outlook.com, www. newcastlecoindealers.co.uk. *Modern British and World Coins/Banknotes.*

John Newman Coins (BNTA)
P O Box 4890, Worthing, BN119WS. Tel: 01903 239 867, email: john@newmancoins.co.uk, www.johnnewmancoins.co.uk. *English hammered coins, British Milled Coins and British Tokens.*

Wayne Nicholls
PO Box 44, Bilston, West Midlands. Tel: 01543 45476. 🅛 *Choice English Coins.*

North Wales Coins Ltd
1b Penrhyn Road, Colwyn Bay, Clwyd. Tel: 01492 533 023. *British Coins.*

NP Collectables
9 Main Street, Gedney Dyke, Spalding, Lincs PE12 0AJ. Tel: 01406 365 211🅿 🅛. *English Hammered and Milled Coins.*🅛

NumisCorner
www.NumisCorner.com
Coins, Banknotes, Medals and Tokens

Numitrading.com
Online market place/trading platform.
Tel: 01702 667420, email: info@numitrading.com, www.numitrading.com.

Odyssey Antiquities
PO Box 61, Southport PR9 0PZ.Tel: 01704 232 494.
Classical Antiquities, Ancient and Hammered Coinage.

Glenn S. Ogden (BNTA)
Tel: 01626 859 350 or 07971 709 427, email: glennogdencoins@hotmail.com,
www. glennogdencoins.com, 🅿 🅛 *English Milled Coinage.*

John Ogden Coins
Hodge Clough Cottage, Moorside, Oldham OL1 4JW. Tel: 0161 678 0709🅿 🅛*Ancient and Hammered.*

Don Oliver Gold Coins
Stanford House, 23 Market Street, Stourbridge, West Midlands DY8 1AB. Tel: 01384 877 901.
British Gold Coins.

Del Parker
PO Box 310 Richmond Hill, GA 31324.
Tel: + 1 2143521475, Email: irishcoins2000@hotmail.com www.irishcoins.com. *Irish, American Coins.*

Pavlos S. Pavlou
58 Davies Streer, Mayfair, London W1K 5JF. Tel: 020 7629 9449, email: pspavlou@hotmail.com. *Ancient to Modern.*

PCGS
Tel:+33 (0) 949 833 0600, email:info@pcgs.com, www.pcgs.com. *Coin Grading and Authentication Service.*

Penrith Coin & Stamp Centre
37 King Street, Penrith, Cumbria CA11 7AY. Tel: 01768 864 185.*World Coins.*

Pentland Coins (IBNS)
Pentland House, 92 High Street, Wick, Caithness KW14 L5. 🅿 *British and general World Coins and Banknotes.*

Philatelic Heritage
35a High Street, Hungerford, RG17 0NF.
Email philatelicheritage@gmx.com. Tel: 01488 684008 Coins & Stamps.

B. C. Pickard
1 Treeside, Christchurch, Dorset BH23 4PF. Tel: 01425 275763, email: bcpickard@fsmail.net). 🅿 *Stone Age, Greek, Roman Items (inc. coins) for sale.*

Pobjoy Mint Ltd (ANA)
Millennium House, Kingswood Park, Bonsor Drive, Kingswood, Surrey KT20 6AY. Tel: 01737 818 182 fax 01737 818199. Europe's largest private mint. *New issues.*

George Rankin Coin Co Ltd (ANA)
Tel: 020 7739 1840. www.rankinsjewellers.co.uk.
*World Coins, banknotes, medals, watches, general
bullion bought and sold.*
Mark Rasmussen (BNTA, IAPN)
PO Box 42, Betchworth, Surrey, RH3 7YR. Tel: 01306
884 880, email: mark.rasmussen@rascoins.com,
www.rascoins.com. ⓟⓛ *Quality Hammered, Milled
Coins.*
Mark T. Ray (see Collectors World)
Rhyl Coin Shop
12 Sussex Street, Rhyl, Clwyd. Tel: 01745 338 112.
World Coins and Banknotes.
Chris Rigby
PO Box 181, Worcester WR1 1YE. Tel: 01905 28028.
ⓟⓛ*Modern British Coins.*
Roderick Richardson (BNTA)
The Old Granary Antiques Centre, King's Staithe
Lane, King's Lynn, PE30 1LZ. Tel: 01553 670
833, www.roderickrichardson.com. ⓛ *English,
Hammered and Early Milled Coins. High quality lists.*
Charles Riley (BNTA)
PO Box 733, Aylesbury HP22 9AX. Tel: 01296
747 598, charlesrileycoins@gmail.com,
www.charlesriley.co.uk. *Coins and Medallions.*
Robin–on–Acle Coins
193 Main Road Essex CO12 3PH. Tel: 01255
554 440, email: enquiries@robin–on–acle–coins.
co.uk. *Ancient to Modern Coins and Paper Money.*
Roma Numismatics
40 Villiers Street, London WC2N 6NJ
Tel: 020 7121 6518, www.romanumismatics.com.
*Dealers and Auctioneers of English, World, Islamic
and Ancient coins..*
Royal Australian Mint
www.ramint.gov.au. *Official new coin issues for
Australia.*
Royal Gold
PO Box 123, Saxonwold, 2132, South Africa,
Tel: +27 11 483 0161, email: royalg@iafrica.com,
www.royalgold.co.za. *Gold Coins 1874–1902 bought
and sold,*
Colin de Rouffignac (BNTA)
57, Wigan Lane, Wigan, Lancs WN1 2LF. Tel: 01942
237 927. *P. English and Scottish Hammered.*
R. P. Coins
PO Box 367, Prestwich, Manchester, M25 9ZH.
Tel: 07802 713 444, www.rpcoins.co.uk.
Coins, Books, Catalogues and Accessories.
Chris Rudd Ltd (IAPN, BNTA)
PO Box 1500, Norwich, NR10 5WS ⓟⓛ
Tel: 01263 735 007 www.celticcoins.com.
Celtic Coins.
Colin Rumney (BNTA)
PO Box 34, Denbighshire, North Wales, LL16 4YQ.
Tel: 01745 890 621. *All world coins including
ancients.*
R & J Coins
21b Alexandra Street, Southend-on-Sea, Essex, SS1
1DA. Tel: 01702 345 995. *World Coins.*
Safe Albums (UK) Ltd
16 Falcon Business Park, 38 Ivanhoe Road,
Finchampstead, Berkshire RG40 4QQ. Tel: 0118 932
8976 fax 0118 932 8612. *Accessories.*
Saltford Coins
Harcourt, Bath Road, Saltford, Bristol, Avon
BS31 3DQ. Tel: 01225 873 512, email: info@
saltfordcoins.com, www.saltfordcoins.com
ⓟ *British, Commonwealth, World Coins and
medallions.*

Satin Coins
PO Box 63, Stockport, Cheshire SK4 5BU.
Tel: 07940 393 583 answer machine.
Scotmint Ltd (BNTA)
68 Sandgate, Ayr, Scotland KA7 1BX
Tel: 01292 268 244, email: rob@scotmint.com,
www.scotmint.com. *Coins, Medals and Banknotes.
Retail shop.*
David Seaman
PO Box 449, Waltham Cross, EN9 3WZ. Tel: 01992
719 723, email: davidseamancoins@outlook.com.
ⓟⓛ *Hammered, Milled, Maundy.*
Mark Senior
553 Falmer Road, Woodingdean, Brighton, Sussex
Tel: 01273 309 359. By appointment only.
ⓟⓛ*Saxon, Norman and English hammered.*
Sharps Pixley
54, St James's Street, London SW1A 1JT Tel: 020
7871 0532, www.sharpspixley.com. *Safe deposit
boxes in St James's, buying and selling Gold Bullion.*
Silbury Coins (BNTA)
PO Box 281, Cirencester, Gloucs GL7 9ET. Tel:
01242 898 107, email: info@silburycoins.com,
www.silburycoins.com. *Iron Age, Roman, Saxon,
Viking, Medieval Coins and later.*
Simmons Gallery (ANA, BNTA, IBNS)
PO Box 104, Leytonstone, London E11 1ND Tel: 020
898 98097, simmonsgallery.co.uk. ⓛ *Coins,
Tokens and Medals.*
E. Smith (ANA, IBNS)
PO Box 348, Lincoln LN6 0TX Tel: 01522 684 681 fax
01522 689 528. Organiser of the Wakefield (formally
known as Leeds) monthly coin fair. ⓟ *World Coins
and Paper Money.*
Neil Smith
PO Box 774, Lincoln LN4 2WX. Tel: 01522 522 772
fax 01522 689 528. *GB and World Gold Coins 1816
to date, including Modern Proof Issues.Organisers of
the Yorkshire Coin Fair.*
Jim Smythe
PO Box 6970, Birmingham B23 7WD. Email:
Jimdens@aol.com.ⓟⓛ*19th/20th Century British
and World Coins.*
Sovereign Rarities Ltd (BNTA)
17–19 Maddox Street, London W1S 2QH Tel: 0203
019 1185, www.sovr.co,uk. *Quality British
and World Coins.*
SP Asimi
Cabinet at The Emporium, 112 High Street,
Hungerford, RG17 ONB. Tel: 01488 686959.
British Milled Coins 1662-1946
Spink & Son Ltd (ANA, BNTA, IAPN, IBNS)
69 Southampton Row, Bloomsbury, London.
WC1B 4ET. Tel: 020 7563 4000, fax 020 7563 4066,
email: info@spinkandson.com, www.spink.com.
Ancient to Modern World Coins. Medals, Banknotes.
Stamford Coins
65–67 Stamford Street, Bradford, West
Yorkshire, BD4 8SD. Tel: 07791 873 595, email:
stamfordcoins@hotmail.co.uk.
Stamp & Collectors Centre
404 York Town Road, College Town, Camberley,
Surrey GU15 4PR. Tel:01276 32587 fax 01276
32505. *World Coins and Medals.*
St Edmunds Coins & Banknotes
PO Box 118, Bury St Edmunds IP33 2NE.
Tel: 01284 761 894.
Sterling Coins & Medals
2 Somerset Road, Boscombe, Bournemouth, Dorset
BH7 6JH. Tel: 01202 423 881. *World Coins & Medals.*

Drake Sterling Numismatics Pty Ltd
GPO Box 2913, Sydney 2001, Australia. UK callers
Tel: 020 7097 1781, www.drakesterling.co.uk. *British
and British Colonial Gold Coins.*

Studio Coins (ANA)
Studio 111, 80 High Street, Winchester, Hants SO23
9AT. Tel: 01962 853 156 email: stephenmitchell13@
bttconnect.com. **P** *English Coins.*

The Britannia Coin Company (BNTA)
*143 High Street, Royal Wootton Bassett,Wilts,
SN4 7AB.Tel: 01793 205007.
wwwbritanniacoincompany.com. Ancient,
Hammered and Milled, Sovereigns, Investment Gold,
Royal Mint New Issues.*

The Coin Cabinet (BNTA)
*First Floor, 60 St James's Street, London,
SW1A 1LE. Tel: 020 3808 5855.
Email: contact@thecoincabinet.com.
www.thecoincabinet.com. World Coin Dealer and
Auctioneer.*

The Coin House
Tel: 01935 824 878, email: thecoinhouse@
btinternet.com. *Quality Investment Coins and Silver
Bars.*

The East India Company
Tel: 0203 205 3394, email: service@
theeastindiacompany.com. *Gold and Silver Coins,
retail premises.Gifts and collectables of historic
interest.*

The Royal Mint
Llantrisant, Pontyclun, CF72 8YT. Tel: 01443 222111.
New coin minter/issuer. Also historic numismatics.

Time Line Originals (BNTA)
PO Box 193, Upminster, RM14 3WH. Tel: 01708
222 384/07775 651 218, email: sales@time–lines.
co.uk.

Stuart J. Timmins
Smallwood Lodge Bookshop, Newport, Salop.
Tel: 01952 813 232. *Numismatic Literature.*

R. Tims
39 Villiers Road, Watford, Herts WD1 4AL.**P L**
Uncirculated World Banknotes.

Michael Trenerry
PO Box 55, Truro, TR1 2YQ. Tel: 01872 277 977,
email: veryfinecoins@aol.com. By
appointment only. **L** *Roman, Celtic and
English Hammered Coins and Tokens.*

Robert Tye
7–9 Clifford Street, York, YO1 9RA. Tel: 0845 4 900
724, email: orders@earlyworlscoins.com.
www.uk–coins.com. Rare Historical Medals

Vale
Tel: 01322 405 911, email: valecoins@ntlworld.com
British Coins and Medals.

Van der Schueren, John-Luc (IAPN)
14 Rue de la Borse, 1,000 Bussels, Belgium. Email:
iapnsecret@compuserve.com, www.coins.be. . *Coins
and Tokens of the World and of the Low Countries.*

M. Veissid & Co (The Collectors Centre) (BNTA)
16 The Parade, St Marys Place, Shrewsbury
SY1 1DL Tel: 01743 600951. *Retail shop offering
coins, medals, notes and emphemera.*

Victory Coins (BNTA)
PO Box 948, Southsea, Hampshire, PO1 9LZ. Tel:
023 92 751908. *British and World Coins.*

Mark J. Vincenzi
Rylands, Earls Colne, Essex CO6 2LE. Tel: 01787
222 555. **P** *Greek, Roman, Hammered.*

Mike Vosper
PO Box 32, Hockwold, Brandon IP26 4HX. Tel:
01842 828 292, email: mikevosper@vosper4coins.
co.uk, www.vosper4coins.co.uk. *Roman,
Hammered.*

Weighton Coin Wonders
50 Market Place, Market Weighton, York, Y043 3AL,
Tel: 01430 879 740, www.weightoncoin.co.uk.
Modern Gold, Silver Proofs and Sets.

Wessex Coins (BNTA)
PO Box 482, Southampton, SO30 9FB. Tel: 02380
972 059, email: info@wessexcoins.co.uk,
www.wessexcoins.co.uk. *Ancient Greek, Roman,
English Hammered Coins and Antiquities, also
Shipwreck Treasure.*

Pam West (IBNS)
PO Box 257, Sutton, Surrey, SM3 9WW. Tel: 020
8641 3224, email: pam@britishnotes.co.uk,
www.britishnotes.co.uk.**P L** *English Banknotes and
related publications.*

West Essex Coin Investments (BNTA, IBNS)
Croft Cottage, Station Road, Alderholt,
Fordingbridge, Hants SP6 3AZ. Tel: 01425 656 459.
British and World Coins and Paper Money.

Whitmore Coins, Tokens & Medals
Tel: 01568 720536, www.whitmorectm.com
Coins, tokens and medals.

West Wicklow Coins
Blessington, Co Wicklow, Ireland. Tel: 00353 45
858 767, email: westwicklowcoins@hotmail.com.
Irish and World Coins.

Trevor Wilkin
PO Box 182 Cammeray, NSW 2602, Australia. Tel:
0061 9438 5040, email trevorsnotes@bigpond.com.
World Banknotes.

Simon Willis Coins
43a St Marys Road, Market Harborough, LE16 7DS.
Tel:07908 240 978, swcoins@simonwilliscoins.com,
www.simonwilliscoins.com. *Quality Hammered and
Early Milled British Coins.*

Worldwide Coins (IBNS)
PO Box 11, Wavertree, Liverpool L15 0FG. Tel: 0845
634 1809, email: sales@worldwidecoins.co.uk,
www.worldwidecoins.co.uk. *World Coins and Paper
Money.*

World Treasure Books
PO Box 5, Newport, Isle of Wight PO30 5QE. Tel:
01983 740 712. **L** *Coins, Books, Metal Detectors.*

Treasure
and the Law

Until the introduction of the new Treasure Act, the legal position regarding articles of gold, silver or bullion, found long after they were hidden or abandoned, was not as simple and straightforward as it might be supposed. Furthermore, this was a case where the law in England and Wales differed fundamentally from that in Scotland.

Treasure Trove was one of the most ancient rights of the Crown, deriving from the age-old right of the monarch to gold, silver or bullion treasure whose owner was not known. In England and Wales, the law applied only to objects made of, or containing, gold or silver, whether in the form of coin, jewellery, plate or bullion. Moreover, the object had to be shown to have been deliberately hidden with intent to retrieve and the owner could not be readily found. The English law therefore excluded precious stones and jewels set in base metals or alloys such as bronze or pewter. It also took no account of artifacts in pottery, stone, bone, wood or glass which might be of immense antiquarian value.

In recent years, as a result of the rise in metal-detecting as a hobby, the archaeological lobby brought pressure to bear on Parliament to change the law and bring it into line with Scotland where the rules on Treasure Trove were far more

rigorously interpreted. In Scotland the Crown is entitled to *all* abandoned property, even if it has not been hidden and is of little value. This applies even to objects dumped in skips on the pavement. Strictly speaking you would be committing a criminal offence if you removed an old chair from a skip without the owner's permission, although in practice such helping oneself rarely proceeds to a prosecution. In 1958 an archaeological expedition from Aberdeen University found several valuable artifacts on St Ninian's Isle, Shetland. These included silver vessels and ornaments, as well as a porpoise bone which had incised decoration on it. The archaeologists challenged the rights of the Crown to this treasure, arguing that the Crown would have to prove that the articles had been deliberately hidden, and that a porpoise bone was in any case not valuable enough to count as treasure. The High Court, however, decided that as long as the property had been abandoned, it belonged

A real treat for any treasure hunter is the finding of a rare or relatively unknown piece. The above coin, a silver unit (Bury Diadem Solar "Anemone Type") dated circa 55–50 BC, depicting a female head left with long pointed nose, wearing a crown and beaded neck torc, was found in Sedgeford, Norfolk. As so often depicted on Celtic coins, the reverse bears the image of a prancing horse. Due to its great rarity, only one other recorded piece is known, and its particularly appealing artistic merit it secured a very impressive £5,500 against a pre-sale estimate of £1,500 when sold by Chris Rudd Auctions in July 2022.

automatically to the Crown. Its value, intrinsic or otherwise, or whether or not it was hidden, did not make any difference. Since then, as a result of this decision in case law, the criteria for Treasure Trove have been very strictly applied in Scotland. It would have only required a similar test case in England or Wales to result in a similar tightening of the rules. This has been resisted, mainly by the detectorist lobby, but inevitably the government considered legislation to control the use of metal detectors, if not to ban them altogether.

In England and Wales a find of gold or silver coins, artifacts or ornaments, or objects which contain some of these metals, which appears to have been concealed by the original owner, was deemed to be Treasure Trove. It was not even necessary for the articles to be buried in the ground; objects concealed in thatched roofs or under the floorboards of buildings have been judged to be Treasure Trove. Such finds had to be notified immediately to the police who then informed the district coroner. He then convened an inquest which decided whether all or part of the find was Treasure Trove. Establishing the gold or silver content was straightforward, but the coroner's inquest had to decide whether the material was hidden deliberately and not just lost or abandoned, and that the owner could not be located. A gold coin found on or near a country footpath might reasonably have been dropped by the original possessor through a hole in pocket or purse and in such cases it was very unlikely that it would be deemed Treasure Trove, even if the coin turned out to be very rare. In this instance the coroner would then have had to determine who was the lawful owner of the find: the actual finder, the owner of the land where it was found or even the tenant of the land. As a rule, however, it was left to the finder and landowner to decide between them who the owner of the coin should

be, and in some cases the matter could only be resolved by referring to a civil court. For this reason it was vital that metal detectorists should secure permission *in writing* from landowners before going on to their land, defining rights and obligations on both sides, in order to determine the disposal or share-out of any finds or proceeds from the sale of finds, *beforehand*.

If the coroner decided that the articles were deliberately concealed, and declared them to be Treasure Trove, the find automatically reverted to the Crown. In practice the find was considered by the Treasure Trove Reviewing Committee of the Treasury. They might decide that although the articles, *invariably coins,* were gold or silver, they were so common that they were not required by the British Museum or one of the other great national collections, and would return them to the finder to dispose of at their discretion. If some or all of the coins were deemed vital for inclusion in a national collection the finder was recompensed with the full market value of the material. On the other hand, if someone found gold or silver which might be Treasure Trove and failed to declare it at the time, that person was liable to prosecution under the Theft Act 1968 should the find subsequently come to light. Not only could they face a heavy fine but the articles would be forfeit to the Crown, and of course no reward or recompense was then payable either.

The anomalies and inconsistencies of existing law on Treasure Trove were eliminated and the position considerably tightened up by the passage, on July 5, 1996, of the Treasure Act.

Announcing that the Treasure Act had received the Royal Assent, Lord Inglewood, National Heritage Minister, said, "This represents the first legislation on Treasure Trove to be passed in England and Wales and will replace Common

Treasure finds are not limited only to terra firma. Deep water excavation has brought to the surface and market, the lost gold of the wreck of the SS Central America which went down in a hurricane on September 3, 1857. Known as the "ship of gold" the first part of the find, graded by NGC, consists of 123 US Liberty Head $20 gold coins (or Double Eagles). Although secured in a San Francisco Mint box, the coins had melded together into one unidentifiable lump. Incredibly, following careful conservation, many of the coins were still in excellent condition despite their long spell on the seabed.

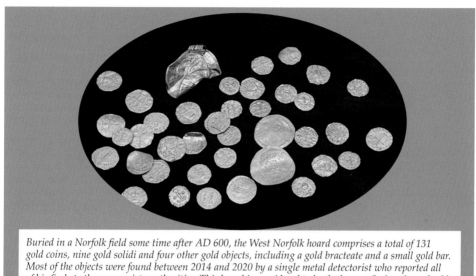

Buried in a Norfolk field some time after AD 600, the West Norfolk hoard comprises a total of 131 gold coins, nine gold solidi and four other gold objects, including a gold bracteate and a small gold bar. Most of the objects were found between 2014 and 2020 by a single metal detectorist who reported all of his finds to the appropriate authorities. This hoard is considered to be the largest find to-date of gold coins from the Anglo-Saxon period in England.

Law precedents and practices dating back to the Middle Ages. The Act, which offers a clearer definition of treasure and simplified procedures for dealing with finds, will come into force after a code of practice has been drawn up and agreed by both Houses of Parliament". The Act came into force in England, Wales and Northern Ireland on September 24, 1997, replacing the Common Law of Treasure Trove.

The act was introduced as a Private Member's Bill by Sir Anthony Grant, after the failure of an earlier attempt by Lord Perth. For the first time, it would be a criminal offence to fail to report within 14 days the discovery of an item which could be declared Treasure Trove. Finders will continue to be rewarded for reporting their discoveries promptly, while landowners and occupiers will also be eligible for rewards for the first time.

The Treasure Act covers man-made objects and defines treasure as objects other than coins which are at least 300 years old and contain at least 10 per cent by weight of gold or silver; coins more than 300 years old which are found in hoards (a minimum of two coins if the precious metal content is more than 10 per cent, and a minimum of 10 coins if the precious metal content is below 10 per cent). The act also embraces all objects found in clear archaeological association with items which are treasure under the above definitions. It also covers any object which would have been Treasure

Trove under the previous definitions (e.g. hoards of 19th century gold or silver coins).

An extension to The Act from January 2003 provides that groups of prehistoric bronze implements are also deemed to be Treasure.

The maximum penalty for failing to report the discovery of treasure within 14 days will be a fine of £5,000 or three months imprisonment, or both.

In Scotland the police pass the goods on to the procurator fiscal who acts as the local representative of the Queen's and Lord Treasurer's Remembrancer. If the articles are of little value, historically or intrinsically, the finder will usually be allowed to keep them. If they are retained for the appropriate national collection then a reward equal to the market value is payable.

A favourite haunt of metal-detectorists these days is the beach, and many hobbyists make quite a lucrative living by sweeping the beaches especially just after a Bank Holiday. It's surprising how much loose change gets lost from pockets and handbags over a holiday weekend. Technically the coins recovered from the beach are lost property, in which case they ought to be surrendered to the police, otherwise the finder may be guilty of theft. In practice, however, the law turns a blind eye to coins, on the sensible grounds that it would be impossible to prove ownership. On the other hand, banknotes are treated as lost property since someone could in theory at least identify a note as his by citing the serial number.

In the case of other objects, such as watches and jewellery, of course the law governing lost property is enforced, and the old adage of "finders keepers" does not apply. Any object of value, identifiable as belonging to someone, that is washed up on the foreshore or found in territorial waters is known technically as "wreck". This includes not just a wrecked ship, but any cargo that was being carried by a ship.

If wreck is not claimed by its owner, it falls to the Crown. In this case it is not necessary to prove deliberate concealment, as in the case of Treasure Trove. This law has a specific numismatic application in the case of the gold and silver coins washed up after storms around our shores, from Shetland to the Scillies. Such coins, emanating from wrecks of Spanish treasure ships and Dutch East Indiamen in particular, are well documented, and any such finds ought to be reported immediately to the police.

Stray finds of coins, as well as other objects of value, on public places, such as the street, a public park or a sports ground, are also subject to law. In this case the finder must take all reasonable steps to locate the owner. Anyone who keeps a coin without making reasonable effort to find the owner could be prosecuted for theft. As with the beach, however, such "reasonable effort" would clearly be impractical. Finding coins on private premises is another matter. In this case large bodies, such as the Post Office, British Rail, the British Airports Authority, bus companies, municipal authorities, hospitals, the owners of department stores, theatre and cinema proprietors and the like, may have bye-laws, rules and regulations for dealing with lost property found within their precincts, or in their vehicles. If you found a purse or wallet on a bus or train, or in a telephone kiosk or a shop, common sense (and your conscience) would tell you to hand it over to the driver, conductor, shopkeeper or official in charge.

As a rule, unclaimed lost property reverts eventually to the finder, but not always; British Rail and some other organisations have a rule that in such cases the property reverts to the organisation. In any event, failure to disclose the find immediately might render you liable to prosecution for stealing by finding.

The Ewerby Hoard, offered by Silbury Coins, consists of some 1,200 silver coins which were found nestled inside a ceramic jug by a detectorist in Lincolnshire. The coins are from the reigns of Henry VIII, Edward VI, Philip and Mary, Elizabeth I, James I and Charles I. It is the largest hoard of its kind ever to be found in that county and one of the largest in the entire country. Its find spot was close to several known Civil War battle sites.